EUROPE & THE M  N

Turn to the pa … try

How to use this Guide / Comment utiliser ce Guide / Benutzerhinweise

To find a hotel by location:

- Turn to the Map of Europe overleaf to identify the country you wish to search.
- Turn to the relevant country section where hotels are featured alphabetically by region and/or by place names.
- Alternatively, turn to the title page of the country required, where you will find a country map. The location of each property appears in red (hotel) or purple (spa hotel) with a number corresponding to the page on which the establishment entry is published.

To find a property by name look for it in the Index from pages 425 - 428.

The indexes also list recommended hotels by their amenities such as SPA, Golf course on site etc.

The Recommendations are split into three categories:

- **Hotels**: properties providing a high standard and wide range of services and facilities
- **Charming Hotels**: properties with a more homely and intimate atmosphere
- **Guest Houses**: properties which are usually owner managed and only serve breakfast

Once you have made your choice please contact the hotel directly. Rates are correct at the time of going to press but should always be checked with the hotel before you make your reservation. When making a booking please mention that Condé Nast Johansens was your source of reference.

We occasionally receive letters from guests who have been charged for accommodation booked in advance but later cancelled. Readers should be aware that by making a reservation with a hotel, either by telephone, e-mail or in writing, they are entering into a legal contract. Under certain circumstances, a hotelier is entitled to make a charge for accommodation when guests fail to arrive, even if notice of the cancellation is given.

All Guides are obtainable from bookshops, or by calling Condé Nast Johansens direct on 0800 269397 (UK) or +44 208 655 7810 (Europe & US). Alternatively, use the order coupons on pages 437 (English), 439 (French) and 441 (German). Guides may also be ordered over the Internet at www.johansens.com/bookshop

Si vous souhaitez trouver un hôtel dans un emplacement spécifique:

- Reportez vous à la carte d'Europe au verso pour identifier le pays que vous souhaitez rechercher.
- Reportez vous à la section du pays désiré, où les hôtels sont présentés par ordre alphabétique par région et/ou nom de la ville.
- Autrement, reportez vous à la première page du pays désiré, où vous trouverez une carte. L'emplacement de chaque hôtel est marqué d'un point rouge (hôtel) ou un point violet (hôtel spa/centre thermal) avec un chiffre correspondant à la page à laquelle l'hôtel est présenté.

Si vous souhaitez trouver un hôtel dont vous connaissez le nom, reportez vous à l'index aux pages 425 - 428.

L'index offre aussi une liste des hôtels recommandés categorisés par leurs aménagements, par exemple Centre thermal, Golf sur site etc.

Les Recommandations se divisent en trois catégories:

- **Hotels**: établissements offrant une prestation haut de gamme ainsi qu'un vaste choix de services
- **Charming Hotels (Hôtels de charme)**: établissements à l'atmosphère plus intime et chaleureuse
- **Guest Houses (Maison d'Hôtes)**: établissements généralement gérés par les propriétaires et ne servant que le petit-déjeuner

Quand vous avez fait votre choix, veuillez contacter l'hôtel directement. Les tarifs indiqués sont corrects au moment de l'impression mais il vous est recommandé de les vérifier auprès de l'établissement concerné avant de réserver. N'oubliez pas de mentionner Condé Nast Johansens comme référence lors de votre réservation.

Il nous arrive parfois de recevoir des lettres de clients qui ont dû payer des chambres réservées à l'avance puis annulées. Les lecteurs doivent savoir qu'en effectuant une réservation auprès d'un hôtel, que ce soit par téléphone, courrier électronique ou lettre, ils passent un contrat légal avec cet hôtel. Dans certaines circonstances, un hôtelier est en droit de facturer une chambre lorsque le client ne se présente pas à l'hôtel même s'il a été avisé de l'annulation.

Tous les Guides peuvent être obtenus en librairies ou en appelant directement Condé Nast Johansens au +44 20 7538 3597. Vous pouvez également utiliser les bons de commande fournis dans ce guide aux pages 437 (anglais), 439 (français) et 441 (allemand). Vous pouvez commander nos Guides sur Internet www.johansens.com/bookshop

Wenn Sie ein Hotel an einem bestimmten Ort suchen:

- Blättern Sie zur Europakarte auf der nächsten Seite, um das Land zu finden, in dem sich das gewünschte Hotel befindet.
- Blättern Sie zu dem relevanten Land - hier finden Sie alle Hotels alphabetisch nach Region und/oder Ortsnamen aufgelistet.
- Alternativ dazu blättern Sie zu der Titelseite des gewünschten Landes – hier finden Sie eine Karte. Die Lage eines jeden Hotels ist mit einem roten Punkt (Hotel) oder einem violetten Punkt (Kurhotel/Spa) auf der Karte markiert und mit einer Zahl versehen, die mit der Seitenzahl des Hoteleintrags übereinstimmt.

Wenn Sie ein Hotel suchen, dessen Namen Sie bereits kennen, hilft Ihnen das Inhaltsverzeichnis auf den Seiten 425 - 428.

Das Inhaltsverzeichnis listet die Hotels auch nach ihren besonderen Einrichtungen auf, wie z.B. Kureinrichtungen, Golfplatz etc.

Alle Empfehlungen sind nach drei Kategorien geordnet:

- **Hotels**: Häuser, die ein hohes Niveau und eine große Auswahl an Service und Einrichtungen bieten
- **Charming Hotels**: kleinere Hotels mit einer heimeligen und familiären Atmosphäre
- **Guest Houses (Pensionen)**: werden normalerweise vom Eigentümer geführt; es wird nur Frühstück serviert

Wenn Sie Ihre Wahl getroffen haben, wenden Sie sich bitte direkt an das Hotel. Die Preise hatten zur Zeit der Drucklegung ihre Gültigkeit. Bitte denken Sie daran, bei jeder Buchung zu erwähnen, dass Sie sich auf Condé Nast Johansens beziehen.

Manchmal erhalten wir Briefe von Gästen, die für stornierte Zimmer eine Hotelrechnung erhalten. Die Leser sollten sich darüber im klaren sein, dass sie bei einer Reservierung per Telefon, E-Mail oder auch schriftlich, einen rechtsgültigen Vertrag mit dem Hotel eingehen. Ein Hotelier kann unter bestimmten Umständen, auch bei rechtzeitiger Stornierung, eine Gebühr verlangen.

Alle Hotelführer sind im Buchhandel erhältlich oder direkt von Condé Nast Johansens unter der Telefonnummer +44 20 7538 3597. Alternativ können auch die Bestellformulare auf Seite 437 (Englisch), Seite 439 (Französisch) und Seite 441 (Deutsch) verwendet werden. Die Guides können auch über das Internet unter www.johansens.com/bookshop bestellt werden.

INTRODUCTION / EINFÜHRUNG

Andrew Warren, Managing Director, Condé Nast Johansens Ltd.

Welcome to the 10th Anniversary edition of our Guide to Europe & The Mediterranean. We are delighted to feature 365 properties, including 122 new recommendations, many from within the new EU countries such as Croatia, Cyprus, Czech Republic, Estonia, Hungary and Slovak Republic.

We encourage your comments as they help us to compile a more useful Guide each year and they also contribute directly to the nominations for our Annual Awards. You may wish to complete a "Guest Survey Report" printed at the back of this Guide or on our new website www.johansens.com where "Special Offers" are available, together with the opportunity to purchase "Gift Vouchers" or visit our Bookshop.

We very much hope that you enjoy using the 2005 edition of our Guide where you will find many favourites and a choice of new recommendations.

Above all, please remember to mention "Condé Nast Johansens" when you make an enquiry or reservation and again when you arrive. You will be especially welcome.

Bienvenue dans la Xe édition de notre guide Europe & Méditerranée. Nous sommes heureux de vous présenter 365 établissements, dont 122 nouvelles recommandations et beaucoup d'hôtels venant des nouveaux pays Européens tels que la Croatie, Chypre, la République Tchèque, l'Estonie, la Hongrie et la Slovaquie.

Plus que jamais nous vous invitons à nous transmettre vos avis et commentaires, ceux-ci nous aident à vous proposer un guide plus pratique chaque année et contribuent aux nominations de nos Prix d'Excellence annuels. Vous pouvez remplir un « Questionnaire de Satisfaction » disponible au dos de ce guide ou sur notre nouveau site internet www.johansens.com où des « Offres Spéciales », des Chèques-Cadeaux, et notre librairie en ligne vous attendent.

Nous espérons sincèrement que vous apprécierez cette édition 2005.

Plus que tout, merci de mentionner « Condé Nast Johansens », lorsque vous demandez un renseignement, faites une réservation ou lors de votre arrivée. Votre accueil n'en sera que meilleur.

Herzlich willkommen zur 10. Ausgabe unseres Guides für Europa und den Mittelmeerraum. Wir freuen uns, Ihnen 365 Etablissements vorstellen zu dürfen, darunter 122 neue Empfehlungen und zahlreiche in den neuen EU-Ländern wie z.B. Kroatien, Zypern, der Tschechischen Republik, Estland, Ungarn und der Slowakischen Republik.

Ihre Kommentare sind uns äußerst wichtig, erstens, um den Guide jedes Jahr verbessern zu können, und zweitens, um die Nominierungen für unsere alljährliche Preisverleihung aufzustellen. Bitte nehmen Sie sich die Zeit, einen „Gastbericht" auszufüllen, den Sie entweder im hinteren Teil dieses Guides oder auf unserer Website www.johansens.com finden, wo auch Sonderangebote, Geschenkgutscheine sowie unser Online-Bookshop angeboten werden.

Wir hoffen sehr, dass Sie mit der 2005 Ausgabe unseres mit vielen Altbekannten und zahlreichen Neulingen gefüllten Guides zufrieden sind.

Und bitte vergessen Sie nicht, bei Anfragen, Buchungen und noch einmal bei der Ankunft „Condé Nast Johansens" zu erwähnen – Sie werden ganz besonders herzlich willkommen geheißen.

Andrew Warren

The Condé Nast Johansens Promise

Condé Nast Johansens is the most comprehensive illustrated reference to annually inspected, independently owned hotels throughout Great Britain, Europe and North America.

It is our objective to maintain the trust of Guide users by recommending through annual inspection a careful choice of accommodation offering quality, excellence and value for money.

Our team of over 50 dedicated Regional Inspectors have visited almost 3000 hotels, country houses, inns and resorts throughout the world to select only the very best for recommendation in the 2005 editions of our Guides.

No hotel can appear in our Guides unless they meet our exacting standards.

L'engagement de Condé Nast Johansens

Condé Nast Johansens est la référence de guides illustrés la plus complète en matière d'hôtels indépendants, inspectés annuellement en Grande-Bretagne, Europe et Amérique du Nord.

C'est notre objectif de maintenir la confiance de nos lecteurs en continuant à recommander, par le biais de nos inspections annuelles, une sélection d'établissements offrant qualité, excellence et un bon rapport qualité-prix.

Notre équipe de plus de 50 inspecteurs régionaux a visité près de 3000 hôtels, country houses, inns et resorts partout dans le monde, pour ne sélectionner que le meilleur en recommandation dans les éditions 2005 de nos Guides.

Aucun hôtel ne peut apparaître dans nos Guides sans répondre exactement à nos standards.

Das Condé Nast Johansens Versprechen

Condé Nast Johansens ist das umfangreichste illustrierte Nachschlagewerk für jährlich inspizierte, privat geführte Hotels in ganz Großbritannien, Europa und Nordamerika.

Unser Ziel ist es, das Vertrauen unserer Leser zu erhalten, indem wir durch jährliche Inspektion eine sorgfältige Auswahl der Häuser treffen, die höchste Qualität bei einem hervorragenden Preis-Leistungs-Verhältnis bieten.

Unser Team aus über 50 regionalen Inspektoren besuchte an die 3000 Hotels, Landhäuser, Inns und Resorts weltweit, um nur die besten Häuser für eine Empfehlung in unseren Guides für 2005 auszuwählen. Jedes in unseren Guides erscheinende Hotel muss unsere extrem hohen Anforderungen erfüllen.

Condé Nast Johansens Guides

Recommending only the finest hotels in the world

As well as this Guide, Condé Nast Johansens also publishes the following titles:
En plus de ce Guide, Condé Nast Johansens publie également les titres suivants:
Außer diesem Guide veröffentlicht Condé Nast Johansens auch folgende Titel:

Recommended Hotels & Spas, Great Britain & Ireland

Unique and luxurious hotels, town houses, castles and manor houses chosen for their superior standards and individual character.

Hôtels luxueux et uniques, hôtels particuliers, châteaux et manoirs sélectionnés pour leurs standards supérieurs et leur caractère individuel.

Einzigartige luxuriöse Hotels, Stadthäuser, Schlösser und Landsitze, ausgewählt aufgrund ihres extrem hohen Niveaus und individuellen Charakters.

Recommended Country Houses, Small Hotels & Inns, Great Britain & Ireland

Smaller, more rural properties, ideal for short breaks or more intimate stays.

Établissements plus petits et le plus souvent à la campagne. Idéal pour des courts séjours ou des escapades romantiques.

Kleinere und eher ländliche Häuser, ideal für Kurztrips oder ein romantisches Wochenende zu zweit.

Recommended Hotels, Inns & Resorts, North America, Bermuda, Caribbean, Mexico, Pacific

A diverse collection of properties across the region, including exotic ocean-front resorts, historic plantation houses and traditional inns.

Une collection variée d'établissements à travers le pays, comprenant des resorts éxotiques en bord de mer, des maisons de plantations historiques et des inns traditionnels.

Eine Vielzahl an Etablissements in der gesamten Region, darunter exotische Resorts am Meer, historische Plantagen und traditionelle Inns.

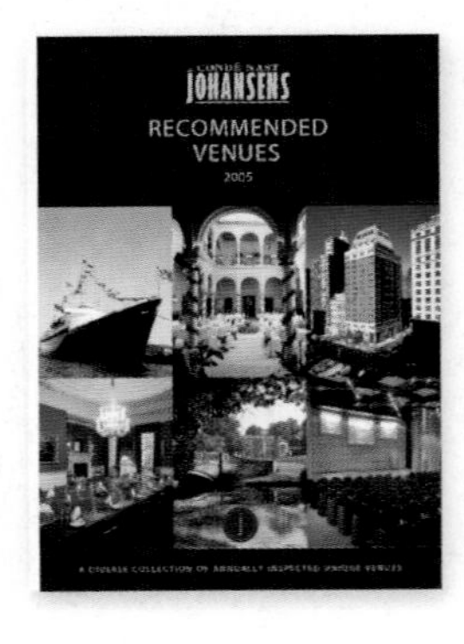

Recommended Venues, Great Britain & Europe

Venues that cater specifically for business meetings, conferences, product launches, events and celebrations.

Des lieux spécifiquement dédiés aux réunions d'affaires, conférences, lancements de produits, évènements et festivités.

Etablissements, die speziell auf Geschäftstreffen, Konferenzen, Produkt-Launches, Veranstaltungen und Festlichkeiten ausgerichtet sind.

To order any Guides please complete the order form on page 437 or call FREEPHONE 0800 269 397

Pour commander les Guides, merci de compléter le bon de commande situé en page 439 ou appelez +44 208 655 7810

Um die Hotelguides zu bestellen, füllen Sie bitte das Bestellformular auf Seite 441 aus oder bestellen Sie direkt unter der Nummer +44 208 655 7810

CONDÉ NAST JOHANSENS

Condé Nast Johansens Ltd, 6-8 Old Bond Street, London W1S 4PH
Tel: +44 (0)20 7499 9080 Fax: +44 (0)20 7152 3565
Find Condé Nast Johansens on the Internet at: www.johansens.com
E-Mail: info@johansens.com

Publishing Director:	Charlotte Evans
European Publishing Executive:	Federica Alecce
Inspectors:	Ana María Brebner
	Suzanne Flanders
	Olivier Hourcade
	Gianna Illari
	Tunde Longmore
	Barbara Marcotulli
	Stéphanie Martinez
	Renzo Miracco
	Murat Özgüç
	Seamus Shortt
	Agnes Szent-Ivanyi Exton
	Danielle Taljaardt
	Christopher Terleski
Production Manager:	Kevin Bradbrook
Production Controller:	Laura Kerry
Senior Designer:	Michael Tompsett
Copywriters:	Clare Barker
	Stephanie Cook
	Sasha Creed
	Norman Flack
	Debra Giles
	Rozanne Paragon
	Leonora Sandwell
Marketing Coordinator:	Siobhan Smith
Marketing Promotions Executive:	Niko Downie
Client Services Director:	Fiona Patrick
P.A. to Managing Director:	Siobhan Smith
Managing Director:	Andrew Warren

Condé Nast Johansens Ltd. is part of The Condé Nast Publications Ltd.

ISBN 1 903665 20 5

Printed in England by St Ives plc
Colour origination by Wyndeham Graphics

Distributed in the UK and Europe by Portfolio, Greenford (bookstores).
In North America by Casemate Publishing, Havertown (Bookstores).

2004 Awards For Excellence

The winners of the Condé Nast Johansens 2004 Awards for Excellence

The winners of the Condé Nast Johansens 2004 Awards for Excellence

The Condé Nast Johansens 2004 Awards for Excellence were presented at the Condé Nast Johansens Annual Luncheon held at The Dorchester on November 10th, 2003. Awards were made to those properties worldwide that represented the finest standards and best value for money in luxury independent travel. An important source of information for these awards was the feedback provided by guests who completed Johansens Guest Survey forms. Guest Survey forms can be found on pages 438 (English), 440 (French) and 442 (German).

Les vainqueurs des Conde Nast Johansens 2004 Awards for Excellence

Les Condé Nast Johansens 2004 Awards for Excellence ont été remis lors du gala déjeuner annuel de Condé Nast Johansens à l'hôtel The Dorchester à Londres le 10 novembre 2003. Ces prix ont été créés afin de rétribuer les établissements qui, à travers le monde, offrent les meilleurs standards et rapport qualité prix dans l'hôtellerie de luxe indépendante. Une source d'information et de sélection importante pour ces prix provient des questionnaires de satisfaction renvoyés par les clients. Les questionnaires de satisfaction sont disponibles page 438 (en anglais), page 440 (en français) et page 442 (en allemand).

Die Gewinner der Condé Nast Johansens 2004 Awards for Excellence

Die Condé Nast Johansens 2004 Awards for Excellence wurden am 10. November 2003 beim jährlichen Condé Nast Johansens Gala-Mittagessen im Londoner Hotel The Dorchester präsentiert. Auszeichnungen erhielten diejenigen Häuser weltweit, die höchste Qualität und das beste Preis-Leistungs-Verhältnis bei privaten Luxusreisen bieten konnten. Eine äußerst wichtige Informationsquelle bei der Entscheidung für diese Auszeichnungen waren die Kommentare derjenigen Gäste, die unsere Johansens-Gastberichte ausgefüllt haben. Formulare für Gastberichte finden Sie auf den Seiten 438 (Englisch), 440 (Französisch) und 442 (Deutsch).

Most Excellent European City Hotel Award

J AND J HISTORIC HOUSE HOTEL – Florence, Italy, p232

"Be mesmerized by the view over the rooftops and hidden courtyards of Florence."

«Soyez hypnotisé par les vues sur les toits et les cours cachés de Florence.»

„Lassen Sie sich von der herrlichen Sicht auf die Dächer und Innenhöfe von Florenz verzaubern."

Most Excellent European Countryside Hotel Award

LE DOMAINE DE DIVONNE CASINO, GOLF & SPA RESORT – Divonne~les~Bains, France, p141

"An abundance of facilities, including an18-hole golf course, Spa, and Casino."

«Une profusion d'installations telles que parcours de golf 18 trous, un spa et un casino.»

„Eine Fülle an Einrichtungen, darunter ein 18-Loch-Golfplatz, Spa und Casino."

2004 Awards For Excellence

The winners of the Condé Nast Johansens 2004 Awards for Excellence

Most Excellent European Waterside Hotel Award

CHÂTEAU EZA – Èze Village, France, p73

"Breathtaking views make this exquisite hotel an ideal romantic retreat."

«Des vues à couper le souffle font de ce ravissant hôtel une étape romantique idéale.»

„Die atemberaubende Sicht macht dieses fantastische Hotel zu einem idealen Ort für Romantiker."

Most Excellent Value for Money Award

ÜRGÜP EVI – Ürgüp-Nevsehir, Turkey, p397

"This extraordinary hotel is a real gem, with stylish bedrooms carved out of the mountain."

«Cet hôtel extraordinaire est un vrai bijou avec des chambres stylées taillées dans la montagne.»

„Dieses außergewöhnliche Hotel ist ein wahres Juwel, seine stilvollen Zimmer sind direkt in die Felswand gehauen."

Most Excellent Spa Hotel Award

NH ALMENARA GOLF HOTEL & SPA – Sotogrande, Spain, p321

"Totally relax in the impressive Spa centre with state-of-the-art treatment rooms."

«La relaxation est totale dans cet impressionnant spa et ses cabines de soins à la pointe.»

„Gönnen Sie sich Entspannung pur im eindrucksvollen Spa mit seinen hochmodernen Behandlungsräumen."

The following award winners are featured within Condé Nast Johansens 2005 Guides to Hotels – Great Britain & Ireland, Country Houses – Great Britain & Ireland, Hotels – North America. See page 4 for details of these Guides.

Les Prix d'Excellence ci-dessous sont présentés dans les Guides 2005 Condé Nast Johansens: Hotels – Great Britain & Ireland, Country Houses – Great Britain & Ireland, Hotels – North America. Voir page 4 pour plus de détails sur ces guides.

Die folgenden Preisträger werden in diesen Condé Nast Johansens 2005 Guides vorgestellt: Hotels – Great Britain & Ireland, Country Houses – Great Britain & Ireland, Hotels – North America. Siehe Seite 4 für Einzelheiten zu diesen Hotelführern.

Most Excellent London Hotel Award
Number Sixteen – London, England

Most Excellent City House Award
Green Bough Hotel – Cheshire, England

Most Excellent Service Award
Riverside House – Derbyshire, England

Most Excellent Restaurant Award
The French Horn – Berkshire, England

Most Excellent Spa Award
Chewton Glen – Hampshire, England

Most Excellent Country House Award
Ballachulish House – Argyll & Bute, Scotland

Most Excellent Traditional Inn Award
The Bell at Skenfrith – Monmouthshire, England

Most Excellent Coastal Hotel Award
Ye Olde Bull's Head – Isle of Anglesey, England

Most Excellent Value for Money Award
Pen-Y-Dyffryn Hall Hotel – Shropshire, England

North America & Caribbean: Most Outstanding City Hotel Award
The Chase Park Plaza – Missouri, USA

North America & Caribbean: Most Outstanding Inn Award
The Lodge at Moosehead Lake – Maine, USA

North America & Caribbean: Most Outstanding Hotel Award
Coral Reef Club – Barbados, Caribbean

North America & Caribbean: Most Outstanding Spa Award
The Bishop's Lodge Resort & Spa – New Mexico, USA

North America & Caribbean: Most Outstanding Resort
Spice Island Beach Resort – Grenada, Caribbean

Knight Frank Award for Outstanding Excellence & Innovation
Richard Ball, Calcot Manor – Gloucestershire, England

Taittinger Wine List of the Year Award
Donnington Valley – Berkshire, England

AUSTRIA

Hotel location shown in red (hotel) or purple (spa hotel) with page number

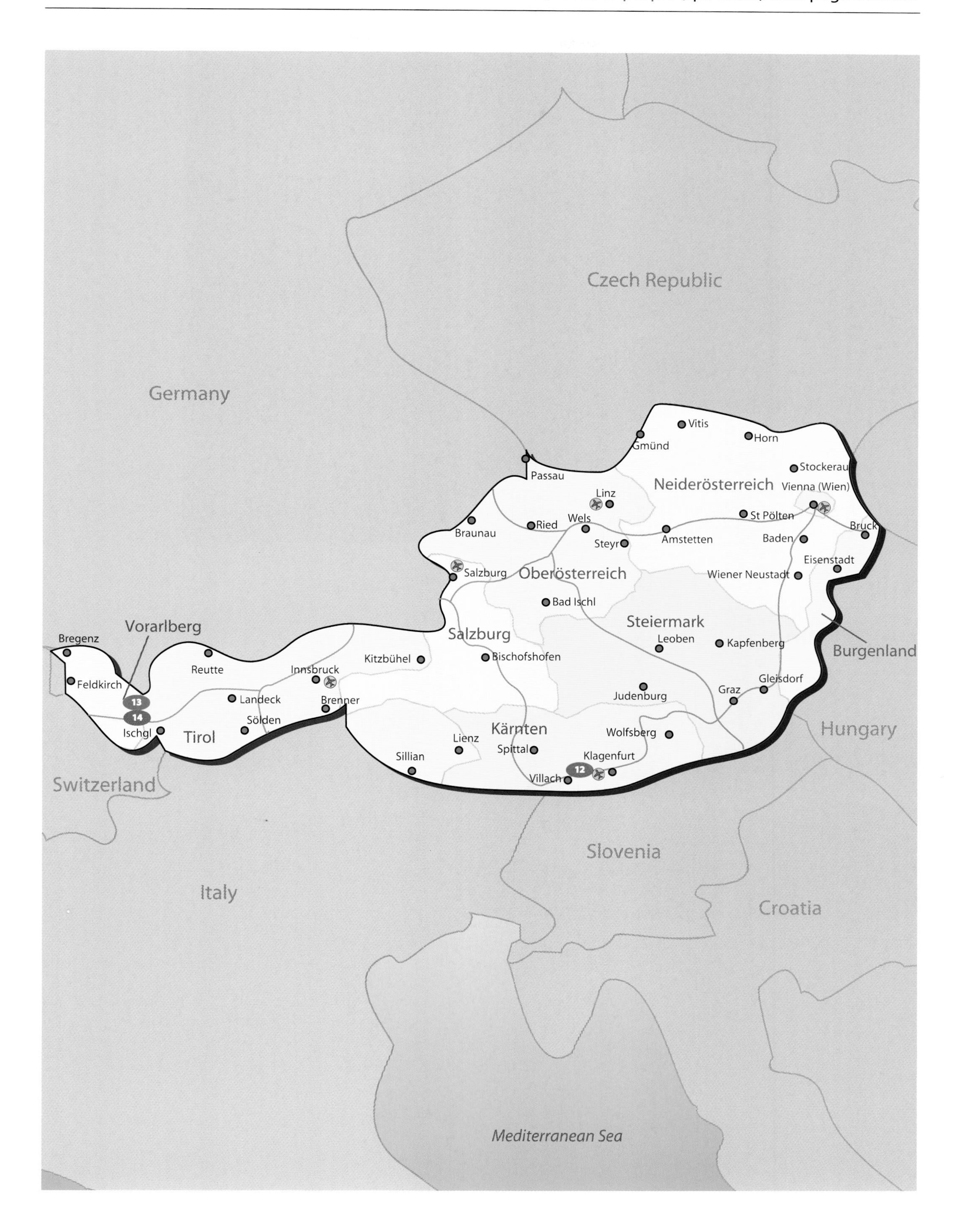

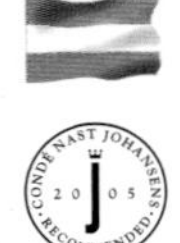

AUSTRIA / KÄRNTEN (VELDEN)

Seeschlössl Velden

KLAGENFURTER STRASSE 34, 9220 VELDEN, AUSTRIA

Directions: Near Velden town centre.

Web: www.johansens.com/seeschlosslvelden
E-mail: seeschloessl@aon.at
Tel: +43 4274 2824
Fax: +43 4274 2824 44

Price Guide:
single/double €120–260
suite €260

With its own private water front and pier, and shielded by a thick wall of imposing trees, this friendly secluded hotel is a mere 5 minutes from Velden's bustling town centre. The public rooms are luxuriously appointed with their panelled walls, polished wooden floors and delightful rustic furnishings. This high level of comfort extends to the bedrooms – all individually designed – some of which have scenic views over the waterfront.

Bénéficiant de son propre quai d'amarrage et entouré d'un mur épais de superbes arbres, cet hôtel sympathique est très calme, tout en étant à 5 minutes du centre bruyant de Velden. Les pièces communes sont luxueusement décorées avec des murs en lambris, des parquets polis et un ameublement délicieusement rustique. Le haut niveau de confort s'étend aux chambres – toutes individuellement décorées – dont certaines ont une vue scénique sur le bord de l'eau.

Dieses freundliche Hotel, durch hohe Bäume von der Außenwelt abgeschirmt und mit eigenem Steg und Anlegestelle, ist nur 5 Minuten vom geschäftigen Stadtzentrum von Velden entfernt. Die Aufenthaltsräume sind luxuriös mit holzverkleideten Wänden, polierten Holzböden und bezaubernden rustikalen Möbeln ausgestattet. Auch die individuell gestalteten Schlafzimmer sind luxuriös und komfortabel, und einige bieten herrliche Blicke auf den See.

Our inspector loved: *The very warm and distinctive welcome.*

Sporthotel Kristiania

OMESBERG 331, 6764 LECH AM ARLBERG, AUSTRIA

Set amidst the most stunning scenery – snow-clad mountains, pine forests and the picturesque mountain hamlet – this enchanting chalet-hotel offers winter sports in a warm and friendly ambience. The bedrooms, furnished with deep-pile rugs, modern chairs and local antiques, are simply a delight. Impeccable service and creative cuisine in the restaurant, with its fine modern art collection adorning the pine walls, is a great retreat after a long day on the piste. Open from 1st December until 15th April (end of season).

Ce charmant hôtel positionné de façon merveilleuse est entouré de montagnes enneigées, de forêts de pins et d'un hameau pittoresque de montagne. Le chalet offre aux fanatiques de sports d'hiver une ambiance chaleureuse et accueillante. Les chambres, meublées avec d'épais tapis, des chaises modernes et des antiquités locales, sont un vrai plaisir. Le restaurant offre un service impeccable et une cuisine créative et présente une collection d'art moderne raffinée sur ses murs en pin, créant un havre excellent après une longue journée sur les pistes. Ouvert le 1 décembre jusqu'au 15 avril.

Schneebedeckte Berge, Kiefernwälder und ein malerisches kleines Bergdorf bilden die Umgebung dieses zauberhaften, freundlichen Chalethotels – ein wahres Paradies für Wintersportler. Die herrlichen Zimmer sind mit flauschigen Teppichen, modernen Sesseln und regionalen Antiquitäten ausgestattet. Das Restaurant, in dem auch eine Sammlung moderner Kunst zu bestaunen ist, bietet kreative Küche und perfekten Service – genau das richtige nach einem langen Tag auf der Piste! Geöffnet vom 1. Dezember bis zum 15. April (Saisonende).

Our inspector loved: *The hotel's fantastic location for skiing and shopping alike. A must for enthusiasts of either!*

Directions: Arlberg tunnel > hotel is on the left just before Lech village.

Web: www.johansens.com/sporthotelkristiania
E-mail: kristiania@lech.at
Tel: +43 5583 25 610
Fax: +43 5583 3550

Price Guide:
single €140–350
double/twin/suite €280–1,500

  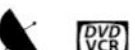   

THURNHERS ALPENHOF

A member of The Leading Small Hotels of the World

6763 ZÜRS – ARLBERG, AUSTRIA

Situated high up in the Alps, Thurnhers is a luxury family-owned chalet hotel exclusively dedicated to winter sports enthusiasts. The interior is well designed, and the owner's interest in antiques is reflected in the plethora of knick-knacks that abound. The atmosphere is very convivial, with visitors mingling in the piano bar before dining in the restaurant. Other facilities include an indoor pool, sauna, steam room and solarium. The hotel has its own sports and facility instructor (certified skiing instructor).

Situé dans les Hautes Alpes, le Thurnhers Alpenhof est un chalet luxueux consacre exclusivement aux fanatiques du sport d'hiver. L'intérieur est fort bien décoré et l'intérêt du propriétaire pour les antiquités se manifeste par le bric-à-brac environnant. L'atmosphère y est fort conviviale, et les clients pourront s'installer au piano bar avant de dîner au restaurant. D'autres équipements incluent une piscine couverte, un sauna, un bain turc et un solarium. L'hôtel a son propre moniteur de ski agréé.

Der Thurnhers Alpenhof liegt wie der Name schon sagt, hoch in den Alpen, ein luxuriöses Chalet-Hotel, das völlig auf Wintersport eingestellt ist. Die Räume sind mit viel Liebe eingerichtet, und das Interesse der Besitzer an Antiquitäten wird anhand der Vielzahl von Kleinigkeiten deutlich. Die Atmosphäre ist sehr herzlich, und die Gäste treffen sich in der Pianobar, bevor sie sich im Restaurant verwöhnen lassen. Zur Entspannung gibt es ein Hallenbad, Sauna, Dampfbad und Solarium. Ein hauseigener Sport- und Freizeitbetreuer (staatl. gepr. Skilehrer) steht zur Verfügung.

Our inspector loved: *The distinctive flair of this sumptuous hotel.*

Directions: Follow signs to Zürs/Arlberg.

Web: www.johansens.com/thunrnhersalpenhof
E-mail: mail@thurnhers-alpenhof.com
Tel: +43 5583 2191
Fax: +43 5583 3330

Price Guide:
single €240–350
double/twin €460–600
suite €550–1,370

Belgium

Hotel location shown in red (hotel) or purple (spa hotel) with page number

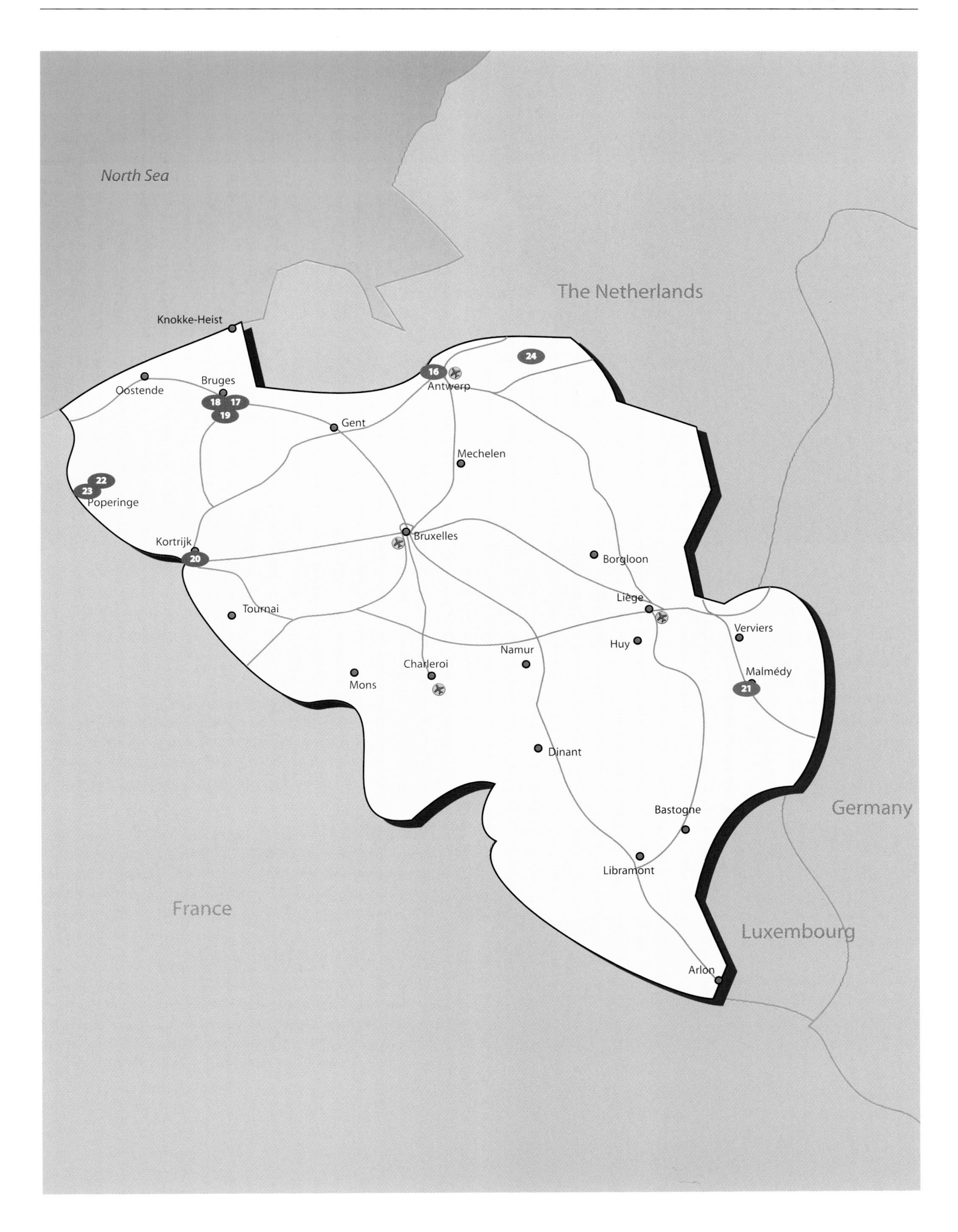

Firean Hotel

KAREL OOMSSTRAAT 6, 2018 ANTWERP, BELGIUM

Set in a quiet residential street minutes away from the centre of picturesque Antwerp, this art deco hotel is a genuine original. Ideally suited for the traveller weary of homogeneous hotel chains, its suave style is all-pervasive, from the stunning entrance right through to the Tiffany enamel and glass in the bedrooms. Renowned for the courtesy of its staff, the Firean's restaurant combines excellent service with the finest of cuisine.

Situé dans une rue résidentielle calme à quelques minutes du centre de la pittoresque ville d'Anvers, cet hôtel art déco est très original. Situé idéalement pour le voyageur lassé des chaînes d'hôtels, son style est suave et partout présent, de l'entrée étonnante à l'émail de Tiffany et aux glaces des chambres. Renommé pour la courtoisie de son personnel, le restaurant du Firean combine un excellent service avec une cuisine raffinée.

In einer ruhigen Straße, nur wenige Minuten vom Zentrum des malerischen Antwerpen entfernt, liegt dieses Art-Deco-Hotel, ideal für die Reisenden geeignet, die eintönigen Hotelketten entgehen wollen. Das stilvolle Ambiente reicht von dem beeindruckenden Eingang bis hin zu den Tiffany-Emaille- und Glaseinrichtungen in den Zimmern. Das hoteleigene Restaurant verbindet exzellenten Service mit köstlicher Küche.

Our inspector loved: *The art deco gates towards the dining area.*

Directions: From A14 > E17, exit 5.

Web: www.johansens.com/firean
E-mail: info@hotelfirean.com
Tel: +32 3 237 02 60
Fax: +32 3 238 11 68

Price Guide:
single €136–141
double/twin €158–169
junior suite €213-229

15

Hotel de Tuilerieën

DYVER 7, 8000 BRUGES, BELGIUM

This elegant 15th-century mansion has recently been converted into a most luxurious small hotel. Great care has been taken to create an extremely stylish interior without sacrificing the integrity of the building's age and character. All the expectations of modern conveniences are met and surpassed, and the stunning location alongside the picturesque canal is only enhanced by the dramatic interiors and Starck designed bathrooms.

Cette élégante maison de maître du XVe siècle a récemment été convertie en un petit hôtel des plus élégants. Un soin particulier a été apporté afin de créer un intérieur raffiné et cossu sans sacrifier au caractère et style d'époque du bâtiment. Toutes les facilités modernes sont présentes, et la situation privilégiée le long d'un canal pittoresque n'en est que mise en valeur par les spectaculaires intérieurs et les salles de bain dessinées par Starck.

Dieses elegante Haus aus dem 15. Jahrhundert wurde kürzlich in ein luxuriöses kleines Hotel umgewandelt, wobei sorgfältig darauf geachtet wurde, dass das stilvolle neue Interieur den Charakter und das Alter des Gebäudes nicht verfälscht. Jeglicher moderner Komfort wird geboten, und das dramatische Décor und die von Starck gestalteten Bäder werden durch die herrliche Lage des Hotels an einem malerischen Kanal perfekt ergänzt.

Our inspector loved: *The hotel's perfect situation and its stylish yet classical décor.*

Directions: E40 from Brussels. A17 from Courthai.

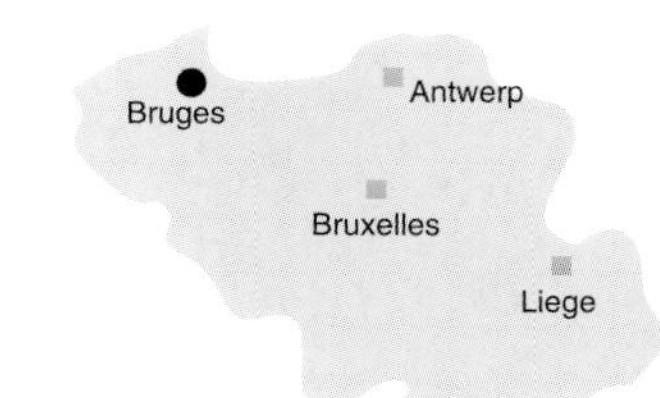

Web: www.johansens.com/hoteltuilerieen
E-mail: info@hoteltuilerieen.com
Tel: +32 50 34 36 91
Fax: +32 50 34 04 00

Price Guide: (breakfast €24, private parking €15 per 24 hours)
single €125-299
double €200-399
executive/suite €250-524

HOTEL DIE SWAENE

1 STEENHOUWERSDIJK (GROENE REI), 8000 BRUGES, BELGIUM

Overlooking one of Bruges' picturesque canals, this luxurious hotel offers a relaxing and romantic ambience. Each of the bedrooms is individually decorated and the hotel's candle-lit restaurant serves cuisine created from regional and organic ingredients. The 18th-century lounge, the former meeting room for the Tailors Guild, features fine tapestries and the 15th-century attic room is ideal for conferences accommodating up to 25 delegates. To relax, guests may use the hotel's indoor swimming pool, sauna and cold bath. Alternatively, drinks can be taken in the cosy bar.

Donnant sur un canal pittoresque, cet hôtel luxueux propose une ambiance romantique et relaxante. Chacune des chambres est décorée de façon unique et le restaurant éclairé à la bougie, sert des plats aux ingrédients régionaux. Le salon, datant du XVIIIe siècle et orné de tapisseries, est l'ancienne salle de réunion pour la guilde de tailleurs. La mansarde date du XVe siècle et offre un endroit idéal pour des conférences pour jusqu'à 25 délégués. Pour se détendre, les hôtes peuvent profiter de la piscine intérieure, la sauna et les bains froids ou prendre un verre dans le bar intime.

Dieses Luxushotel mit Blick auf einen der malerischen Kanäle Brügges besitzt ein entspanntes, romantisches Ambiente. Alle Zimmer sind unterschiedlich gestaltet, und im kerzenbeleuchteten Restaurant kann man Köstlichkeiten aus regionalen und biologisch angebauten Zutaten genießen. Im Aufenthaltsraum aus dem 18. Jahrhundert – dem einstigen Versammlungssaal der Schneidergilde – findet man edle Wandteppiche. Der Speicher aus dem 15. Jahrhundert ist ideal für Konferenzen für bis zu 25 Personen. Entspannung findet man im Hallenbad, der Sauna und dem Kaltbad oder bei einem Drink in der gemütlichen Bar.

Our inspector loved: *The altar reception desk and tapestries in the lounge.*

Directions: Take the E40 to Bruges in the direction of Ostend. Brussels (Zaventem) is the nearest airport.

Web: www.johansens.com/swaene
E-mail: info@dieswaene.com
Tel: +32 50 34 27 98
Fax: +32 50 33 66 74

Price Guide: (breakfast €15)
single €160
double €185-295
suite €350-460

HOTEL PRINSENHOF

ONTVANGERSSTRAAT 9, 8000 BRUGES, BELGIUM

This elegant 20th-century Flemish mansion, hidden down a quiet side street, is a superb and welcoming hideaway just minutes from the pulsating heart of Bruges. Renovated with great flair, the Burgundy-style interior, rich with chandeliers, antiques and moulded ceilings, has an air of opulence, which extends into the charming breakfast room, where an excellent buffet is served. The bedrooms are furnished in traditional style and provide thoughtful extras including exceptional robes in the en-suite bathrooms. Member of "Relais du Silence".

Cet élégant manoir flamand du XXe siècle, caché au fond d'une rue calme, est une étape accueillante à quelques minutes du centre animé de Bruges. Récemment renovée avec beaucoup de goût, la décoration intérieure, qui foisonne de chandelliers, de plafonds à moulures et d'antiquités dégage une atmosphère d'opulence, qui s'étend à la salle du petit déjeuner où un délicieux buffet est servi le matin. Les chambres sont décorées avec soin dans un style traditionnel et proposent des petits plus tels que des peignoirs dans les salles de bains. Membre de "Relais du Silence".

Dieses elegante flämische Haus aus dem 20. Jahrhundert liegt in einer ruhigen Seitenstraße, nur wenige Minuten vom pulsierenden Herzen Brügges entfernt. Das Hotel wurde herrlich renoviert, und das Interieur im Burgunder Stil vermittelt mit seinen Lüstern, verzierten Decken und Antiquitäten ein Gefühl von Opulenz, das sich bis zum Frühstücksraum erstreckt, in dem morgens ein Buffet serviert wird. Die exquisiten Zimmer haben eigene Bäder, sind traditionell gestaltet und bieten Extras wie herrlich luxuriöse Bademäntel. Mitglied der "Relais du Silence".

Our inspector loved: *The classic décor and welcoming staff.*

Directions: E40 > exit 8 marked "Brugge" > follow N31 > in the centre of Bruges.

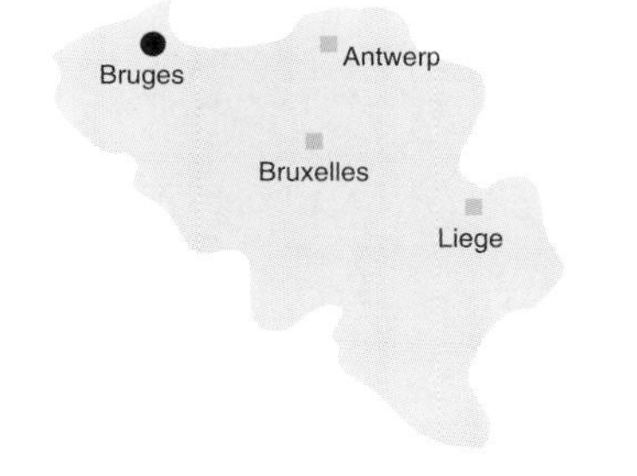

Web: www.johansens.com/prinsenhof
E-mail: info@prinsenhof.be
Tel: +32 50 34 26 90
Fax: +32 50 34 23 21

Price Guide: (breakfast €15)
single €130–285
double/twin €140–295
suite €285

Hotel Damier

GROTE MARKT 41, 8500 KORTRIJK, BELGIUM

This exquisite Rococo building is right in the town centre and ideally located for sightseeing, shopping and visiting the city museums. The hotel is one of the oldest in Belgium and is charmingly appointed with period features, elegant bedrooms and marble bathrooms. Its previous guests include Margaret Thatcher and President George Bush, who would have sampled the hotel's legendary silver service that takes place during functions in the dining room.

Ce immeuble raffiné de style rococo est situé en plein centre de ville, dans une location idéale pour visiter la ville et ses musées, et pour faire du shopping. Cet hôtel, l'un des plus vieux de Belgique, est aménagé de manière charmante avec des décors d'époque, de chambres élégantes et des salles de bain en marbre. Parmi ses hôtes précédents, on trouve Margaret Thatcher et le Président George Bush, qui ont pu apprécier le célèbre service stylé des grandes fonctions qui se tiennent dans la salle à manger.

Dieses bezaubernde Rokoko-Gebäude ist eines der ältesten Hotels in Belgien und liegt mitten im Stadtzentrum - ideal für Stadtbesichtigungen, Einkäufe und Museumsbesuche. Es ist liebevoll eingerichtet, die Zimmer sind elegant, die Bäder in Marmor gehalten. Zu den Gästen zählten bereits Margaret Thatcher und Präsident George Bush, die sicherlich in den Genuss des legendären "Silbernen Service" kamen, der während feierlicher Anlässe im Speisesaal stattfindet.

Our inspector loved: *This beautiful first-rate hotel with great artwork adorning the walls.*

Directions: 42km from Bruges. Take the E40 from Bruges to Kortrijk centre, the hotel is in market square.

Web: www.johansens.com/damier
E-mail: info@hoteldamier.be
Tel: +32 56 22 15 47
Fax: +32 56 22 86 31

Price Guide:
single €119–180
double €139–195
suites €199–359

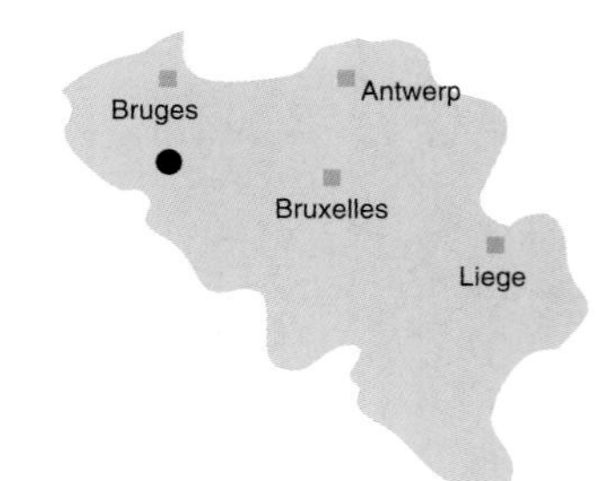

Hostellerie Trôs Marets

ROUTE DES TRÔS MARETS, 4960 MALMÉDY, BELGIUM

Set at the foot of the Hautes Fagnes National Park and offering a panoramic view across the surrounding valleys, the Trôs Marets is the epitome of modern style and comfort. The elegant furnishings immediately catch the eye, but the spectacular views from the lounge and dining room are undoubtedly the hotel's chief attraction. In addition to an al fresco terrace, there is an outstanding restaurant, where succulent dishes are complemented by fine wines.

Hostellerie située au pied du Parc Naturel des Hautes Fagnes avec vue panoramique sur les vallées avoisinantes, le Trôs Marets est l'incarnation même du style moderne et du confort. Les meubles élégants attirent le regard, et les vues spectaculaires du salon et de la salle à manger forment indubitablement la principale attraction de l'hôtel. Outre la terrace alfresco, l'établissement a un restaurant exceptionnel, où des plats délicieux sont agrémentés de vins fins.

Das Trôs Marets, am Fuße des Nationalparks Hautes Fagnes gelegen und mit Panoramablick auf die umliegenden Täler, ist die Verkörperung modernen Stils und Komforts. Die elegante Einrichtung sticht sofort ins Auge, doch die Trumpfkarte des Hotels sind zweifellos die spektakulären Aussichten vom Aufenthaltsraum und Speisesaal. Neben einer Sonnenterrasse gibt es ein exquisites Restaurant, das mit köstlichen Speisen und erlesenen Weinen für das leibliche Wohl sorgt.

Our inspector loved: *The serene setting in the scenic National Park.*

Directions: Liège > E40 > Malmédy > Eupen 6 km. 1 hour and 30 minutes from Brussels. 2 hours from Luxembourg.

Web: www.johansens.com/trosmarets
E-mail: info@trosmarets.be
Tel: +32 80 33 79 17
Fax: +32 80 33 79 10

Price Guide:
single €102
double/twin €134–206
suite €223–459

11 10

Hotel Recour

GUIDO GEZELLESTRAAT 7, 8970 POPERINGE, BELGIUM

Directions: A25 from Lille - Dunkerque (gate 13). From Brussels E40 > E17-A19. Hotel Recour is a 5-minute drive from Ypres.

Web: www.johansens.com/hotelrecour
E-mail: info@pegasusrecour.be
Tel: +32 57 33 57 25
Fax: +32 57 33 54 25

Price Guide: (breakfast €14, 50% discount valid until 31st December 2005. Please contact hotel for availability.)
single €125-200
double €150-250
suite €325

Bruges
Antwerp
Bruxelles
Liege

This 18th-century residential home, located in the heart of hop country, is only 100 metres from Poperinge town market square. The original luxury and opulence has been restored and now features magnificent pieces of furniture and exquisite details. Each of the 8 beautiful, individually furnished en suite bedrooms has every modern amenity including DVD players and internet access. The hotel's restaurant, Pegasus, serves sumptuous meals influenced by Mediterranean cuisine, created from the freshest ingredients. There are also 2 conference rooms with state-of-the-art equipment available.

Situé au coeur de la culture du houblon, cette maison datant du XVIIIe siècle est à 100 mètres de la place du marché de Poperinge. Le luxe original ayant été restauré, aujourd'hui l'hôtel est orné de meubles magnifiques et de détails exquis. Chacune des 8 chambres salle de bains attenante est meublée de manière individuelle, et est munie de tout équipement, incluant DVD et Internet. Pegasus, le restaurant de l'hôtel, sert des plats délicieux, influencés par la cuisine méditerranéenne et crées avec les ingrédients les plus frais. Il y a 2 salles de conférences du dernier cri disponibles.

Diese Residenz aus dem 18. Jahrhundert befindet sich mitten im Hopfenanbaugebiet, nur 100 Meter vom Marktplatz der Stadt Poperinge entfernt. Die einstige luxuriöse Pracht des Hotels zeigt sich am herrlichen Mobiliar und exquisiten Details. Jedes der 8 unterschiedlich eingerichteten hübschen Zimmer hat ein eigenes Bad und bietet jeden modernen Komfort wie z.B. DVD-Player und Internetanschluss. Im Hotelrestaurant Pegasus werden frisch zubereitete, mediterran geprägte Speisen serviert. Es stehen 2 Konferenzräume mit hochmoderner Ausstattung zur Verfügung.

Our inspector loved: *The exquisite bathrooms in this old residence.*

Manoir Ogygia

VEURNESTRAAT 108, 8970 POPERINGE, BELGIUM

Carefully constructed to create a replica renovated 19th-century manor, Ogygia successfully combines bygone charm with modern-day luxury. Warm wooden furnishings and thoughtful touches create a homely quality in sophisticated surroundings. The 9 guest rooms, including 2 duplex rooms featuring 2 separate sleeping areas, are individually decorated and ground floor rooms boast direct access to the garden. Views of the castle park can be admired during a buffet breakfast. The top floor relaxation area includes a Jacuzzi, sauna, steam shower and bar.

Construit avec soin afin de créer une réplique améliorée d'un manoir du XIXe siècle, Ogygia mélange avec succès le charme d'autrefois et le luxe d'aujourd'hui. Le mobilier chaleureux en bois et les petites touches attentionnées créent une atmosphère accueillante dans un environnement sophistiqué. Les 9 chambres, dont 2 en duplex avec coin chambre séparé, sont individuellement décorées et les chambres du rez de chaussée ont accès direct sur le jardin. Des vues sur le parc du château peuvent être admirées en dégustant le petit-déjeuner buffet. L'aire de relaxation au dernier étage comprend jacuzzi, sauna, cabine de vapeur et un bar.

Dieses sorgfältig konstruierte Haus gleicht einem Landsitz aus dem 19. Jahrhundert und ist die perfekte Verbindung aus dem Charme vergangener Zeit und modernem Luxus. Warme Holzmöbel und liebevolle Details schaffen ein heimeliges Gefühl in eleganter Umgebung. Die 9 Zimmer, darunter 2 Duplexzimmer mit 2 separaten Schlafbereichen sind individuell gestaltet, und diejenigen im Erdgeschoß haben Zugang zum Garten. Beim Frühstücksbuffet kann man die Sicht auf den Schlosspark bewundern, und zur Entspannung bietet die oberste Etage Jacuzzi, Sauna, Dampfbad und Bar.

Our inspector loved: *The charming hospitality and secluded park setting.*

Directions: A25 from Lille (France) > Dunkerque (Gate 13). From Brussels take the E40, E17 or A19. 5 minutes from Ypres.

Web: www.johansens.com/ogygia
E-mail: info@ogygia.be
Tel: +32 57 33 88 38
Fax: +32 57 33 88 77

Bruges
Antwerp
Bruxelles
Liege

Price Guide:
double €115-135

Hostellerie Ter Driezen

HERENTALSSTRAAT 18, 2300 TURNHOUT, BELGIUM

Formerly the official residence of the mayor of Turnhout, today this 18th-century house offers modern accommodation alongside professional service managed by Gust and Liesbeth Keersmaekers, owners for 28 years. Public rooms feature classic furnishings, crystal chandeliers, Oriental rugs and wooden floors and bedrooms provide relaxing havens in warm tones. Enjoy pre-dinner drinks by the fireplace before dining in one of the 8 fine restaurants within 5 minutes, walk in the centre of town. During summer, al fresco dining in the garden can be arranged.

Ancienne résidence officielle du maire de Turnhout, cette maison du XVIIIe siècle est aujourd'hui un hôtel moderne bénéficiant du service professionnel de Gust et Liesbeth Keersmaekers, propriétaires depuis 28 ans. Les pièces communes sont aménagées avec un mobilier classique, des chandeliers en cristal, des tapis orientaux et des planchers et les chambres sont des havres de paix dans des tons chaleureux. Dégustez un apéritif près de la cheminée avant de dîner à l'un des 8 restaurants excellents au centre ville. Pendant l'été, des dîners dans le jardin peuvent être arrangés.

Dieses Haus aus dem 18. Jahrhundert war einst die offizielle Residenz des Bürgermeisters von Turnhout, und ist nun ein modernes Hotel, seit nunmehr 28 Jahren professionell geführt von Gust und Liesbeth Keersmaekers. Die Aufenthaltsräume sind klassisch mit Kristalllüstern, orientalischen Teppichen und Holzböden gestaltet, und die Zimmer sind in warmen Farbtönen gehalten. Ein Apéritif am offenen Kamin ist der ideale Auftakt für ein Essen in einem der 8 nur 5 Gehminuten entfernten Restaurants im Stadtzentrum. Im Sommer kann man auch im Garten dinieren.

Our inspector loved: *Entering a bygone era, and the owners' warm hospitality.*

Directions: Antwerpen > E34 > Turnhout.

Web: www.johansens.com/terdriezen
E-mail: terdriezen@yahoo.com
Tel: +32 14 41 87 57
Fax: +32 14 42 03 10

Price Guide:
single €110
double €135-145

HILDON
NATURAL MINERAL WATER
ESTABLISHED
1989
HILDON
AN ENGLISH
NATURAL MINERAL WATER
OF EXCEPTIONAL TASTE
DELIGHTFULLY STILL
HILDON
AN ENGLISH
NATURAL MINERAL WATER
OF EXCEPTIONAL TASTE
GENTLY CARBONATED
Hildon Ltd., Broughton, Hampshire SO20 8DQ
www.hildon.com

CROATIA

Hotel location shown in red (hotel) or purple (spa hotel) with page number

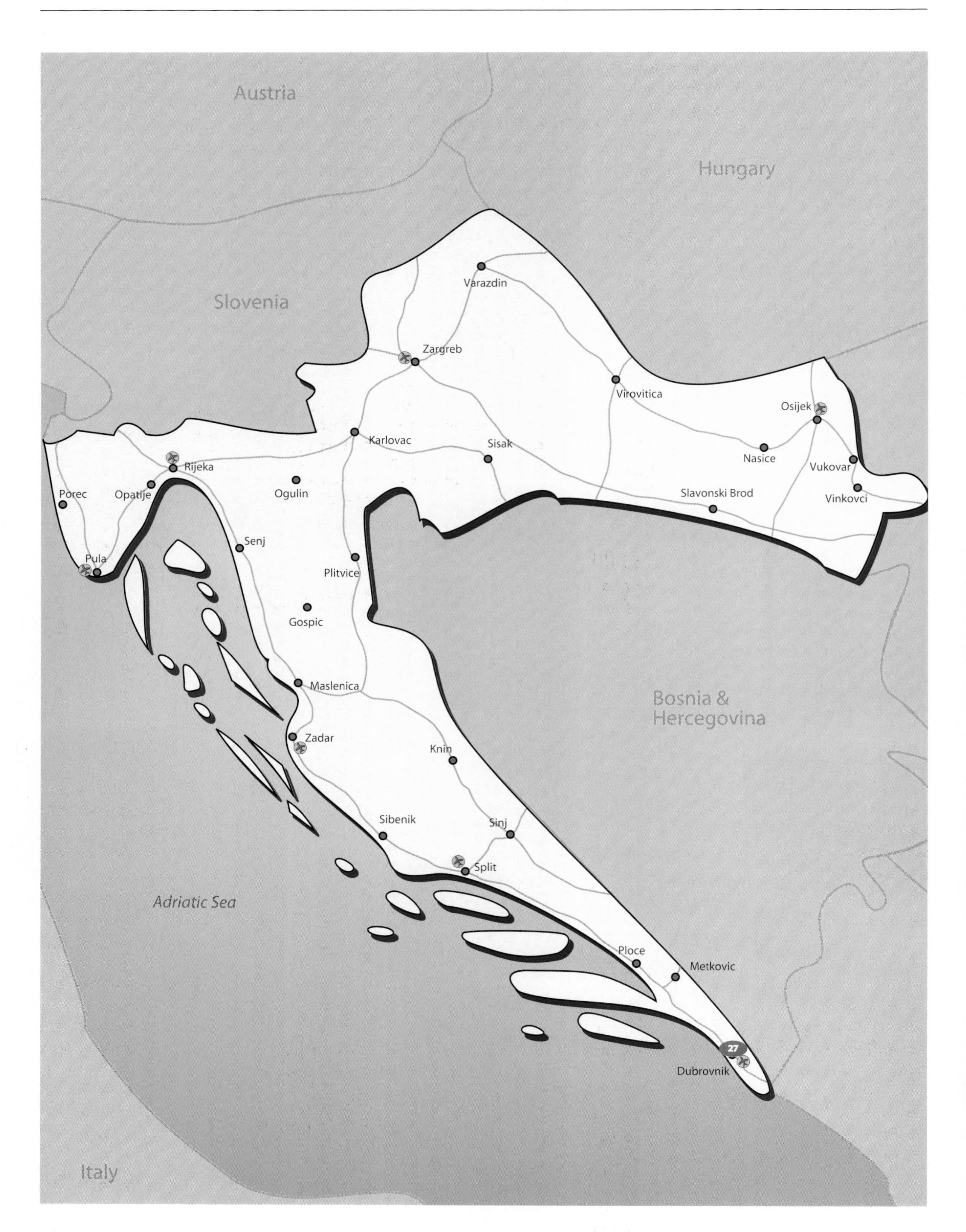

GRAND VILLA ARGENTINA

FRANA SUPILA 14, 20000 DUBROVNIK, CROATIA

4 exclusive villas and a hotel comprise this unique property, which reflects the spirit, history and cultural heritage of Dubrovnik. Surrounded by charming terraced gardens, each villa is tastefully appointed; standard guest rooms are spacious, and the sea view rooms look across the gardens to the Island of Lokrum. The restaurants serve gourmet Dalmatian and international cuisine, and the Wellness Centre offers health and beauty treatments. Grand Villa Argentina is the ideal place to discover the old city, only a 10-minute walk away. Versatile congress and banqueting facilities are available.

Cette propriété unique qui reflète parfaitement l'héritage spirituel, historique et culturel de Dubrovnik, est composée de 4 villas exclusives et d'un hôtel. Entourés de charmants jardins en terrasses, chaque villa est décorée avec goût. Les chambres standard sont spacieuses, et les chambres côté mer offrent des vues allant du jardin à l'île de Lokrum. Les restaurants servent cuisine gourmet dalmate et internationale et le centre de bien-être offre des soins de santé et de beauté. C'est l'endroit idéal pour découvrir la vieille ville, seulement à 10 minutes a pied. L'interieur de salons de banquets et réunions s'adapte selon vos besoins.

Dieses einzigartige, aus 4 exklusiven Villen und einem Hotel bestehende Anwesen spiegelt perfekt die Geschichte und das kulturelle Erbe Dubrovniks wider. Die von zauberhaften terrassenartigen Gärten umgebenen Villen sind geschmackvoll gestaltet, die Standard-Zimmer sind großzügig, und die mit Meerblick haben eine Sicht bis hin zur Insel Lokrum. Im Restaurants werden dalmatinische und internationale Gerichte serviert, und das Wellness-Zentrum bietet Gesundheits- und Schönheitsbehandlungen. Der ideale Ort, um die nur 10 Minuten entfernte Altstadt zu besichtigen. Einrichtungen für Feiern und Konferenzen sind vorhanden.

Our inspector loved: *Dining on one of the terraces - a gastronomic adventure!*

Directions: 20 minutes from Dubrovnik International Airport. Follow city centre > the hotel is signposted.

Web: www.johansens.com/grandvillaargentina
E-mail: sales@hoteli-argentina.hr
Tel: +385 20 440555
Fax: +385 20 432 524

Price Guide: (excluding local tax)
single €136-268
double €174-334
suite €390-470

Cyprus

Hotel location shown in red (hotel) or purple (spa hotel) with page number

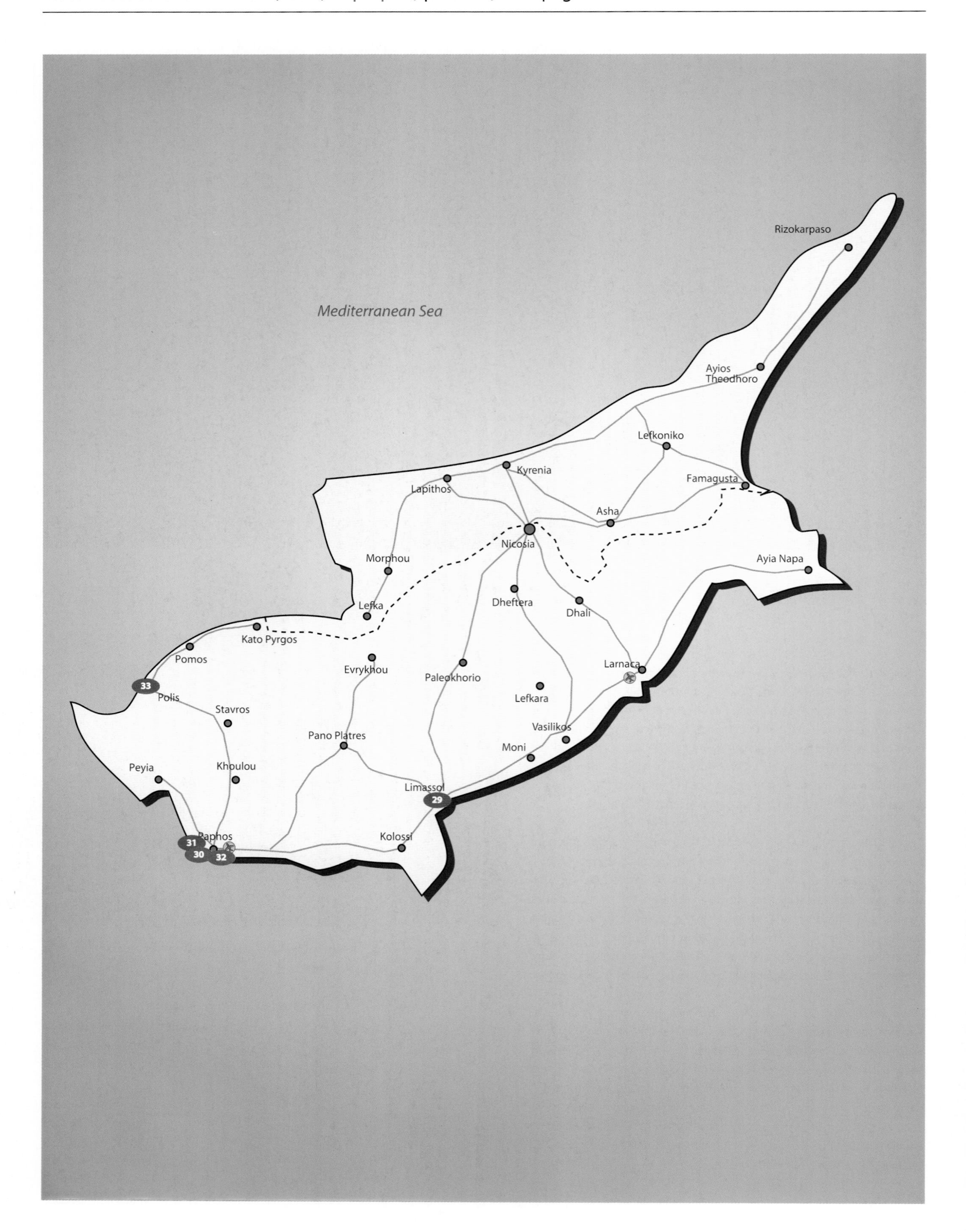

FOUR SEASONS HOTEL

PO BOX 57222, 3313 LIMASSOL, CYPRUS

This exceptional, prestigious hotel stands on the edge of a sandy beach, a short drive from Limassol. It combines 5-star amenities with elegant décor, superb cuisine and excellent service. Public areas are elegant and guest rooms range from classic superior bedrooms to spacious garden studios, to uniquely designed, opulent suites. A member of Chaîne des Rôtisseurs - International Gastronomic Association, 4 restaurants offer imaginative dining experiences to satisfy all tastes. Leisure facilities include a thalasso spa. A complete hotel refurbishment is planned for winter 2004-2005.

Ce prestigieux hôtel se situe au bord d'une plage de sable, près du centre de la cosmopolite ville de Limassol. L'hôtel offre tous les équipements d'un 5* avec un décor élégant, une délicieuse cuisine et un excellent service. Les salons sont élégants et l'hébergement varie de chambres supérieures classiques, aux larges garden studios, aux suites exclusives et opulentes. 4 restaurants, membres de Chaîne des Rôtisseurs (confrérie internationale de la gastronomie), proposent une cuisine imaginative. Il y a un centre thalasso, et une remise à neuf de tout l,hôtel est envisagé pour l'hiver de 2004/2005.

Dieses prestigereiche Hotel befindet sich am Rand eines Sandstrandes nur wenige Autominuten vom Zentrum des kosmopoliten Limassol entfernt. 5-Sterne-Einrichtungen verbinden sich mit elegantem Décor, exzellenter Küche und hervorragendem Service. Die Aufenthaltsräume sind elegant, und zur Auswahl stehen klassische Doppelzimmer, geräumige Garden Studios und einzigartige opulente Suiten. 4 Restaurants, Mitglied der Chaîne des Rôtisseurs (internationaler Gastronomie-Verband) bieten kulinarischen Genuss für jeden Geschmack. Es gibt ein Thalasso-Spa und für Winter 2004/2005 ist eine Komplett-Renovierung des ganzen Hotels vorgesehen.

Our inspector loved: *The garden studios with outdoor Jacuzzis - adults only.*

Directions: From Larnaca > highway to Limassol > exit Agios Tychonas > turn left > the traffic lights (T-junction) > turn right > entrance is 30m on the left.

Web: www.johansens.com/fourseasons
E-mail: inquiries@fourseasons.com.cy
Tel: +357 258 58000
Fax: +357 253 10887

Price Guide:
single CY£103–138
double/twin CY£128–198
studio room (double occupancy) CY£214–226
garden studio (double occupancy CY£282–316
suite CY£350-1,300

ALMYRA

design hotels

POSEIDONOS AVENUE, 8042 PAPHOS, CYPRUS

Directions: Highway to Paphos > Kato Paphos > Poseidonos Avenue > hotel is located on the left-hand side (on the seafront next to The Annabelle Hotel). Paphos Airport is 15 minutes away. Larnaca Airport is 1 hour and 30 minutes away.

Web: www.johansens.com/almyra
E-mail: almyra@thanoshotels.com and sales@thanoshotels.com
Tel: +357 26 93 30 91
Fax: +357 26 94 28 18

Nicosia
Paphos
Limassol

Price Guide:
single CY£48-82
double CY£47-112
suite CY£250-395

Located directly on the seafront in the delightful town of Paphos, Almyra has been totally refurbished over the past 18 months and is now the ultimate in contemporary design. Beautifully styled and ultra modern, it remains extremely comfortable and appeals to both couples and families. There are 3 restaurants, the most notable being the Notios where stunning dishes are created with a special culinary ideology as well as the ethos of Almyra.

Situé en bord de mer dans la charmante ville de Paphos, Almyra a été complètement restauré ces 18 derniers mois et est maintenant le summum du design contemporain et minimaliste. Magnifiquement stylé et ultra moderne, l'hôtel reste extrêmement confortable et attire aussi bien les couples que les familles. Il y a 3 restaurants, le plus remarquable étant Notios où des plats impressionants sont créés suivant une idéologie spéciale culinaire ainsi que la culture d'Almyra.

Das direkt am Ufer der hübschen Stadt Paphos gelegene Almyra wurde die letzen eineinhalb Jahre komplett renoviert und bietet nun ultimatives zeitgenössisch-minimalistisches Design. Das herrlich gestaltete ultramoderne Hotel ist extrem komfortabel und spricht sowohl Paare als auch Familien an. Es gibt 3 Restaurants, das bekannteste davon das Notios, wo eindrucksvolle Speisen gemäß einer speziellen kulinarischen Ideologie und gemäß dem Ethos von Almyra zubereitet werden.

Our inspector loved: *Dining al fresco facing the Mediterranean and sampling Rob Shipman's (Nobu) fusion Japanese/Mediterranean cuisine.*

Elysium

QUEEN VERENIKIS STREET, PO BOX 60701, 8107 PAPHOS, CYPRUS

Visitors cannot but be impressed by initial impressions of this palatial hotel. First they cross a drawbridge and then go through a medieval arch before being attentively welcomed into a lovely colonnaded reception area. Situated on the coastal road from Paphos to Coral Bay, Elysium benefits from an exceptional location next to the Tomb of Kings and enjoys uninterrupted sea views. This is one of the country's luxury "concept" hotels designed to provide complete relaxation for guests and offer the best in comfort, leisure facilities and cuisine.

Les visiteurs ne peuvent qu'être subjugués des premières impressions offertes par cet hôtel grandiose. En premier lieu, ils traversent un pont-levis et passent sous une voûte datant du moyen-âge avant d'âtre attentivement accueillis dans la superbe réception à colonnades. Situé sur la route côtière entre Paphos et Coral Bay, Elysium profite d'un magnifique emplacement à côté du Tombeau des Rois et jouit de vues mer à l'infini. Cet hôtel est l'un des 'concepts' hôtels les plus luxueux du pays, conçu afin d'offrir une relaxation totale à ses hôtes dans le meilleur du confort, de la cuisine et des équipements de loisirs.

Der erste Eindruck dieses palastartigen Hotels ist einfach umwerfend. Man gelangt über eine Zugbrücke zu einem mittelalterlichen Torbogen, bevor man die hübsche, einladende, von Säulen umrahmte Rezeption betritt. Das an der Küstenstraße von Paphos nach Coral Bay direkt neben dem Grabmal der Könige gelegene Elysium bietet eine ungebrochene Sicht auf das Meer. Dieses Hotel ist eines der luxuriösen „Konzepthotels" des Landes, das seinen Gästen Entspannung pur und das Beste an Komfort, Freizeitmöglichkeiten und kulinarischem Genuss verspricht.

Our inspector loved: *Café Oriental for the Byzantine coffee and sweet delicacies.*

Directions: From Paphos: road to Polis/Coral Bay > turn left at Tomb of the Kings.

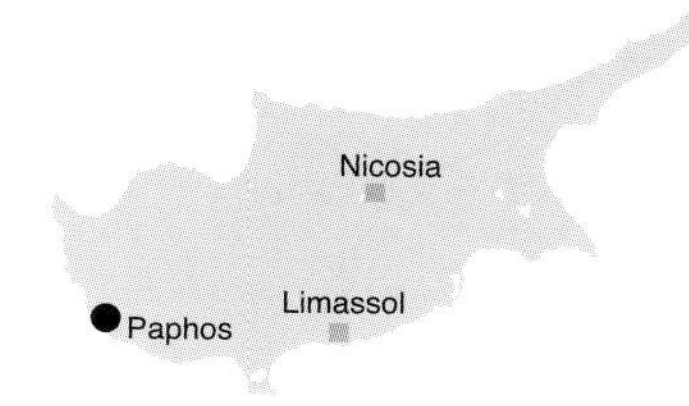

Web: www.johansens.com/elysium
E-mail: info@elysium.com.cy
Tel: +357 26 844 444
Fax: +357 26 844 333

Price Guide:
single CY£90-192
double/twin CY£112-240
studio CY£160-227
villa CY£244-335
suite CY£170-1,250

THE ANNABELLE HOTEL

POSEIDONOS AVENUE, 8042 PAPHOS, CYPRUS

Directions: Highway to Paphos > Kato Paphos > Poseidonos Avenue > hotel is located on the left-hand side, on the seafront. Paphos Airport is 15 minutes away. Larnaca Airport is 1 hour and 30 minutes away.

Web: www.johansens.com/annabelle
E-mail: the-annabelle@thanoshotels.com and sales@thanoshotels.com
Tel: +357 26 938 333
Fax: +357 26 945 502

Price Guide:
single CY£62-140
double CY£74-190
suite CY£134-316

Idyllically located on the seafront at Paphos, The Annabelle is a stunning and luxurious hotel, where every care is taken to ensure guests' total comfort and relaxation. Decorated in soft, muted colours, the atmosphere is cool and tranquil, with views onto tropical gardens, waterfalls and pools, and out towards the old fort of Paphos. The service is attentive and discreet with the feeling of being part of a small family-run hotel, and a choice of 3 stunning restaurants, both indoor and outdoor, ensures there is something to suit all tastes.

Idéalement situé en bord de mer à Paphos, l'Annabelle est un magnifique et luxueux hôtel où tout est mis en place pour assurer le repos et le confort total du client. Décoré dans des tons pales et des couleurs sourdes, l'atmosphère y est tranquille et agréable avec des vues sur les jardins tropicaux, cascades, bassins et plus loin sur la vieille forteresse de Paphos. Le service est attentionné et discret avec le sentiment d'être dans un petit hôtel de famille. Tous les goûts culinaires sont satisfaits avec un choix de 3 superbes restaurants, à l'intérieur et à l'extérieur.

Das idyllisch direkt am Meer bei Paphos gelegene Annabelle ist ein eindrucksvolles und luxuriöses Hotel, das jedem Gast Komfort und Entspannung pur bietet. Sanfte, gedämpfte Farben sorgen für ein kühles, ruhiges Ambiente, und man blickt auf tropische Gärten, Wasserfälle und Pools bis zur alten Festung von Paphos. Der Service ist aufmerksam und diskret, man fühlt sich wie ein Teil eines kleinen, familiengeführten Hotels. 3 hervorragende, drinnen und draußen gelegene Restaurants garantieren Gaumenfreuden für jeden Geschmack.

Our inspector loved: *The relaxed, secluded environment at this seafront hotel.*

ANASSA

PO BOX 66006, LATSI, 8830 POLIS, CYPRUS

This stunning resort has established itself as one of the most luxurious in the Mediterranean, built within the traditions of a Cypriot village, complete with Byzantine-style chapel and village square. Panoramic views over magnificent unspoilt sandy beaches complement the white-washed villas and terracotta tiled roofs. Elegant bedrooms are spacious and light with private balconies overlooking the bay and gardens. There are 2 outdoor swimming pools and a superb thalassa spa as well as plenty of watersports available.

Ce somptueux resort, construit dans la tradition des villages chypriotes avec une chapelle de style byzantin et une place de village, s'est établi comme l'un des plus luxueux en Méditerranée. Les vues panoramiques sur les magnifiques plages de sable désertes mettent en valeur les maisons de chaux blanche et les toits en tuiles de terre cuite. Les chambres élégantes sont spacieuses et claires avec des balcons privés surplombant la baie et les jardins. Il y a 2 piscines extérieures, un superbe thalasso spa et de nombreux sports nautiques disponibles.

Dieses fantastische Resort hat sich bereits als eines der luxuriösesten im Mittelmeerraum etabliert. Im Stil eines traditionellen zypriotischen Dorfes erbaut, bietet es neben einer byzantinischen Kapelle und einem Dorfplatz Panoramablicke auf herrlich einsame Strände, weiß getünchte Villen und Dächer aus Terrakotta-Ziegeln. Die eleganten, geräumigen Zimmer haben eigene Balkone mit Blick auf die Bucht und die Gärten. Es gibt 2 Swimmingpools und ein wunderbares Thalasso-Spa sowie zahlreiche Wassersportmöglichkeiten.

Our inspector loved: *The luxurious suites with pretty terraces and private pools.*

Directions: Paphos > Polis > Baths of Aphrodite > the hotel is on the left-hand side before Baths of Aphrodite. 45 minutes from Paphos Airport. 2 hours and 30 minutes from Larnaca Airport.

Web: www.johansens.com/anassa
E-mail: anassa@thanoshotels.com and sales@thanoshotels.com
Tel: +357 26 888 000
Fax: +357 26 322 900

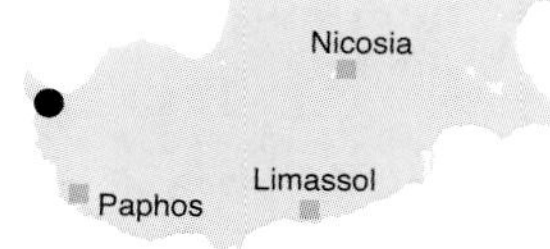

Price Guide:
single CY£150-228
double CY£196-298
suite CY£220-370

Czech Republic

Hotel location shown in red (hotel) or purple (spa hotel) with page number

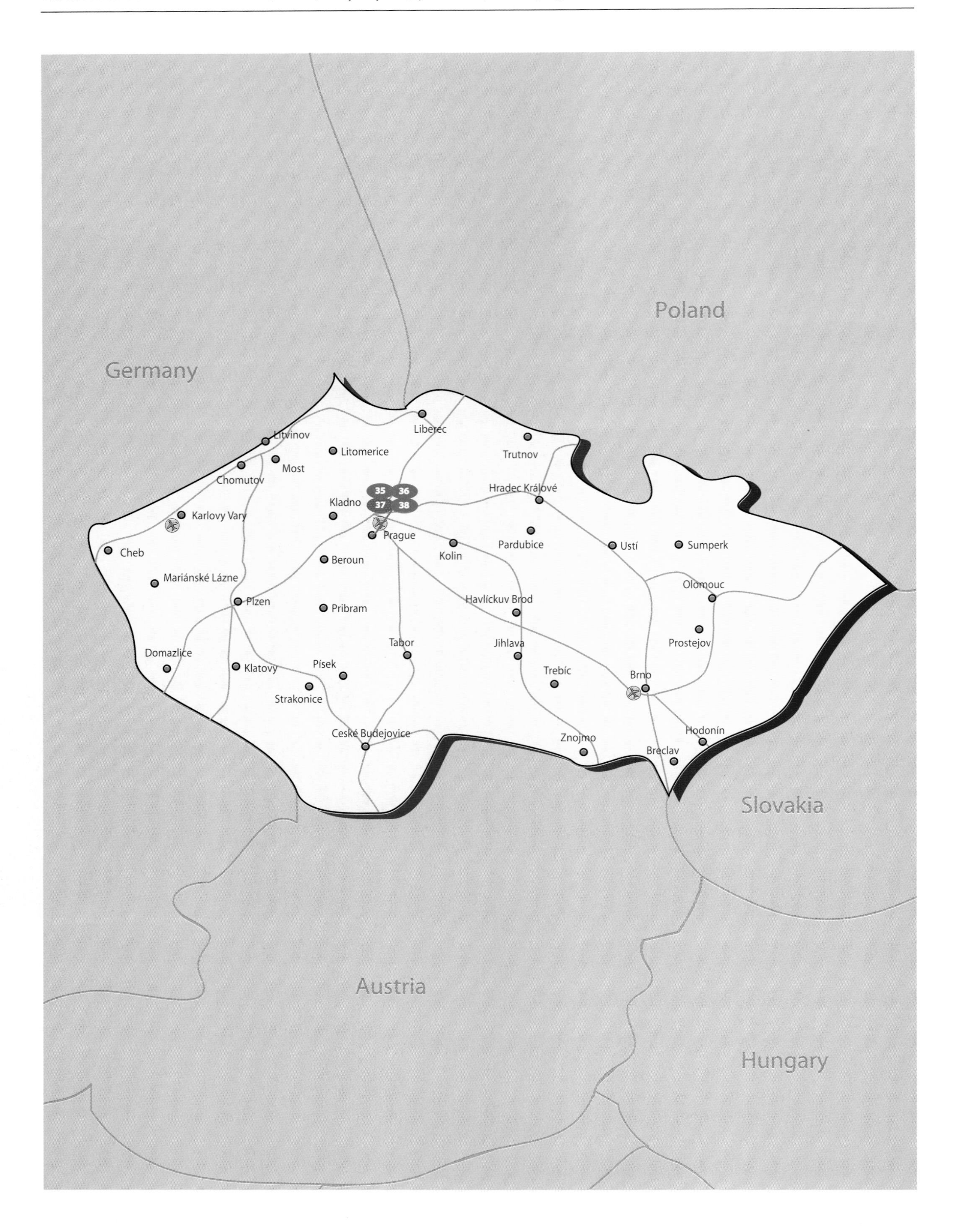

Art Hotel Prague

NAD KRÁLOVSKOU OBOROU 53, 170 00 PRAGUE 7, CZECH REPUBLIC

Two famous artists, Jan and Pravoslav Kotik, provided the inspiration for this artistic hotel, which is located only a 10-minute walk from the city centre. The hotel was recently designed and built by the architect Martin Kotik, ensuring that its long artistic tradition is kept within this well-known family, but made available to guests. Each floor of the 6-storey building presents a thematic mini collection of works by the Kotiks, as well as Pavel Stecha, famous for photographs of architectural detail, and Pavel Roucka, a painter and graphic artist.

Deux artistes de renom, Jan et Pravoslav Kotik, sont à l'origine de cet hôtel artistique, situé à quelques minutes à pied du centre ville. L'hôtel à été récemment conçu et construit par l'architecte Martin Kotik, garantissant ainsi que la tradition artistique reste dans cette célèbre famille tout en en faisant profiter les clients. Chaque étage, de cet immeuble de 6 niveaux, présente une mini collection thématique des œuvres des Kotiks ainsi que de Pavel Stecha, photographe reconnu de détails d'architecture, et de Pavel Rouchka, un peintre et artiste graphique.

Zwei bekannte Künstler, Jan und Pravoslav Kotik inspirierten den Bau dieses Künstlerhotels, das nur 10 Minuten vom Stadtzentrum entfernt ist. Das Hotel wurde erst kürzlich von dem Architekten Martin Kotik erbaut und designt, der Wert darauf legte, dass die lange künstlerische Tradition in der Familie blieb, aber dennoch den Hotelgästen zugänglich gemacht wurde. Jede der 6 Etagen bietet eine kleine Sammlung von Kunstwerken der Kotiks, sowie von Pavel Stecha, bekannt für Fotografien architektonischer Details, und Pavel Roucka, einem Maler und Grafiker.

Our inspector loved: *The black and white photographs in the breakfast room depicting life in this former 1970s socialist state.*

Directions: The hotel is 12km from Prague Ruzyne Airport.

Web: www.johansens.com/arthotel
E-mail: johansens@arthotel.cz
Tel: +420 233 101 331
Fax: +420 233 101 311

Prague
Olomouc
Tábor

Price Guide:
single €140
double €160
suite €190

Bellagio Hotel Prague

U MILOSRDNYCH 2, 110 00 PRAGUE 1, CZECH REPUBLIC

Directions: Situated in the old Jewish district between Cechuv and Stefanikuv bridge.

Web: www.johansens.com/bellagio
E-mail: kvetaf@bellagiohotel.cz
Tel: +420 221 778 999
Fax: +420 221 778 900

Price Guide:
single €144-189
double €163-211
suite €188-259

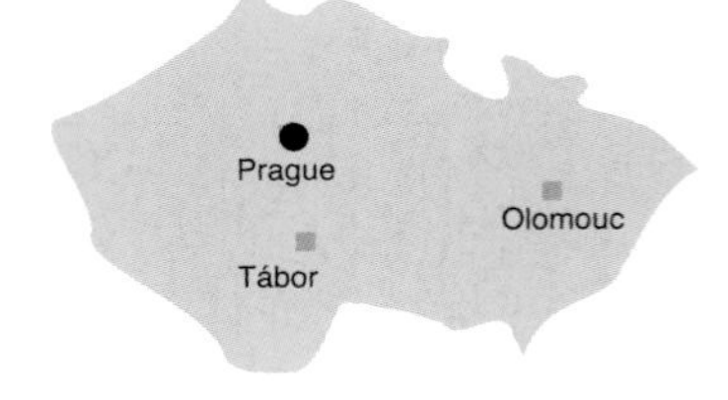

Located in a quiet yet accessible part of historical Prague, within walking distance of the Old Town Square, the magnificent Hotel Bellagio has been completely renovated in recent years. Italian chic is the theme throughout, and the building is embellished with stylish Italian furnishings and fabrics creating a warm, romantic ambience. Guests find the convivial staff helpful and courteous, in particular Swedish chef Lars Sjostrand is on hand to fulfil any unique request from gourmet guests!

Situé dans un endroit calme mais accessible de la ville historique de Prague, et seulement quelques minutes à pied de la place principale de la vieille ville, le magnifique hôtel Bellagio a été récemment complètement rénové. Le chic italien est le thème général et le bâtiment est embelli par de superbes meubles et tissus italiens, créant ainsi une atmosphère chaleureuse et romantique. Le personnel est convivial, courtois et serviable ; en particulier le Chef Suèdois Lars Sjostrand qui est toujours prêt à répondre à n'importe quel désir des ses hôtes gastronomes.

Das in einem ruhigen und doch leicht erreichbaren Teil des historischen Prag gelegene und nur ein paar Gehminuten vom Hauptplatz der Altstadt entfernte Hotel Bellagio wurde über die letzten Jahre hinweg gründlich renoviert. Das Motto ist italienischer Chic, und überall findet man elegante italienische Möbel und Stoffe, die eine warme, romantische Atmosphäre schaffen. Das Personal ist freundlich und hilfsbereit, und insbesondere der schwedische Chefkoch Lars Sjostrand ist ständig zur Stelle, um auch die ausgefallensten Wünsche der anspruchsvollen Gäste zu erfüllen.

Our inspector loved: *The Swedish chef Lars Sjostrand, who creates inventive menus and suggests the perfect wine to accompany the meal.*

HOTEL HOFFMEISTER

POD BRUSKOU 7, MALÁ STRANA, 11800 PRAGUE 1, CZECH REPUBLIC

This charming hotel has recently undergone extensive refurbishment. Great thought has been paid to 3 superbly designed new suites, furnished with beautiful antique effects and situated in a medieval house opposite the main building. The original restaurant has been divided in 2 and replaced by a coffee lounge, ideal for light lunches, and an elegant dining room, complete with Bohemian crystal glassware. Guests can take advantage of the relaxing spa, which incorporates the walls of ancient Prague in its design.

Cet hôtel de charme vient juste d'être entièrement rénové. Une attention toute particulière à été portée au design des 3 magnifiques nouvelles suites, meublées avec de superbes antiquités et situées dans une maison médiévale en face du bâtiment principal. Le restaurant d'origine a été séparé en deux et remplacé par un café lounge, idéal pour les déjeuners légers, et par une salle à manger très élégante avec un service en cristal de Bohême. Les hôtes peuvent profiter du spa, qui comprend, dans sa conception, les murs de l'ancien Prague.

Dieses bezaubernde Hotel wurde kürzlich ausgiebig renoviert, wobei 3 herrlich gestaltete neue Suiten besonders viel Aufmerksamkeit bekamen – sie sind mit wundervollen Antiquitäten eingerichtet und befinden sich in einem mittelalterlichen Haus gegenüber des Haupthotels. Das ursprüngliche Restaurant wurde in 2 geteilt, eine Lounge für Kaffee und leichte Mittagessen, und einen eleganten Speisesaal, in dem überall echtes böhmisches Kristallglas zu finden ist. Zur Entspannung gibt es ein Spa, dessen Wände mit Abbildungen des alten Prag gestaltet sind.

Our inspector loved: *The newly reconstructed Bohemian-style restaurant and spa in the old building's cellar, set amidst the medieval city walls.*

Directions: The hotel is situated between Mánesuu bridge and Prague castle.

Web: www.johansens.com/hoffmeister
E-mail: hotel@hoffmeister.cz
Tel: +420 251 017 111
Fax: +420 251 017 100

Prague
Olomouc
Tábor

Price Guide:
single €165-220
double/twin €225-310
suite €275-430

Romantik Hotel U Raka

CERNÍNSKÁ 10/93, 11800 PRAGUE 1, CZECH REPUBLIC

Directions: In the centre of Prague's Castle area, near Loretta.

Web: www.johansens.com/uraka
E-mail: uraka@login.cz
Tel: +420 2205 111 00
Fax: +420 2333 580 41

Price Guide:
single €185-210
double €205-230
suite €240-260

Located on the castle hill in the Hradcany area, this enchanting hotel in the centre of Prague is an oasis of peace and seclusion – the ideal place for those who wish to escape the hustle and bustle of modern life, withdraw with a book and discover the city on a leisurely walk. With its cosy bedrooms and warming fireplaces, the atmosphere is more that of a private home than a hotel. The hotel serves snacks and drinks, whilst for dinner guests will find numerous restaurants in the vicinity.

Situé sur la colline du château dans le quartier de Hradcany, cet hôtel enchanteur du centre de Prague est un havre de paix et d'isolement -- l'endroit idéal pour ceux qui veulent échapper au tourbillon de la vie moderne, se retirer avec un livre et découvrir la ville au rythme d'une promenade. Avec ses chambres douillettes et de chaleureux coins cheminée, l'atmosphère ressemble plus à celle d'une maison privée que d'un hôtel. L'hôtel sert des en-cas et boissons, alors que pour le dîner les hôtes pourront faire leur choix parmi les nombreux restaurants du voisinage.

Dieses zauberhafte, auf dem Schlosshügel nahe des Hradschin gelegene Hotel ist eine wahre Oase der Ruhe und Abgeschiedenheit – der ideale Ort, um der Hektik des Alltags zu entfliehen, sich mit einem Buch zurückzuziehen und gemächliche Spaziergänge zu unternehmen. Mit seinen gemütlichen Zimmern und wärmenden Kaminen erinnert die Atmosphäre eher an ein Privathaus als an ein Hotel. Kleine Mahlzeiten und Getränke werden hier serviert, und zahlreiche Restaurants befinden sich in der Nähe.

***Our inspector loved:** The romantic breakfast room reminiscent of an old kitchen.*

DENMARK

Hotel location shown in red (hotel) or purple (spa hotel) with page number

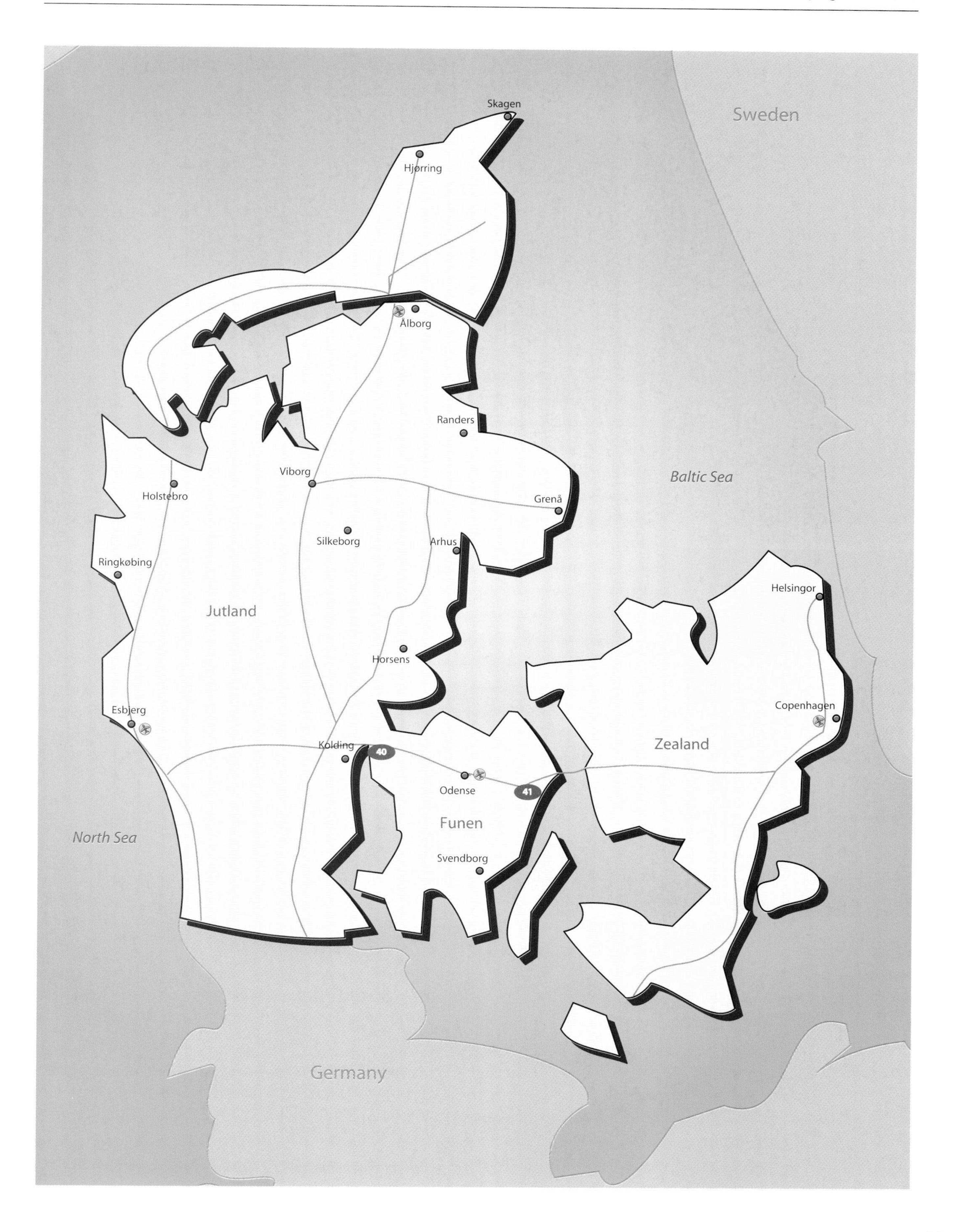

HINDSGAVL SLOT

HINDSGAVL ALLÉ 7, 5500 MIDDELFART, DENMARK

Directions: E20 > Route 161 Middelfart.

Web: www.johansens.com/hindsgavl
E-mail: hindsgavl@hindsgavl.dk
Tel: +45 64 41 88 00
Fax: +45 64 41 88 11

Price Guide:
single €134
double €162
suite €202

Hindsgavl Slot dates back to the 12th century and has a very impressive history. Today, the castle stands in 125 acres of garden, park, meadow and forest and provides modern comfort alongside old traditions within a fairytale atmosphere. Exquisite works of art and rare antiques feature throughout the relaxing rooms of the house, and the serene grounds offer great walking trails, with castle ruins and farm buildings, to explore. Traditional Danish and French cuisine is prepared in the restaurant.

Hindsgavl Slot date du 12ème siècle et peut se vanter d'un passé historique impressionnant. Aujourd'hui, le château se dresse au cœur de 50 hectares de jardins, parcs, prairies et forêts et offre tout le confort moderne allié aux anciennes traditions dans une atmosphère de conte de fées. De superbes œuvres d'art et d'uniques antiquités ornent les pièces de la maison. Les terres offrent de beaux sentiers de randonnée ainsi que des ruines de château et des fermes à explorer. Une cuisine traditionnelle danoise et française est préparée au restaurant.

Die eindrucksvolle Geschichte dieses Hotels geht bis ins 12. Jahrhundert zurück. Heute liegt Hindsgavl Slot inmitten von 50ha Garten, Park, Wiese und Wald und verbindet modernen Komfort mit alten Traditionen in einem märchenhaften Ambiente. Exquisite Kunstwerke und seltene Antiquitäten zieren die erholsamen Zimmer des Hauses, und das Hotelgelände bietet hervorragende Wanderwege, Burgruinen und Bauernhäuser. Im Restaurant wird traditionelle dänische und französische Küche serviert.

Our inspector loved: *The tranquillity of the castle's private grounds.*

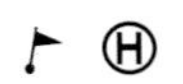

Hotel Hesselet

CHRISTIANSLUNDSVEJ 119, 5800 NYBORG, DENMARK

Situated on the island of Funen and surrounded by woodland, the renowned Hesselet offers simply awe-inspiring views over the sea. The Japanese influenced architecture is one of the hotel's most outstanding features, and visitors are not disappointed by the tasteful interior and spacious airy rooms. More active guests will enjoy the indoor pool with fitness equipment or may prefer to swim from the hotel jetty or play tennis.

Situé sur l'île de Funen et entouré de bois, le fameux Hesselet offre des vues extraordinaires sur la mer. L'architecture d'influence japonaise est un des traits de caractères principaux de l'hôtel et les visiteurs ne seront pas déçus de l'intérieur superbe et des chambres aériennes et luxueuses. Les visiteurs les plus actifs pourront profiter de la piscine couverte avec ses équipements sportifs ou pourront préférer une nage depuis la jetée ou jouer au tennis.

Das renommierte Hotel Hesselet auf der Insel Funen ist von Waldlandschaft umgeben und bietet atemberaubende Aussichten über das Meer. Die japanisch beeinflusste Architektur ist eine seiner Besonderheiten, und die geschmackvolle Inneneinrichtung und die geräumigen, luftigen Zimmern sind nicht weniger beeindruckend. Sportliche Gäste können Hallenbad und Fitnessgeräte nutzen, Tennis spielen oder vom hoteleigenen Steg aus schwimmen.

Our inspector loved: *The beautiful seafront location.*

Directions: E20 > exit 45 > Nyborg.

Web: www.johansens.com/hesselet
E-mail: hotel@hesselet.dk
Tel: +45 65 31 30 29
Fax: +45 65 31 29 58

Price Guide:
single DKK1,180–1,280
double/twin DKK1,680–1,780
suite DKK2,400–2,800

47 70

Estonia

Hotel location shown in red (hotel) or purple (spa hotel) with page number

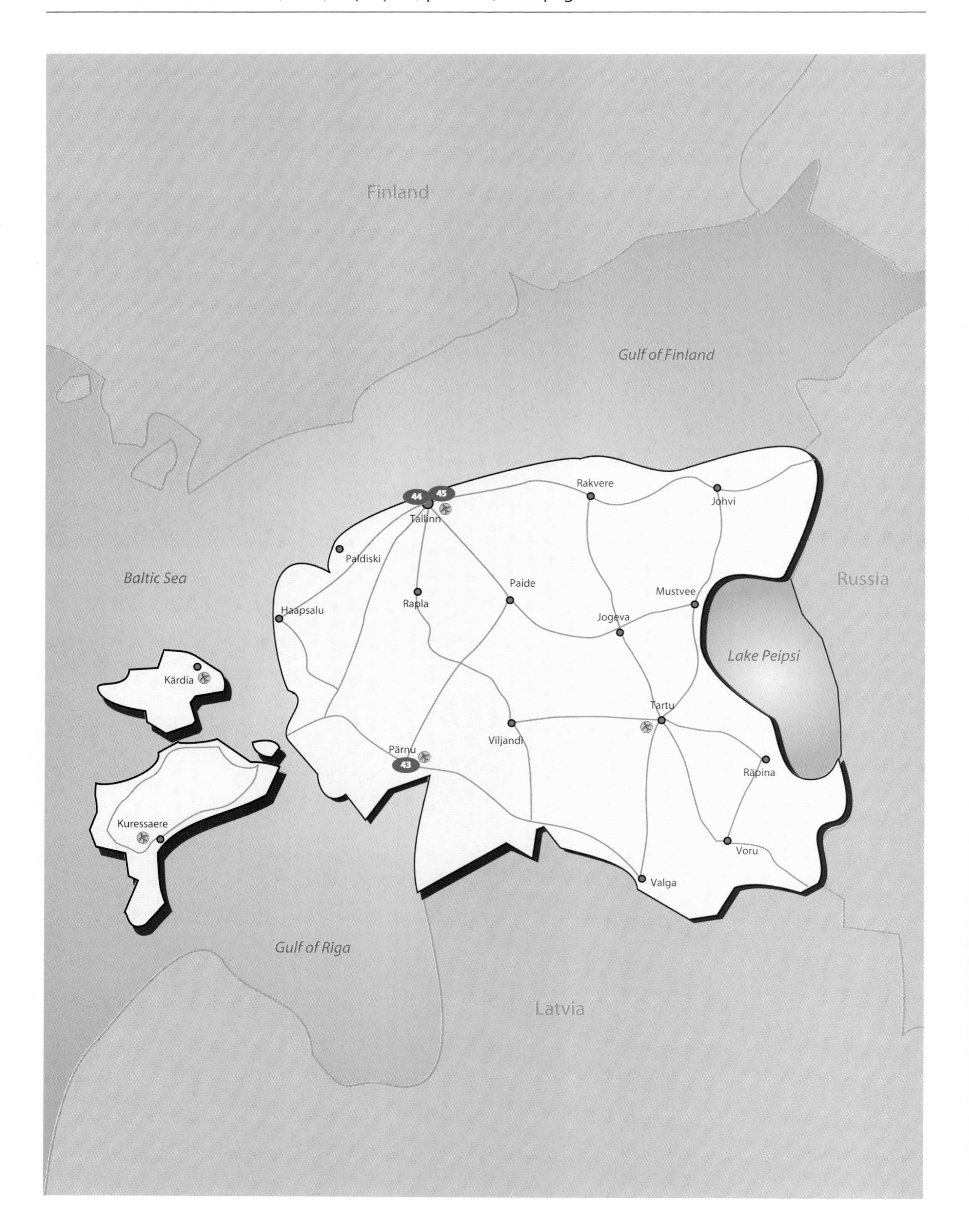

AMMENDE VILLA

MERE PST 7, 80010 PÄRNU, ESTONIA

Set in a romantic park close to the sea, this art nouveau hotel, built at the beginning of the 20th century, is Estonia's most fascinating building of its kind. All bedrooms are suites or de luxe rooms decorated with restored original furniture and period details. The Suite Ammende boasts a sauna and whirlpool bath. Guests can enjoy French and Mediterranean cuisine accompanied by fine Old World wines in the elegant blue dining room, the green "wine room" or the crimson "hunting room". The famous Spa is only minutes away.

Dans un pareprès de la mer, cet hôtel art nouveau construit au début du XXe siècle, est l'un des bâtiments d'Estonie les plus fascinants de son genre. Toutes les chambres sont des suites ou chambres de luxe, décorées avec des meubles restaurés et des détails d'époque. La Suite Ammende contient un sauna et un bain à remous. Les invités peuvent apprécier, dans l'élégante salle à manger bleue, dans la « salle de vin » verte ou la « salle de chasse » rouge foncée, une cuisine française et méditerranéenne accompagnée de vins fins. Les célèbres bains ne sont qu'à quelques minutes.

In einem romantischen Park am Strand liegt dieses Anfang des 20. Jahrhunderts erbaute Jugendstil-Hotel, Estlands faszinierendstes Gebäude seiner Art. Alle Zimmer sind Suiten oder Deluxe-Zimmer und mit restaurierten Originalmöbeln und dazugehörigen Details eingerichtet. Die Suite Ammende bietet Sauna und Bad mit Whirlpool. Französische und mediterrane Gerichte sowie feine Weine der Alten Welt werden im historischen blauen Speisesaal, grünen Weinsaal oder purpurfarbenen Jadgsaal serviert. Das berühmte Spa ist nur ein paar Minuten entfernt.

Our inspector loved: *The spacious common rooms - arthaus style.*

Directions: On main road between Tallinn and Riga. 2 hours from Tallinn, 3 hours from Riga.

Web: www.johansens.com/villaammende
E-mail: johansens@ammende.ee
Tel: +372 44 73888
Fax: +372 44 73887

Tallinn
Mustvee
Pärnu

Price Guide:
de luxe €125–195
suite €205–415

DOMINA CITY

VANA POSTI, 11/13, 10146 TALLINN, ESTONIA

Domina City's aim is to provide guests with a memorable and unique experience together with swift and smooth responsive service, and is ideal for business and independent travellers alike. Ideally situated in the heart of Tallinn, the hotel is surrounded by fashionable shops, restaurants, casinos and nightclubs. Each of the 68 guest rooms and suites has high standards of modern facilities and comforts and à la carte menus are offered in the basement restaurant.

Le Domina City est l'endroit idéal pour les visiteurs d'affaires et les hôtes indépendants. Son but est de procurer à ses hôtes une expérience unique et inoubliable avec un service rapide et efficace. Idéalement situé au cœur de Tallinn, cet hôtel est cerné de magasins à la mode, de restaurants, casinos et discothèques. Chacune de ses 68 chambres et suites offre les meilleurs équipements et conforts et un menu à la carte est disponible au restaurant en sous-sol.

Das Domina City ist gleichermaßen ideal für Geschäftsreisende und Urlauber. Höchste Priorität ist, den Gästen einen einzigartigen und unvergeßlichen Aufenthalt mit schnellem, aufmerksamen Service zu bieten. Das Hotel liegt ideal im Zentrum Tallinns, umgeben von modernen Geschäften, Restaurants, Casinos und Nachtclubs. Jedes der 68 Zimmer und Suiten bietet ein sehr hohes Niveau an Komfort und Einrichtungen, und im Kellerrestaurant werden Menüs à la carte serviert.

Our inspector loved: *The central location, near to shopping and nightclubs.*

Directions: Situated in a central location in the old town. The nearest airport is Tallinn.

Web: www.johansens.com/dominacity
E-mail: city@domina.ee
Tel: +372 681 3900
Fax: +372 681 3901

Price Guide:
single €65-150
double €120-170
suite €176-240

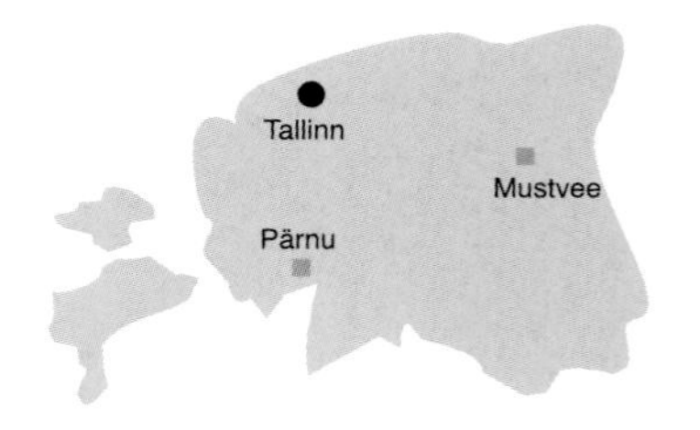

design hotels

THE THREE SISTERS HOTEL

PIKK 71/TOLLI 2, 10133 TALLINN, ESTONIA

This recently rebuilt hotel is situated just inside the walls of the 800-year-old Estonian capital of Tallinn, just a short walk through cobblestone streets to the attractions of the main square and harbour. Welcoming and friendly, The Three Sisters Hotel is a combination of 3 adjoining medieval houses whose old stone and woodwork has been retained and combined with modern, stylish design and comforts. Service is excellent and even includes, if required, breakfast in bed until 6pm and limousine travel to private picnics.

Cet hôtel récemment reconstruit est situé à l'intérieur des murs de Tallin, la vieille capitale estonienne de 800 ans, tout proche via les rues pavées, des attractions de la place principale et du port. Accueillant et amical, l'hôtel The Three Sisters est la combinaison de 3 maisons médiévales adjacentes dont la vieille pierre et l'ébénisterie ont été sauvegardées. L'hôtel offre un service excellent qui inclut même, si demandé, petit déjeuner au lit jusqu'à 18 heures et transport en limousines à des pique-niques privés.

Dieses kürzlich wieder erbaute Hotel liegt innerhalb der Stadtmauern der 800 Jahre alten Landeshauptstadt, nur einen kurzen Weg über gepflasterte Straßen von den Attraktionen des Hauptplatzes und des Hafens entfernt. Das einladende, freundliche Three Sisters besteht aus 3 mit einander verbundenen Häusern aus dem Mittelalter, deren alte Steinwände und Holzarbeiten erhalten blieben und den modernen Komfort und das stilvolle Design perfekt ergänzen. Der Service ist hervorragend, einschließlich, falls gewünscht, Frühstück im Bett bis 18 Uhr und Limousinentransfer zu privaten Picknicks.

Our inspector loved: *The homely feeling of the elegant Piano Suite.*

Directions: Tallinn Airport > old town, close to the harbour.

Web: www.johansens.com/threesisters
E-mail: johansens@threesistershotel.com
Tel: +372 630 6300
Fax: +372 630 6301

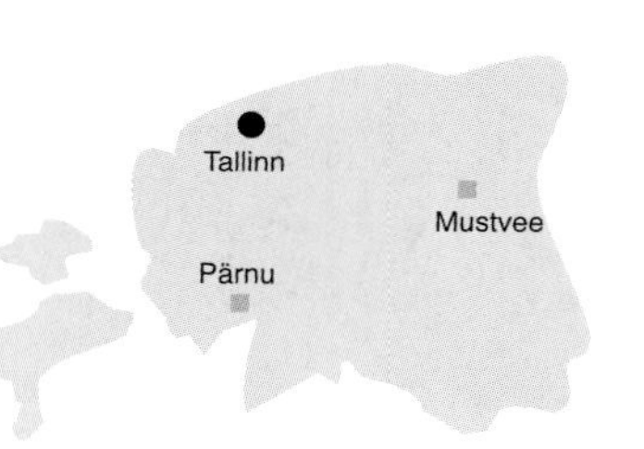

Price Guide:
single €178-400
double €200-430
suite €300-590

France

Hotel location shown in red (hotel) or purple (spa hotel) with page number

HOSTELLERIE LE MARÉCHAL

4 PLACE SIX MONTAGNES NOIRES, PETITE VENISE, 68000 COLMAR, FRANCE

Set beside a canal in Colmar's most beautiful quarter, "Little Venice", this charming house is renowned for its exquisite cuisine, superb Alsatian wines and warm hospitality. After 2 years of renovation, the 4-star hotel now provides 30 delightful bedrooms, all named after famous musicians and equipped with air conditioning, satellite television and comfortable bathrooms. L'Echevin serves Alsatian delicacies by candlelight and classical music. This is the perfect place for a romantic weekend!

Située en bordure d'un canal dans le plus beau quartier de Colmar, "La Petite Venise", cette maison charmante est réputée pour sa cuisine, ses vins alsaciens et sa chaleureuse hospitalité. Après deux ans de rénovation, cet hôtel 4 étoiles a 30 chambres superbes, qui portent toutes le nom d'un musicien célèbre. Elles possèdent la climatisation, la télévision et par satellite ainsi que des salles de bain confortables. L'Echevin sert les plats fins alsaciens à la lueur des chandelles et au son de la musique classique. L'endroit idéal pour un week-end romantique!

An einem Kanal in "Petite Venise", dem schönsten Viertel Colmars liegt dieses 4-Sterne Hotel, das für seine exquisite Küche, köstlichen elsässischen Weine und herzliche Gastfreundschaft bekannt ist. Nach zweijähriger Renovierung stehen nun 30 zauberhafte Zimmer bereit, alle nach berühmten Musikern benannt und mit Klimaanlage, Satellitenfernsehen und komfortablen Bädern ausgestattet. Im L'Echevin werden bei Kerzenschein und klassischer Musik elsässische Köstlichkeiten serviert. Der perfekte Ort für ein romantisches Wochenende!

Our inspector loved: *The "Debussy" bedroom with its four poster bed.*

Directions: From Strasbourg turn off the highway for Colmar Sud. Then follow the directions to Petite Venise.

Web: www.johansens.com/marechal
E-mail: marechal@calixo.net
Tel: +33 3 89 41 60 32
Fax: +33 3 89 24 59 40

Price Guide: (room only)
single €95–185
double €95–215
suite €245

Hôtel Les Têtes

19 RUE DES TÊTES, 68000 COLMAR, FRANCE

Situated at the heart of this labyrinthine cathedral town, this beautiful Renaissance hotel is truly unique. Covered by 105 grotesque masks, the Baroque theme extends into the interior, where an intimate courtyard allows guests to relax over coffee and cool drinks in summer. The bedrooms, complete with ancient beamed ceilings and attractive stonework, are highly atmospheric. The hotel's welcoming owner, Marc Rohfritsch, prepares sumptuous dishes served under glittering chandeliers in the restaurant La Maison des Têtes.

Situé au coeur de cette ville tentaculaire avec sa cathédrale, ce magnifique hôtel Renaissance est vraiment exceptionnel. Décoré de 105 masques de style grotesque, le thème baroque s'étend à l'intérieur, où une cour intime permet aux clients de se détendre autour d'un café ou de boissons rafraîchissantes en été. Les chambres, avec leurs poutres anciennes et leurs beaux murs en pierre, dégagent une ambiance extraordinaire. L'accueillant maître des lieux, Marc Rohfritsch, prépare de somptueux repas dans son restaurant La Maison des Têtes.

Inmitten dieser labyrinthischen Domstadt liegt dieses einzigartige Renaissancehotel. Das Barockthema wird mit 105 grotesken Masken im Interieur fortgesetzt, wo ein intimer Innenhof die Gäste zu Kaffee oder einem kühlen Drink im Sommer einlädt. Die Zimmer, mit alten Balkendecken und attraktiven Steinarbeiten verziert, sind besonders stimmungsvoll. Marc Rohfritsch, der Besitzer des Hotels, bereitet köstliche Speisen, die im Restaurant La Maison des Têtes unter glänzenden Lüstern serviert werden.

Our inspector loved: *The warm welcome and friendliness of the staff.*

Directions: Colmar city centre.

Web: www.johansens.com/lestetes
Tel: +33 3 89 24 43 43
Fax: +33 3 89 24 58 34

Price Guide: (room only)
single €95-168
double/twin €95–168
suite €230

CHÂTEAU D'ISENBOURG

68250 ROUFFACH, FRANCE

Peace, comfort, luxury, discreet charm and attentive service are the hallmarks of this imposing, hillside château hotel which overlooks colourful gardens and vineyards towards the Vosges forest. Built on 12th and 14th-century cellars d'Isenbourg is a superb historical and gourmet retreat on the Alsace wine route. Its restaurants are famed, its bedrooms elegantly spacious and leisure facilities are excellent.

Paix, confort, charme discret et service attentif sont les marques de cet imposant hôtel-château, posé sur les coteaux et surplombant des jardins colorés et des vignobles en direction de la forêt de Vosges. Construit sur les celliers d'Isenbourg datant du XIIe et XIVe siecle, c'est une superbe retraite historique gastronomique sur la route des vins d'Alsace. Ses restaurants sont célèbres, ses chambres élégantes sont spacieuses et ses équipements de loisirs sont excellents.

Ruhe, Komfort, Luxus, unaufdringlicher Charme und aufmerksamer Service sind die Maximen dieses eindrucksvollen, auf einem Hügel gelegenen Schlosshotels, das auf farbenfrohe Gärten und Weinberge in Richtung Vogesen blickt. Das auf Weinkellern aus dem 12. und 14. Jahrhundert erbaute Château d'Isenbourg ist ein einmaliges historisches und gastronomisches Erlebnis auf der Elsässer Weinroute. Seine Restaurants genießen einen exzellenten Ruf, die eleganten Zimmer sind geräumig und das Freizeitangebot ist hervorragend.

Our inspector loved: *The cosy bar.*

Directions: A35 > exit Colmar.

Web: www.johansens.com/isenbourg
E-mail: isenbourg@grandesetapes.fr
Tel: +33 3 89 78 58 50
Fax: +33 3 89 78 53 70

Price Guide: (room only)
single €110–360
double €110–360
suite €400–515

41

HOSTELLERIE LES BAS RUPTS

88400 GÉRARDMER, VOSGES, FRANCE

Directions: Paris > Nancy > Remiremont > Gérardmer.

Web: www.johansens.com/lesbasrupts
E-mail: basrupts@relaischateaux.com
Tel: +33 3 29 63 09 25
Fax: +33 3 29 63 00 40

Price Guide: (room only)
single €140-180
double/twin €119–198
suite €240-280

Close to Lake Gérardmer, in the heart of Les Vosges Mountain region, the Hostellerie and its adjoining Chalet Fleuri is a magical retreat all year round. A homely and welcoming ambience is accompanied by warm hospitality – the bedrooms are comfortable and uniquely attractive, with hand-painted flowers adorning the walls and doors. The succulent dishes, an inspired interpretation of local specialities are complemented by fine wines and served in the panoramic restaurant.

Tout près du lac de Gérardmer, au coeur des Vosges, l'Hostellerie Les Bas Rupts et son annexe, le Chalet Fleuri, offrent une retraite idyllique tout au long de l'année. L'accueil cordial est complété par une atmosphère intime et chaleureuse - les chambres sont confortables et très jolies, avec des portes et des murs ornés de fleurs peintes à la main. Des plats succulents, une brillante interprétation des spécialités locales, accompagnés de vins exceptionnels sont servis dans le restaurant panoramique.

Nahe am Géradmer See und inmitten der Vogesen liegt die Hostellerie Les Bas Rupts und das dazugehörende Chalet Fleuri. Eine heimelige und warme Atmosphäre verbindet sich hier mit herzlicher Gastfreundschaft – die zauberhaften Zimmer sind gemütlich eingerichtet und die Wände und Türen mit Blumen handbemalt. Köstliche Speisen, eine gelungene Interpretation einheimischer Spezialitäten, und erlesene Weine werden im Panoramarestaurant serviert.

Our inspector loved: *The smell of wood burning in the fireplace in this lovely mountain chalet.*

Hostellerie St Barnabé

68530 MURBACH – BUHL, FRANCE

The warmest of welcomes and the chance to really get away from it all are offered by this marvellous hostellerie in the heart of the Alsace. Set amidst spectacular forest scenery and beside a meandering mountain stream, each of the charming beamed bedrooms is named after one of the Alsatian grand cru wines. One of the cosy chalets has its own wood-burning stove. The hosts are true professionals and will ensure guests of impeccable service and breathtaking views.

Un accueil des plus chaleureux vous attend dans cette merveilleuse hostellerie alsacienne où vous pourrez vous reposer loin de tout. Construite au milieu d'une magnifique forêt et au bord d'un ruisseau de montagne, elle offre de ravissantes chambres aux poutres apparentes, qui portent toutes des noms de grands crus d'Alsace. Un poêle à bois chauffe l'un des chalets douillets. Les patrons sont de vrais professionnels, qui garantissent aux visiteurs un service impeccable, dont ils peuvent profiter en admirant des vues à couper le souffle.

Ein herzlicher Empfang erwartet Gäste in dieser wunderbaren Hostellerie im Herzen des Elsass. Inmitten atemberaubender Waldumgebung und neben einem Gebirgsbach gelegen, ist dies ein idealer Ort, um jeglichem Alltagsstress zu entkommen. Die bezaubernden Zimmer sind alle nach elsässischen Grand Cru Weinen benannt, und eines der gemütlichen Chalets hat einen eigenen Holzofen. Die Gastgeber sind wahre Experten und garantieren ihren Gästen makellosen Service und traumhafte Umgebung.

Our inspector loved: *The friendly welcome from all the staff.*

Directions: D429 to Guebwiller > Murbach D429II.

Web: www.johansens.com/stbarnabe
E-mail: hostellerie.st.barnabe@wanadoo.fr
Tel: +33 3 89 62 14 14
Fax: +33 3 89 62 14 15

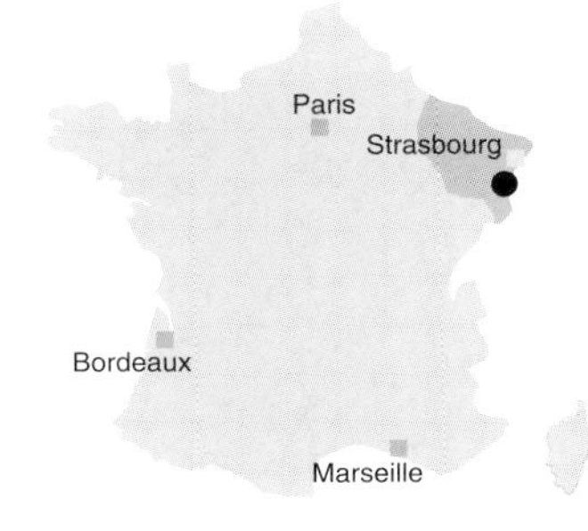

Price Guide: (room only)
single €95-190
double €95-190

27

FRANCE / ALSACE~LORRAINE (OBERNAI)

Hotel à la Cour d'Alsace

3 RUE DE GAIL, 67210 OBERNAI, FRANCE

Within the medieval old town of Obernai, 23 carefully restored houses surround a central courtyard to create this unique hotel. Light and airy guest rooms feature original beamed ceilings and overlook the courtyard or garden. Traditional Alsatian cuisine is served in the hotel's restaurants whilst dinner may be enjoyed in the garden during the summer. This is an ideal base from which to explore Alsace and its vineyards; alternatively the hotel's wine tavern boasts many regional specialities to sample.

Situé dans la ville médiévale d'Obernai, 23 maisons rénovées avec le plus grand soin entourent une cour centrale afin de créer cet hôtel unique. Les chambres claires et spacieuses aux poutres originales apparentes donnent sur la cour ou sur le jardin. Une cuisine traditionnelle alsacienne est servie dans les restaurants et le dîner peut-être servi dans le jardin en été. Cet hôtel est une base idéale pour explorer l'Alsace et ses vignes. La taverne de l'hôtel propose de nombreux vins régionaux à déguster.

Inmitten der mittelalterlichen Stadt Obernai gelegen, besteht dieses einzigartige Hotel aus 23 sorgfältig restaurierten, um einen Innenhof angesiedelten Häusern. Die hellen, luftigen Zimmer bieten originale Balkendecken und Blick auf den Hof oder Garten. Traditionelle Elsässer Küche wird in den Hotelrestaurants serviert, und im Sommer diniert man im Garten. Dies ist der ideale Ausgangspunkt, um das Elsass und seine Weinberge zu erkunden; man kann aber auch bereits in der Weintaverne des Hotels zahlreiche regionale Spezialitäten probieren.

Our inspector loved: *The collection of buildings, which make up the courtyard area.*

Directions: A35 > exit 11 > Obernai town centre > top of the town. The nearest airport is Strasbourg.

Web: www.johansens.com/couralsace
E-mail: info@cour-alsace.com
Tel: +33 3 88 95 07 00
Fax: +33 3 88 95 19 21

Price Guide: (room only)
single €109-129
double €149-179
suite €266

Romantik Hotel Beaucour Baumann

5 RUE DES BOUCHERS, 67000 STRASBOURG, FRANCE

Just a stone's throw from the cathedral, this authentic timber-framed hotel is ideally situated for discovering Strasbourg. Built around a narrow courtyard, its exposed beams, warm colours and hand-painted frescoes create a homely and comfortable Alsatian ambience. Bedrooms are individually decorated and have Jacuzzi baths. A sumptuous breakfast is served daily, and guests can relax in the cosy lounge with its log fire. All visitors are given a hearty welcome from the staff and also the resident talking parrot!

A deux pas de la cathédrale, cet hôtel en style typique de la région est parfaitement situé pour découvrir Strasbourg. Construit autour d'une cour intérieure étroite, ses poutres apparentes, des couleurs chaudes et des fresques peintes à la main créent une ambiance confortable et alsacienne. Les chambres sont décorées de façon individuelle et disposent d'un Jacuzzi. Un petit déjeuner somptueux est servi tous les jours et les hôtes peuvent se détendre dans le salon intime autour du feu de bois. Le personnel, ainsi que le perroquet parlant, attend tous les visiteurs avec un accueil chaleureux!

Dieses mit echtem Fachwerk geschmückte Hotel liegt nur einen Katzensprung von der Kathedrale entfernt, ideal um Straßburg zu erkunden. Das Haus ist um einen schmalen Innenhof herum gebaut, und Holzbalken, warme Farben und handbemalte Fresken schaffen eine heimelige, typisch elsässische Atmosphäre. Die unterschiedlich gestalteten Zimmer haben Jacuzzibäder. Täglich wird ein üppiges Frühstück serviert, und Gäste entspannen sich in der gemütlichen Lounge mit offenem Kamin. Das Personal sorgt für einen herzlichen Empfang – und ebenso der sprechende Papagei!

Our inspector loved: *The pretty courtyard.*

Directions: The hotel is in the town centre, near the old customs house. The nearest airport is Strasbourg. Parking available opposite the hotel, €7 per day.

Web: www.johansens.com/beaucour
E-mail: info@hotel-beaucour.com
Tel: +33 3 88 76 72 00
Fax: +33 3 88 76 72 60

Price Guide: (room only)
single €64-112
double €128
junior suite €156-172

Château de L'Ile

4 QUAI HEYDT, 67540 OSTWALD, FRANCE

Directions: A35 > exit Ostwald.

Web: www.johansens.com/chateaudelile
E-mail: ile@grandesetapes.fr
Tel: +33 3 88 66 85 00
Fax: +33 3 88 66 85 49

Price Guide: (room only)
single €180–405
double €180–405
suite €500–615

Here is total luxury and absolute quality. Nestling in 10 acres of parkland in a loop of the river Ill, this gorgeous château is elegant and spacious while at the same time being intimate and cosy. Individually decorated guest rooms with their refined bathrooms, air conditioning and balconies are simply a dream. Diners enjoy views over river and woods. Spa treatments are available by arrangement. There is a large indoor pool and fitness centre.

Tout ici est synonyme de luxe et de complète qualité. Niché au cœur de 4 hectares de parc dans un méandre de l'Ill, ce superbe château est élégant et spacieux tout en bénéficiant d'une atmosphère intime et douillette. Les chambres à la décoration unique avec balcon, salles de bain raffinées et disposant de l'air conditionné sont de vraies merveilles. Les dîneurs peuvent profiter de la vue sur la rivière et les bois. Le spa offre des traitements sur demande, et il y a une grande piscine couverte et un centre de remise en forme.

Hier findet man Luxus und Qualität der höchsten Güte. Dieses wundervolle, inmitten von 4ha Parklandschaft an einer Schleife des Flusses Ill gelegene Château ist elegant und geräumig, hat jedoch eine gemütliche und intime Atmosphäre. Die unterschiedlich gestalteten Zimmer haben elegante Bäder, Klimaanlage und Balkone. Beim Abendessen kann man die Sicht auf den Fluss und die Wälder genießen. Im Spa werden auf Anfrage Behandlungen angeboten, und es gibt ein großes Hallenbad mit Fitnessraum.

Our inspector loved: *The sumptuous cuisine.*

ROMANTIK HOTEL L'HORIZON

50 ROUTE DU CRÈVE~CŒUR, 57100 THIONVILLE, FRANCE

Set on the Crève-Cœur hill overlooking Thionville and the surrounding countryside, this 3-star hotel is the perfect base from which to explore the beautiful Lorraine region. The individually decorated bedrooms are furnished with antiques and offer all modern comforts. Panoramic views can be enjoyed from the terrace and the popular restaurant where guests can sample delicious, simple dishes complemented by excellent wines. Luxembourg is within easy reach and guests can visit several Maginot Line forts nearby.

Situé sur la colline de Crève-Cœur surplombant Thionville et la campagne environnante, cet hôtel trois étoiles est la base idéale à partir de laquelle explorer la belle région de Lorraine. Les chambres décorées individuellement sont meublées avec des antiquités et offrent tout le confort moderne. Les vues panoramiques peuvent être appréciées de la terrasse et le restaurant reputé ou les hôtes peuvent déguster des plats délicieux quoique simples, accompagnés d'excellents vins. Le Luxembourg est facile d'accès et les hôtes peuvent visiter la ligne Maginot toute proche.

Dieses auf dem Crève-Cœur-Hügel gelegene 3-Sterne-Hotel mit Blick auf Thionville und die Umgebung ist der ideale Ausgangspunkt, um Lothringen zu erkunden. Die mit Antiquitäten gefüllten, individuell gestalteten Zimmer sind mit jeglichem modernen Komfort ausgestattet. Panoramablicke bieten sich von der Terrasse und dem beliebten Restaurant, wo köstliche Gerichte und erlesene Weine serviert werden. Luxemburg ist nicht weit, und mehrere Festungen der Maginot-Linie können in der Nähe besichtigt werden.

Our inspector loved: *The friendly welcome.*

Directions: A31> exit 40 > follow signs for Crève-Cœur.

Paris
Strasbourg
Bordeaux
Marseille

Web: www.johansens.com/lhorizonfrance
E-mail: hotel@lhorizon.fr
Tel: +33 3 82 88 53 65
Fax: +33 3 82 34 55 84

Price Guide: (room only)
single €85–96
double €96–138
suite €180

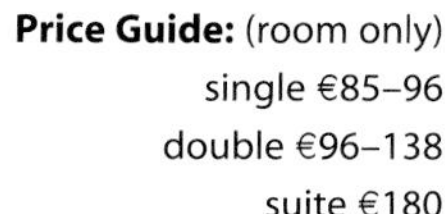

Les Violettes

THIERENBACH, 68500 JUNGHOLTZ, FRANCE

This stunning newly built mountain chalet hotel could have existed for centuries. Bedrooms feature rich colours and furnishings, romantic bathrooms and ready-to-light log fires. In the Honeymoon Suite a ceiling mounted mirror appears at the flick of a button! The lounge and first dining room are wood clad and cosy, whilst the second dining room is a veranda, which gives beautiful views across the mountains and valley.

Ce superbe hôtel-chalet de montagne tout neuf pourrait avoir été là depuis des siècles. Les chambres présentent des couleurs riches, des salles de bain romantiques et des feux de bois prêts à allumer. Dans la suite Lune de Miel, un miroir au plafond apparaît sur simple pression d'un interrupteur! Le salon et la première salle à manger en lambris sont douillets, alors que la seconde salle à manger est une véranda qui offre de fantastiques vues sur la montagne et la vallée.

Fast könnte man meinen, dass dieses fantastische neue Bergchalet schon seit Jahrhunderten hier steht. Die Zimmer sind mit kräftigen Farben und üppigem Mobiliar ausgestattet und bieten romantische Bäder und offene Kamine. In der Flitterwochen-Suite erscheint auf Knopfdruck ein Spiegel an der Decke! Der Aufenthaltsraum und einer der Speisesäle sind mit Holz verschalt und sehr gemütlich, und der zweite Speisesaal ist eine Veranda mit herrlicher Sicht auf die Berge und das Tal.

***Our inspector loved:** The incredibly romantic atmosphere.*

Directions: Mulhouse Basel Airport > D430 > exit 3 towards Guebwiller > Soultz > Jungholtz > Thirenbach > left after the church.

Web: www.johansens.com/lesviolettes
E-mail: lesviolettes2@wanadoo.fr
Tel: +33 3 89 76 91 19
Fax: +33 3 89 74 29 12

Price Guide: (room only)
single €150-195
double €150-195
suites €210-300

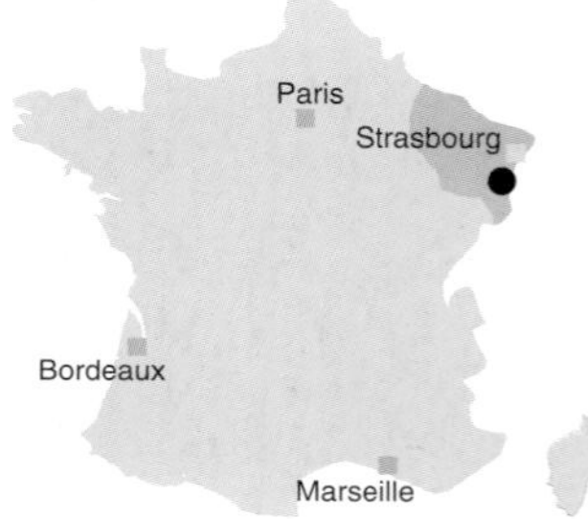

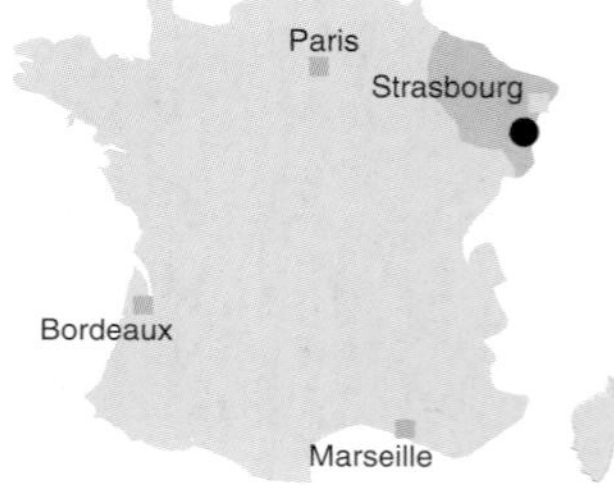

Domaine de Rochevilaine

POINTE DE PEN LAN, 56190 BILLIERS, FRANCE

Perched on the edge of the rocky Pointe de Pen Lan, this historic manor house affords a panoramic vista across the waterfront. The bedrooms are all designed in a stylish manner, whilst Aubusson tapestries adorn the walls of the comfortable lounge, where visitors enjoy pre-prandial drinks. Afterwards they can revel in the delicious French cuisine that chef Patrice Caillaut crafts from the freshest of local produce.

Perché sur la pointe rocheuse de Pen Lan, ce manoir historique bénéficie d'une vue panoramique sur le bord de mer. Les chambres sont toutes décorées avec soin. Les tapisseries d'Aubusson décorent les murs du confortable salon et le visiteur se délectera d'apéritifs délicieux. Ensuite, il pourra évoluer vers la divine table française que le chef Patrice Caillaut concocte à partir des meilleurs produits locaux.

Dieses historische Herrenhaus liegt auf der Felspitze von Pen Lan und bietet eine traumhafte Sicht auf die Küste. Die Zimmer sind höchst elegant, Aubusson-Gobelins zieren die Wände des gemütlichen Aufenthaltsraums, in dem sich die Gäste auf einen Apéritif treffen. Für die herrlichen französischen Speisen verwendet Chefkoch Patrice Caillaut die frischesten und besten Zutaten der Region.

Our inspector loved: *The Nomads massage in the Moorish massage parlour.*

Directions: From Nantes > E60 > Vannes > Billiers > Pen Lan.

Web: www.johansens.com/domainederochevilaine
E-mail: domaine@domainerochevilaine.com
Tel: +33 2 97 41 61 61
Fax: +33 2 97 41 44 85

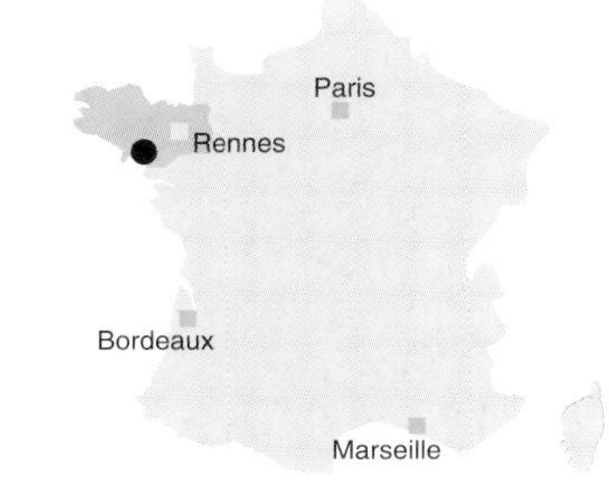

Price Guide: (room only)
single €120–357
double/twin €110–357
suites €330–490

CHÂTEAU HOTEL DE BRÉLIDY

NOBLANCE, 22140 BRÉLIDY, FRANCE

Directions: The nearest airport is Lannion. N12 > exit Guigam > towards Lannion on D767 > Bégard > D12 > Brélidy.

Web: www.johansens.com/brelidy
E-mail: chateau.brelidy@worldonline.fr
Tel: +33 1 96 95 69 38
Fax: +33 2 96 95 18 03

Price Guide: (room only)
single €68-84
double €91-125
suite €126-212

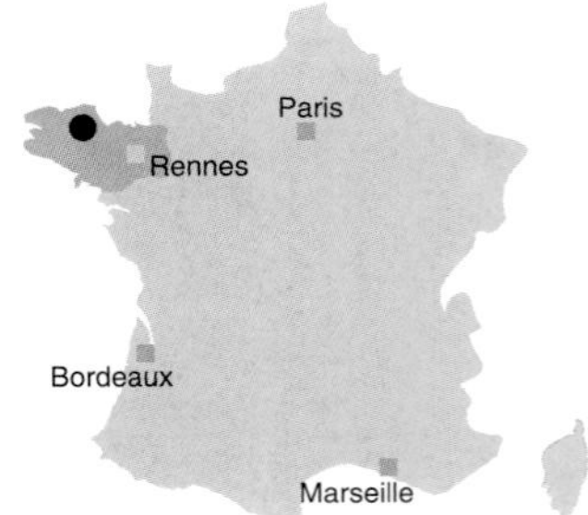

Surrounded by 85 acres of spectacular Brittany countryside, with private lake and streams, stands this carefully restored granite 16th-century château. A warm welcome is created by the large Baronial fireplaces in the public rooms, which feature high beamed ceilings and exposed brickwork. Bedrooms display genuine Louis XIII furnishings and some have a terrace opening onto the colourful garden; the former castle's chapel is a luxury suite. Activities include trout fishing, walking and hiking. Alternatively, relax by the pool and admire the scenery.

Au sein de 35 ha d'une spectaculaire campagne bretonne, avec lac privé et ruisseaux, se tient ce château de granite, soigneusement restauré, du XVIe siècle. Un accueil chaleureux est créé par les grandes cheminées seigneuriales des pièces communes, aux hauts plafonds à poutres et briquetage apparents. Les chambres sont meublées en authentique Louis XIII et certaines bénéficient d'une terrasse qui ouvre sur un jardin coloré ; l'ancienne chapelle du chateau est une suite luxueuse. Les activités incluent pêche à la truite, randonnées ; sinon, détendez-vous au bord de la piscine et appréciez le paysage.

Umgeben von 35ha spektakulärer bretonischer Landschaft, mit eigenem See und Flüssen, steht dieses sorgfältig restaurierte, aus Granitstein erbaute Château aus dem 16. Jahrhundert. Die Kamine in den Aufenthaltsräumen mit ihren hohen Balkendecken und freiliegendem Mauerwerk sorgen für einen warmen Empfang. In den Zimmern findet man Möbel aus der Zeit Ludwigs XIII., und einige bieten Terrassen, die in den Garten führen. Die einstige Kappelle ist heute eine Luxussuite. Man kann Forellen fischen, wandern oder am Pool entspannen und sich an der hübschen Umgebung erfreuen.

Our inspector loved: *The bedroom "Lys" for its stunning views.*

CHÂTEAU DE BONABAN

35350 LA GOUESNIÈRE, FRANCE

Situated on a wooded estate in the midst of the Pays Malouin, this 17th-century château offers best service in a friendly ambience. Boasting an opulently decorated chapel and a vast marble staircase, this idyllic country hideaway gives the impression of time standing still. Guest rooms offer panoramic views of Mont-Saint-Michel bay or attractive pond. Gastronomic, sumptuous French fare is served in the restaurant created by a chef who has studied with the greats. 5 high-quality golf courses are in close proximity.

Situé au coeur de la région boisée du Pays Malouin, ce château du XVIIe siècle offre le meilleur service dans un environnement où le temps amicale. Exhibant une chapelle superbement décorée et une cage d'escalier en marbre, cette retraite idyllique campagnarde évoque une ambiance où le temps s'arrête. Les chambres offrent une vue panoramique sur la baie du Mont-Saint-Michel ou sur l'étang. Les salons du restaurant invitent les clients au plaisir somptueux d'un menu français gastronomique réalisé par un chef, émule des plus grands. 5 superbes parcours de golf sont situés à proximité.

Auf einem bewaldeten Gut inmitten des Pays Malouin bietet dieses Schloss aus dem 17. Jahrhundert anspruchsvollen Service in einem freundlichen Ambiente. Mit einer opulent gestalteten Kapelle und einer riesigen Marmortreppe erweckt dieses idyllische ländliche Versteck den Eindruck, als ob hier die Zeit stehengeblieben wäre. Die Zimmer bieten Panoramablick auf den Mont-Saint-Michel oder den malerischen Teich. Im Restaurant wird üppige, französische Gourmetküche serviert, die ein von den besten Lehrmeistern geschulter Koch zubereitet. 5 hervorragende Golfplätze liegen in der Nähe.

Our inspector loved: *The candle-lit dinner in the small dining room.*

Directions: N137 > St Malo > La Gouesnière > signposts.

Web: www.johansens.com/chateaudebonaban
E-mail: chateau.bonaban@wanadoo.fr
Tel: +33 2 99 58 24 50
Fax: +33 2 99 58 28 41

Paris
Rennes
Bordeaux
Marseille

Price Guide: (room only)
single €70–210
double/twin €70–210
suite €205–285

19 165

Domaine de Bodeuc

ROUTE SAINT DOLAY, LA ROCHE~BERNARD, 56130 NIVILLAC, FRANCE

This beautiful 19th-century manor house stands in 35 acres of parkland, 15 minutes from Atlantic beaches and 5 minutes from the port city of La Roche Bernard. This tranquil haven, managed by English owners, offers intimate public rooms and 14 individually decorated en-suite bedrooms, 4 of which are located in the old stable block. An international menu is prepared by the owner from fresh ingredients bought from the local market. For leisure, guests may wish to use the heated pool, go cycling, take walks in the park and have picnics in the grounds.

Ce magnifique manoir du XIXe siècle se dresse dans un parc de 15 hectares, à 5 minutes du port de la Roche Bernard et à 15 minutes des plages de l'Atlantique. Cet havre de paix, propriété d'une famille anglaise, offre une atmosphère intime qui se retrouve dans les 14 chambres, toutes décorées individuellement et dont 4 d'entre elles sont situées dans les anciennes écuries. Une carte de cuisine internationale est préparée à partir des produits frais du marché. Pour les loisirs, les clients ont accès à la piscine chauffée et peuvent faire de vélo, se promener au park ou avoir des pique-niques.

Dieser traumhafte Herrensitz aus dem 19. Jahrhundert liegt inmitten von 15ha Parklandschaft, 15 Minuten von den Stränden des Atlantik und 5 Minuten von der Hafenstadt La Roche Bernard entfernt. Diese von englischen Besitzern geführte Oase der Ruhe bietet gemütliche Aufenthaltsräume und 14 individuell gestaltete Zimmer mit Bad, von denen sich 4 in den alten Stallungen befinden. Köstliche internationale Speisen werden mit frischen Zutaten vom Markt zubereitet. Ein beheizter Pool steht zur Verfügung, man kann Rad fahren, im Park spazieren gehen oder ein Picknick veranstalten.

Directions: The nearest airport is Nantes. Leave the N165 at exit 16 toward Nivillac. At the roundabout turn right then take the first left. After 4 kilometres turn right then a further 1 kilometre on turn right again.

Web: www.johansens.com/hotelbodeuc
E-mail: hotelbodeuc@hotelbodeuc.com
Tel: +33 2 99 90 89 63
Fax: +33 2 99 90 90 32

Price Guide:
single €85-210
double €85-210

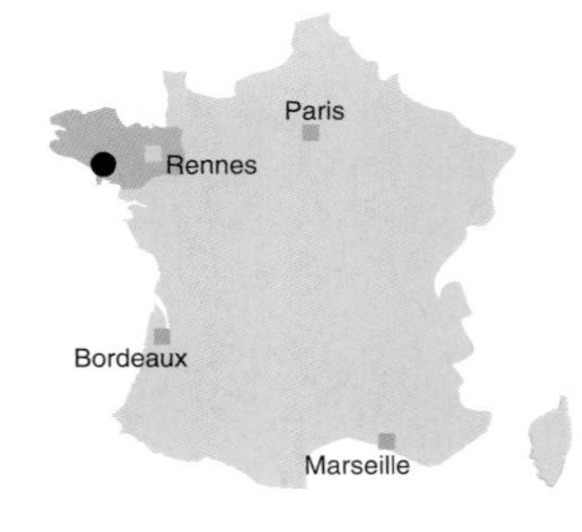

Our inspector loved: *The warm welcome and the country house feeling.*

14 14

Manoir de Kertalg

ROUTE DE RIEC~SUR~BELON, 29350 MOËLAN~SUR~MER, FRANCE

Set in a huge park filled with a variety of trees, this country house offers tranquillity, discreet luxury and a truly warm welcome. The owner's paintings adorn the walls, and fresh flowers can be found everywhere. The hotel has recently been elegantly refurbished, including bedrooms and bathrooms. Breakfast is served in the conservatory or on the sun terrace overlooking the park. Although there is no restaurant at the hotel, numerous gastronomic venues can be found in the vicinity.

Blotti au milieu d'un parc peuplé de différentes espèces d'arbres, ce manoir vous accueille cordialement dans un cadre au luxe discret baigné d'une douce tranquillité. Les tableaux du propriétaire ornent les murs, et des fleurs fraîches égayent toute la demeure. L'hôtel a récemment été remis à neuf de manière très élégante, incluant les chambres et salles de bains. Le petit déjeuner est servi dans le jardin d'hiver ou sur la terrasse avec vue sur le parc. L'hôtel n'a pas de restaurant, mais les environs regorgent d'établissements gastronomiques.

Dieses Landhaus liegt inmitten eines riesigen, mit verschiedensten Bäumen gefüllten Parks und bietet Ruhe, unaufdringlichen Luxus und warme Gastfreundschaft. Eigene Bilder des Besitzers zieren die Wände und frische Blumen sind im ganzen Haus zu finden. Das Hotel wurde kürzlich komplett überholt und elegant gestaltet, einschließlich die Zimmer und Bäder. Das Frühstück genießt man im Wintergarten oder auf der Terrasse mit Blick auf den Park. Zwar wird kein Abendessen serviert, aber zahlreiche Gourmetrestaurants liegen in nächster Nähe.

Our inspector loved: *The superb welcome and friendliness.*

Directions: N165 > exit at Quimperlé centre.

Web: www.johansens.com/manoirdekertalg
E-mail: kertalg@free.fr
Tel: +33 2 98 39 77 77
Fax: +33 2 98 39 72 07

Price Guide: (breakfast €10)
single/double/twin €95–180
suite €230

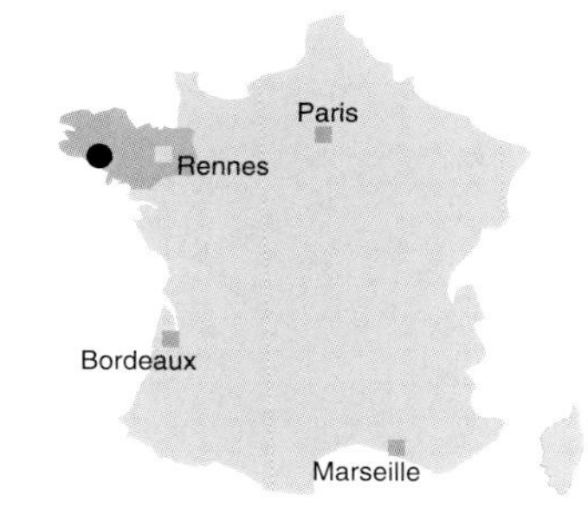

MANOIR DU VAUMADEUC

22130 PLEVEN, FRANCE

Directions: N168 > Planceot > Lamballe > Pleven.

Web: www.johansens.com/manoirduvaumadeuc
E-mail: manoir@vaumadeuc.com
Tel: +33 2 96 84 46 17
Fax: +33 2 96 84 40 16

Price Guide: (room only)
single €90-195
double/twin €90–195
suites €205

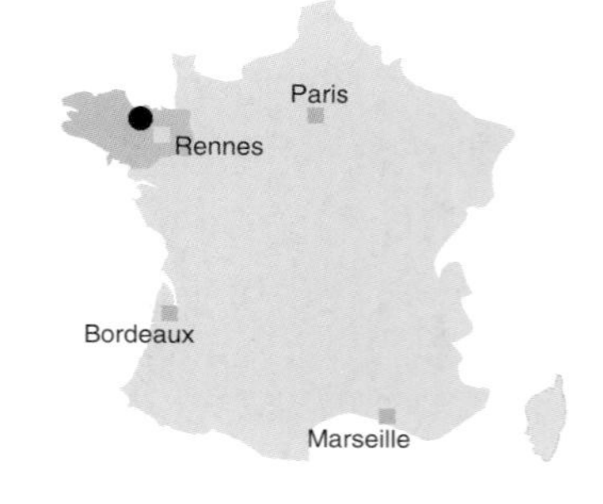

The magnificent Hunaudaye forest encompasses this luxurious former 15th-century manor house, which fuses modern comfort and medieval grandeur. Sculpted beams, ornate fireplaces and wooden floors set the tone in the public rooms, whilst an imposing granite staircase leads to the individually decorated rooms. Exclusive use of the château is available; this is an ideal venue for a special family function.

La somptueuse forêt de Hunaudaye abrite ce luxueux et ancien manoir du XVe siècle, qui allie un cadre médiéval authentique avec le confort moderne. Des poutres sculptées, des cheminées ornées et des parquets en bois plantent le décor des salons, alors qu'un magnifique escalier en granit vous amène aux chambres décorées de manière individuelle. L'utilisation exclusive du château est disponible; c'est l'endroit idéal pour des fêtes en famille.

Der herrliche Hunaudaye Forst umgibt dieses luxuriöse Herrenhaus aus dem 15. Jahrhundert, eine Mischung aus modernem Komfort und mittelalterlicher Opulenz. Zierbalken, prunkvolle Kamine und Holzböden verleihen den Empfangsräumen einen besonderen Charakter, und die Zimmer können über eine imposante Granittreppe erreicht werden. Das Château kann exklusiv gemietet werden und ist der ideale Ort für eine ganz besondere Familienfeier.

Our inspector loved: *The warm and personal welcome from the proprietor.*

Ti Al Lannec

14 ALLÉE DE MÉZO~GUEN, BP 3, 22560 TREBEURDEN, FRANCE

This Breton manor house commands imposing views, perched high on a cliff top overlooking the rose granite coast – one of the most spectacular reaches of Brittany. Professionalism is key here with a warm welcome from the attentive staff and a keen eye for detail. The public rooms are well-appointed and inviting, whilst the bedrooms are luxurious, with many having private balconies and sea views.

Ce manoir breton, à la vue incroyable, est solidement posé sur la colline surplombant la côte de granite rose — l'une des plus spectaculaires de Bretagne. Ici le professionnalisme est de mise, accompagné d'un accueil chaleureux de la part d'un personnel attentif et d'une attention particulière pour le détail. Les salles communes sont bien placées et accueillantes, alors que les chambres sont luxueuses, beaucoup d'entre elles ayant un balcon privé et vue sur la mer.

Dieses bretonische Herrenhaus befindet sich an einem der spektakulärsten Orte der Bretagne und bietet von seiner Lage hoch auf einer Klippe atemberaubende Blicke auf die Küste. Professionalität und ein Auge fürs Detail sind das Erfolgsrezept des Hotels, und das Personal bereitet jedem Gast einen herzlichen Empfang. Die attraktiven Aufenthaltsräume sind sehr einladend und viele der luxuriösen Gästezimmer haben einen eigenen Balkon und Blick auf das Meer.

Our inspector loved: *The friendliness of every staff member.*

Directions: From north > towards Lannion > then towards Trebeurden.

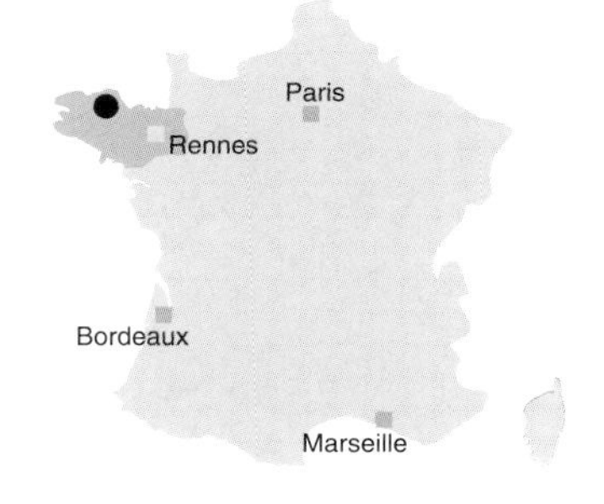

Web: www.johansens.com/tiallannec
E-mail: resa@tiallannec.com
Tel: +33 296 15 01 01
Fax: +33 2 96 23 62 14

Price Guide: (room only)
single €80-105
double €148-257
suite €317-349

CHÂTEAU DE VAULT DE LUGNY

11 RUE DU CHÂTEAU, 89200 AVALLON, FRANCE

Dating from the 16th century, this magical rural hideaway is surrounded by an authentic 13th-century moat weaving its way through the verdant estate. The interior is no less dramatic, with its marvellous panelling, elaborate fireplaces and ornate ceilings. Some of the splendid bedrooms have four-poster beds and fireplaces. The château is renowned for the variety of its food, which is taken around a large table exclusively for hotel residents (closed on Wednesdays), and its magnificent 100-acre garden and vegetable garden. There is also a terrace overlooking the river.

Ce ravissant château du XVIe siècle est encerclé de ses douves authentiques du XIIIe siècle. L'intérieur est tout aussi impressionnant, avec ses lambris magnifiques, ses cheminées élaborées et ses plafonds à la Française. Certaines chambres splendides ont des lits à baldaquins et des cheminées. Le château est renommé pour sa table d'hôte (restauration exclusivement pour résidents de l'hôtel, fermé le mecredi) et son magnifique jardin de 40 ha et potager. Terrasse sur la rivière.

Dieses zauberhafte Landversteck aus dem 16. Jahrhundert liegt inmitten eines üppigen Parks und ist von einem Burggraben aus dem 13. Jahrhundert umgeben. Im Inneren sorgen herrliche Holzvertäfelung, opulente Kamine und reichverzierte Decken für ein dramatisches Ambiente. Einige der prachtvollen Schlafzimmer besitzen Himmelbett und offenen Kamin. Das Château ist bekannt für seine große kulinarische Auswahl, die am "Table d'hôte" serviert wird (exklusiv für Hotelgäste, mittwochs geschlossen) und für seinen 40ha großen Garten und Gemüsegarten sowie eine Terrasse mit Blick auf den Fluss.

Our inspector loved: *The beautiful lawn and park where ducks, peacocks and hens roam freely.*

Directions: A6 > Avallon > Vezelay > Pontaubert.

Web: www.johansens.com/vaultdelugny
E-mail: hotel@lugny.fr
Tel: +33 3 86 34 07 86
Fax: +33 3 86 34 16 36

Price Guide:
double/twin €160–480
suite €450

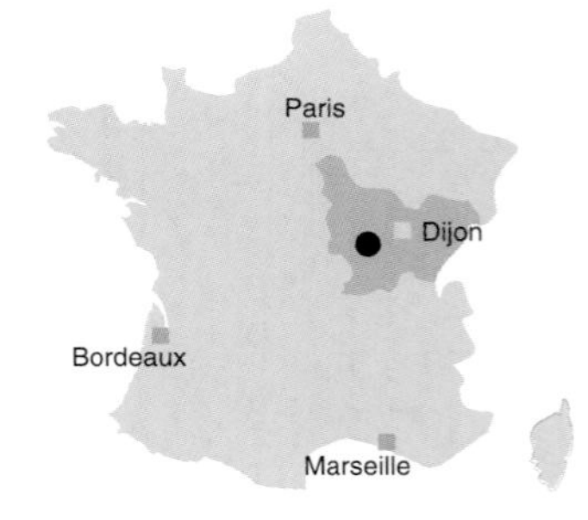

Ermitage de Corton

R.N. 74, 21200 CHOREY~LES~BEAUNE, FRANCE

Set in acres of glorious vineyards, this old Burgundy-style mansion offers comfortable accommodation and warm hospitality in fine surroundings. The individually decorated rooms range from the grandiose to the simple yet elegant. The restaurant is undoubtedly the centre-point; the traditional French fare is prepared by a maître cuisinier de France, and is complemented by a fine selection of wines.

Entouré d'hectares de merveilleux vignobles, ce vieux manoir de style bourguignon offre des séjours confortables et une chaleureuse hospitalité dans un beau cadre. Les chambres décorées de manière individuelle varient d'un style grandiose au simple et élégant. Le restaurant est sans nul doute l'attraction centrale; la cuisine traditionnel le française est préparé par un Maître Cuisinier de France, et est complété par une fine sélection de vins.

Inmitten herrlicher Weinberge liegt dieses alte Haus im Burgunder Stil, das seinen Gästen ein herzliches Willkommen bietet. Die gemütlichen Zimmer sind in unterschiedlichen Stilen gestaltet, von prunkvoll bis einfach aber elegant. Das Restaurant, zweifellos Mittelpunkt des Hotels, serviert unvergleichliche französische Küche, kreiert von einem „Maître Cuisinier de France", und durch eine erlesene Auswahl an Weinen ergänzt.

Our inspector loved: *The superb dining room with views over the vineyards.*

Directions: A6 > Beaune > exit 24 > Dijon.

Web: www.johansens.com/ermitagedecorton
E-mail: ermitage.corton@wanadoo.fr
Tel: +33 3 80 22 05 28
Fax: +33 3 80 24 64 51

Paris
Dijon
Bordeaux
Marseille

Price Guide: (Continental breakfast €25, lunch €40, dinner €40, à la carte menu €65-100, excl VAT)
double/twin €210-285
suite €250-350

HOSTELLERIE DES MONTS DE VAUX

LES MONTS DE VAUX, 39800 POLIGNY, FRANCE

Directions: N5 from Poligny towards Switzerland.

Web: www.johansens.com/montdevaux
E-mail: mtsvaux@hostellerie.com
Tel: +33 3 84 37 12 50
Fax: +33 3 84 37 09 07

Price Guide: (breakfast €13.50)
rooms and apartments €145-220

This wonderful family-run coaching inn perched high on a mountain top is of beautifully old-fashioned charm. With its traditional décor and furnishings, it takes you back into a bygone era. It is a true home from home, with warming logfires in the lounges creating a cosy and welcoming atmosphere. After a day spent exploring the breathtaking surroundings by bicycle or on foot, guests can enjoy the extensive menu featuring delicious regional cuisine, complemented by an extraordinary wine list.

Perchée au sommet d'une montagne, cette superbe auberge familiale dégage un charme merveilleusement ancien. Son décor et son mobilier traditionnels vous transportent dans l'ancien temps. On se sent vraiment chez soi à la lueur des feux de bois qui réchauffent les salons en créant une atmosphère douillètte et accueillante. Après une journée passée à explorer les alentours pittoresques à vélo ou à pied, les clients pourront apprécier le menu complet qui propose une délicieuse cuisine régionale, accompagné d'une carte des vins extraordinaire.

Diese zauberhafte, familiengeführte alte Poststation liegt hoch auf einem Berg im Jura, und versprüht einen herrlich altmodischen Charme. Die traditionelle Einrichtung erinnert an längst vergangene Zeiten. Hier fühlt man sich wie zu Hause, und wärmende offene Kamine schaffen eine gemütliche und freundliche Atmosphäre. Die Gäste können die traumhaft schöne Umgebung zu Fuß oder mit dem Fahrrad erkunden, bevor sie sich von den regionalen Köstlichkeiten auf der umfangreichen Speisekarte und der phantastischen Weinkarte verwöhnen lassen..

Our inspector loved: *The magnificent wine list.*

CHÂTEAU DE GILLY

GILLY~LES~CÎTEAUX, 21640 VOUGEOT, FRANCE

With its moats, parkland gardens and magnificent 14th-century vaulted dining room this former residence of the Priors of the Cistercian Abbey in the heart of Burgundy is a superb hotel of history. Restoration, refurbishment, modernisation in no way diminished its authenticity and charm. The architecture is superb, the interior décor and furnishings stunning and guest rooms are of the highest standard.

Avec ses douves, son parc et sa magnifique salle à manger sous voûtes, cette ancienne résidence des moines de l'abbaye cistercienne au cœur de la Bourgogne est un splendide monument historique. Restauration, redécoration et modernisation n'ont en rien diminué son authenticité et son charme. L'architecture est superbe, les intérieurs et le mobilier magnifiques et les chambres d'un niveau exceptionnel.

Diese ehemalige Residenz der Priore der Zisterzienserabtei im Herzen des Burgund mit ihren Gräben, parkartigen Gärten und herrlichem Speisesaal mit gewölbter Decke aus dem 14. Jahrhundert ist ein einzigartiges und geschichtsträchtiges Hotel. Restaurierungs- und Modernisierungsarbeiten konnten der Authentizität und dem Charakter keinen Abbruch tun. Die Architektur ist atemberaubend, das Décor und die Einrichtung der Innenräume einmalig, und die Zimmer bieten höchsten Komfort.

Our inspector loved: *The very impressive vaulted dining room and the many activities organised for children.*

Directions: A6 > A31 > exit Nuits-Saint-Georges > follow signs to Gilly-Les-Cîteaux.

Paris
Dijon
Bordeaux
Marseille

Web: www.johansens.com/gilly
E-mail: gilly@grandesetapes.fr
Tel: +33 3 80 62 89 98
Fax: +33 3 80 62 82 34

Price Guide: (room only)
double €150–290
suite €690

Château d'Etoges

51270 ETOGES~EN~CHAMPAGNE, FRANCE

Nestling in the Champagne Region on the Paris-Strasbourg road, this magnificent château is surrounded by a moat and 45 acres of parkland and gardens sprinkled with fountains and water features. Formerly a medieval fortress, the château was rebuilt in the 17th century by the counts of Anglure and prior to the revolution was a favourite stopping point for French royalty. Bright and spacious public rooms create a comfortable ambience, whilst the bedrooms are individually decorated and furnished, some in period style, others more cosy and intimate.

Niché au coeur de la Champagne, sur la route de Paris á Strasbourg, ce magnifique château est entouré de larges douves et d'un parc de 18ha. Ancien château-fort, il fut reconstruit au XVIIe siècle par les Comtes d'Anglure et fut, avant la Révolution, la halte privilégiée des Rois de France. Les chambres, intimes et confortables, sont aménagées et décorées avec raffinement. Mobilier authentique et vastes salons sont les témoins précieux des fastes du passé d'Etoges.

Dieses herrliche Château bei Etoges an der Straße von Paris nach Straßburg ist umgeben von einem Burggraben und 18ha Park mit zahlreichen Springbrunnen und Wasseranlagen. Diese einstige mittelalterliche Festung wurde im 17. Jahrhundert von den Grafen zu Anglure wieder erbaut und war vor der Revolution ein beliebter Rastort für Mitglieder der französischen Königsfamilie. Helle, geräumige Aufenthaltsräume schaffen ein freundliches Ambiente, und die Zimmer sind unterschiedlich eingerichtet und gestaltet, einige im Originalstil, andere eher klein und gemütlich.

Our inspector loved: *The terrace area overlooking the moat.*

Directions: The hotel is situated beside the D933 Montmirail, Chalons en Champagne road. The nearest airport is Paris Roissy.

Web: www.johansens.com/etoges
E-mail: contact@etoges.com
Tel: +33 3 26 59 30 08
Fax: +33 3 26 59 35 57

Price Guide: (room only)
single €80-110
double €110-190

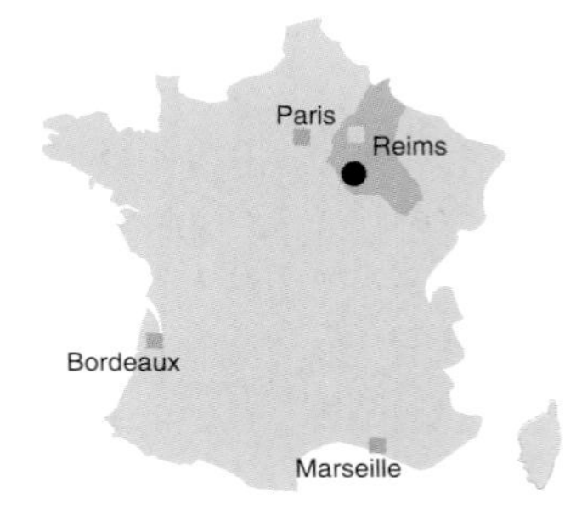

CHÂTEAU DE FÈRE

02130 FÈRE~EN~TARDENOIS, FRANCE

Side by side with the impressive ruins of a medieval castle, this grand and exclusive 18th-century château is situated in beautiful, wooded countryside just 1 hour's drive from Paris. The guest rooms are tastefully furnished, maintained to the highest standard and offer spectacular views. Excellent gourmet meals are served in 3 individual and stylishly designed dining rooms where the service is impeccable. The treasures of the Champagne region can be enjoyed on a tour of the Château's cellars.

Dominé par les ruines impressionnantes d'un château fort, cet hôtel de luxe occupe un magnifique château du XVIIIe siècle, au milieu d'un beau parc boisé, à une heure seulement de Paris. Des chambres de premier ordre, meublées avec goût, offrent des vues spectaculaires sur les environs. 3 salles à manger différentes proposent des menus gourmands dans un cadre élégant. Le service est d'une qualité irréprochable. Un tour des caves du château permet aux œnophiles de savourer les délices de la région champenoise.

Inmitten der imposanten Ruinen einer mittelalterlichen Burg und umgeben von herrlicher Waldlandschaft liegt dieses elegante und exklusive Schloss aus dem 18. Jahrhundert, nur eine Stunde Fahrt von Paris entfernt. Die Zimmer sind geschmackvoll eingerichtet und bieten höchstes Niveau und eindrucksvolle Aussichten. In 3 unterschiedlichen, eleganten Speisesälen werden exzellente Gerichte serviert; der Service ist tadellos. Champagnerfreunde werden sich über die Champagnerkeller des Schlosses freuen.

Our inspector loved: *The totally committed and friendly staff.*

Directions: From Paris on the A4 > exit at Château-Thierry. From Calais on the A26 > exit at Reims.

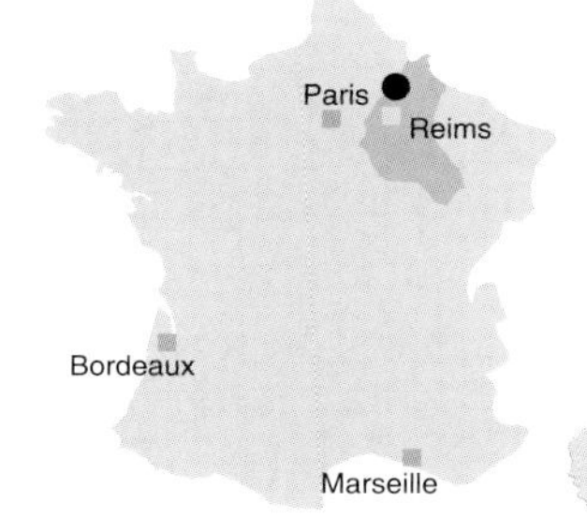

Web: www.johansens.com/chateaudefere
E-mail: chateau.fere@wanadoo.fr
Tel: +33 3 23 82 21 13
Fax: +33 3 23 82 37 81

Price Guide: (room only)
single/double/twin €150–340
suites €230–390

FRANCE / CHAMPAGNE~ARDENNES (SAINTE PREUVE)

Domaine du Château de Barive

02350 SAINTE-PREUVE, FRANCE

This perfectly restored stone built hotel is accessed through an ornamental gateway, which gives way to a manicured garden and courtyard area. Although the atmosphere is one of relaxed elegance, there is amazing attention to detail. Public rooms are furnished in a modern style in contrast with the historic ambience, and bedrooms are light, spacious and airy. Classic French cooking can be sampled in the restaurant, and guests may enjoy the pool, sauna and gymnasium. Ideally located for exploring the World War I battlefields and numerous champagne cellars.

Cet hôtel, magnifiquement restauré, est accessible par une entrée ornementale qui s'ouvre sur des jardins et une cour très soignés. L'atmosphère décontractée mais élégante n'empêche pas une impressionnante attention du détail. Les pièces communes sont meublées avec une touche moderne dans cette ambiance historique. Les chambres sont claires et spacieuses. Une cuisine classique peut-être dégustée au restaurant et les clients ont accès à la piscine, au sauna et à la salle de gym. Cet hôtel est idéalement situé pour explorer les champs de bataille de la première guerre mondiale et les caves de champagne.

Dieses perfekt restaurierte, Hotel ist über eine prunkvolle Pforte erreichbar, die den Blick auf einen gepflegten Garten und Innenhof freigibt. Die Atmosphäre ist entspannt und elegant, und Liebe zum Detail ist überall sichtbar. Der moderne Stil der Aufenthaltsräume kontrastiert wunderbar mit dem historischen Ambiente, und die Zimmer sind hell und geräumig. Im Restaurant wird klassische französische Küche serviert, und Swimmingpool, Sauna und Fitnessraum stehen zur Verfügung. Ideal für Besuche der Champagnerkellereien und der Schlachtfelder des 1. Weltkriegs.

Our inspector loved: *The quiet and peaceful library.*

Directions: A26 > exit 13 > N2 towards Laon > D977 to Chivres en Laonnais. The nearest airport is Rheims, a free bus transfer to and from the airport and train station is available.

Web: www.johansens.com/barive
E-mail: contact@lesepicuriens.com
Tel: +33 3 23 22 15 15
Fax: +33 3 23 22 08 39

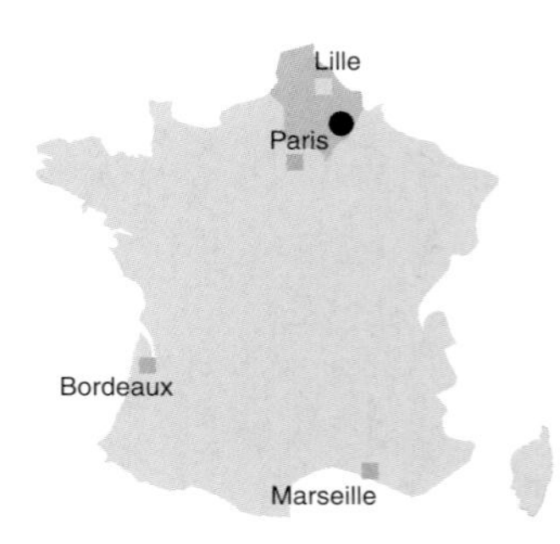

Price Guide: (breakfast €16)
single €120-220
double €120-220
suite €200

L'Assiette Champenoise

40 AVENUE PAUL VAILLANT COUTURIER, 51430 TINQUEUX, FRANCE

A truly warm welcome awaits visitors to this family-orientated hotel, highly reputed for its delicious modern and traditional cuisine. Complemented by a cosy and welcoming bar, a superb dining room opens out onto an amazing terrace. Guests may relax in the lawned gardens filled with trees and flowers, take advantage of the indoor swimming pool and sauna or visit Reims and some of the numerous champagne cellars in the vicinity, some of which house the finest bottles in the world.

Un accueil très chaleureux vous attend dans cet hôtel hautement réputé pour sa délicieuse cuisine moderne et traditionnelle. Complétée par un bar intime, l'élégante salle de restaurant s'ouvre sur une magnifique terrasse. Les visiteurs se reposent sur les pelouses du jardin rempli de fleurs et d'arbres, profitent de la piscine et du sauna ou visitent Reims et les innombrables caves à champagne des environs, dont certaines renferment les meilleures bouteilles du monde.

Ein herzlicher Empfang erwartet Besucher dieses familienorientierten Hotels, das für seine köstliche moderne und traditionelle Küche weithin bekannt ist. Es gibt eine gemütliche Bar, und ein eleganter Speisesaal führt auf eine fantastische Terrasse hinaus. Die Gäste entspannen sich im gepflegten, mit Bäumen und Blumen gefüllten Garten, Hallenbad oder in der Sauna oder erkunden Reims und die zahllosen Champagnerkeller in der Umgebung, von denen einige die besten Champagnersorten der Welt beherbergen.

Our inspector loved: *The new breakfast room.*

Directions: A4 > exit Tinqueux.

Web: www.johansens.com/lassiettechampenoise
E-mail: info@assiettechampenoise.com
Tel: +33 3 26 84 64 64
Fax: +33 3 26 04 15 69

Price Guide: (breakfast €14)
double/twin €125–175
suite €245

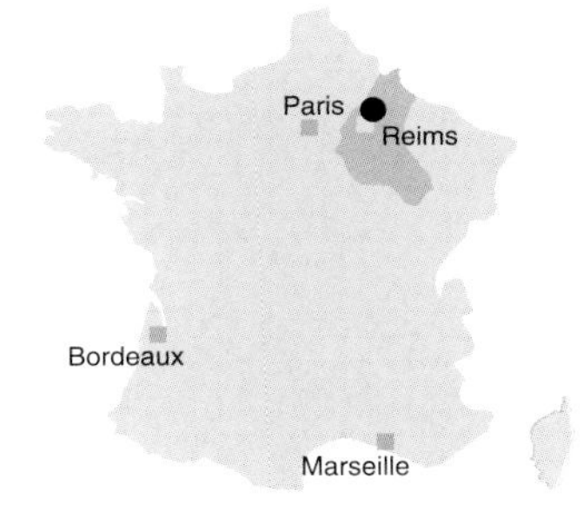

Bastide du Calalou

VILLAGE DE MOISSAC-BELLEVUE, 83630 AUPS, FRANCE

Directions: From the A8 > exit either St Maximin or Le Muy.

Web: www.johansens.com/calalou
E-mail: info@bastide-du-calalou.com
Tel: +33 4 94 70 17 91
Fax: +33 4 94 70 50 11

Price Guide: (room only)
double €75-191
apartment €180-230

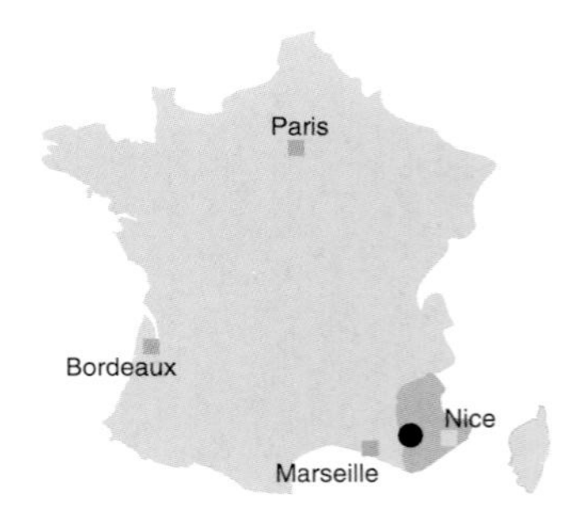

Perched on a hill, at an altitude of 550m, within the Nature Park of Verdon and amidst 10 acres of century-old olive trees, Bastide du Calalou is a delightful and relaxing retreat. The lounges, library, bar and restaurant are all decorated with antiques and family pictures, as are the bedrooms, which overlook the garden, swimming pool or surrounding valley. Breakfast, lunch and apéritifs are served on the terrace under olive trees, and refined Provençal cuisine can be enjoyed in the restaurant with open fire. Numerous attractions of the Var region include the Gorges du Verdon and St-Tropez.

Perché sur le flanc d'une colline à 550 m d'altitude, au milieu de 4 ha d'oliviers multicentenaires au milieu du Parc Naturel Régional du Verdon, la Bastide du Calalou est synonyme de charme et de repos. Elle est décorée de meubles antiques et tableaux de famille depuis les salons TV, bibliothèque, bar, restaurant jusqu'aux chambres qui font toutes face au jardin, à la piscine et à la vallée environnante. Le petit-déjeuner, le déjeuner et les apéritifs sont servis en terrasse, sous les oliviers, et le restaurant avec feu ouvert propose une cuisine provençale raffinée. La région du Var comporte de nombreux sites à visiter, comme les Gorges du Verdon et St-Tropez.

550m hoch auf einem Hügel inmitten des Naturparks von Verdon und umgeben von jahrhundertealten Olivenbäumen liegt diese Oase der Ruhe. Die Aufenthaltsräume, Bibliothek, Bar und das Restaurant sind mit Antiquitäten und Familienbildern geschmückt, ebenso die Zimmer, alle mit Blick auf Garten, Pool oder Tal. Frühstück, Mittagessen und Apéritif werden auf der Terrasse unter Olivenbäumen serviert, und im Restaurant genießt man raffinierte provenzalische Küche bei offenem Kamin. Sehenswürdigkeiten der Var-Region sind z.B. die Gorges du Verdon und St-Tropez.

***Our inspector loved:** The breathtaking views and the very warm welcome.*

Château Eza

Rue de la Pise, 06360 Èze Village, France

From its vantage point, 1,300ft above the Mediterranean Sea, Château Eza enchants its guests as its location and history suggest. Completely refurbished in a contemporary style, original stone walls, oak beams and fireplaces of several 13th-century houses have been preserved. 10 sumptuous suites, 7 with their own balcony, have all been tastefully redecorated with superb fabrics and feature every modern facility. Breathtaking views are guaranteed as an accompaniment to the award-winning meals served on the outdoor terrace or panoramic restaurant.

Perché à plus de 400 mètres au-dessus de la Méditerranée, Château Eza émerveille les visiteurs par sa situation et son histoire privilégiées. Complètement remis à neuf au style contemporain, la propriété a gardé les murs de pierre originaux, les poutres en chêne et les cheminées de plusieurs maisons du XIIIe siècle. Les 10 suites somptueuses, 7 d'entre elles avec leur propre balcon, ont été redécorées avec goût utilisant des tissus superbes et offrant tout le confort moderne. Des vues spectaculaires accompagnent la dégustation des plats primés servis sur la terrasse ou dans le restaurant panoramique.

Das etwa 450m über dem Mittelmeer gelegene Châtau Eza verzaubert seine Gäste durch seine Aussicht und seine Geschichte. Bei der kompletten Renovierung wurden die ursprünglichen Steinwände, Eichenbalken und Kamine einiger der Häuser aus dem 13. Jahrhundert erhalten. 10 prunkvolle Suiten - 7 mit eigenem Balkon - wurden mit herrlichen Stoffen geschmackvoll neu gestaltet und bieten jeglichen modernen Komfort. Eine atemberaubende Aussicht begleitet preisgekrönte Gaumenfreuden, die auf der Außenterrasse oder im Panorama-Restaurant serviert werden.

Our inspector loved: *The restaurant's private little balconies; amazing views.*

Directions: On Moyenne Corniche between Nice and Monaco.

Web: www.johansens.com/eza
E-mail: reservations@luxurylifestylehotels.com
Tel: +33 4 93 41 12 24
Fax: +33 4 93 41 16 64

Price Guide:
double/twin €230–530
suite €580–880

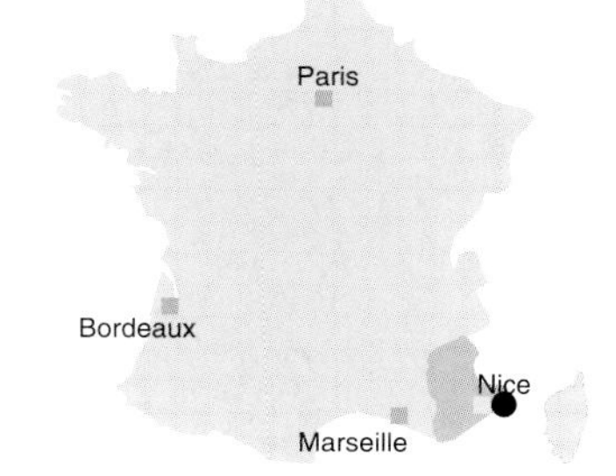

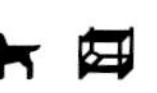

Bastide Saint Mathieu

35 CHEMIN DE BLUMENTHAL, 06130 SAINT MATHIEU, GRASSE, FRANCE

This 18th-century Provençal Bastide is situated in the heart of the "Golden Triangle," just south east of the perfume town of Grasse. Owners, Mr and Mrs van Osch, personally welcome guests into this exclusive yet homely country residence. Each of the individually designed and spacious suites feature exquisite antiques and luxurious cashmere blankets. Breakfast may be taken on the terrace overlooking the sloping hills of Mougins and Cannes or in the intimate stone breakfast room. Within the beautiful, extensive gardens the secluded pool offers a relaxing haven.

Cette bastide provençale, datant du XVIIIe siècle est située au coeur du "triangle d'or" au sud-est de la ville de Grasse, célèbre pour le parfum. Les propriétaires, M et Mme van Osch, accueillent leurs hôtes personnellement dans cette résidence de campagne, qui est également exclusive et confortable. Toutes les suites, spacieuses et décorées de manière individuelle, sont parées d,antiquités et de couvertures luxueuses de cachemire. Le petit déjeuner est servi sur la terrasse donnant sur les collines de Mougins et de Cannes, ou dans la petite salle à manger construite en pierre. Dans les beaux jardins vastes, la piscine isolée offre un havre relaxant.

Diese provenzalische Bastide befindet sich im Herzen des "Goldenen Dreiecks", südöstlich der Parfümstadt Grasse. Die Eigentümer, Herr und Frau van Osch heißen ihre Gäste persönlich in ihrem exklusiven und familiären Landsitz willkommen. Jede der individuell gestalteten geräumigen Suiten bietet exquisite Antiquitäten und Kaschmirdecken. Das Frühstück wird auf der Terrasse mit Blick auf die Hügel von Mougins und Cannes oder im gemütlichen Frühstücksraum serviert. Innerhalb der herrlichen weitläufigen Gärten sorgt ein abgeschiedener Pool für Entspannung.

Our inspector loved: *The superb and original toiletries.*

Directions: A8 > exit at 42 Cannes / Mougins / Grasse > Grasse > exit Grasse Sud. The nearest airport is Nice, Côte d'Azur.

Web: www.johansens.com/saintmathieu
E-mail: info@bastidestmathieu.com
Tel: +33 4 97 01 10 00
Fax: +33 4 97 0110 09

Price Guide:
single €230-340
double €230-340

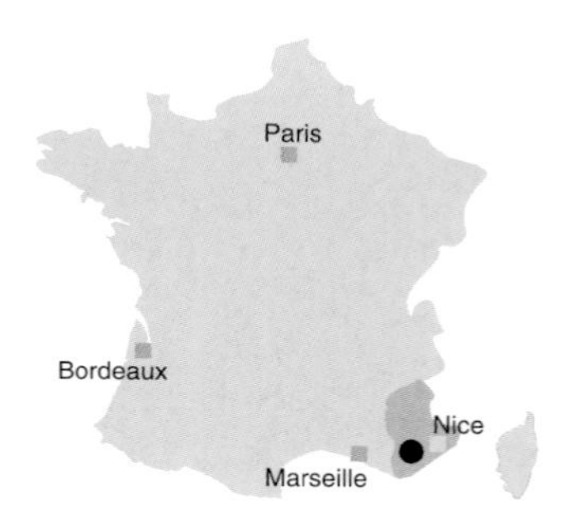

HÔTEL JUANA

LA PINÈDE, AVENUE G. GALLICE, 06160 ANTIBES JUAN~LES~PINS, FRANCE

Built in 1931 and recently extensively restored, this art deco hotel is a real gem. Its heritage has been carefully preserved with bespoke furniture and fabrics, and the tastefully decorated bedrooms have elegant marble bathrooms featuring handmade tiles. At La Terrasse, awarded 2 Michelin stars and 5 diamonds, guests can enjoy traditional Provençal cuisine and fine wines in a romantic setting. There is a small white marble swimming pool, whilst the hotel's sandy beach is a 3-minute walk away, offering another 3 restaurants.

Construit en 1931 et récemment rénové, cet hôtel art déco est un vrai joyau. Son héritage a été soigneusement préservé par un ameublement sur mesures, et les chambres sont décorées avec goût avec des salles de bains en marbre et carrelages fait-main. A La Terrasse, 2 étoiles au Michelin et 5 diamants, les hôtes peuvent déguster une cuisine provençale typique et des vins délicats dans un cadre romantique. Pour les nageurs, il y a une petite piscine en marbre blanc, et la plage de sable de l'hôtel est à 3 minutes à pied, proposant 3 restaurants.

Dieses 1932 erbaute und ausgiebig restaurierte Art-Deco-Hotel ist ein wahres Juwel, dessen Erbe mit eigens angefertigten Möbeln und Stoffen bewahrt wurde. Die geschmackvoll eingerichteten Zimmer haben elegante Bäder mit handgefertigten Kacheln. Im mit 2 Michelinsternen und 5 Diamanten ausgezeichneten La Terrasse werden traditionelle provenzalische Küche und feine Weine in romantischem Ambiente serviert. Ein kleiner Marmorswimmingpool steht zur Verfügung und der Sandstrand ist nur 3 Minuten zu Fuß entfernt. Hier findet man 3 weitere Restaurants.

Our inspector loved: *The panoramic views from the top floor bedrooms.*

Directions: A8 > exit Antibes/Juan-les-Pins > hotel is signposted.

Web: www.johansens.com/juana
E-mail: reservation@hotel-juana.com
Tel: +33 4 93 61 08 70
Fax: +33 4 93 61 76 60

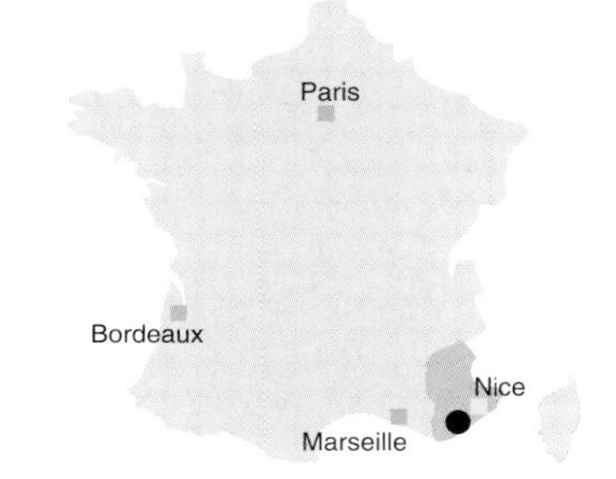

Price Guide:
double €235-635
suite upon request

Le Bailli de Suffren

AVENUE DES AMÉRICAINS, GOLFE DE SAINT~TROPEZ, 83820 LE RAYOL – CANADEL, FRANCE

This superb hotel facing the islands of Port-Cros and Levant is located in one of the most beautiful coves of the Saint-Tropez Gulf. Spacious and cosy lounges overlook the sea and the 53 junior suites are tastefully decorated in a Provençal style with balconies and terraces which boast views of the islands. Guests may dine at the gastronomic restaurant La Praya or the beach restaurant L'Escale, which is ideal for lunch by the sea. There is a heated swimming pool overlooking the sea, fitness room, sauna, private beach and yacht; all the ingredients for a fantastic break.

Ce superbe hôtel est situé face aux îles de Port-Cros et du Levant, au bord d'une des criques les plus séduisantes du Golfe de Saint-Tropez, dans un site totalement préservé. Vastes salons ouverts sur la mer, 53 suites junior décorées avec goût dans le style provençal avec balcons et terrasses orientés vers les îles, piscine d'eau douce chauffée surplombant la mer, salle de fitness, sauna, plage privée de sable fin, splendide voilier; tous les ingrédients de la Dolce Vita s'y trouvent réunis. Restaurant gastronomique La Praya et restaurant de plage 'L'Escale' pour déjeuner les pieds dans l'eau.

Dieses einmalige Hotel mit Blick auf die Inseln Port-Cros und Levant befindet sich in einer der schönsten Buchten am Golf von Saint-Tropez. Die geräumigen, gemütlichen Aufenthaltsräume blicken auf das Meer und die 53 Junior-Suiten sind geschmackvoll im provenzalischen Stil eingerichtet. Von den Balkonen und Terrassen sieht man die Inseln. Man kann im Gourmetrestaurant La Praya oder im Strandrestaurant L'Escale essen - der ideale Ort für ein Mittagessen direkt am Meer. Es gibt einen beheizten Swimmingpool mit Meerblick, Fitnessraum, Sauna, Privatstrand und eine herrliche Jacht: alles Zutaten für einen wunderbaren Aufenthalt.

Our inspector loved: *Its superb seaside location with breathtaking views.*

Directions: A8 > exit Le Muy > Saint Tropez > Cavalaire > Le Rayol - Canadel.

Web: www.johansens.com/lebaillidesuffren
E-mail: info@lebaillidesuffren.com
Tel: +33 4 98 04 47 00
Fax: +33 4 98 04 47 99

Price Guide:
double €154–550
junior suite €154–550

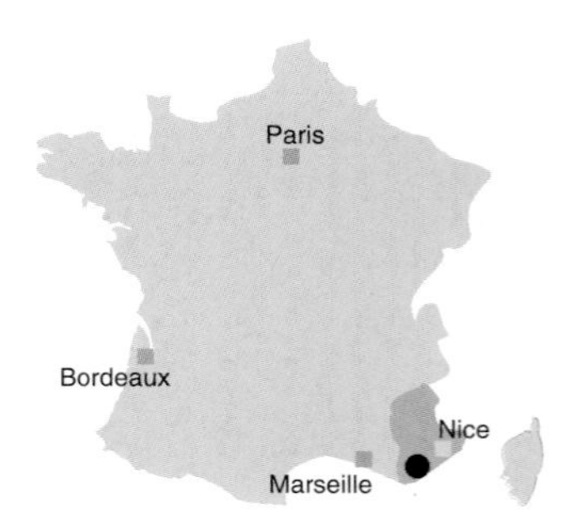

Les Muscadins

18 BOULEVARD COURTELINE, 06250 MOUGINS, FRANCE

This charming property, located in the heart of the picturesque village of Mougins, is located within walking distance of Le Mas Candille, where guests can enjoy such facilities as the Shiseido Spa, a swimming pool and fitness area. 11 beautiful bedrooms of all shapes and sizes are scattered around the old house and overlook the village and Alps or the fantastic bay of Cannes. Breakfast and dinner can be savoured on the terrace, whilst the bar and restaurant are flamboyant in décor and style.

Cet établissement de charme, situé au cœur du magnifique village de Mougins, est à quelques minutes à pied du Mas Candille où les clients peuvent profiter entre autres du Spa Shiseido, de la piscine et de la salle de l'air de fitness. 11 superbes chambres toutes différentes sont dispersées dans cette ancienne demeure et offrent des vues époustouflantes sur le village et les Alpes ou sur la baie de Cannes. Le petit-déjeuner et le dîner peuvent être dégustés sur la terrasse ou dans le restaurant au décor et style magistral.

Dieses bezaubernde Anwesen im Herzen des hübschen Dörfchens Mougins ist nur ein paar Schritte vom Mas Candille entfernt, dessen Einrichtungen wie z.B. das Shiseido-Spa, den Swimmingpool und den Fitnessraum die Gäste benutzen dürfen. 11 attraktive Zimmer in allen Größen und Formen befinden sich im alten Haus und blicken auf das Dorf, die Alpen oder die herrliche Bucht von Cannes. Frühstück und Abendessen können auf der Terrasse serviert werden, während Stil und Décor der Bar und des Restaurants einen etwas ausgefalleneren Hintergrund bieten.

Our inspector loved: *Savouring the amazing views whilst being in the heart of an old Provençal village.*

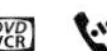

Directions: A8 > exit Mougins > exit at Mougins Centre > signs to Centre Ville/Vieux Village.

Web: www.johansens.com/muscadins
E-mail: info@lemascandille.com
Tel: +33 4 92 28 28 28
Fax: +33 4 92 28 43 40

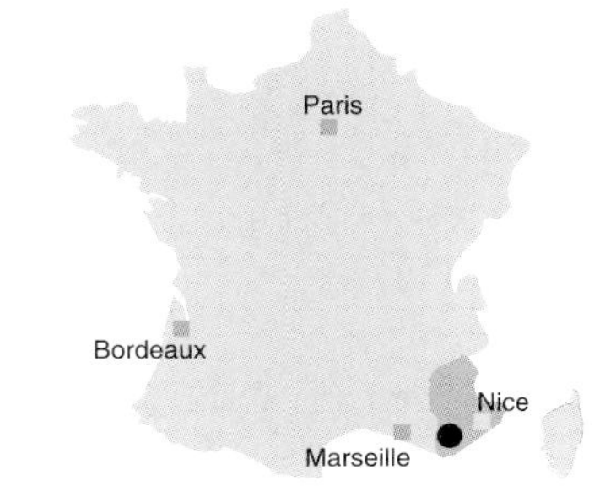

Price Guide:
single €129-279
double €139-279
suite €245-399

HÔTEL LA PÉROUSE

11, QUAI RAUBA~CAPEU, 06300 NICE, FRANCE

Perched high on a hill overlooking the Baie des Anges, the Hôtel la Perouse enjoys a unique and peaceful setting in the heart of the city. Completely renovated in 2000, the hotel offers a comfortable stay in charming surroundings, enhanced by elegant bedrooms decorated in Provençal style and flower-filled terraces and gardens. There is an outdoor swimming pool, gymnasium, sauna and Jacuzzi as well as a sun terrace with panoramic view of the surroundings. From May to September, simple Provençal dishes are served on the terrace in the shade of the lemon trees.

Dominant la Baie des Anges, l'Hôtel la Perouse bénéficie d'une situation privilégiée, véritable havre de paix en plein centre ville. Entièrement renové en 2000, l'hôtel offre un grand confort dans une atmosphère de charme et de convivialité avec ses chambres élégantes de style provençal, ses terrasses fleuries et ses jardins ombragés. L'hôtel dispose d'une piscine extérieure d'un solarium panoramique avec salle de gymnastique, sauna et jacuzzi au dernier étage avec vue imprenable sur la mer. Une cuisine provençale simple et fraîche est servie en terrasse à l'ombre des citronniers de mai à septembre.

Mit seiner herrlichen Lage am Schlossberg mit Blick auf die Baie des Anges ist dieses Hotel eine Oase der Ruhe mitten in der Stadt. Nach umfassender Renovierung im Jahr 2000 bietet das Hotel mit seinen eleganten Zimmern im provenzalischen Stil, blumengeschmückten Terrassen und schattenspendenden Gärten großen Komfort in charmanter Atmosphäre. Es gibt einen Außenpool, Fitnessraum, Sauna und Jacuzzi sowie eine Sonnenterrasse mit Panoramablick auf die Umgebung. Von Mai bis September wird auf der Terrasse im Schatten der Zitronenbäume einfache provenzalische Küche serviert.

Our inspector loved: *The superb top floor terrace with panoramic views.*

Directions: Situated on the Promenade des Anglais, round the corner from the Nice port and old Nice.

Web: www.johansens.com/hotellaperouse
E-mail: lp@hroy.com
Tel: +33 4 93 62 34 63
Fax: +33 4 93 62 59 41

Price Guide: (breakfast €19)
single €155-420
double €155-420
suite €630-850
Special conditions for Johansens readers

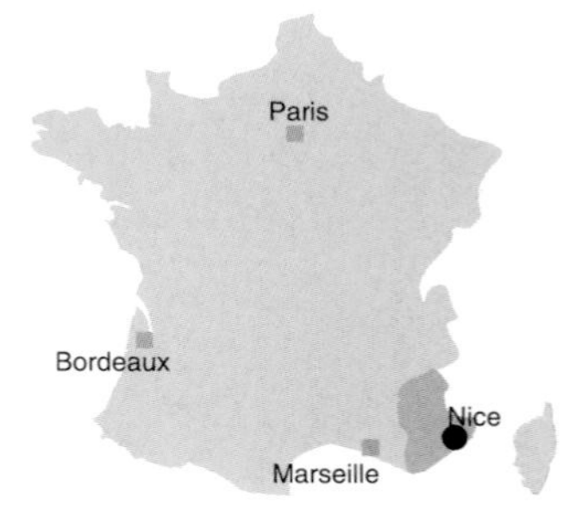

LE MAS D'ARTIGNY

ROUTE DE LA COLLE, 06570 SAINT~PAUL~DE~VENCE, FRANCE

Le Mas d'Artigny stands in 20 acres of hillside pine forest overlooking the Mediterranean and the medieval city of Saint-Paul-de-Vence between Nice and Cannes. Guests have the choice of bedroom, apartment or 2 to 8-bedroom villa with garden. All are spacious and individually decorated. Award-winning cuisine is served in an elegant restaurant with panoramic views. Extensive leisure and sport facilities.

Le Mas d'Artigny se tient au sein de 8ha de forêt de pins sur les côteaux de collines surplombant la Méditerranée et la cité médiévale de Saint-Paul-de-Vence entre Nice et Cannes. Les hôtes ont le choix entre chambres, appartements ou villas de 2 à 8 chambres avec jardin. Tous ces logements sont spacieux et décorés individuellement. Une cuisine primée est servie dans un restaurant élégant avec vue panoramique. De nombreux loisirs et sports sont disponibles.

Le Mas d'Artigny liegt zwischen Nizza und Cannes inmitten von 8ha hügeligem Pinienwald mit Blick auf das Mittelmeer und die mittelalterliche Stadt Saint-Paul-de-Vence. Man hat die Wahl zwischen einem Zimmer, Appartement oder einer Villa mit 2 bis 8 Zimmern und Garten. Alle Räumlichkeiten sind großzügig und individuell gestaltet. In einem eleganten Restaurant mit Panoramablick wird preisgekrönte Küche serviert. Das Sport- und Freizeitangebot ist sehr umfangreich.

Our inspector loved: *The giant chess board by the swimming pool.*

Directions: A8 from Nice, exit Cagnes-sur-Mer > follow signs to Vence > Saint Paul.

Web: www.johansens.com/masdartigny
E-mail: mas@grandesetapes.fr
Tel: +33 4 93 32 84 54
Fax: +33 4 93 32 95 36

Price Guide:
single €150–380
double €150–380
suite €450–1,200

LA FERME D'AUGUSTIN

PLAGE DE TAHITI, 83350 RAMATUELLE, NEAR SAINT~TROPEZ, FRANCE

This delightful family-run hotel combines traditional French charm with modern hospitality to create an idyllic retreat from the buzzing pace of the Côte d'Azur. The pretty bedrooms and suites are furnished with antiques and have whirlpool baths – some even have private gardens. A hydrotherapy pool in the charming gardens and wonderful homemade cooking create a sense of luxury and complement the impeccable standards set by the owners, the Vallet family.

La famille Vallet a complété le charme français traditionnel de cet hôtel séduisant par un accueil moderne pour créer un havre de paix idyllique, à l'écart de la vie trépidante de la Côte d'Azur. Les jolies chambres et suites sont pourvues de meubles anciens et d'un bain bouillonnant, parfois même d'un jardin privatif. La piscine hydrothérapique aménagée dans le ravissant jardin et la cuisine maison succulente soulignent le caractère luxueux et la qualité exceptionnelle de cet établissement.

Dieses freundliche, familiengeführte Hotel, das traditionelles französisches Flair mit moderner Gastfreundschaft verbindet, liegt idyllisch fernab vom geschäftigen Treiben Côte d'Azur. Die hübschen Zimmer und Suiten sind mit Antiquitäten ausgestattet und haben Jacuzzibäder. Einige bieten auch einen privaten Garten. Ein Hydrotherapie-Pool im Garten und köstliche Hausmannskost schaffen ein Gefühl von Luxus und spiegeln perfekt das hohe Niveau wider, das sich die Eigentümer, die Familie Vallet, zum Ziel gesetzt haben.

Our inspector loved: *The friendliness of the staff and the relaxed atmosphere.*

Directions: A8 > exit Le Muy > Saint-Tropez > Plage de Tahiti.

Web: www.johansens.com/fermedaugustin
E-mail: info@fermeaugustin.com
Tel: +33 4 94 55 97 00
Fax: +33 4 94 97 59 76

Price Guide: (breakfast €12)
double/twin €135–200
suite €250-490

HÔTEL CANTEMERLE

258 CHEMIN CANTEMERLE, 06140 VENCE, FRANCE

Nestling on a wooded hillside, this hotel is a haven of peace. Everything seems far away, yet Cannes, Nice and the airport, the sea and a few museums are within easy reach, and the towns of Vence and Saint-Paul, whose Provençal charm has inspired great artists such as Matisse and Chagall, are nearby. The comfortable rooms and suites have private terraces and each has its own individual style. Large lawns border the pool and the solarium, overlooking the Mediterranean. The indoor pool and Turkish bath, the lounges, the bar and the restaurant open onto large terraces.

Cet hôtel se niche sur une colline boisée et est un vrai havre de calme. Tout semble très loin, quand tout n'est qu'à quelques minutes: Cannes, Nice et son aéroport, la mer, les musées, et, à deux pas, Vence et Saint-Paul, petites cités dont le charme provençal a inspiré les plus grands artistes, comme Matisse ou Chagall. Les chambres et les duplex confortables avec terrasse privée offrent une grande diversité de décors raffinés. Une grande pelouse borde la piscine et le solarium, face à la Méditerranée. La piscine couverte et son hammam, les salons, le bar et le restaurant s'ouvrent sur de vastes terrasses.

Dieses auf einem Hügel gelegene Hotel ist eine Oase der Ruhe, scheinbar abgeschieden, doch unweit von Cannes, Nizza, dem Flughafen, dem Meer, ein paar Museen, und den Städtchen Vence und Saint-Paul, die bereits große Meister wie Matisse und Chagall mit ihrem provenzalischen Charme bezauberten. Die individuell gestalteten, komfortablen Zimmer und Suiten haben eigene Terrassen. Ein Swimmingpool ist von Rasen umgeben und das Solarium blickt auf das Meer. Das Hallenbad, Türkische Bad, die Aufenthaltsräume, Bar und Restaurant öffnen sich auf große Terrassen.

Our inspector loved: *The bedrooms in the new building where the exceptional steam bath is located.*

Directions: A8 > exit Cagnes-sur-Mer > follow signs to Vence. The hotel is signposted.

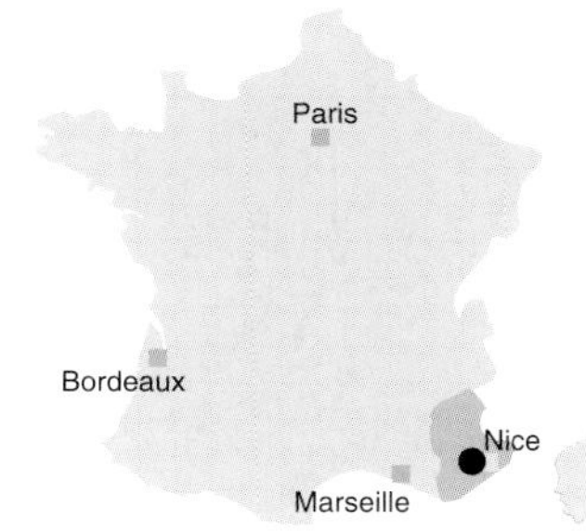

Web: www.johansens.com/hotelcantemerle
E-mail: info@hotelcantemerle.com
Tel: +33 4 93 58 08 18
Fax: +33 4 93 58 32 89

Price Guide: (room only)
double €200-220
duplex €225-295

Château de Pray

ROUTE DE CHARGÉ, 37400 AMBOISE, FRANCE

Nestled on the sunny terraced slopes overlooking the tranquil Loire river, Château de Pray is simply steeped in history. Surrounded by peaceful gardens, the imposing round towers bear witness to its Renaissance origins. The traditional ambience extends to the interior, where wood panelling, heavy beams and rich fabrics abound. The en-suite bedrooms, many of which have stunning views, are tastefully furnished. Award-winning gourmet cuisine is served in the restaurant.

Niché sur les côteaux ensoleillés des collines des eaux tranquilles de la Loire, Le Château de Pray est imprégné d'histoire. Entouré de jardins paisibles, ses tours rondes sont témoins de son origine Renaissance. L'ambiance traditionnelle s'étend à l'intérieur où les boiseries, les lourdes poutres et riches étoffes abondent. Les chambres dont la plupart ont de superbes vues, sont meublées avec goût. La cuisine y est gourmande et soignée.

In die sonnigen, terrassenförmigen Hänge oberhalb der Loire schmiegt sich das geschichtsträchtige Château de Pray. Umgeben von ruhigen Gärten zeugen die imposanten runden Türme von seinen Ursprüngen aus der Renaissance. Das traditionsreiche Ambiente wird durch reichlich vorhandene Holzvertäfelung sowie schwere Balken und üppige Stoffe betont. Ausblick. Im Restaurant wird feinste Gourmetküche serviert.

Our inspector loved: *The very attentive and friendly staff.*

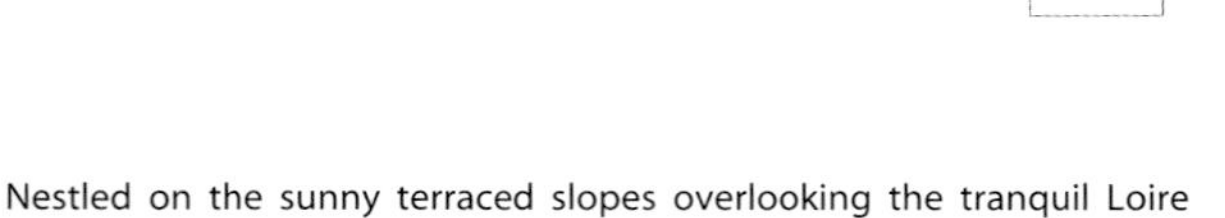

Directions: D31 > Blois.

Web: www.johansens.com/chateaudepray
E-mail: chateau.depray@wanadoo.fr
Tel: +33 2 47 57 23 67
Fax: +33 2 47 57 32 50

Price Guide: (room only)
single €95-170
double/twin €95-170
suite €185-230

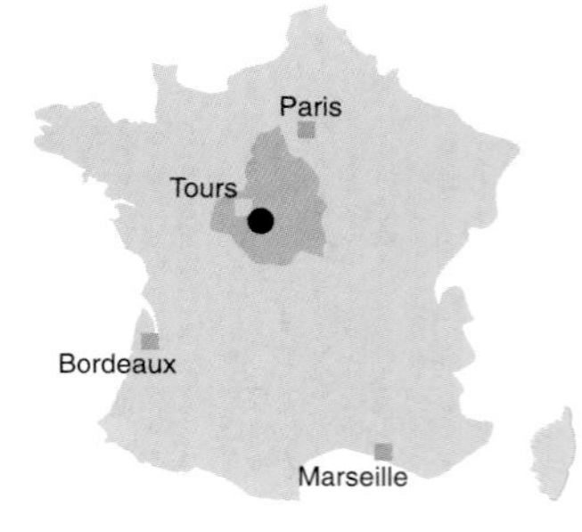

Le Choiseul

36 QUAI CHARLES GUINOT, 37400 AMBOISE, FRANCE

Situated in a quiet and charming area around Amboise, Le Choiseul lies tucked between the hillside and the Loire river. The surrounding grounds of this ensemble of 3 delightful 18th-century houses feature a labyrinth of superb Italian-style terraced gardens. 32 tastefully decorated guest rooms with elegant bathrooms offer every comfort and there is excellent dining in a refined restaurant with panoramic views.

Situé dans un coin charmant et calme près d'Amboise, Le Choiseul est blotti entre les flancs de coteaux et la Loire. Sur les terrains environnants de ce complexe de 3 demeures charmantes du XVIIIe siècle, existe un labyrinthe de jardins en terrasses, dessiné dans un style italien superbe. Les 32 chambres décorées avec goût et disposant d'élégantes salles de bain offrent tout le confort et les dîners servis dans un restaurant raffiné avec vue panoramique sont délicieux.

In der ruhigen, zauberhaften Gegend um Amboise befindet sich Le Choiseul, ganz versteckt zwischen einem Hügel und der Loire. Die Umgebung dieser 3 herrlichen Häuser aus dem 18. Jahrhundert besteht aus einem Labyrinth aus wundervollen terrassenförmigen Gärten in 32 geschmackvoll eingerichteten Zimmer mit ihren eleganten Bädern bieten jeglichen Komfort, und im stilvollen Restaurant genießt man hervorragende Küche mit Panoramablick.

Our inspector loved: *Bistro 36 for its inventive lunch menu.*

Directions: D751 east of town centre.

Web: www.johansens.com/lechoiseul
E-mail: choiseul@grandesetapes.fr
Tel: +33 2 47 30 45 45
Fax: +33 2 47 30 46 10

Price Guide: (room only)
single €125–270
double €125–270
suite €290–335

32

Le Manoir Les Minimes

34 QUAI CHARLES GUINOT, 37400 AMBOISE, FRANCE

Directions: A10 > exit Amboise > D751 on the south bank of the river.

Web: www.johansens.com/lemanoirlesminimes
E-mail: manoir-les-minimes@wanadoo.fr
Tel: +33 2 47 30 40 40
Fax: +33 2 47 30 40 77

Price Guide: (room only)
single €90–170
double €90–170
suite €195–240

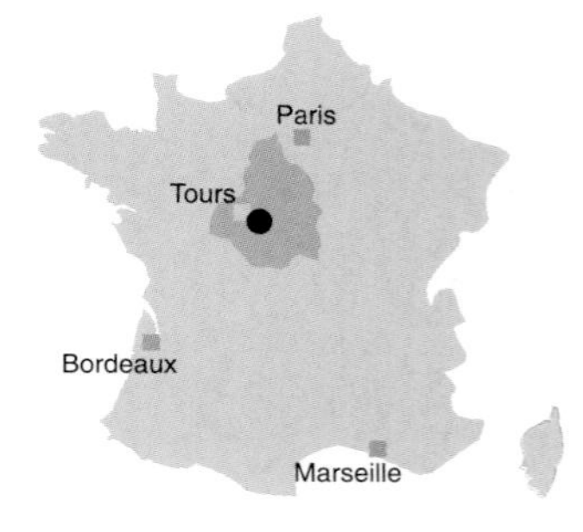

This authentic 18th-century manor house was built on the foundations of the ancient medieval Monastère des Minimes and is situated in proximity of the old town. It is the ideal place from which to explore the châteaux and vineyards of the Loire Valley. This selected stopping place offers its visitors comfort "à la française," a harmonious blend of sophistication and intimacy, whilst affording glorious views of the Château Royale d'Amboise and the River Loire. Air-conditioned rooms; private enclosed parking; no restaurant.

Authentique demeure du XVIIIe siècle, érigée sur les fondations de l'ancien monastère médiéval des Minimes, située à proximité immédiate de la vieille ville. Le Manoir les Minimes est un lieu de villégiature rêvé pour découvrir les châteaux et les vignobles de la Loire. Cette halte de choix offre à ses visiteurs ce confort "à la française", harmonieux dosage de délicatesse et d'intimité, avec une vue exceptionnelle sur le Château Royale d'Amboise et la Loire. Chambres climatisées et parking privé clos. Sans restaurant.

Dieses authentische Herrenhaus aus dem 18. Jahrhundert wurde auf dem Fundament des mittelalterlichen Klosters Monastère des Minimes erbaut und befindet sich in unmittelbarer Nähe zur Altstadt. Es liegt ideal, um die Schlösser und Weinberge des Loire-Tals zu erkunden und bietet typischen Komfort "à la française", eine harmonische Mischung aus Intimität und Raffinesse, mit atemberaubenden Blicken auf das Château Royale d'Amboise und die Loire. Klimatisierte Zimmer; private, abgeschlossene Parkplätze; kein Restaurant.

Our inspector loved: *The total attention to detail.*

Château de Rochecotte

37130 SAINT~PATRICE, (NEAR LANGEAIS) FRANCE

Formerly the home of Prince Talleyrand, this exquisite château is surrounded by acres of immaculate parkland. The salons are spacious and inviting, and the exceptional Italianate terrace overlooks the French gardens. The bedrooms are ethereal, furnished with delicately patterned chintz and antiques. The delightful dining room has terracotta columns, palm trees and splendid views over the park.

Autrefois la demeure du Prince de Talleyrand, cet exquis château est entouré d'un immense parc magnifique. Les salons sont accueillants et la terrace d'inspiration italienne surplombe les jardins français. Les chambres sont divines, avec des chintz délicats et des antiquités. La superbe salle à manger a des colonnes en terracotta, des palmiers et une vue splendide sur le parc.

Dieses exquisite Château, einst Heim des Prinzen Talleyrand, ist von einem herrlichen, weitläufigen Park umgeben. Die großzügigen Aufenthaltsräume laden zum Verweilen ein, und eine italienisch geprägte Terrasse gibt den Blick auf die französischen Gärten frei. Die traumhaften Schlafzimmer sind mit delikat gemustertem Chintz und feinen Antiquitäten ausgestattet. Vom Speisesaal mit seinen Terrakotta-Säulen und Palmen hat man eine fantastische Sicht auf den Park.

Our inspector loved: *The floral decoration in the restaurant.*

Directions: A10 towards Tours > exit 24 > A85 > Langeais > N152 Saint Patrice > D35. The nearest airport is Tours.

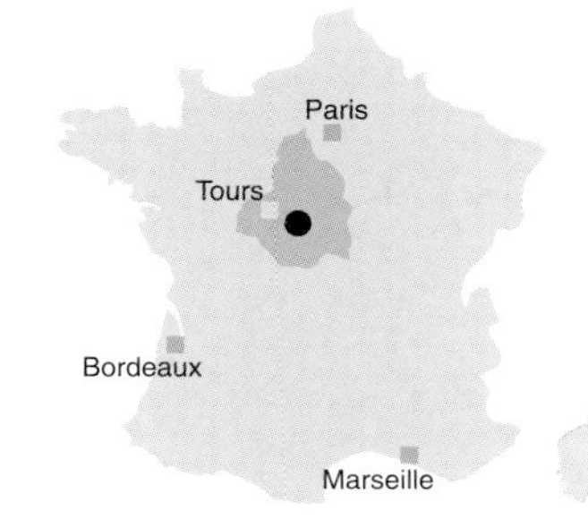

Web: www.johansens.com/rochecotte
E-mail: chateau.rochecotte@wanadoo.fr
Tel: +33 2 47 96 16 16
Fax: +33 2 47 96 90 59

Price Guide:(room only)
double/twin €130–212
suite €275

FRANCE / LOIRE VALLEY (SAINT~AMOND MONTROND)

Château de la Commanderie

FARGES ALLICHAMPS, 18200 SAINT~AMAND DE MONTROND, FRANCE

Directions: A71 > exit 8 > D925 > Nozières (D92) > Farges Allichamps. The nearest airport is Clermond Ferrand.

Web: www.johansens.com/commanderie
E-mail: chateaudelacommanderie@wanadoo.fr
Tel: +33 2 48 61 04 19
Fax: +33 2 48 61 01 84

Price Guide:
single €105-210
double €145-210
suite €210

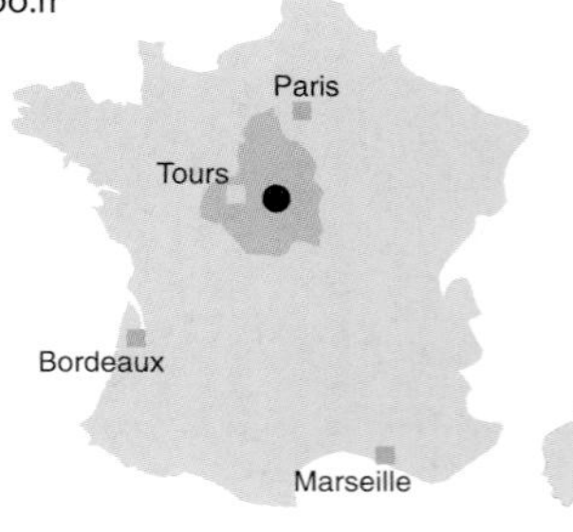

Château de la Commanderie brings together an ancient manor house and a beautiful Renaissance castle. Guests will be made to feel most welcome in this fairytale retreat, ideal for those who wish to indulge in the elegant splendour of a bygone era. All rooms are authentically decorated with beautiful antiques, customised porcelain and crystal glassware to create a homely and luxurious atmosphere. There is a large private garden to explore or golf, horse riding and tennis nearby.

Château de la Commanderie réunit un ancien manoir et un superbe château de la renaissance. Les hôtes seront chaleureusement accueillis dans ce lieu digne d'un conte de fée, idéale pour ceux qui souhaitent se relaxer dans la splendeur d'une époque passée. Toutes les pièces sont décorées avec authenticité avec de magnifiques antiquités, de la porcelaine personnalisée et la verrerie en cristal afin de créer une atmosphère luxueuse et accueillante. Il y a un vaste jardin dans lequel flâner ou de nombreuses activités à proximité telles que golf, équitation et tennis.

Hier treffen ein altes Herrenhaus und ein wunderschönes Schloss aus der Renaissance zusammen. Ein herzlicher Empfang erwartet jeden Gast in diesem Märchenschloss, der ideale Ort für jeden, der in die elegante Pracht einer längst vergangenen Zeit entfliehen möchte. Die Atmosphäre ist heimelig und luxuriös, und alle Zimmer sind authentisch gestaltet und bieten herrliche Antiquitäten, speziell angefertigtes Porzellan und Kristallglas. Ein großer privater Garten lädt zur Erkundung ein, und in der Nähe kann man Golf spielen, reiten und Tennis spielen.

Our inspector loved: *The conviviality and hospitality of Laura and Umberto, the resident proprietors.*

HOSTELLERIE DES HAUTS DE SAINTE MAURE

2-4 AVENUE DU GÉNÉRAL-DE-GAULLE, 37800 SAINTE~MAURE~DE~TOURAINE, FRANCE

This charming, former 16th-century coaching inn has been sympathetically restored to its former glory. Encircling a peaceful courtyard and surrounded by a flower-filled garden with secluded, heated swimming pool, it is situated on the main Paris to Bordeaux road and is an ideal base for touring the Loire Valley. Modern bathrooms and spacious, air-conditioned bedrooms are intimate and delightful; some have four-poster beds. The beamed restaurant prides itself on offering authentic regional cuisine.

Ce charmant relais du XVIe siècle a été agréablement restauré dans sa gloire ancienne. Au sein d'une cour paisible et entouré d'un jardin de fleurs avec une piscine chauffée et à l'écart, il est situé sur l'axe principal Paris-Bordeaux et est la base idéale pour explorer la Vallée de la Loire. Les salles de bain sont modernes et spacieuses, les chambres avec climatisation, intimes et délicieuses; certaines ont même des lits à baldaquins. Le restaurant à poutres apparentes se glorifie d'offrir une cuisine régionale authentique.

Diese zauberhafte, einstige Poststation aus dem 16. Jahrhundert erlangte durch liebevolle Restaurierung ihre einstige Pracht wieder. Das um einen friedlichen Innenhof angelegte und von einem blumenbedeckten Garten mit beheiztem Swimmingpool umgebene Hotel liegt auf der Strecke von Paris nach Bordeaux und ist der ideale Ausgangspunkt, um das Loire-Tal zu erkunden. Die geräumigen, klimatisierten Zimmer haben moderne Bäder und sind sehr gemütlich, einige bieten Himmelbetten. Im Restaurant werden authentische Köstlichkeiten der Region serviert.

Directions: N10 south from Tours >the hotel is on the right. Maure or A10 > exit 25 > turn left at lights > hotel is on the hill, on the left. The nearest airport is Tours.

Web: www.johansens.com/saintemaure
E-mail: hauts-de-ste-maure@wanadoo.fr
Tel: +33 2 47 65 51 18
Fax: +33 2 47 65 60 24

Price Guide: (room only)
single €104-135
double €104-135
suite €180

Our inspector loved: *The view from the restaurant into the cellar.*

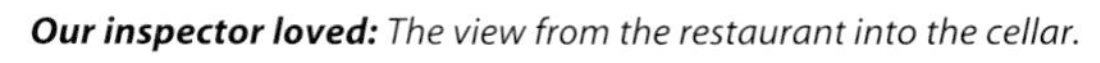

LE PRIEURÉ

49350 CHÊNEHUTTE~LES~TUFFEAUX, FRANCE

This historic, local stone built former priory stands majestically in 17 acres of magnificent parkland featuring centuries-old trees just 7km from Saumur, the Loire Valley's capital city of horse riding. Guests are accommodated in the elegant château or small, modern chalets in the grounds. All are extremely comfortable and offer stunning views. There is an excellent restaurant with equally good, friendly service. Heated pool.

Cet ancien prieuré historique construit en pierre locale, se tient majestueusement dans les 7 hectares d'un parc magnifique aux arbres centenaires et à seulement 7 kilomètres de Saumur, la capitale de l'équitation de la vallée de la Loire. Les hôtes sont logés dans l'élégant château ou dans des petits pavillons modernes. Tous sont extrêmement confortables et offrent une vue imprenable. Le restaurant est excellent avec un service amical. Piscine chauffée.

Diese historische, aus einheimischem Stein erbaute ehemalige Abtei steht majestätisch inmitten von 7ha Parklandschaft mit jahrhundertealten Bäumen, nur 7km von Saumur, der Reiterhauptstadt des Loiretales entfernt. Man wohnt entweder im eleganten Château oder in kleinen, modernen Chalets auf dem Grundstück. Alle Zimmer sind extrem komfortabel und bieten herrliche Ausblicke. Im Restaurant genießt man hervorragende Küche, der Service ist sehr freundlich. Ein beheizter Swimmingpool ist vorhanden.

Our inspector loved: *The views from the restaurant.*

Directions: On the D751 between Saumur and Gennes.

Web: www.johansens.com/leprieure
E-mail: prieure@grandesetapes.fr
Tel: +33 2 41 67 90 14
Fax: +33 2 41 67 92 24

Price Guide:
single €92–275
double €92–295
suite €295–325

Celebration Gourmet Dinners or Prestigious 2 Night Breaks. (Flowers, a bottle of Champagne and bathrobes)

A VIP welcome, candlelit dinner, a lakeside walk, breakfast in bed overlooking the gardens full of flowers.

Offer the Unforgettable

M. & Madame JAULIN
are delighted to offer
M. & Madame Pierre Hecquet
a prestigious all inclusive one night stay
in one of the Grandes Etapes Françaises
Please mention the following reference when making your booking xxxxx-xxxxx
This invitation is valid for 2 persons until 01/12/03

There are certain moments which merit a truly exceptional gift

THE ELEGANCE AND THE DISTINCTION OF AN INVITATION

A personalised invitation which clearly explains, without indication of price, the gift that is being offered, (dinner or a break in the selected category) is sent to your guest.

THE PRIVILEGE OF HAVING FREEDOM OF CHOICE

He or she can choose from amongst any of the 10, 4 star " GRANDES ETAPES FRANÇAISES " hotels, the location, the date of stay - the gift voucher is valid for 1 year.

PARIS
121 54 49 90 83 88 91 67 140 79

Discover 10 different ways to offer the truly unforgettable in any one of our 10, 4 star châteaux hotels.

For further information and bookings contact +33 1 40 02 99 99 or E-mail : cadeaux@grandesetapes.fr

GRANDES ETAPES FRANÇAISES

DOMAINE DE BEAUVOIS

LE PONT CLOUET, ROUTE DE CLÉRÉ~LES~PINS, 37230 LUYNES, FRANCE

Situated on the banks of Lake Briffaut, in the heart of peaceful Tourain countryside, this gracious former manor house offers stunning views over beautiful gardens and 350 acres of glorious woodland. It is a true and historically attractive getaway hotel providing visitors with every comfort and excellent cuisine and service. Lounges are intimate, dining rooms elegant, bedrooms superb – and silence almost absolute.

Situé sur les rives du Lac Briffaut, au cœur de la paisible Touraine, cet élégant ancien manoir offre une vue imprenable sur des beaux jardins et plus de 140 hectares de bois magnifiques. Cet hôtel procure un véritable échappatoire à ses visiteurs dans un confort total, une cuisine et un service excellents, avec des salons à l'atmosphère feutrée, des salles à manger élégantes et des chambres superbes – le tout dans un silence presque absolu.

Mit seiner Lage am Ufer des Briffaut Sees im Herzen der friedlichen Landschaft westlich von Tours bietet dieses anmutige ehemalige Herrenhaus eine atemberaubende Sicht auf wundervolle Gärten und 140ha Waldlandschaft. Das historisch faszinierende Hotel ist ein wahres Versteck und gewährt seinen Gästen jeden Komfort bei exquisiter Küche und hervorragendem Service. Die Aufenthaltsräume sind gemütlich und intim, die Speisesäle elegant und die Gästezimmer einfach herrlich – und Ruhe ist garantiert.

Our inspector loved: *Room 22 for a romantic stay.*

Directions: N152 Tours - Langeais > exit at Luynes > direction Cléré.

Web: www.johansens.com/domianedebeauvois
E-mail: beauvois@grandesetapes.fr
Tel: +33 2 47 55 50 11
Fax: +33 2 47 55 59 62

Price Guide: (room only)
single €180–270
double €180–270
suite €210–295

CHÂTEAU D'ARTIGNY

37250 MONTBAZON, FRANCE

Built by the perfumer Coty in 18th-century style, this palatial hotel creates an immediate impression. Its startling white exterior with soaring entrance pillars is in striking contrast to the lush greens of the surrounding 25 acres of parkland and formal gardens. The interior is equally majestic with imposing stone staircase, stunning public rooms, superb spacious bedrooms and 2 elegant gourmet restaurants.

Construit par le parfumeur Coty dans un style du XVIIIe siècle, cet hôtel magnifique fait une impression immédiate. Ses saisissants extérieurs blancs et l'entrée aux piliers élancés créent un contraste frappant avec les verts luxuriants des 10 hectares de parc et jardins alentours. L'intérieur est tout aussi majestueux avec d'impressionnants escaliers de pierre, d'incroyables salles communes, des superbes chambres spacieuses et 2 élégants restaurants gastronomiques.

Dieses vom Parfumeur Coty im Stil des 18. Jahrhunderts erbaute palastartige Hotel beeindruckt schon auf den ersten Blick. Das strahlend weiße Exterieur mit seinen eleganten Eingangssäulen steht in starkem Gegensatz zu der üppig grünen Umgebung der 10ha Parklandschaft und Gärten. Das Interieur ist ebenso majestätisch, hier findet man ein eindrucksvolles steinernes Treppenhaus, herrliche Aufenthaltsräume, wundervolle Gästezimmer und 2 elegante Feinschmeckerrestaurants.

Our inspector loved: *The circular dining room and the views.*

Directions: A10 exit 23 > direction Montbazon > in the centre of the village turn right.

Web: www.johansens.com/dartigny
E-mail: artigny@grandesetapes.fr
Tel: +33 2 47 34 30 30
Fax: +33 2 47 34 30 39

Price Guide: (room only)
single €160–315
double €160–315
suite €400

DOMAINE DE LA TORTINIÈRE

ROUTE DE BALLAN~MIRÉ, 37250 MONTBAZON, FRANCE

This fairytale château lies in the very heart of the Loire Valley and has breathtaking views over the Indre River. The welcome is warm and genuine and indicative of a winning formula that creates a sense of intimacy amongst classically elegant high ceilings, moulded doors and grand mirrors. Each of the bedrooms is individually decorated, whilst the "cottage rooms" in the park outbuildings are enchanting and even older than the château itself.

Ce château de conte de fées se situe au cœur de la Vallée de la Loire et a une vue à couper le souffle sur l'Indre. L'accueil est chaleureux, sincère et indicatif de la recette gagnante qui crée une sensation d'intimité au sein de hauts plafonds classiques et élégants, de portes à moulures et de grands miroirs. Chaque chambre est décorée individuellement, alors que les pavillons dans le parc, plus anciens que le château lui-même, sont absolument enchanteurs.

Dieses mitten im Herzen des Loiretales gelegene Märchenschloss bietet eine traumhafte Sicht über den Fluss Indre. Gäste erwartet ein warmer und herzlicher Empfang und ein Gefühl von Vertrautheit inmitten des mit klassisch hohen Decken, verzierten Türen und edlen Spiegeln geschmückten Interieurs. Die Zimmer sind individuell gestaltet, und die zauberhaften Cottagezimmer in den Außengebäuden im Park sind sogar noch älter als das Schloss selbst.

Our inspector loved: *Suite 6, with its comfortable lounge and bedroom in the tower.*

Directions: A10 > exit 23 direction Montbazon > turn right in the direction of Ballan-Miré.

Web: www.johansens.com/domainetortiniere
E-mail: domaine.tortiniere@wanadoo.fr
Tel: +33 2 47 34 35 00
Fax: +33 2 47 65 95 70

Price Guide: (room only)
single €98–180
double €98–180
suite €285

LE GRAND ECUYER

HAUT DE LA CITÉ, 81170 CORDES~SUR~CIEL, FRANCE

The beautiful medieval village of Cordes sits atop a hill, and Le Grand Ecuyer is located within its cobbled streets. Once home to the Comte de Toulouse, it is furnished in a medieval style with wonderfully rich furniture and fabrics. Most bedrooms have four-poster beds and views across the surrounding countryside. Renowned chef Yves Thuriès creates delicious and creative gourmet cuisine, and dinner is served in one of 3 impressive dining rooms. Nearby places of interest include Toulouse, Albi and Gaillac, a wine-producing region.

Le beau village médiéval de Cordes se situe au sommet d'une colline et le Grand Ecuyer dans le dédale de ses rues pavées. Autrefois le foyer du Comte de Toulouse, il est meublé dans le style médiéval avec un superbe mobilier et des tissus riches. La plupart des chambres ont des lits à baldaquin et vue sur la campagne environnante. Le célèbre chef Yves Thuriès créé une cuisine délicieuse en trilogie, et le dîner est servi dans l'une des 3 impressionnantes salles à manger. A visiter tout près, Toulouse, Albi et la région viticole de Gaillac.

Mitten in dem auf einem Hügel gelegenen mittelalterlichen Dorf Cordes mit seinen Kopfsteingässchen liegt das zauberhafte Le Grand Ecuyer. Das einstige Zuhause des Comte de Toulouse ist in mittelalterlichem Stil mit üppigen Stoffen und Möbeln eingerichtet. Die meisten Zimmer bieten Himmelbetten und eine herrliche Sicht auf die Umgebung. Der bekannte Chefkoch Yves Thuriès kreiert köstliche, kreative Gourmetspeisen, die in 3 eindrucksvollen Speisesälen serviert werden. Ausflugsziele in der Nähe sind Toulouse, Albi und die Weingegend Gaillac.

Our inspector loved: *The feeling of being in another era.*

Directions: A68 > exit between Toulouse and Albi > follow signs to Cordes.

Web: www.johansens.com/grandecuyer
E-mail: grand.ecuyer@thuries.fr
Tel: +33 5 63 53 79 50
Fax: +33 5 63 53 79 51

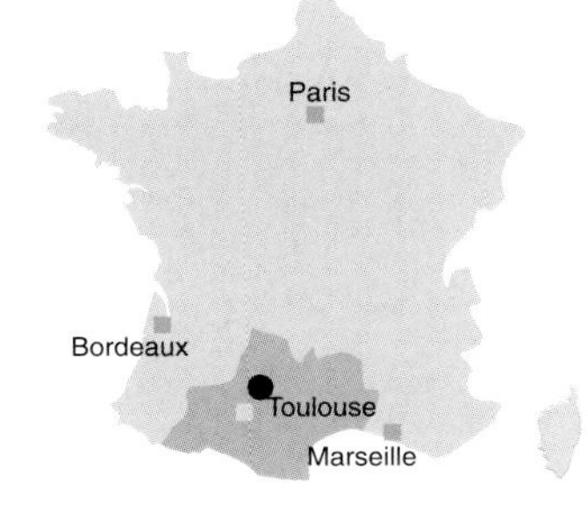

Price Guide:
double €90–155
suite €230

  13   20 

CHÂTEAU DE FLOURE

SYMBOLES de FRANCE

1, ALLÉE GASTON BONHEUR, 11800 FLOURE, FRANCE

Directions: A61 > exit Carcassonne Est, no. 24 > RN113 towards Narbonne.

Web: www.johansens.com/floure
E-mail: contact@chateau-de-floure.com
Tel: +33 4 68 79 11 29
Fax: +33 4 68 79 04 61

Price Guide: (room only)
double €100-170
suite €230

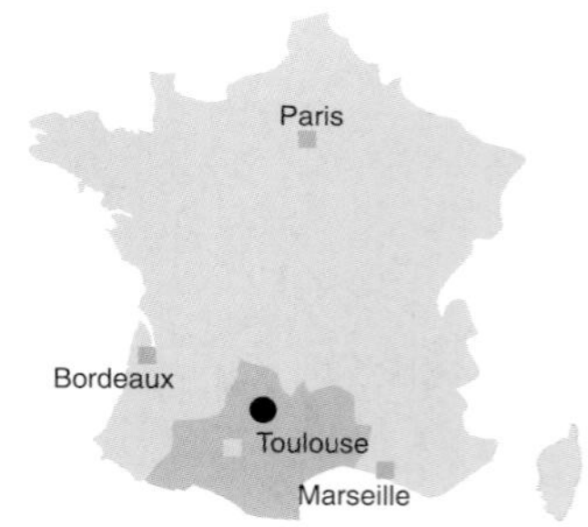

Only 10 minutes from Carcassonne, facing the majestic Mount Alaric, this beautiful château, which was formerly the residence of French writer Gaston Bonheur, lies peacefully within a lush park, surrounded by vineyards and exquisite traditional French gardens. Charming bedrooms are the ultimate in comfort whilst irresistible French cuisine and superb wines are served in the 17th-century restaurant, featuring impressive original woodwork. Guests can stroll through the grounds, play tennis or swim in the pool.

A seulement 10 minutes de Carcassonne, face au mont Alaric, le beau Château de Floure, ancienne résidence de Gaston Bonheur l'écrivain, se niche au cœur d'un parc luxuriant entouré de vignobles et d'adorables jardins typiques de la région. Les chambres charmantes sont ultra confortables et une cuisine succulente accompagnée de vins délicieux est servie au restaurant dans un cadre du XVIIe siècle à l'ébénisterie impressionnante. Les hôtes peuvent se promener dans le parc, jouer au tennis ou profiter de la piscine.

Nur 10 Minuten von Carcassonne entfernt und mit Blick auf den majestätischen Mont Alaric liegt dieses Château, die einstige Residenz des französischen Schriftstellers Gaston Bonheur, umgeben von üppiger Parklandschaft, Weinbergen und herrlichen traditionellen Gärten. Die bezaubernden Zimmer bieten höchsten Komfort, und im Restaurant aus dem 17. Jahrhundert mit seinen eindrucksvollen ursprünglichen Holzarbeiten werden unwiderstehliche französische Küche und edle Weine serviert. Man kann herrliche Spaziergänge machen, Tennis spielen oder im Pool schwimmen.

Our inspector loved: *The bedrooms in the garden with their private terraces.*

Domaine Saint Clair, Le Donjon

CHEMIN DE SAINT CLAIR, 76790 ETRETAT, FRANCE

The colour and character of this ivy-clad château are as inspiring as its breathtaking coastal views. Rooms are cosy and intimate with antique furnishings, and each of the superb newly decorated bedrooms in the adjoining villa are themed after a person who lived as a house guest between 1890 and 1920. After a delicious dinner in one of 3 unique dining rooms guests can retire to the cigar lounge, relax in the pretty courtyard or enjoy a drink on the poolside terrace.

La couleur et le caractère de ce château couvert de vigne vierge sont tout aussi inspirants par leur beauté qu'est la vue à couper le souffle sur la côte. Les pièces sont douillettes et intimes avec des antiquités pour mobilier, et chaque chambre de la villa adjacente, a été superbement décorée récemment selon quelqu'un qui a séjourné dans la maison entre 1890 et 1920. Après un délicieux dîner dans l'une des 3 salles à manger, les hôtes peuvent se retirer dans le salon, se détendre dans la petite cour intérieure ou déguster un verre sur la terrasse près de la piscine.

Farben und Charakter dieses efeubewachsenen Schlosses sind ebenso atemberaubend wie die Sicht auf die Küste. Die Zimmer sind herrlich gemütlich und mit Antiquitäten eingerichtet, und jedes der eindrucksvollen Zimmer in der anliegenden Villa wurde nach einer bestimmten Person gestaltet, die hier zwischen 1890 und 1920 zu Gast war. Nach einem köstlichen Abendessen in einem der 3 einzigartigen Speisesäle kann man sich ins Zigarrenzimmer zurückziehen, im Innenhof entspannen oder auf der Terrasse am Pool einen Drink genießen.

Our inspector loved: *The cry of the seagulls flying above the garden.*

Directions: Town centre > follow signs.

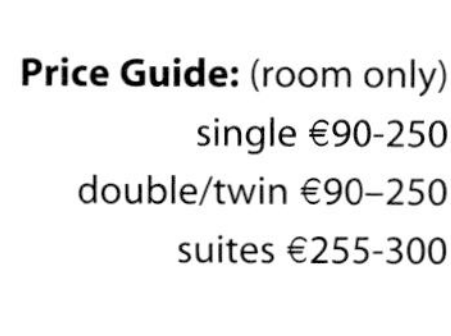

Rouen
Paris
Bordeaux
Marseille

Web: www.johansens.com/donjon
E-mail: info@hoteletretat.com
Tel: +33 2 35 27 08 23
Fax: +33 2 35 29 92 24

Price Guide: (room only)
single €90-250
double/twin €90–250
suites €255-300

Château de Sassetot

76540 SASSETOT~LE~MAUCONDUIT, FRANCE

Elegance, charm and gracious hospitality are hallmarks of this imposing 18th-century château situated in 28 acres of parkland, close to the Normandy clifftops. An ideal retreat for those seeking the peaceful joys of a countryside rich in culture and history. The new owners have restored the château to its former glory with comfortable guest rooms, many of which enjoy views over the parkland. Classic gastronomic cuisine is offered in 2 attractive dining rooms.

Elégance, charme et accueil courtois sont les particularités de cet imposant château du 18ème siècle, situé dans un parc de 11 hectares proche des falaises de Normandie. C'est un lieu idéal pour ceux à la recherche des plaisirs paisibles d'une région riche en culture et en histoire. Les nouveaux propriétaires ont restauré le château en lui rendant ses fastes d'autrefois, avec des chambres confortables et une vue sur le parc. Une cuisine gastronomique est servie dans de très belles salles à manger.

Eleganz, Charme und herzliche Gastfreundschaft sind die Markenzeichen dieses eindrucksvollen Châteaus aus dem 18. Jahrhundert, das inmitten von 11ha Parklandschaft nahe der Steilküste der Normandie gelegen ist. Ideal für diejenigen, die eine ruhige, von Kultur und Geschichte erfüllte Landschaft schätzen. Die neuen Besitzer haben die einstige Pracht des Châteaus wieder hergestellt und komfortable Zimmer geschaffen, viele davon mit Blick auf den Park. In 2 attraktiven Speisesälen wird klassische Gourmetküche serviert.

Our inspector loved: *The cosy lounge with its log fire and views over the park.*

Directions: A29 >exit 4 > D926 towards Fécamp > 9km after Fauville > D17 towards Valmont > Sassetot. The nearest airport is Beauvais.

Web: www.johansens.com/sassetot
E-mail: reception@chateau-de-sassetot.com
Tel: +33 2 35 28 00 11
Fax: +33 2 35 28 50 00

Price Guide: (room only)
single €78-158
double €78-158
suite €164-314

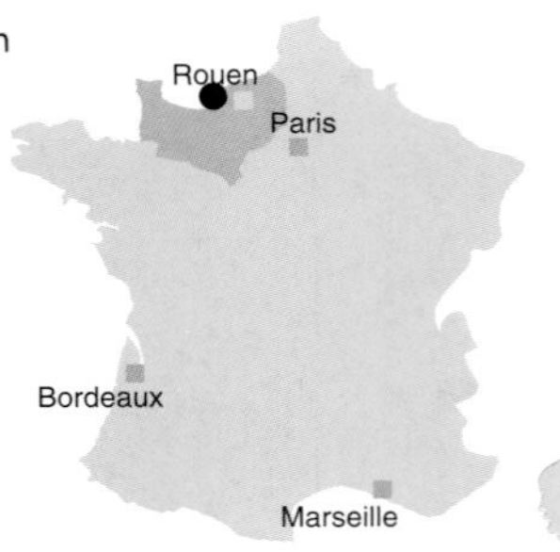

Manoir de la Poterie

CHEMIN PAUL RUEL, 14113 CRICQUEBOEUF, FRANCE

Situated between Honfleur and Trouville, the Manoir de la Poterie combines the atmosphere of a grand country manor with the hospitality and elegance of a small château. Fine cuisine is served in the dining room, whilst guests can also enjoy a drink in the American Bar or relax in the salon with its fireplace. The bedrooms are luxuriously appointed, featuring marble bathrooms and stunning views of the sea or the surrounding countryside, which beckons to be explored on a leisurely walk along the coast. A swimming pool, sauna, hammam and Jacuzzi are planned for June 2005.

Entre Honfleur et Trouville, le Manoir de la Poterie offre l'espace d'une grande propriété de campagne ajouté à la chaleur et l'élégance d'un petit château. La salle à manger où est servie une cuisine raffinée est complétée par un Bar Américain et salon avec cheminée. Les chambres luxueuses avec salle de bain en marbre ont vue sur la mer ou sur la campagne. De nombreux endroits vous attendent pour d'agréables promenades le long de la côte. Une piscine, un sauna, un hammam et un jacuzzi sont envisagés pour juin 2005.

Das zwischen Honfleur und Trouville gelegene Manoir de la Poterie bietet die Geräumigkeit eines vornehmen Landhauses und die Eleganz und Freundlichkeit eines kleinen Schlosses. Im Speisesaal werden erlesene Gerichte serviert, daneben gibt es eine Amerikanische Bar und einen Aufenthaltsraum mit Kamin. Die luxuriösen Zimmer haben Marmorbäder und Blick auf das Meer oder die Umgebung, und die schöne Landschaft lädt zu Spaziergängen entlang der Küste ein. Für Juni 2005 sind Swimmingpool, Sauna, Dampfbad und Jacuzzi geplant.

Our inspector loved: *The artistic crockery in the restaurant.*

Directions: Detailed directions available from the hotel.

Web: www.johansens.com/manoirdelapoterie
E-mail: info@honfleur-hotel.com
Tel: +33 2 31 88 10 40
Fax: +33 2 31 88 10 90

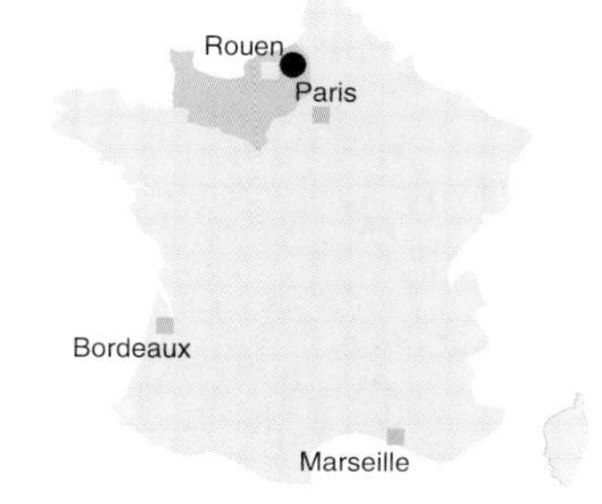

Price Guide: (room only)
single €116–200
double €116–200
suites €160–200

HÔTEL ROYAL PICARDIE

AVENUE DU GÉNÉRAL LECLERC, 80300 ALBERT, FRANCE

Directions: A1 > Paris > Lille exit 14 > D929 Amiens/Albert. The hotel is immediately south west of Albert. The nearest airport is Lille or Charles de Gaulle.

Web: www.johansens.com/royalpicardie
E-mail: royalpicardie@wanadoo.fr
Tel: +33 3 22 75 37 00
Fax: +33 3 22 75 60 19

Price Guide: (breakfast €10)
single €97
double €97-153

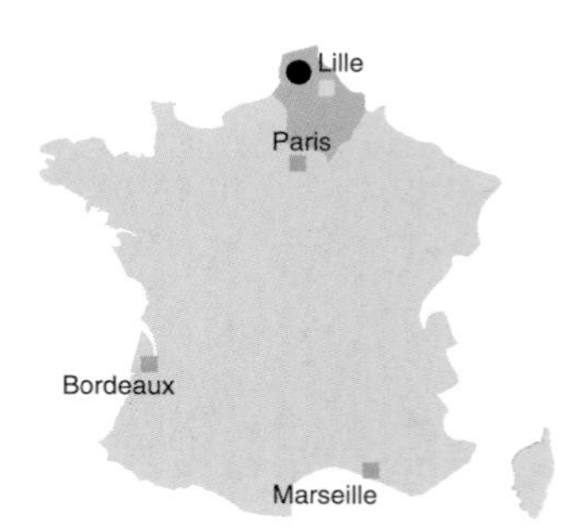

With its location close to Lille and Arras, in the heart of Picardy and its First World War battlefields, just 1 hour from the bay of Somme, this splendid white stone building offers plenty to discover nearby. Particular care has been taken in the comfortable en suite bedrooms, which feature marble bathrooms. Before sampling seasonal gastronomic cuisine in the light and elegant Louis-XIV-style dining room, guests may relax in the bar by the inviting fireplace. The restaurant, conference rooms, bar, reception area and a number of other rooms in the hotel are air-conditioned.

Tout proche de Lille et Arras, au coeur de la Picardie et de ses champs de batailles de la 1ère guerre mondiale, à 1 heure de la baie de Somme, cette splendide construction de pierres blanches offre beaucoup de choses à découvrir à proximité. Son architecture s'inspire des châteaux forts d'autrefois et les hôtes sont traités royalement. Les chambres sont de grand confort avec salles de bain en marbre. Avant de savourer la cuisine gastronomique dans la salle à manger lumineuse et élégamment décorée en style Louis XIV, les hôtes peuvent se détendre au bar. Le restaurant, le bar, la réception les salles de séminaires et certaines chambres sont climatisées.

Mit seiner Lage nahe bei Lille und Arras im Herzen der Picardie mit ihren Schlachtfeldern aus dem 1. Weltkrieg nur 1 Stunde von der Somme-Bucht entfernt, bietet dieses strahlend weiße Steingebäude einiges an Attraktionen in der Umgebung. Die Architektur ist von alten Festungen inspiriert, und jeder Gast wird hier wie ein König behandelt. Jedes komfortable, liebevoll gestaltete Zimmer hat ein eigenes Marmorbad. Bevor man im hellen, eleganten Speisesaal im Stil Ludwigs des XIV. gastronomische Köstlichkeiten genießt, entspannt man sich am Kamin in der Bar. Restaurant, Konferenzräume, Bar, Rezeption und einige Zimmer sind klimatisiert.

Our inspector loved: *The 2 pageboy statues in the entrance hall.*

La Chartreuse du Val Saint Esprit

62199 GOSNAY, FRANCE

Situated in the heart of the Pas-de-Calais region, this superb former Carthusian monastery is steeped in history and legend. Particular care has been taken to personalise each of the elegant bedrooms and everything is done to ensure the utmost comfort. Local gastronomic dishes can be savoured in any of the 3 restaurants. As well as several historic and cultural attractions, there is a dry-ski slope nearby.

Situé dans le cœur du Pas de Calais, cette superbe ancienne chartreuse est ancrée dans l'histoire et la légende. Un soin particulier a été apporte pour que chacune des élégantes chambres soit personnalisée, et tout est fait pour assurer le plus grand confort. Une gastronomie locale peut être appréciée dans chacun des 3 restaurants. Ajoutant à l'attraction historique de l'hôtel, une piste de ski artificielle est à proximité.

Um diese geschichtsreiche, im Herzen der Region Pas-de-Calais gelegenes ehemaliges Karthäuserkloster ranken sich zahlreiche Legenden. Jedes der eleganten Zimmer wurde mit viel Liebe eingerichtet, und höchster Komfort ist geboten. In 3 Restaurants kann man köstliche Feinschmeckerküche der Region genießen. Außer zahlreichen historischen und kulturellen Attraktionen gibt es ganz in der Nähe eine Trockenskipiste.

Our inspector loved: *The beautifully decorated corridors.*

Directions: A26 > exit 6 for Bethune.

Web: www.johansens.com/lachartreuse
E-mail: levalsaintesprit@lachartreuse.com
Tel: +33 3 21 62 80 00
Fax: +33 3 21 62 42 50

Price Guide: (room only)
single €85–121
double €96–302
suite €302

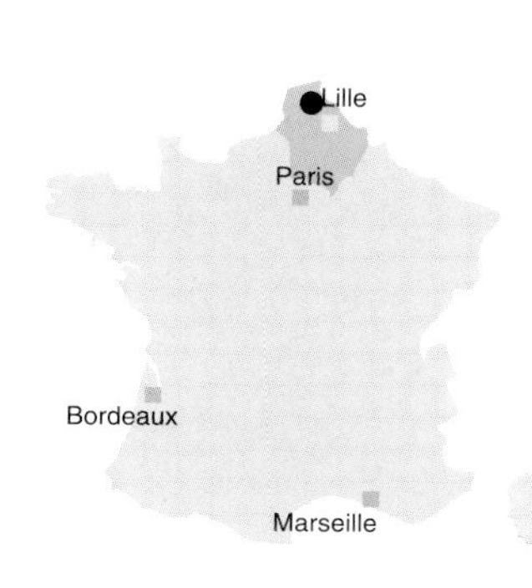

67

FRANCE / NORTH - PICARDY (CALAIS - RECQUES~SUR~HEM)

Château de Cocove

SYMBOLES de FRANCE

62890 RECQUES~SUR~HEM, FRANCE

This classically proportioned château nestles within 11 hectares of its own pretty parkland and is an idyllic setting in which to enjoy fine regional cuisine. The elegant and panoramic dining room is the backdrop for romantic candle-lit dinners, whilst afternoon tea and apéritifs served by attentive staff can be savoured from the terrace. A carefully planned menu and fine wine selection ensure a gastronomic delight.

Ce château de style XVIIIe niché au sein des 11 ha de son joli parc, est l'endroit idéal où apprécier une cuisine régionale raffinée. La salle à manger panoramique élégante est la toile de fond pour des dîners romantiques aux chandelles, alors que le thé de l'après-midi et les apéritifs servis par un personnel attentif peuvent être dégustés sur la terrasse. Un menu soigneusement planifié et une sélection de vins fins sont la garantie d'un régal gastronomique.

Dieses klassische Schloss befindet sich inmitten von 11 ha Parklandschaft und ist ein idyllischer Ort, um feinste regionale Küche zu genießen. Der elegante Speisesaal mit Panoramablick bietet den idealen Hintergrund für ein romantisches Abendessen bei Kerzenschein, und auf der Terrasse serviert das aufmerksame Personal Nachmittagstee und Apéritifs. Die sorgfältig zusammengestellte Speisekarte und eindrucksvolle Weinkarte versprechen gastronomischen Hochgenuss.

Our inspector loved: *The wonderful selection of cheeses.*

Directions: A26 > Calais > Paris exit No. 2 > Cocove.

Web: www.johansens.com/chateaudecocove
E-mail: chateaudecocove@hotmail.com
Tel: +33 3 21 82 68 29
Fax: +33 3 21 82 72 59

Price Guide: (breakfast €12)
single €80–162
double €90–162

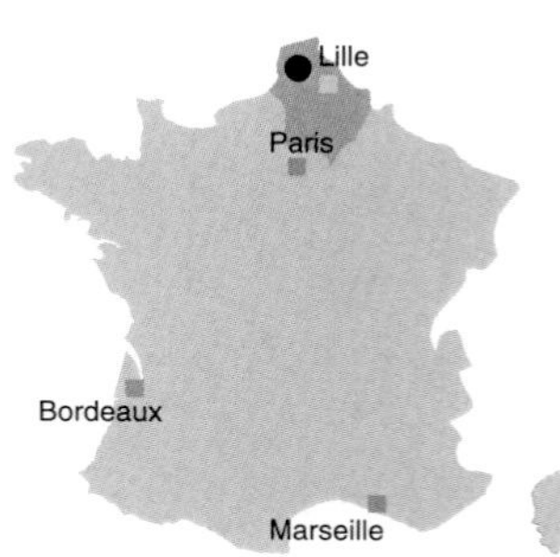

Carlton Hotel

RUE DE PARIS, 59000 LILLE, FRANCE

A new health and fitness facility and solarium as well as stunning new double floor luxury suite are the latest additions to this historic city centre hotel. Situated in the Cupole, the suite has its own lounge, bar and bathroom, and is the ideal place in which to relax after a day enjoying Lille's shopping, museums and opera. The hotel is furnished in Louis XV and XVI styles and is easily accessible by plane or rail.

Un centre de remise en forme et un solarium ainsi qu'une superbe suite luxueuse sur deux niveaux sont les dernières nouveautés de cet hôtel historique du centre ville. Située dans la coupole la suite a son propre salon, bar et salle de bain et est l'endroit idéal pour se détendre après avoir profiter d'une journée de shopping, de musées et d'opéra à Lille. L'hôtel est meublé en style Louis XV et Louis XVI et est d'accès facile par avion ou train.

Ein neues Gesundheits- und Fitnesszentrum mit Solarium sowie eine atemberaubende, zweistöckige Luxussuite sind die neuesten Ergänzungen dieses historischen Hotels im Zentrum von Lille. Die in der Kuppel untergebrachte Suite mit Lounge, Bar und Bad ist der ideale Ort, um sich nach einem mit Einkaufen, Museumsbesuchen und Oper gefüllten Tag zu entspannen. Das im Stil Ludwigs des XV. und XVI. eingerichtete Hotel ist vom Flughafen oder Bahnhof gut zu erreichen.

Our inspector loved: *The fitness room.*

Directions: In the heart of Lille, near the opera, in the main square. The nearest airport is Lille Lesquin.

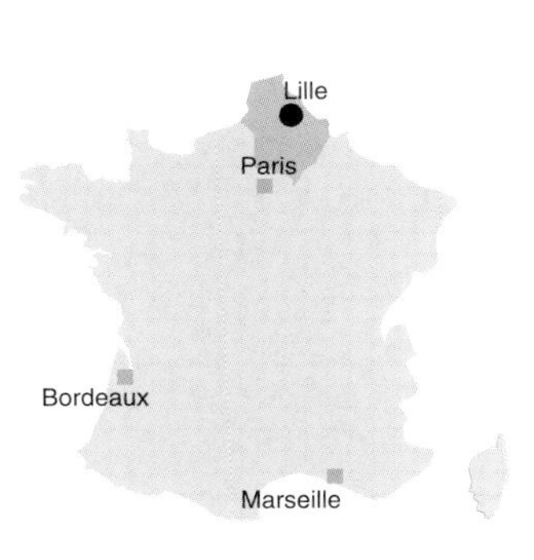

Web: www.johansens.com/carltonlille
E-mail: carlton@carltonlille.com
Tel: +33 3 20 13 33 13
Fax: +33 3 20 51 48 17

Price Guide: (breakfast €17)
single/double €220
suite €250-1,180

La Tour du Roy

02140 VERVINS, FRANCE

Directions: Between Paris and Brussels on the N2. A26 from Calais to Reims > exit 13 > N2 towards Vervins.

Web: www.johansens.com/tourduroy
E-mail: latourduroy@wanadoo.fr
Tel: +33 3 23 98 00 11
Fax: +33 3 23 98 00 72

Price Guide: (breakfast €15)
single €65-185
double €100–185
suite €230

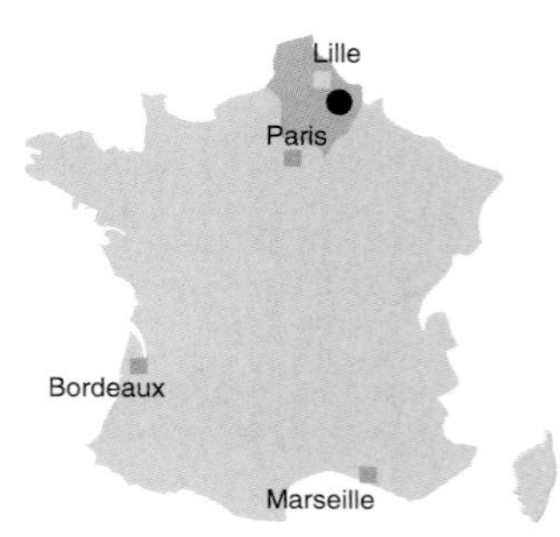

Steeped in history this charming hotel is set in the 11th-century ramparts of the town. A warm welcome is assured from the host, who has lovingly restored this building over the past 33 years to create a real home from home atmosphere. Now fully refurbished, bedrooms boast spectacular views of the valley and 4 of the romantic, antique-style bathrooms have Jacuzzi baths, whilst the suite, high in the tower, is a true gem. The dining room is home to stunning antiques and is clad in wood and marble, making this an inviting setting in which to sample some of Madame Annie's excellent cuisine.

Imprégné d'histoire, ce charmant hôtel se dresse sur les remparts du XIe siècle de la ville. Le propriétaire, qui a restauré le bâtiment au fil des 33 dernières années et a créé une atmosphère familiale, vous y réserve un accueil chaleureux. Entièrement remises à neuf, les chambres jouissent de vues sur la vallée et 4 des salles de bains ont jacuzzi. La suite, qui occupe le haut de la tour, est une véritable merveille. La salle à manger habillée de bois et de marbre abrite de belles antiquités et offre un cadre attrayant, où il fait bon savourer la cuisine renommée de la patronne Annie. Cordon bleu aux doigts de fée (Ducasse) fait la cuisine comme l'oiseau chante (Courtine).

Dieses bezaubernde, geschichtsträchtige Hotel liegt in einem Stadtteil aus dem 11. Jahrhundert. Der Besitzer, der das Gebäude über die letzten 33 Jahre liebevoll restauriert und eine heimelige Atmosphäre geschaffen hat, heißt seine Gäste hier herzlich willkommen. Die Zimmer, perfekt renoviert, haben herrliche Sicht auf das Tal und 4 der im antiken Stil gehaltenen Badezimmer haben Jacuzzibäder. Die Suite im oberen Teil des Turmes ist ein wahres Juwel, und der mit Holz und Marmor gestaltete Speisesaal bietet die ideale Umgebung, um Madame Annies köstliche Speisen zu probieren.

Our inspector loved: *The pin cushion sewing kits in the bathrooms.*

Paris

Hotel location shown in red (hotel) or purple (spa hotel) with page number

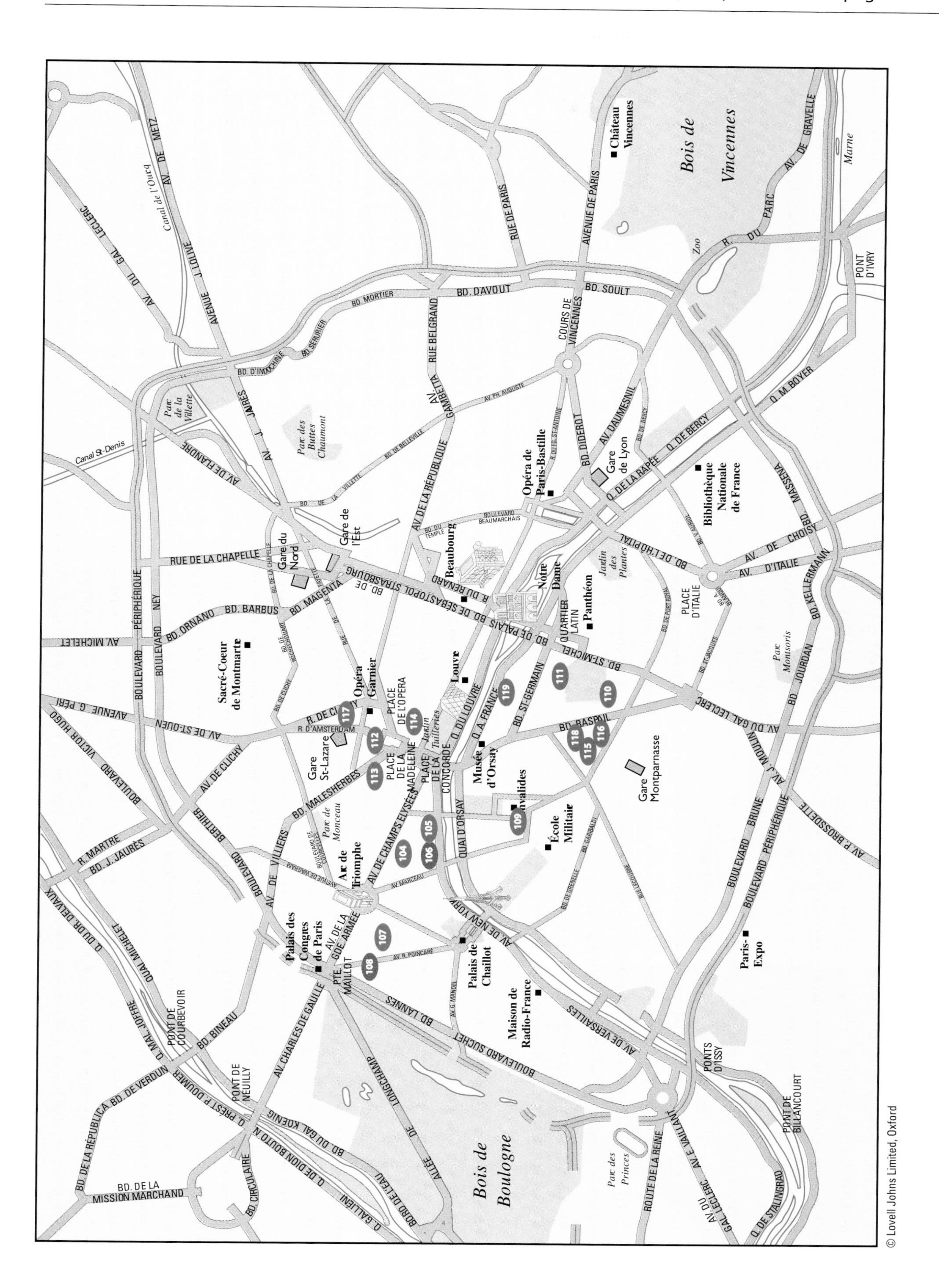

Hôtel Plaza Athénée

25 AVENUE MONTAIGNE, 75008 PARIS, FRANCE

Directions: Centre of Paris, 5-minute walk from Champs-Elysées.

Web: www.johansens.com/plazaathenee
E-mail: reservation@plaza-athenee-paris.com
Tel: +33 1 53 67 66 65
Fax: +33 1 53 67 66 66

Price Guide: (Continental breakfast €35, American breakfast €46)
standard €555
superior €690
de luxe €750
suite from €910

Since opening in 1911 this elegant hotel has become synonymous with luxury and charm. Situated on the exclusive Avenue Montaigne in the heart of Paris, the Hôtel Plaza Athénée has undergone a complete redecoration, preserving and combining classical French and art deco styling on the top 2 floors with 21st-century facilities in all rooms. Alain Ducasse opened his gastronomic restaurant at the Plaza Athénée, and also oversees the other restaurants, the Relais Plaza and the summer courtyard restaurant. A member of the Dorchester group.

Depuis son ouverture en 1911, cet élégant hôtel est devenu un symbole de luxe et de charme. Il se dresse au coeur de Paris, sur l'avenue Montaigne, une des rues les plus chics de la capitale. Entièrement re-décoré, le Plaza Athénée a su garder son style français classique et innover avec le style art déco aux 2 derniers étages, tout en intégrant les commodités du XXIe siècle. Alain Ducasse a ouvert son restaurant gastronomique au Plaza Athénée; il supervise également les autres restaurants, le Relais Plaza, et l'été la Cour Jardin. Un membre du groupe Dorchester.

Seit seiner Eröffnung 1911 ist dieses elegante Hotel zu einem Symbol von Luxus und Charme geworden. An der exklusiven Avenue Montaigne im Herzen von Paris gelegen, wurde das Hôtel Plaza Athénée vollständig renoviert und vereint sein klassisch Französisches Dekor mit dem Art-Dekor-Stil (auf den 2 obersten Etagen) perfekt mit dem Komfort des 21. Jahrhunderts. Alain Ducasse eröffnete hier sein Gourmetrestaurant und leitet daneben auch die anderen Restaurants: Le Relais Plaza und La Cour Jardin, das Sommerrestaurant. Mitglied der Dorchestergruppe.

Our inspector loved: *The innovative and stylish bar - the place to be in Paris!*

HÔTEL SAN RÉGIS

12 RUE JEAN GOUJON, 75008 PARIS, FRANCE

Deep in the heart of Paris's fashion district lies this small, intimate and beautifully appointed hotel. Built in 1857, the interior charmingly combines modern comforts with 19th-century furniture and antiques. Each of the 44 bedrooms has been individually decorated and boasts a marble bathroom as well as all modern conveniences. The restaurant, set in an old library, is a haven of tranquillity and serves simply impeccable fare.

Ce luxueux petit hôtel parisien à l'atmosphère intime jouit d'une situation privilégiée au coeur du quartier de la mode. Construit en 1857, le San Régis marie à merveille des meubles et des objets d'art du XIXe siècle avec un confort des plus modernes. Chacune des 44 chambres a son propre charme et dispose d'une salle de bains en marbre et des dernières commodités. Le restaurant, aménagé dans une ancienne bibliothèque, est un havre de paix propice à la dégustation de mets exquis.

Dieses persönliche und attraktive Hotel wurde im Jahr 1857 errichtet und liegt mitten im Pariser Modeviertel. Moderner Komfort verbindet sich perfekt mit Möbeln und Antiquitäten aus dem 19. Jahrhundert. Die 44 Zimmer sind individuell gestaltet und besitzen Marmorbäder und jegliche modernen Annehmlichkeiten. Das herrlich ruhige Restaurant liegt in einer alten Bibliothek und serviert hervorragende Gerichte.

Our inspector loved: *The top floor suites with little balconies.*

Directions: Rue Jean Goujon is off the Champs-Elysées and Avenue Montaigne.

Paris
Bordeaux
Marseille

Web: www.johansens.com/sanregis
E-mail: message@hotel-sanregis.fr
Tel: +33 1 44 95 16 16
Fax: +33 1 45 61 05 48

Price Guide: (room only)
single €315–415
double/twin €415–565
suite €620–1,025

LA TRÉMOILLE

14 RUE DE LA TRÉMOILLE, 75008 PARIS, FRANCE

Recently reopened after extensive refurbishment this boutique-style hotel is now the epitome of 21st-century elegance. The bedrooms are beautifully designed in muted tones with inspiring use of fabric and equipped to a high standard (Internet access, CD and DVD players). The public rooms house a superb collection of Parisian photographic artwork. The restaurant and bar Senso offers superb French cuisine in an original setting designed by Sir Terence Conran. There is a new health and beauty centre with sauna, fitness facilities and superb treatment and massage rooms.

Récemment ré-ouvert après un programme de rénovations ce boutique hôtel est l'exemple même de l'élégance du XXIe siècle. Les chambres sont décorées dans des tons doux avec une utilisation inhabituelle des tissus et offrent un équipement très haut de gamme (accès internet, lecteur CD & DVD). Les pièces communes abritent une collection d'ouvres photographiques sur Paris. Le restaurant and bar Senso offre le meilleur de la cuisine française dans un décor original imaginé par le célèbre decorateur Sir Terence Conran. Nouveau centre de remise en forme avec sauna et des salons de beauté et de massage.

Dieses nach umfangreicher Renovierung wieder eröffnete Boutiquehotel ist nun der Inbegriff innovativer Eleganz des 21. Jahrhunderts. Die Zimmer sind mit gedämpften Tönen und interessanten Stoffen gestaltet und bieten Internetzugang, CD- und DVD-Player. Die Aufenthaltsräume beherbergen eine Sammlung Pariser Kunstfotografien. Das Restaurant und die Bar Senso bietet beste französische Küche in originellem, von Sir Terence Conran gestalteten Ambiente. Ein neues Health- und Beautyzentrum mit Sauna, Fitness und Schönheits- und Massagesalons steht zur Verfügung.

Directions: Metro stations: Alma-Marceau or Franklin Roosevelt.

Web: www.johansens.com/tremoille
E-mail: reservation@hotel-tremoille.com
Tel: +33 1 56 52 14 00
Fax: +33 1 40 70 01 08

Price Guide: (room only)
double/twin from €399
suite from €600

Our inspector loved: *The "Hatch" for room service without disturbance.*

design hotels

L'Hôtel Pergolèse

3 RUE PERGOLÈSE, 75116 PARIS, FRANCE

This impressive 19th-century stone building houses today a very sophisticated hotel. Guests in this elegant establishment, which has been designed by Rena Dumas Hermès, are immediately struck by the warmth, light and colours pervading the reception area, and the charm enhanced by light wooden flooring and beautiful leather armchairs. Bright, friendly colours and original furniture create a feeling of comfort and serenity in the bedrooms. Tables by Starck and paintings by Hilton McConnico set the tone in the breakfast room and the salons leading onto a small courtyard garden.

Cet immeuble en pierre de taille du XIXe siècle abrite aujourd'hui un hôtel très sophistiqué. Dans cet établissement élégant décoré par Rena Dumas Hermès, les visiteurs sont d'emblée frappés par la chaleur, la clarté et les couleurs qui règnent dans les pièces de réception et par le charme que donnent le parquet blond et les beaux fauteuils de cuir. Confort et sérénité caractérisent les chambres aux couleurs gaies et au mobilier original. Les tables de Starck, les tableaux d'Hilton McConnico donnent le ton à la salle des petit-déjeuners et aux salons ouvrant sur le petit jardin intérieur.

Dieses eindrucksvolle Steingebäude aus dem 19. Jahrhundert beherbergt heute ein prestigereiches Hotel. Das elegante, von Rena Dumas Hermès gestaltete Haus besticht sofort durch seine Wärme, Helligkeit und die Farben der Empfangsräume, und durch seinen Charme, der durch helle Parkettböden und Ledersessel noch verstärkt wird. Komfort und Ruhe zeichnen die Zimmer mit ihren fröhlichen Farben und Originalmöbeln aus. Im Frühstückssaal und in den auf einen Innenhof führenden Aufenthaltsräumen geben Starck-Tische und Bilder von Hilton McConnico den Ton an.

Our inspector loved: *The superb design of the public rooms.*

40

Directions: Between Porte Maillot and the Arc de Triomphe.

Web: www.johansens.com/pergolese
E-mail: hotel@pergolese.com
Tel: +33 1 53 64 04 04
Fax: +33 1 53 64 04 40

Paris
Bordeaux
Marseille

Price Guide: (room only)
single €175–240
double/twin €195–280
de luxe room €350

LA VILLA MAILLOT

143 AVENUE DE MALAKOFF, 75116 PARIS, FRANCE

A short walk from the Champs-Elysées, the Villa Maillot is a charming, elegant and discreet haven in the centre of Paris. Behind the façade of this unique historic residence lies a friendly, modern interior, with pastel colours, fireplace and wooden floors creating creating an atmosphere of warmth and hospitality. The bedrooms are all well appointed and have rose-coloured marble bathrooms. Breakfast, selected from the enticing buffet, may be enjoyed in the newly redesigned garden conservatory.

A deux pas des Champs-Elysées, la Villa Maillot est un havre de charme, élégant et discret au coeur de la capitale. La façade de cet ancien hôtel particulier cache un hôtel moderne et amical, avec de subtiles nuances de pastels, une cheminée et des sols de bois créant une atmosphère chaleureuse et conviviale. Les chambres sont toutes bien équipées et offrent des salles de bains en marbre rose. Un superbe buffet petit déjeuner dressé dans les salons est servi dans la verrière complètement reconçue, nichée dans un jardin.

Nur einen kurzen Spaziergang von den Champs-Élysées entfernt liegt die charmante Villa Maillot, die Eleganz und Diskretion mitten im Stadtzentrum bietet. Hinter der Fassade dieses außergewöhnlichen alten Hotels versteckt sich ein freundliches, modernes Interieur, das mit Pastellfarben, Kamin und Holzböden ein behagliches und einladendes Ambiente schafft. Die Zimmer sind alle bestens ausgestattet und verfügen über Marmorbäder in Rosétönen. Ein herrliches Frühstücksbuffet steht im Salon bereit und wird im neugestalteten Wintergarten serviert.

Our inspector loved: *The newly opened spa with steam bath, sauna and massage service; well designed with a relaxing atmosphere.*

Directions: Close to Champs-Elysées.

Web: www.johansens.com/lavillamaillot
E-mail: resa@lavillamaillot.fr
Tel: +33 1 53 64 52 52
Fax: +33 1 45 00 60 61

Price Guide: (room only, excluding VAT)
double/twin €250–370
suite €350–495

HÔTEL LE TOURVILLE

16 AVENUE DE TOURVILLE, 75007 PARIS, FRANCE

Though located in the heart of Paris, close to the Eiffel Tower, this neo-classical hotel enjoys a unique atmosphere of refined tranquillity. Soft pastel colours form a warm ambience and ideal background for the wealth of antique furniture and paintings that grace its salons and bedrooms. Guests are cosseted by the fine breakfasts served in the vaulted cellar room and the large range of toiletries that are thoughtfully provided in the marble bathrooms.

Bien qu'il se situe au coeur de Paris, à deux pas de la Tour Eiffel, cet hôtel néoclassique jouit d'une tranquillité raffinée. Les couleurs pastel créent une ambiance chaleureuse et soulignent à merveille la beauté des nombreux meubles et objets d'art anciens qui ornent les salons et les chambres. Les visiteurs choyés dégustent d'excellents petits déjeuners dans la cave voûtée et profitent du vaste choix d'articles de toilette gracieusement mis à leur disposition dans les salles de bains en marbre.

Trotz seiner Lage im Herzen von Paris und in der Nähe des Eiffelturms genießt dieses neoklassizistische Hotel eine Atmosphäre herrlicher Ruhe. Sanfte Pastellfarben schaffen ein warmes Ambiente und einen idealen Hintergrund für die Vielfalt antiker Möbel und Gemälde, welche die Salons und Schlafzimmer schmücken. Die Gäste werden durch das erlesene Frühstück im Gewölbekeller verwöhnt, des Weiteren durch das große Angebot an Toilettenartikeln, die sorgfältig ausgewählt in den Marmorbadezimmern bereitstehen.

Our inspector loved: *The superb top-floor suite.*

Directions: Between the Eiffel Tower and Les Invalides.

Web: www.johansens.com/tourville
E-mail: hotel@tourville.com
Tel: +33 1 47 05 62 62
Fax: +33 1 47 05 43 90

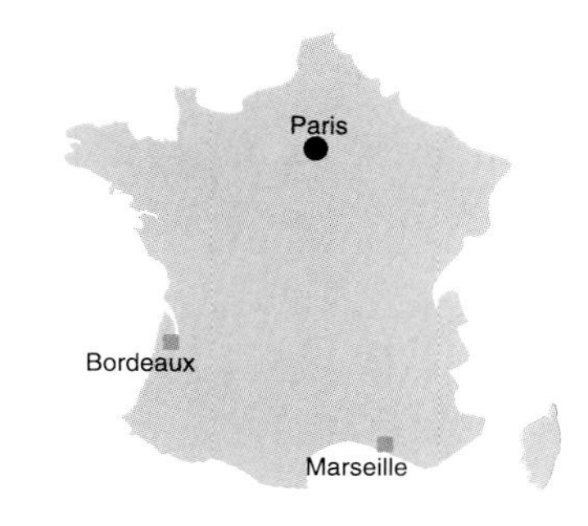

Price Guide: (breakfast €12)
double/twin €165–240
junior suite €310

Le Sainte~Beuve

9 RUE SAINTE~BEUVE, 75006 PARIS, FRANCE

Directions: Between Saint~Germain~des~Prés and Jardin du Luxembourg.

Web: www.johansens.com/saintebeuve
E-mail: saintebeuve@wanadoo.fr
Tel: +33 1 45 48 20 07
Fax: +33 1 45 48 67 52

Price Guide: (breakfast €14)
Rooms €130–325

Situated on a quiet street, this superbly renovated hotel is excellently positioned near to Saint-Germain-des-Près, Saint-Sulpice and the Jardin du Luxembourg. The charming Le Sainte-Beuve has the atmosphere of a chic Parisian home, complemented by friendly and welcoming service. The bedrooms are attractively decorated with pastel colours and antique furnishings, whilst the suite is simply beautiful. The fashionable shops and cultural attractions of central Paris are all within easy reach.

Dans une rue calme et idéalement situé près de Saint-Germain-des-Prés, Saint-Sulpice et les Jardins du Luxembourg, l'hôtel Sainte-Beuve a l'atmosphère d'une maison chic parisienne, complétée par un service amical et accueillant. Toutes les chambres sont agréablement décorées avec des couleurs pastel et un mobilier ancien, alors que la suite est tout simplement superbe. Les magasins en vogue et attractions culturelles du centre de Paris sont tous d'accès facile.

Dieses charmante, perfekt renovierte Hotel liegt in einer ruhigen Straße in der Nähe von Saint-Germain-des-Près, Saint-Sulpice und dem Jardin du Luxembourg. Die Atmosphäre ist die eines eleganten Pariser Privathauses, und wird durch den freundlichen, herzlichen Service noch verstärkt. Die Zimmer sind wunderschön mit Antiquitäten eingerichtet und in Pastellfarben gehalten, und die Suite ist einfach traumhaft. Die zahlreichen Einkaufsmöglichkeiten und kulturellen Attraktionen von Paris liegen alle in nächster Nähe.

Our inspector loved: *Room number 20, "Sainte-Beuve".*

Relais Médicis

23 RUE RACINE, 75006 PARIS, FRANCE

Tucked away just a few minutes from l'Odéon, the Jardin du Luxembourg and the Boulevard St Germain, this delightful hotel is arranged around a charming patio that is lavishly planted between April and September. Antique pieces, painted woodwork, Impressionist-style printed curtains and vintage photographs create a warm atmosphere. The 16 cosy bedrooms are surprisingly spacious and decorated with cheerful colours reminiscent of Provence and Italy; all have marble bathrooms and air conditioning. Numerous sights and attractions are within easy reach.

Situé à quelques minutes du Jardin du Luxembourg et du Boulevard St. Germain, cet hôtel de charme est construit autour d'une fontaine et d'un joli patio très fleuri des mois d'Avril à Septembre. Des meubles antiques, des boiseries peintes, des rideaux "impressionnistes" et des photos très anciennes créent une ambiance chaleureuse. Les 16 chambres sont à la fois intimes et spacieuses et sont décorées de couleurs qui rappellent celles de Provence et de l'Italie. Elles disposent toutes de salles de bain en marbre et sont climatisées. De nombreuses attractions sont d'accès facile.

Dieses zauberhafte, nur ein paar Minuten dem Jardin du Luxembourg und dem Boulevard St Germain entfernte Hotel ist um eine hübsche Terrasse herum gebaut, die von April bis September üppig bepflanzt ist. Antiquitäten, bemaltes Holz, impressionistisch bedruckte Vorhänge und alte Fotografien sorgen für ein warmes Ambiente. Die 16 gemütlichen Zimmer sind überraschend geräumig und mit bunten, an die Provence und Italien erinnernden Farben dekoriert. Alle haben Marmorbäder und Klimaanlange. Zahlreiche Sehenswürdigkeiten liegen in nächster Nähe.

Our inspector loved: *The lounge that gives the feeling of being in a private home.*

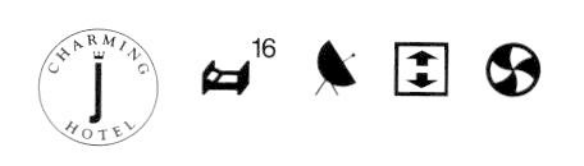

Directions: The hotel is a few yards from Place de l'Odéon and a few minutes from Boulevard Saint-Germain.

Paris
Bordeaux
Marseille

Web: www.johansens.com/medicis
E-mail: reservation@relaismedicis.com
Tel: +33 1 43 26 00 60
Fax: +33 1 40 46 83 39

Price Guide: (room only, excluding VAT)
single €138-188
double/twin €168-239
double de luxe €215-258

Hôtel de L'Arcade

9 RUE DE L'ARCADE, 75008 PARIS, FRANCE

This 19th-century town house is ideally located just a few steps from the Opéra Gamier, the Place de la Concorde and the "grands magasins" on boulevard Haussman. This private home has been designed for those looking for discreet elegance. The subtly coloured lounges create a tranquil atmosphere, whilst the bedrooms are decorated in soft tones and have a functional design. Bathrooms boast marble and ceramic from Sardinia. Only breakfast is served here, but numerous cafés and restaurants can be found within easy reach.

L'Hôtel de l'Arcade, maison de ville du XIXe siècle, est idéalement situé à quelques minutes de l'Opéra Gamier, de la place de la Concorde et des grands magasins du boulevard Haussman. Cette maison privée a été conçue pour les amoureux à la recherche d'une élégance discrète. Décorés en couleurs subtiles, les salons créent une atmosphère de tranquillité. Les chambres en teintes douces sont lumineuses et fonctionnelles. Marbre et céramique de Sardaigne dans les salles de bains. Seul le petit-déjeuner y est servi mais de nombreux cafés et restaurants se situent dans les environs.

Dieses Stadthaus aus dem 19. Jahrhundert liegt ideal nur ein paar Minuten von der Opéra Gamier, der Place de la Concorde und den "grands magasins" des Boulevard Haussman entfernt. Dieses Privathaus ist ein Traum für diejenigen, die diskrete Eleganz lieben. Die Aufenthaltsräume sind mit subtilen, eine ruhige Atmosphäre schaffenden Farben gestaltet, und die Zimmer sind funktionell und in sanften Tönen gehalten. In den Bädern findet man Marmor und Keramik aus Sardinien. Das Hotel serviert nur Frühstück, doch zahlreiche Restaurants und Cafés liegen in nächster Nähe.

Our inspector loved: *The superb and welcoming lounge with its fireplace and bouquets of fresh flowers.*

Directions: Off Place de la Madeleine.

Web: www.johansens.com/larcade
E mail: reservation@hotel-arcade.com
Tel: +33 1 53 30 60 00
Fax: +33 1 40 07 03 07

Price Guide:
single €140-163
double/twin €180
duplex apartment €215

Hôtel Le Lavoisier

21 RUE LAVOISIER, 75008 PARIS, FRANCE

One of the most chic hotels in Paris, Hôtel le Lavoisier is mere minutes away from Place de la Concorde and the famous shops of the Boulevard Haussman. Well-chosen antique furniture and warm, elegant colour schemes compose a refinement that makes this hotel an ideal retreat from the busy streets of Paris. The intimacy of communal areas such as the cellar breakfast room, and the attentive service of the staff are suggestive of comforts from outside the city.

L'Hôtel Le Lavoisier, l'un des plus chics de Paris, n'est qu'à quelques minutes de la place de la Concorde et des célèbres magasins du boulevard Haussmann. Les meubles anciens choisis avec soin et les couleurs élégantes et chaleureuses du décor créent une ambiance raffinée qui fait de cet hôtel un refuge idéal pour échapper à la fébrilité des rues parisiennes. L'intimité des salles communes, telles que la petite salle à manger occupant la cave, et la prévenance du personnel évoquent le charme des hôtels provinciaux.

Dieses nur wenige Minuten vom Place de la Concorde und den Geschäften des Boulevard Haussman entfernt gelegene Hotel ist eines der elegantesten von Paris. Geschmackvolles, antikes Mobiliar und warme, elegante Farben schaffen eine erlesene Atmosphäre, die dieses Hotel zu einer Oase inmitten der geschäftigen Straßen von Paris macht. Die Abgeschiedenheit der Aufenthaltsräume, z. B. des Frühstücksraums im Kellergewölbe, sowie aufmerksamster Service bieten einen Komfort, wie man ihn sonst nur außerhalb der Stadt erwarten würde.

Our inspector loved: *The superb decoration of the lounge including the 19th-century paintings of children.*

Directions: Near Place Saint-Augustin.

Web: www.johansens.com/lelavoisier
E-mail: info@hotellavoisier.com
Tel: +33 1 53 30 06 06
Fax: +33 1 53 30 23 00

Price Guide: (room only, excluding VAT)
double/twin €215–230
suite €285–415

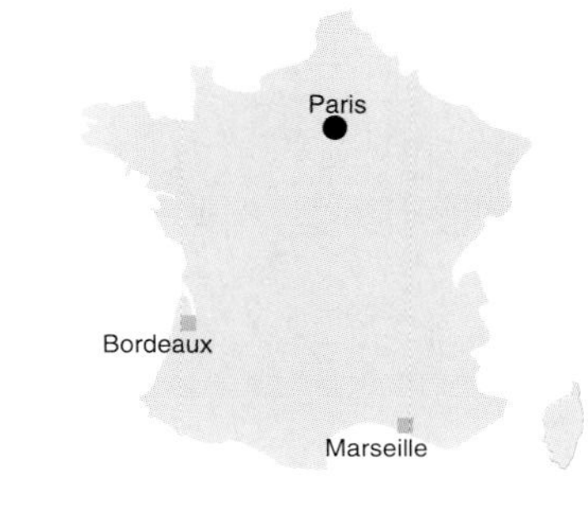

Hôtel Opéra Richepanse

14 RUE DU CHEVALIER DE SAINT-GEORGE, 75001 PARIS, FRANCE

This art deco hotel, which is located in the heart of historic Paris, next to rue Saint-Honoré and Place de la Madeleine, and between rue Royale and Place Vendôme, exudes a typically Parisian elegance. 3 suites and some of the rooms are particularly generously sized, perfect for families or businessmen who wish to hold their meetings in a welcoming setting. The hotel is ideally located for exploring the city on foot: luxury boutiques and shopping centres, museums, monuments, restaurants and events can be found nearby. A friendly and competent team helps organise your stay.

Au cœur du Paris historique, cet hôtel art déco à côté de la rue Saint-Honoré et de la Place de la Madeleine, entre la rue Royale et la Place Vendôme, est d'une élégance très parisienne. Les 3 suites et certaines chambres sont particulièrement grandes, pouvant accueillir des familles ou des hommes d'affaires à la recherche d'un espace convivial pour leurs rendez-vous professionnels. C'est le lieu idéal pour se rendre partout à pied: boutiques de luxe, grands magasins, musées, monuments, restaurants et spectacles. Une équipe acceuillante et compétente vous aidera à organiser votre séjour.

Dieses Art Déco Hotel im historischen Herzen von Paris, an der Rue Saint-Honoré und Place de la Madeleine, und zwischen der Rue Royale and Place Vendôme, besitzt eine typische Pariser Eleganz. Die 3 Suiten und einige der Zimmer sind besonders geräumig und somit ideal für Familien oder Geschäftsleute, die hier ihre Treffen abhalten möchten. Der ideale Ort, um die Stadt zu Fuß zu erkunden: Luxusboutiquen, Kaufhäuser, Museen, Monumente, Restaurants und Veranstaltungen sind ganz in der Nähe zu finden. Ein herzliches und kompetentes Team steht ständig zur Hilfe bereit.

Our inspector loved: *The beautiful art déco furniture.*

Directions: Centrally located, near to la Madeleine and Place de la Concorde.

Web: www.johansens.com/richepanse
E-mail: richepanseotel@wanadoo.fr
Tel: +33 1 42 60 36 00
Fax: +33 1 42 60 13 03

Price Guide: (room only)
double €230-350
suite €450-590

HÔTEL MAYET

3 RUE MAYET, 75006 PARIS, FRANCE

Set in the heart of the vibrant Rive Gauche quarter, this beautiful small hotel is the ideal place for a young and energetic clientele, who wish to experience a relaxed yet sophisticated atmosphere. The carefully furnished public rooms feature great attention to detail, and the bright and comfortable bedrooms offer modern design, with grey-and-raspberry coloured walls. Complimentary breakfast can be enjoyed in a beautiful room with vaulted ceiling and exposed stone walls, and is served on a long table d'hôte.

Situé au coeur de la rive gauche, ce petit hôtel est l'endroit idéal pour une clientéle jeune et pleine d'énergie, désirant profiter d'une atmosphère détendue et sophistiquée. Les parties communes sont soigneusement aménagées avec une attention particuliére pour les détails. Les chambres claires et confortables ont un design moderne avec des murs gris et framboise. Le petit déjeuner offert est servi sur une longue table d'hôte dans une cave voutée aux pierres apparentes.

Dieses hübsche kleine Hotel im Herzen des lebhaften Rive Gauche ist der ideale Ort für ein junges, dynamisches Publikum, das eine gediegene und doch entspannte Atmosphäre schätzt. Die Aufenthaltsräume sind sorgfältig und mit viel Liebe zum Detail eingerichtet, und die hellen, komfortablen Zimmer sind modern gestaltet und haben grau und himbeerfarbene Wände. Frühstück ist inklusive und wird am Table d,hôte in einem herrlichen Raum mit hohen Decken und freiliegendem Mauerwerk serviert.

Our inspector loved: *The brilliant concept of this hotel and its lively atmosphere as well as its excellent value for money.*

Directions: In the centre of Paris, close to Duroc métro station.

Web: www.johansens.com/mayet
E-mail: hotel@mayet.com
Tel: +33 1 47 83 21 35
Fax: +33 1 40 65 95 78

Price Guide:
single €100-140

VICTORIA PALACE HÔTEL

6, RUE BLAISE DESGOFFE, 75006 PARIS, FRANCE

Conveniently situated on the left bank, within walking distance of most tourist sights in the city, this charming hotel has friendly, attentive staff and an atmosphere of luxury and elegance. Beautiful public rooms are decorated in a traditional Victorian style with eye-catching colour schemes, comfortable furniture and stunning works of art. A delicious buffet breakfast is served and there is also a 24-hour concierge service. The hotel is ideally situated for exploring the city's numerous attractions.

Bien situé sur la rive gauche, avec les attractions touristiques d'accès facile à pied, cet hôtel charmant a un personnel accueillant qui répond au moindre désir des clients et une ambiance de luxe et d'élégance. Les belles salles publiques sont décorées en style traditionnel victorien avec une combinaison de couleurs qui tire l'œil, des meubles confortables et des œuvres d'art magnifiques. Le petit déjeuner-buffet est servi et il y a un service concierge disponible 24h/24. L'hôtel est parfaitement situé pour explorer les nombreuses attractions de la ville.

Dieses charmante Hotel mit seiner günstigen Lage am linken Seineufer und nicht weit von zahlreichen Attraktionen der Stadt entfernt bietet freundliches, aufmerksames Personal und eine Atmosphäre von Luxus und Eleganz. Die herrlichen Aufenthaltsräume sind traditionell viktorianisch mit auffallenden Farben gestaltet und mit bequemen Möbeln und eindrucksvollen Kunstwerken gefüllt. Das Frühstück ist ein verlockendes Buffet, und ein Concierge steht rund um die Uhr zur Verfügung. Das Hotel liegt ideal, um die vielen Sehenswürdigkeiten von Paris zu erkunden.

Our inspector loved: *The beautifully decorated bedrooms, each with superb paintings.*

Directions: The hotel is situated between rue de Renner and rue de Vaugirard, close to Saint Placide tube station.

Web: www.johansens.com/victoriapalace
E-mail: info@victoriapalace.com
Tel: +33 1 45 49 70 00
Fax: +33 1 45 49 23 75

Price Guide: (room only)
double €305-365
suite €595-765

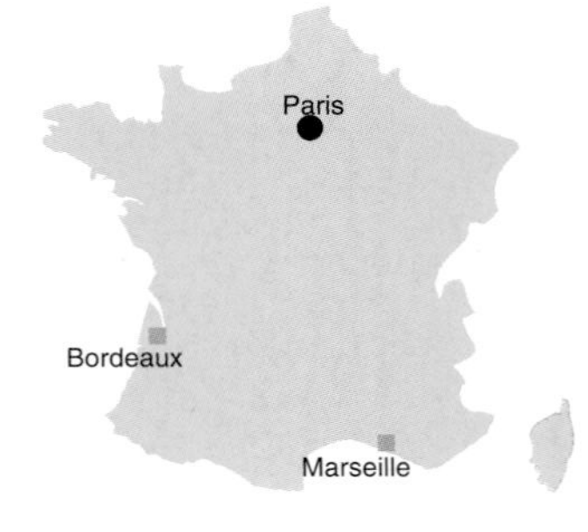

Pavillon de Paris

7 RUE DE PARME, 75009 PARIS, FRANCE

Guests will be forgiven for confusing this contemporary-style townhouse hotel with an art gallery: abstract paintings and black and white pictures adorn the walls, combined with subtle lighting and designer décor. The financial district is easily accessible. Feng Shui influences each room, from the minimalist reception area to the inviting lounge and homely guest rooms decorated in ivory and blue. Room service offers French, Japanese and Chinese cuisine whilst breakfast may be taken under the warm glass-domed ceiling in the Breakfast Room.

Cet hôtel de style contemporain pourrait facilement être confondu avec une galerie d'art : peintures abstraites et photos en noir et blanc ornent les murs, associées à une lumière subtile et à une décoration de designer. Le quartier financier de Paris est facilement accessible. On trouve des influences Feng Shui dans toutes les pièces, de la réception minimaliste au lounge attrayant et aux chambres accueillantes décorées dans des combinaisons de bleu et d'ivoire. La carte du room service propose une cuisine française, japonaise ou chinoise et le petit-déjeuner peut-être pris sous la verrière.

Fast könnte man dieses zeitgenössische Stadthaushotel mit einer Kunstgalerie verwechseln: abstrakte Gemälde und Schwarzweißfotografien, gedämpfte Beleuchtung und Designer-Décor zieren das Hotel, das nicht weit vom Finanzviertel liegt. Feng Shui ist allgegenwärtig, von der minimalistischen Rezeption bis hin zur einladenden Lounge und den in Elfenbein und Blautönen gehaltenen Zimmern. Zimmerservice bietet französische, japanische und chinesische Küche, und Frühstück wird unter dem warmen Glaskuppeldach im Frühstücksraum serviert.

Our inspector loved: *The reception desk area.*

Directions: The hotel is located midway between Montmartre and Opéra. The nearest metro station is Liege.

Web: www.johansens.com/pavillonparis
E-mail: mail@pavillondeparis.com
Tel: +33 1 55 31 60 00
Fax: +33 1 55 31 60 01

Price Guide:
single €195-230
double €245-285

HÔTEL LE SAINT~GRÉGOIRE

43 RUE DE L'ABBÉ GRÉGOIRE, 75006 PARIS, FRANCE

Directions: Near rue du Bac. St Placide and Rennes are the closest metro stations.

Web: www.johansens.com/saintgregoire
E-mail: hotel@saintgregoire.com
Tel: 33 1 45 48 23 23
Fax: +33 1 45 48 33 95

Price Guide: (room only, excluding VAT)
single €175
double/twin €175-215
suite €248

Set at the heart of the Rive Gauche, this small 18th-century hotel offers guests refined elegance in a tranquil environment. Overlooking the interior garden, the charming lobby with an open fire becomes a cosy retreat during winter. 20 unique bedrooms are adorned with period paintings and antiques and offer every modern amenity. Guests enjoy an imaginative breakfast in the stonewall cellar before exploring the Saint Germain quarter.

Situé en plein coeur de la Rive Gauche, cet hôtel du XVIIIe siècle offre à ses visiteurs une élégance raffinée dans un environnement tranquille. Surplombant le jardin intérieur, le charmant hall de réception est encore plus attrayant en hiver avec son feu de cheminée. Les 20 chambres, toutes uniques, sont décorées de peintures d'époques et d'antiquités et offrent tout le confort moderne. Les hôtes peuvent déguster un petit déjeuner imaginatif dans la salle voutée aux murs de pierre, avant d'explorer le quartier Saint-Germain.

Mitten im Herzen des rechten Seine-Ufers gelegen bietet dieses kleine Hotel aus dem 18. Jahrhundert subtile Eleganz in einer ruhigen Umgebung. Der auf den Garten blickende Empfangsraum sorgt mit seinem offenen Kaminfeuer im Winter für Behaglichkeit. 20 einzigartige Zimmer sind mit Bildern und Antiquitäten des 18. Jahrhunderts geschmückt und bieten modernsten Komfort. Im Kellergeschoss mit seinen Steinwänden genießt man ein einfallsreiches Frühstück, bevor Saint Germain mit seinen vielen Attraktionen lockt.

Our inspector loved: *The manager's warm welcome and the feeling of entering a private home.*

FRANCE / PARIS (SAINT~GERMAIN)

L' HÔTEL

13, RUE DES BEAUX ARTS, 75006 PARIS, FRANCE

Brimming with history, L' Hôtel was once visited by artists and other distinguished guests. Today a magnificent refurbishment keeps its spirit alive with stunning effect. Enchanting bedrooms, each with their own theme and style, descend from the magnificent skylight which looks out into the Paris sky. The sophisticated public rooms are superbly decorated; especially in the intimate bar and gourmet restaurant, Le Bélier, with its patio and fountain. Downstairs, a swimming pool reminiscent of old Roman hot baths awaits guests.

Lieu historique, l'hôtel était autrefois privilégié par les artistes et autres hôtes de marque. Récemment rénové, il a préservé son esprit de manière remarquable. Des chambres enchanteresses, chacune avec son propre thème et style, sont disposées sous la magnifique coupole qui s'ouvre sur le ciel de Paris. Les pièces communes sont décorées avec sophistication; surtout un bar intime et le restaurant gastronomique, Le Bélier, son patio et fontaine. Au sous-sol, une piscine qui évoque les vieux Bains chauds romains est à la disposition des hôtes.

Das geschichtsträchtige L' Hôtel wurde einst von Künstlern und anderen distinguierten Gästen besucht. Durch gekonnte Renovierung blieb der alte Geist des Hauses erhalten. Zauberhafte, nach unterschiedlichen Motiven gestaltete Zimmer reihen sich um ein fantastisches Deckenfenster mit Blick auf den Pariser Himmel. Die eleganten Aufenthaltsräume sind wundervoll eingerichtet, vor allem die gemütliche Bar und das Gourmetrestaurant Le Bélier mit Terrasse und Springbrunnen. Ein Swimmingpool, der an römische Thermen erinnert, steht zur Verfügung.

Our inspector loved: *The amazing attention to detail with which the hotel has been decorated. Each bedroom has its own history and story to tell.*

Directions: Within the heart of Saint-Germain. Saint Germain is the nearest métro station.

Paris

Bordeaux

Marseille

Web: www.johansens.com/lhotel
E-mail: reservation@l-hotel.com
Tel: +33 1 44 41 99 00
Fax: +33 1 43 25 64 81

Price Guide:
double €255–640
suite €540–640
apartment €640–740

20 40

LE MANOIR DE GRESSY

77410 GRESSY~EN~FRANCE, ROISSY CDG, NEAR PARIS, FRANCE

Built on the site of a 17th-century fortified farmhouse, Le Manoir de Gressy is a restful country retreat that recreates the cosy atmosphere of an old-fashioned inn. Whether relaxing by the pool or cycling through the countryside, Le Manoir's tranquil surroundings offer respite from the bustle of everyday life. On the terrace, a selection of the very best fresh produce form the market is served. The luxuriously appointed bedrooms are charmingly decorated and look out over the pool and landscaped courtyard garden.

Sur le site d'une ferme fortifiée du XVIIe siècle, le Manoir vous offre un cadre reposant à la campagne. Redécouvrez l'atmosphère feutrée d'une étape d'autrefois. A bicyclette le long des chemins de halage ou bien autour de la piscine, le Manoir de Gressy offre un cadre privilégié à tous ceux qui désirent oublier leur vie trépidante. Dans une ambiance chaleureuse, dégustez une sélection des meilleurs produits du marché sur la terrasse. Les chambres raffinées, d'un charme et d'un luxe discret, s'ouvrent toutes sur la piscine et le jardin intérieur paysager.

An der Stelle eines befestigten Landgutes aus dem 17. Jahrhundert befindet sich das idyllische Manoir de Gressy. Hier fühlt man sich wahrlich in eine vergangene Zeit zurückversetzt. Ob man mit dem Fahrrad die Gegend erkundet oder sich am Pool erholt, hier findet man Ruhe vom hektischen Alltagsleben. In herzlicher Atmosphäre wird auf der Terrasse eine verlockende Auswahl an frischen Produkten vom Markt serviert. Die zauberhaften, eleganten Zimmer bieten diskreten Luxus und alle haben Blick auf den Pool und den gepflegten Garten.

Our inspector loved: *The courtyard garden and the pool.*

Directions: Paris > A1 or A3 > A104, N2 > D212 > Gressy.

Web: www.johansens.com/manoirdegressy
E-mail: information@manoirdegressy.com
Tel: +33 1 60 26 68 00
Fax: +33 1 60 26 45 46

Price Guide:
luxury single/double €149-200
terrace single/double €149-230
suite single/double €260
special weekend offers are available

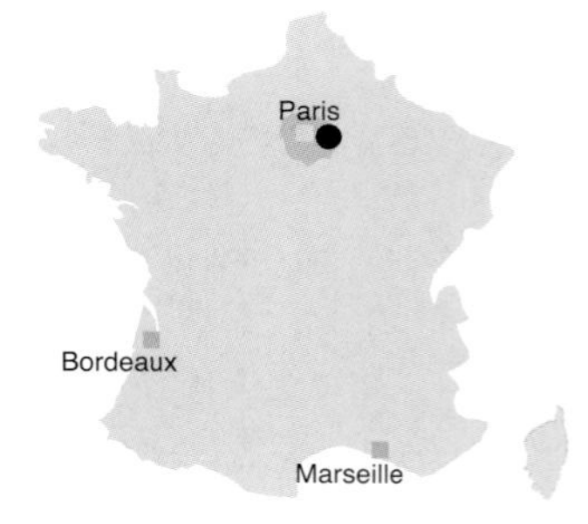

Château d'Esclimont

28700 SAINT SYMPHORIEN~LE~CHÂTEAU, FRANCE

A French château as it should be - tranquil moat, colourful gardens, picturesque towers, acres of parkland, large lake. And inside, high ceiling rooms, period elegance and delicate décor reminiscent of d'Esclimont's original 15th to 16th-century era. Spacious en-suite guest rooms have every comfort, whilst excellent cuisine is prepared by leading chef Olivier Dupart with inventive pre-dinner cocktails served by master barman Jean Jacques Venneugges.

Un château français comme il se doit. Des douves tranquilles, des jardins colorés, des tours pittoresques, des hectares de parc, un grand lac. Et à l'intérieur, des hauts plafonds, une élégance d'époque et un décor délicat évocateurs de l'original Esclimont du XVe et XVIe siècles. Les chambres spacieuses ont tout le confort. Une cuisine excellente est préparée par le chef Olivier Dupart avec des cocktails d'apéritifs inventifs servis par le barman Jean Jacques Venneugges.

Genau so sollte ein französisches Château aussehen: ein ruhiger Burggraben, farbenprächtige Gärten, malerische Türmchen, weite Parklandschaft und ein großer See, und im Inneren hohe Decken, Eleganz vergangener Zeiten und erlesenes Décor, das an Esclimonts Zeit im 15. und 16. Jahrhundert erinnert. Die geräumigen Zimmer mit eigenen Bädern bieten jeglichen Komfort. Chefkoch Olivier Dupart kreiert exzellente Speisen, und vor dem Abendessen serviert Bartender Jean Jacques Venneugges einfallsreiche Cocktails.

Our inspector loved: *Taking a picnic by the hotel's lake.*

Directions: A11 > exit 1 > Ablis > direction of Chartres.

Web: www.johansens.com/esclimont
E-mail: esclimont@grandesetapes.fr
Tel: +33 2 37 31 15 15
Fax: +33 2 37 31 57 91

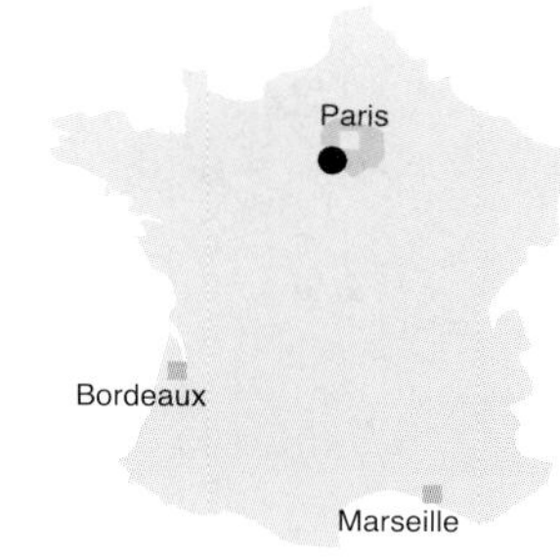

Price Guide: (room only)
room €170–470
double €170–470
suite €690–1,280

Château de L'Yeuse

65 RUE DE BELLEVUE, QUARTIER DE L'ECHASSIER, 16100 CHÂTEAUBERNARD, FRANCE

Directions: N141 from Angoulème > turn right in the direction of L'Echassier.

Web: www.johansens.com/chateaudelyeuse
E-mail: reservations.yeuse@wanadoo.fr
Tel: +33 5 45 36 82 60
Fax: +33 5 45 35 06 32

Price Guide: (room only)
single €92–157
double €92–157
suite €205–314

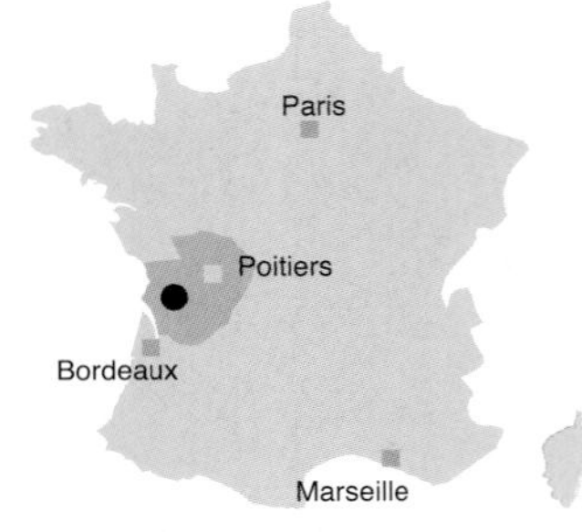

Perfectly enlarged and restored with tasteful interiors, the château's superb décor includes wonderful furnishings and fabrics. Beautiful suites have stunning views across the park, the river Charente and surrounding countryside and are adjoined by spacious, well-equipped bathrooms. In the elegant high-ceilinged dining room attentive staff serve inventive local cuisine. There is an outdoor pool and indoor Jacuzzi and sauna, and guests can choose to relax on the large sun terrace or beneath the shade of the ancient oak trees, or "Yeuses".

Agrandie et restaurée parfaitement avec goût, le superbe décor du Château inclut un fantastique ameublement et tissus. Les suites superbes, avec salle de bain contiguë spacieuse et parfaitement équipée, ont une vue imprenable sur le parc, la Charente et la campagne environnante. Dans l'élégante salle à manger à hauts plafonds, un personnel attentif sert une cuisine locale inventive. Les hôtes peuvent choisir d'utiliser la piscine extérieure ou le jacuzzi en salle, ou encore de se détendre sur la grande terrasse ensoleillée ou à l'ombre des vieux chênes appelés Yeuses.

Dieses restaurierte, erweiterte Schloss besitzt ein geschmackvolles Interieur mit einem Décor aus wundervollen Einrichtungen und Stoffen. Die Suiten bieten herrliche Ausblicke auf den Park, den Fluss Charente und die Umgebung und haben geräumige Bäder. Im eleganten Speisesaal serviert aufmerksames Personal kreative regionale Küche. Ein Außenswimmingpool sowie ein Jacuzzi und eine Sauna stehen zur Verfügung, und man kann sich auf der großen Sonnenterrasse oder im Schatten der alten Eichenbäume („Yeuses") entspannen.

Our inspector loved: *The cognac library.*

Château de Crazannes

17350 CRAZANNES, FRANCE

This magnificent 15th-century château has been lovingly restored and welcomes guests in a most friendly and professional manner. The bedrooms in the main building feature period furniture and stunning views over the park, whilst those in the newly renovated dungeon boast exposed stonework and beams. For relaxation the heated swimming pool is never overcrowded and the rooftop sun terrace affords breathtaking views as far as the eye can see.

Ce magnifique château du XVe siècle a été soigneusement décoré et accueille ses hôtes de manière amicale et professionnelle. Les chambres dans le bâtiment principal sont meublées d'antiquités et offrent de magnifiques vues sur le parc, celles dans le donjon, récemment rénové, ont de belles pierres et de superbes poutres. Pour la relaxation, la piscine chauffée n'est jamais surchargée et le solarium sur le toit offre des vues vers l'infini à couper le souffle.

Dieses herrliche, liebevoll restaurierte Château aus dem 15. Jahrhundert heißt seine Gäste auf extrem freundliche und professionelle Weise willkommen. Die Zimmer im Hauptgebäude sind mit Stilmöbeln gefüllt und blicken auf den Park, während die im neu renovierten einstigen Kerker freigelegtes Mauerwerk und Holzbalken zu bieten haben. Am beheizten Swimmingpool ist nie zu viel los, und von der Dachterrasse hat man eine atemberaubende Sicht soweit das Auge reicht.

Our inspector loved: *The secluded swimming pool area.*

Directions: A10 > exit 6 > N137 towards Rochefort > D119 towards Plassay > Crazannes. The nearest airport is Bordeaux.

Web: www.johansens.com/chateaudecrazannes
E-mail: crazannes@worldonline.fr
Tel: +33 6 80 65 40 96
Fax: +33 5 46 91 34 46

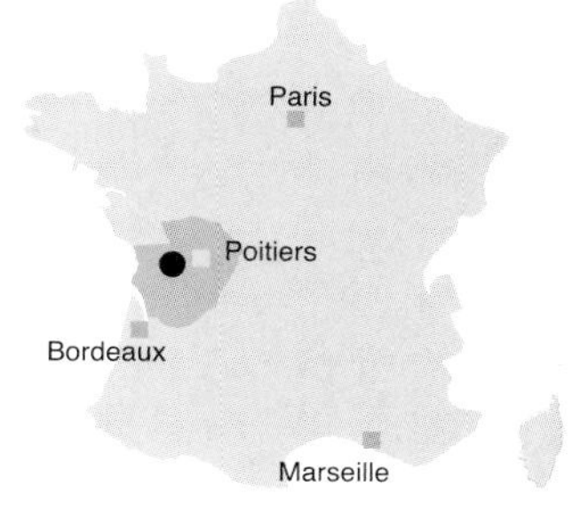

Price Guide:
single €90-140
double/twin €110-190
suite €170-230

DOMAINE DES ETANGS

16310 MASSIGNAC, FRANCE

The Domaine is a vast, partially wooded property of over 2,000 acres including 76 acres of ponds and over 25km of private roads. Dotted around this immaculately kept piece of nature are an elegant château and 7 hamlets, housing 17 4-star guest rooms and suites. Most of the rooms, which are charmingly decorated with stone, glass, wood and copper, have impressive fireplaces, which can also be found in the salons and the Les Tournelles restaurant, where guests can enjoy delicious seasonal cuisine. Activities include tennis, swimming in the pool, boating on the lake and much more.

Le Domaine est une vaste propriété partiellement boisée de 850 ha, ponctués de 31 ha d'étangs et 25 km de routes privées. Dans une nature soigneusement préservée, se dressent un élégant château et 7 hameaux principaux dans lesquels sont aménagées 17 chambres ou suites 4 étoiles. La plupart des pièces, chaleureusement décorées en pierre, verre, bois et cuivre, possède une imposante cheminée a l'instar des salons d'accueil et du restaurant Les Tournelles, qui sert une délicieuse cuisine de saison. Pour la détente, le domaine propose le court de tennis, la piscine chauffée, le canotage et toutes sortes de loisirs.

Dieses weitläufige, teilweise bewaldete Anwesen umfasst 850ha Land mit 31ha Teichen und 25km Privatstraßen. In sorgfältig gepflegter Natur befinden sich ein elegantes Schloss und 7 kleine Dörfchen mit 17 4-Sterne-Zimmern und Suiten. Die meisten der mit Stein, Glas, Holz und Kupfer gestalteten, einladenden Zimmer bieten eindrucksvolle Kamine, wie man sie auch in den Aufenthaltsräumen und im Les Tournelles findet, das erlesene, saisonbedingte Küche serviert. Aktivitäten sind Tennis, Schwimmen im Pool, Bootfahren und vieles mehr.

Our inspector loved: *The total feeling of freedom, peace and quiet.*

Directions: Nearest airport: Limoges; nearest station: Angoulême (45 minutes). Angoulême > Limoges road N141; at La Rochefoucauld, go towards Montemboeuf (D13).

Web: www.johansens.com/etangs
E-mail: info@domainedesetangs.fr
Tel: +33 5 45 61 85 00
Fax: +33 5 45 61 85 01

Price Guide: (room only)
single €137-242
double €137-242
suite €222-242

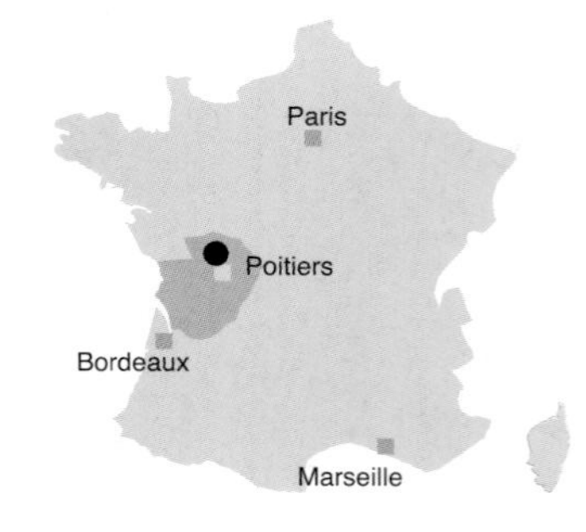

MOULIN DU VAL DE SEUGNE

MARCOUZE, 17240 MOSNAC, FRANCE

Sheltered by ash trees and poplars, this converted 16th-century water mill is surrounded by cognac vineyards. The River Seugne flows along the mill's walls, and riverside guest rooms overlook Wooded Island, home to hens, peacocks, ducks, sheep and Pyjama, the goat. Each spacious bedroom has a desk area and lounge. Gastronomic cuisine is complemented by an extensive wine list featuring nearby Bordeaux samples. Fishing on nearby River Maine is a must; alternatively visit the cave baths, balneotherapy pool and aquacentre at Jonzac.

Sous les par des frênes et des peupliers, ce moulin à eau reconverti du XVIe siècle est entouré des vignobles de Cognac. La Seugne coule le long des murs du moulin, et les chambres d'amis côte rivière donnent sur l'Ile aux Bois, foyer de poules d'eau, paons, canards, moutons et Pyjama la chèvre. Chaque chambre spacieuse a un coin bureau et salon. Une cuisine gastronomique est complétée d'une bonne carte de vins dont des Bordeaux locaux. La pêche dans La Seugne est une obligation ; sinon il faut visiter les bains troglodytes, la piscine de balnéothérapie et le centre aquatique de Jonzac.

Diese von Eschen und Pappeln beschattete umgebaute Wassermühle aus dem 16. Jahrhundert ist von Kognacweinbergen umgeben. Die Seugne fließt entlang ihrer Wände, und die Zimmer an der Flussseite blicken auf eine bewaldete Insel, auf der Hühner, Pfaue, Enten, Schafe und die Ziege Pyjama leben. Jedes der geräumigen Zimmer hat einen Schreibtisch und einen Wohnbereich. Gourmet-Küche wird durch eine umfassende Weinkarte ergänzt, auf der Weine des nahegelegenen Bordeaux zu finden sind. Angeln der Seugne ist ein Muss, ebenso ein Besuch der Höhlenbäder, Balneotherapiebecken und des Aquazentrums in Jonzac.

Our inspector loved: *Watching Pyjama the goat playing with Gideon the goose.*

Directions: Situated between Cognac and Bordeaux, 30mins from the sea. A10 > exit 36 towards Pons > N137 towards Saint Genis > left in Belluire > D134 toards Mosnac. The nearest airport is Bordeaux.

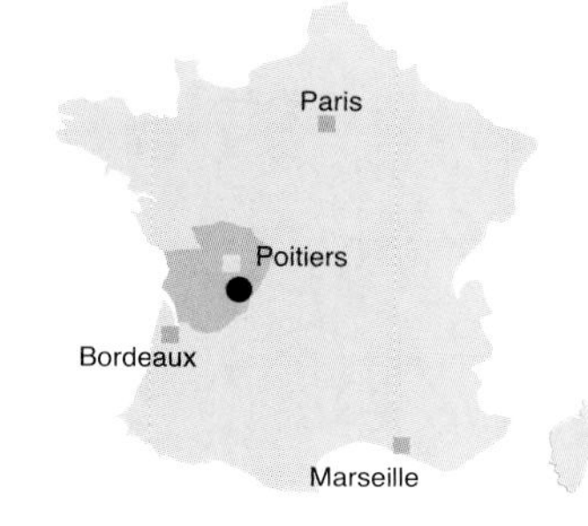

Web: www.johansens.com/valdeseugne
E-mail: moulin@valdeseugne.com
Tel: +33 5 46 70 46 16
Fax: +33 5 46 70 48 14

Price Guide: (room only)
single €90-110
double €90-110
suite €145

LE LOGIS SAINT MARTIN

CHEMIN DE PISSOT, 79400 SAINT~MAIXENT~L'ECOLE, FRANCE

Renowned for its excellent gastronomic restaurant, this charmingly restored 17th-century manor is nestled in the peaceful surroundings of the beautiful Poitou valley. Delicious and inventive cuisine is served in the elegant dining room, complemented by fine wines and great vintages, rare liquors and a choice of cigars. Friendly and attentive staff cater for every need. Guests may relax on the terrace or by the swimming pool, explore the beautiful countryside and enjoy golf, horse riding and fishing.

Réputé pour son excellent restaurant gastronomique, ce charmant pavillon restauré du XVIIe siècle est niché au calme dans la superbe vallée du Poitou. La cuisine délicieuse et inventive est servie dans l'élégante salle à manger et est agrémentée de vins fins, de grands crus, de digestifs uniques et d'un large choix de cigares. Le personnel, prévenant et accueillant, répond au moindre besoin. Les hôtes peuvent se relaxer sur la terrasse ou à la piscine, explorer les superbes environs ou pratiquer le golf, l'équitation ou la pêche.

Dieses herrlich renovierte Haus aus dem 17. Jahrhundert liegt im friedvollen und traumhaft schönen Tal von Poitou und ist berühmt für sein exzellentes Gourmetrestaurant. Im eleganten Speisesaal wird köstliche und einfallsreiche Küche serviert, begleitet von erlesenen Spitzenweinen, seltenen Likören und einer großen Auswahl an Zigarren. Das freundliche und aufmerksame Personal erfüllt jeden Wunsch. Die Gäste können auf der Terrasse oder am Pool entspannen, die herrliche Landschaft erkunden und Golf spielen, reiten oder angeln.

Our inspector loved: *The constant quality year in, year out.*

Directions: A10 > exit 32.

Web: www.johansens.com/logisstmartin
E-mail: contact@logis-saint-martin.com
Tel: +33 549 0558 68
Fax: +33 549 7619 93

Price Guide: (room only)
single €105–115
double/twin €105–140
suite €145

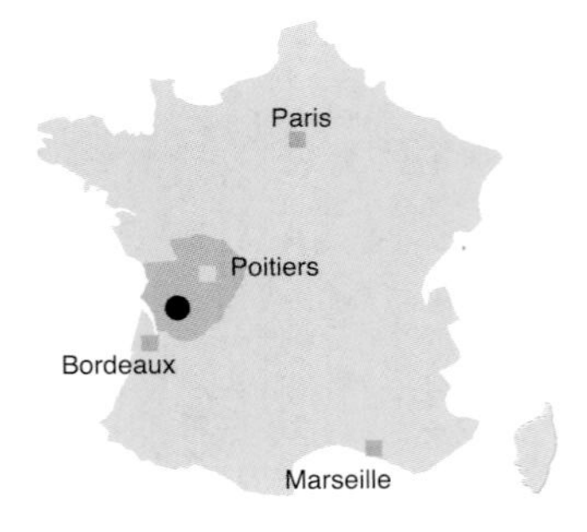

LE PIGONNET

5 AVENUE DU PIGONNET, 13090 AIX~EN~PROVENCE, FRANCE

This beautiful Bastide Provençale lies in the heart of Aix-en-Provence, less than a 5-minute walk from the town centre. The décor is typically Provençal in its use of fabric and colour, and is both elegant and extremely welcoming. Many of the bedrooms overlook the beautiful manicured grounds with wide varieties of plants, flowers and trees and stunning fountains, whilst the typical regional cuisine will have guests returning time and again. A new wifi system and business centre are available, as are hammam, fitness room and massage service.

Cette belle bastide provençale se situe au cœur d'Aix-en-Provence, à moins de 5 minutes à pied du centre ville. Le décor est typiquement provençal dans son utilisation de tissus et couleurs, et est à la fois élégant et accueillant. La plupart de ses chambres surplombent les jardins superbement entretenus avec toute une variété de plantes, fleurs, arbres et fantastiques fontaines, alors que la cuisine typiquement régionale verra ses hôtes revenir encore et encore. Un nouveau système wi-fi et un centre des affaires sont disponibles, ainsi qu'un hammam, une salle de remise en forme et des massages.

Diese wundervolle Bastide Provençale liegt inmitten eines Parks in Aix-en-Provence, knapp 5 Minuten zu Fuß vom Stadtzentrum entfernt. Das Décor aus typisch provenzalischen Stoffen und Farben schafft eine elegante und freundliche Atmosphäre. Viele Zimmer haben Blick auf die herrlich mit den verschiedensten Blumen, Bäumen und faszinierenden Springbrunnen gestalteten Gärten, und die köstliche regionale Küche sorgt dafür, dass Gäste immer wieder hierher kommen. Ein neues Wi-Fi-System und Business-Zentrum sind vorhanden, ebenso ein Dampfbad, Fitnessraum und Massageservice.

Our inspector loved: *The quiet park surrounding this town centre hotel.*

Directions: A8 > exit Pont de l'Arc > follow signs to town centre > after roundabout the hotel is located at the third red light on the left.

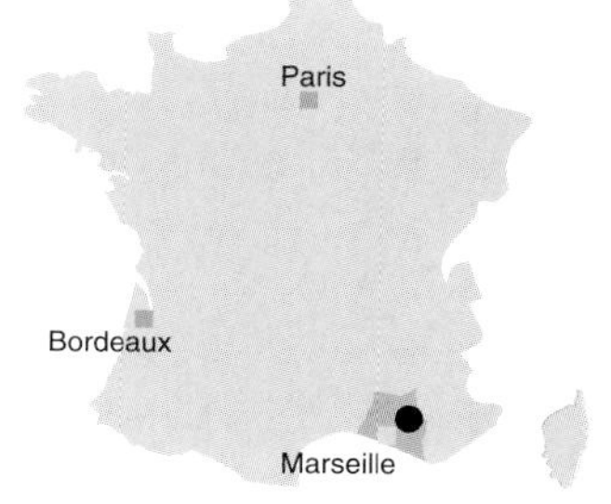

Web: www.johansens.com/lepigonnet
E-mail: reservation@hotelpigonnet.com
Tel: +33 4 42 59 02 90
Fax: +33 4 42 59 47 77

Price Guide:
single €150-300
double €180-400
suite from €500

L'Hôtel Particulier

4 RUE DE LA MONNAIE, 13200 ARLES, FRANCE

This little gem of a hotel lies tucked away in the heart of Arles. A collection of 18th-century buildings clustered around a central courtyard, it is the ultimate in chic sophistication. Just 7 stylish bedrooms, a breathtaking swimming pool and delightful gardens combine with an excellent homemade breakfast and unswerving attention to detail to create a first-class reputation. A new Spa will be built in November.

Ce petit bijou d'hôtel est caché en plein cœur de la ville d'Arles. Un ensemble de bâtiments du XVIIIe siècle entourent une cour centrale, c'est le summum de la sophistication. 7 chambres stylées, une superbe piscine et de ravissants jardins ajoutés à un délicieux petit-déjeuner maison et une constante attention au détail donnent à cet hôtel une réputation de premier ordre. Un nouveau Spa sera construit en novembre.

Dieses kleine Juwel von einem Hotel liegt versteckt im Herzen von Arles und besteht aus einer Ansammlung von Gebäuden aus dem 18. Jahrhundert, die um einen zentralen Innenhof herum angesiedelt sind. Das Hotel bietet ultimativen Chic und Eleganz: Nur 7 edle Zimmer, ein atemberaubender Swimmingpool und herrliche Gärten zusammen mit hervorragendem, hausgemachten Frühstück und nie endender Aufmerksamkeit sorgen für einen absolut erstklassigen Ruf. Im November wird ein neues Spa gebaut.

Our inspector loved: *The bedrooms in the opposite building, with their private terraces.*

Directions: A9/A54 > exit Arles or Arles centre.

Web: www.johansens.com/particulier
E-mail: contact@hotel-particulier.com
Tel: +33 4 90 52 51 40
Fax: +33 4 90 96 16 70

Price Guide: (room only, excluding VAT)
double €159-209
suite €189-279
breakfast €14.50 per person

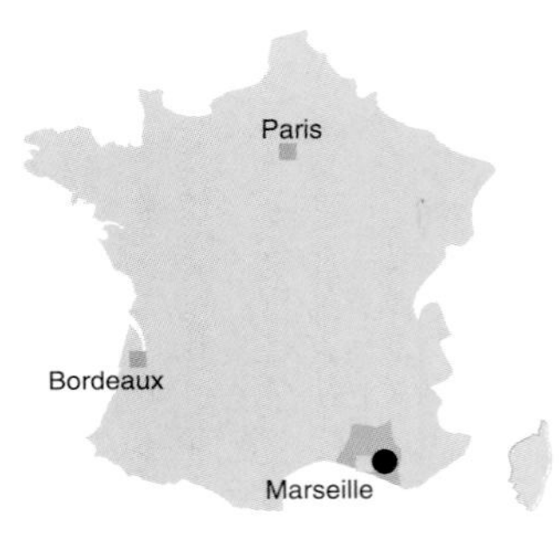

LA BASTIDE DE CAPELONGUE

84480 BONNIEUX~EN~PROVENCE, FRANCE

This beautiful property, set in the heart of the Lubéron region, overlooks the delightful old village of Bonnieux and is surrounded by lavender fields and rolling plains. The attention to detail throughout the hotel is immaculate; the spacious bedrooms are decorated with elegant soft furnishings and neutral pastel tones and offer terrace or balcony. Stunning panoramic views can be enjoyed from the superb restaurant, which overlooks the beautiful garden and its hidden swimming pool.

Cette belle propriété, située au cœur du Lubéron, donne sur le vieux village charmant de Bonnieux et est entourée par des champs de lavande et des pleines onduleuses. L'attention apportée au détail dans tout l'hôtel est impeccable; les chambres spacieuses sont ornées avec des ameublements doux et des tons pastel neutres, et offrent une terrasse ou balcon. On peut jouir de vues panoramiques à couper le souffle depuis le restaurant superbe, qui donne sur le beau jardin et sa piscine cachée.

Dieses wundervolle Hotel befindet sich im Herzen des Lubéron mit Blick auf das hübsche alte Dorf Bonnieux und ist umgeben von Lavendelfeldern und weiten Ebenen. Liebe zum Detail ist überall sichtbar, und die geräumigen Zimmer sind elegant in neutralen Pastelltönen eingerichtet und bieten Terrasse oder Balkon. Vom exquisiten Restaurant hat man einen herrlichen Panoramablick auf den traumhaften Garten und den versteckten Swimmingpool.

Our inspector loved: *The beautiful garden full of lavender, and the breathtaking views.*

Directions: A7 > exit Avignon Sud > Apt. Bonnieux is then signposted.

Web: www.johansens.com/capelongue
E-mail: contact@capelongue.com
Tel: +33 4 90 75 89 78
Fax: +33 4 90 75 93 03

Price Guide: (room only)
double €160-320
junior suite €280-380

17 20

LE CLAIR DE LA PLUME

PLACE DU MAIL, 26230 GRIGNAN, FRANCE

Situated at the foot of an imposing castle in the picturesque village of Grignan, in the heart of the Drôme Provençale, this delightful guesthouse is a true gem and was originally constructed in the 17th century. Breakfast is prepared in a vaulted-ceiling kitchen, the legacy of the monks who founded the site. The charming bedrooms are individually designed with typical Provençal bedcovers and curtains. Grignan with its numerous restaurants and attractions offers plenty of entertainment.

Situé au pied de l'imposant château dans le village médiéval de Grignan, au cœur de la Drôme provençale, cette adorable maison d'hôtes est un véritable joyau construit au XVIIe siècle. Le petit déjeuner est préparé dans la cuisiné voûtée héritage des moines à l'origine des lieux. Les chambres charmantes ont toutes une décoration unique, avec dessus de lits et rideaux typiquement provençaux. De nombreux loisirs sont disponibles a Grignan, avec entre autres de nombreux restaurants.

Am Fuße einer eindrucksvollen Burg im malerischen Dorf Grignan mitten im Drôme Provençale liegt dieses einladende Gästehaus, ein wahres Juwel, das ursprünglich im 17. Jahrhundert erbaut wurde. Das Frühstück wird in einer Küche mit gewölbter Decke zubereitet, ein Andenken an die Mönche, die diese Stätte gründeten. Die zauberhaften Zimmer sind individuell mit typisch provenzalischen Bettdecken und Vorhängen gestaltet. Grignan mit seinen Restaurants und Attraktionen bietet zahlreiche Unterhaltungsmöglichkeiten.

Our inspector loved: *The hotel's intimate atmosphere and the owner's warm welcome.*

Directions: From North > A7 > exit 18 Montelimar Sud > D541 to Nyons > hotel in the heart of Grignan. From South > A7 > exit 19 Bollene > D26 to St Paul 3 châteaux > D59 then D71 to Grignan > hotel in the heart of Grignan.

Web: www.johansens.com/leclairdelaplume
E-mail: plume2@wanadoo.fr
Tel: +33 4 75 91 81 30
Fax: +33 4 75 91 81 31

Price Guide: (breakfast €10)
double €90–165

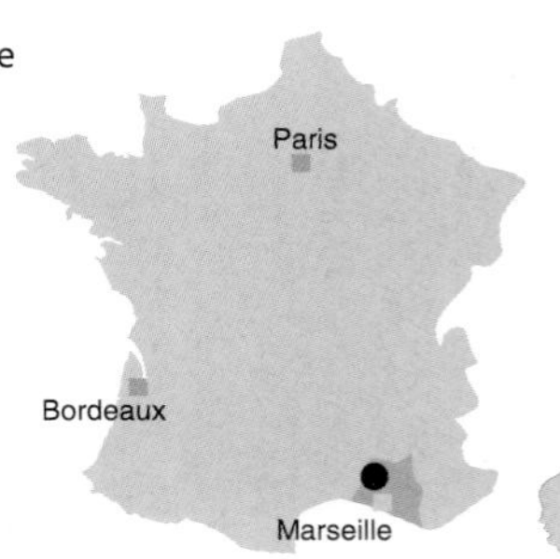

Manoir de la Roseraie

Route de Valréas, 26230 Grignan, France

Situated in the Drôme Provençale and surrounded by 5 acres of lush lawns and gardens that seem to explode into a riot of colours, this is a luxurious and welcoming 19th-century manor. Fusing past and contemporary décor, the interior has been appointed in stylish fabrics and comfortable furnishings. The fresh taste of home-grown vegetables and fruit entices visitors towards the restaurant, where the inspired dishes are complemented by a selection of fine wines.

Situé en Drôme Provençale et entouré de 2 hectares de parc, de pelouses et de jardins qui semblent exploser dans une fête colorée, il s'agît ici d'un accueillant et luxueux manoir du XIXe siècle. Mariant le passé et le présent, la décoration a été arrangée avec de beaux tissus et des meubles confortables. Les légumes et les fruits cultivés sur place ajoutent à l'authenticité du restaurant, où les plats inspirés sont complétés par une sélection de vins fins.

Dieses luxuriöse und einladende Haus aus dem 19. Jahrhundert liegt im Drôme Provençale, inmitten von 2ha grünem Rasen und farbenfrohen Gärten. Vergangenheit vermischt sich mit zeitgenössischem Décor, die Innenräume sind mit stilvollen Stoffen und bequemem Mobiliar eingerichtet. Der köstliche Geschmack von Gemüse und Obst aus eigenem Anbau lockt die Gäste ins Restaurant, wo einfallsreiche Gerichte von einer Auswahl erlesener Weine ergänzt werden.

Our inspector loved: *The magnificent garden with hundreds of different varieties of roses.*

Directions: A7 > Montelimar Sud > Nyons Sud.

Web: www.johansens.com/manoirdelaroseraie
E-mail: roseraie.hotel@wanadoo.fr
Tel: +33 4 75 46 58 15
Fax: +33 4 75 46 91 55

Price Guide:
double/twin €162–213
suite €310–340

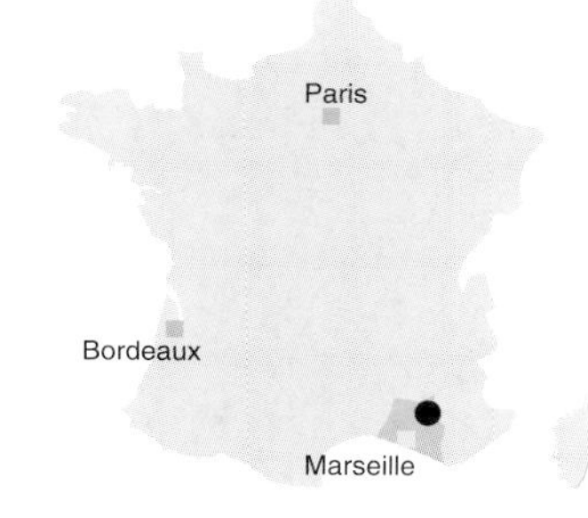

MAS DE L'OULIVIÉ

13520 LES~BAUX~DE~PROVENCE, FRANCE

Directions: 2 km from the village towards Fontvieille/Arles on the D78f secondary road.

Web: www.johansens.com/masdeloulivie
E-mail: contact@masdeloulivie.com
Tel: +33 4 90 54 35 78
Fax: +33 4 90 54 44 31

Price Guide: (breakfast €11-15)
double/twin €100–245
suite €290–410

Surrounded by olive trees, this beautiful and very welcoming "mas provençal" nestles at the bottom of one of the most amazing villages in Provence. All bedrooms are decorated with rustic wood furniture and Provençal fabrics. 2 beautiful suites, one of which has it's own terrace and garden are also available. The stunning pool and Jacuzzi are an oasis of peace, and here, a variety of snacks and salads are served at lunchtime. After a day of sightseeing, this is the perfect place to enjoy the colours and overwhelming scents that are so typical of the region.

Niché au pied de l'un des plus prestigieux villages de Provence, ce beau mas provençal entouré d'oliviers cache une hospitalité cordiale. Toutes les chambres sont agrémentées de meubles en bois rustiques et de tissus provençaux. Deux belles suites, dont l'une s'ouvre sur une terrasse et un jardin privatifs, sont également disponibles. La magnifique piscine et le jacuzzi forment une oasis de paix où sont servies diverses collations légères et salades à midi. Après une journée d'exploration, le mas est l'endroit rêvé pour se laisser griser par les couleurs et les parfums enivrants de la région.

Umgeben von Olivenbäumen liegt dieses zauberhafte "Mas provençal" am Fuße eines der außergewöhnlichsten Dörfer der Provence. Alle Zimmer sind mit rustikalem Mobiliar und provenzalischen Stoffen ausgestattet, und eine der beiden schönen Suiten mit Terrasse besitzt einen eigenen Garten. Der herrliche Pool und Jacuzzi verbreiten eine Atmosphäre der Ruhe, und mittags wird hier eine Vielzahl von Snacks und Salaten serviert. Nach einem langen Erkundungstag ist dies der ideale Ort, um die typischen Farben und Gerüche der Region zu genießen.

Our inspector loved: *The superb swimming pool with its unusual stone features and the Jacuzzi.*

LE MOULIN DE LOURMARIN

84160 LOURMARIN, PROVENCE, FRANCE

This 18th-century former mill is located in the delightful village of Lourmarin in the heart of the Lubéron, and boasts a winning combination of contemporary style within a traditional stone building. Wrought iron blends effortlessly with dark wooden furniture, and the impressive vaulted dining room opens onto a stunning terrace with ancient olive trees. The exquisite cuisine is prepared by Edouard Loubet, the youngest chef in France to be awarded 2 Michelin stars.

Cet ancien moulin datant du XVIIIe siècle est situé dans l'adorable village de Lourmarin au cœur du Lubéron, et s'enorgueillit d'un mélange réussi de style contemporain dans un bâtiment traditionnel en pierre. Les fers forgés se fondent parfaitement avec les bois foncés, et l'impressionnante salle à manger sous voûte ouvre sur une superbe terrasse aux vieux oliviers. La délicieuse cuisine est préparée par Edouard Loubet, le plus jeune chef en France à s'être vu décerner 2 étoiles Michelin.

Diese einstige Mühle aus dem 18. Jahrhundert befindet sich in dem hübschen Dorf Lourmarin im Herzen des Lubéron und bietet eine wundervolle Mischung aus zeitgenössischem Stil in einem traditionellen Steingebäude. Schmiedeeiserne Gegenstände schmiegen sich an Möbel aus dunklem Holz und der eindrucksvolle Speisesaal mit seiner gewölbten Decke öffnet sich auf eine herrliche, von alten Olivenbäumen umgebene Terrasse. Die exquisiten Speisen werden von Edouard Loubet zubereitet, dem jüngsten Koch Frankreichs mit 2 Michelinsternen.

Our inspector loved: *The beautiful public areas on 2 levels and the wheat on the ceiling.*

Directions: A7 > exit Sénas > D973 towards Pertuis > follow the signs to Lourmarin.

Web: www.johansens.com/moulindelourmarin
E-mail: info@moulindelourmarin.com
Tel: +33 4 90 68 06 69
Fax: +33 4 90 68 31 76

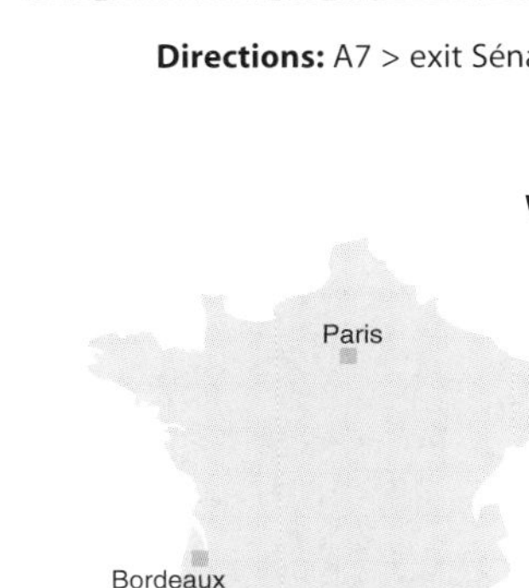

Price Guide: (room only)
double €190-310
suite €430-655

CHÂTEAU DE MAZAN

PLACE NAPOLÉON, 84380 MAZAN, FRANCE

Directions: From the A7 > exit Avignon Nord > Carpentras on D942 > from Carpentras follow Mont Ventoux then Mazan > in Mazan the hotel is in first road on the right.

Web: www.johansens.com/mazan
E-mail: contact@chateaudemazan.fr
Tel: +33 4 90 69 62 61
Fax: +33 4 90 69 76 62

Price Guide: (room only)
double €120-255
suite €255-400

Built in 1720, the hotel is the former residence of the Marquis de Sade. Its setting in the heart of Mazan, a typical Provençal village, is a magnificent park filled with mulberry trees, paths of lavender and centuries old olive trees. Inside, the 30 bedrooms are all individually decorated in a traditional style. Attention to detail is evident everywhere from the high ceilings to the impressive ancient tiled floors dating back to the 19th century. Food is innovative and highlights fresh local ingredients.

Construit en 1720, cet hôtel était la résidence du Marquis de Sade. Sa situation au cœur de Mazan, village provençal typique, est un parc magnifique de mûriers, de chemins de lavande et d'oliviers centenaires. A l'intérieur, les 30 chambres sont toutes individuellement décorées dans le style traditionnel. L'attention au détail est partout évidente, des hauts plafonds aux impressionnants carrelages anciens datant du XIXe siècle. La cuisine est originale et met en valeur les ingrédients frais locaux.

Dieses 1720 erbaute Hotel ist der einstige Wohnsitz des Marquis de Sade. Es liegt inmitten eines herrlichen, mit Maulbeerbäumen, Lavendel und jahrhundertealten Olivenbäumen gefüllten Parks im Herzen von Mazan, einem typisch provenzalischen Dorf. Die 30 Gästezimmer sind unterschiedlich im traditionellen Stil gestaltet, und Liebe zum Detail ist überall sichtbar, von den hohen Decken bis hin zu eindrucksvollen alten Fliesenböden aus dem 19. Jahrhundert. Das Essen ist innovativ und basiert hauptsächlich auf frischen einheimischen Zutaten.

Our inspector loved: *The superb and original bathrooms in the superior garden rooms and suites.*

LE SPINAKER

POINTE DE LA PRESQU'ÎLE, PORT CAMARGUE, 30240 LE GRAU~DU~ROI, FRANCE

Set in the heart of the marina, this idyllic retreat is an oasis of greenery, palm trees and pines in an impressive peninsula location. 21 stylish guest rooms and suites lie scattered around a central swimming pool, each individually decorated and with its own private terrace overlooking the garden or harbour. The restaurant, Le Carré des Gourmets, is blissful, offering an invitation to enjoy the flavours of the south and the sea.

Situé à la pointe d'une presqu'île, le Spinaker est un oasis de verdure, de palmiers et de pins au coeur du port de plaisance. 21 chambres chics et individuellement décorées sont reparties autour de la piscine centrale, chacune avec sa propre terrasse avec vue sur le jardin ou le port. Le restaurant, le Carré des Gourmets, est un enchantement, et une invitation à apprécier les saveurs du Sud et de la mer.

Dieses idyllische, dramatisch auf einer Halbinsel direkt an der Uferpromenade gelegene Anwesen ist eine grüne Oase, umgeben von Palmen und Pinienbäumen. 21 hübsche Zimmer und Suiten sind in Bungalows um einen Swimmingpool herum angeordnet, jeder individuell gestaltet und mit eigener Terrasse mit Blick auf den Garten oder den Hafen. Das Restaurant, Le Carré des Gourmets, ist ein wahres Paradies für Feinschmecker, in dem man die Aromen des Südens und des Meeres genießen kann.

Our inspector loved: *Its perfect location in the middle of Port Camargue.*

Directions: From Nîmes > exit Gallargues. From Montpellier > exit airport. 16km from Montpellier Airport. 45km from Nîmes Airport. The hotel advises guests to rent a car.

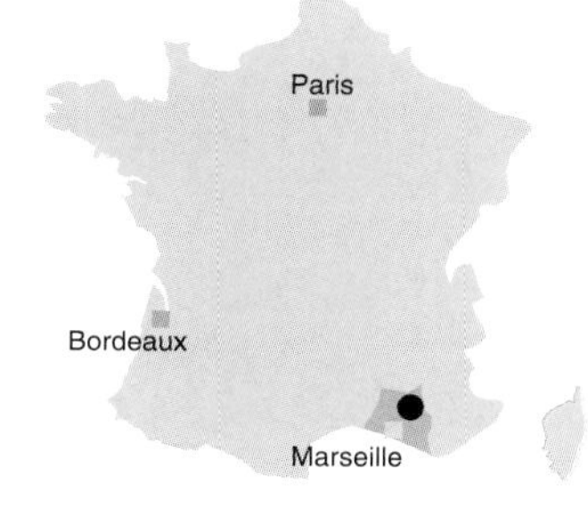

Web: www.johansens.com/spinaker
E-mail: spinaker@wanadoo.fr
Tel: +33 4 66 53 36 37
Fax: +33 4 66 53 17 47

Price Guide: (room only, excluding VAT)
double €109
suite €230
junior suite €135

Château des Alpilles

ROUTE DÉPARTEMENTALE 31, ANCIENNE ROUTE DU GRÈS, 13210 SAINT~RÉMY~DE~PROVENCE, FRANCE

Surrounded by verdant grounds in which rare old trees offer a touch of the exotic, this elegant 19th-century château offers wonderful seclusion. The salons reflect its age-old grandeur, with moulded ceilings, mosaic floors, tapestries and enormous gilt mirrors. Many bedrooms reflect this ancient splendour, whilst some are more contemporary. Adjoining the cosy bar is the dining room, where visitors can enjoy simple regional dishes.

Entouré de terrains verdoyants où de vieux arbres offrent une touche exotique, cet élégant château du XIXe siècle offre une merveilleuse occasion de retraite. La salon reflète la grandeur d'époque, avec moulures, sols en mosaïque, tâpisseries et d'énormes miroirs dorés. La plupart des chambres reflète cette grandeur ancienne, alors que certaines sont plus contemporaines. A côté du bar chaleureux se trouve le restaurant, où les visiteurs peuvent déguster des plats régionaux simples.

Umgeben von einer Parkanlage mit seltenen alten Bäumen bietet dieses elegante Château aus dem 19. Jahrhundert herrliche Abgeschiedenheit. Die Salons spiegeln mit ihren Stuckverzierungen, Mosaikböden, Gobelins und riesigen vergoldeten Spiegeln eine Erhabenheit aus vergangenen Zeiten wider. Einige Zimmer zeigen die gleiche ehrwürdige Pracht, andere sind modern gestaltet. Neben der behaglichen Bar können die Gäste einfache, regionale Gerichte im Speisesaal genießen.

Our inspector loved: *The superb park surrounding the château, with its swimming pool and tennis courts.*

Directions: D31 > Tarascon.

Web: www.johansens.com/chateaudesalpilles
E-mail: chateau.alpilles@wanadoo.fr
Tel: +33 4 90 92 03 33
Fax: +33 4 90 92 45 17

Price Guide:
single €180
double/twin €180–230
suite €258–360

Les Demeures du Ranquet

TORNAC, 30140 ANDUZE, FRANCE

This skilfully restored mansion offers visitors a combination of charm, relaxation and comfort with the traditional, rustic and contemporary in a beautiful countryside location, within easy reach of many tourist attractions. The lovely, dry-stone built main building houses a delightful, beamed restaurant overlooking the garden and swimming pool and serving excellent local and Mediterranean-inspired cuisine. 4 lodges within the grounds have every amenity, together with terrace and private entrance.

Cette demeure, habilement restaurée, marie le charme, la relaxation et le confort avec le traditionnel, le rustique et le contemporain dans un cadre magnifique de campagne et à proximité des attractions touristiques. Le ravissant restaurant aux poutres apparentes se trouve dans le bâtiment principal construit en pierres sèches et a vue sur la piscine et le jardin. On y sert une délicieuse cuisine d'inspiration locale et méditerranéenne. Les chambres sont dans des lodges répartis dans le domaine et possèdent tous les équipements, une terrasse et une entrée privée.

Diese kunstvoll restaurierte Residenz bietet ihren Gästen eine Mischung aus Charme, Entspannung und Komfort und traditionellem, rustikalen, zeitgenössischen Stil in herrlich ländlicher Lage, unweit zahlreicher Attraktionen. Das hübsche, steinerne Hauptebäude beherbergt ein bezauberndes Restaurant mit Blick auf den Garten und den Swimmingpool, wo hervorragende einheimische und Mittelmeerküche serviert wird. 4 kleinere Häuser auf dem Grundstück bieten jeglichen Komfort sowie Terrasse und eigenen Eingang.

Our inspector loved: *The glass ceiling wine cellar beneath the restaurant.*

Directions: A7 > exit Bollène > follow Alès > follow Anduze > follow signs.
A9 > exit Lunel > follow Sommières > follow Quissac > follow signs.

Web: www.johansens.com/ranquet
E-mail: ranquet@tiscali.fr
Tel: +33 4 66 77 51 63
Fax: +33 4 66 77 55 62

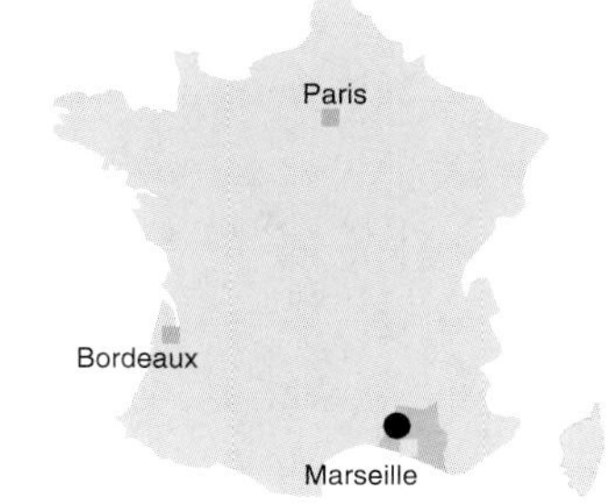

Price Guide: (room only, excluding VAT)
single €95-150
double €120-190

LE BEAU RIVAGE

2 RUE DU BEAU-RIVAGE, 69420 CONDRIEU, FRANCE

On the banks of the Rhône, close to the vineyards of Condrieu and the hills of Côtes Roties, this former fishermen,s house has been magnificently renovated and extended. Each guest room, some with private terraces, is individually furnished and decorated with fresh flowers. Lyonnaise-style cuisine, created from local produce, is accompanied by the finest wines of the Rhône Valley in the spacious restaurant. Alfresco dining is available during the summer months. Explore the garden or relax in the bar, lounge or terrace whilst admiring the serene surroundings.

Sur les rives du Rhône, proche des vignobles de Condrieu et collines des Côtes Roties, cette ancienne maison de pêcheurs a été magnifiquement rénovée et agrandie. Chaque chambre, dont certaines avec terrasses privées, est individuellement meublée et décorée de fleurs fraîches. Une cuisine de style lyonnaise conçue à partir de produits frais et accompagnée de vins de premier choix est servie dans le spacieux restaurant. Il est possible de dîner à l'extérieur pendant les mois d'été. Les hôtes peuvent se promener dans le jardin ou se relaxer au bar, au salon ou sur la terrasse en admirant les alentours.

Am Ufer der Rhône, nahe der Weinberge von Condrieu und der Hügel der Côtes Roties befindet sich dieses einstige Fischerhaus, das herrlich renoviert und erweitert wurde. Alle Zimmer, manche mit eigener Terrasse, sind individuell eingerichtet und mit frischen Blumen geschmückt. Aus einheimischen Zutaten zubereitete Lyonnaiser Speisen werden mit edlen Weinen des Rhône-Tales im großzügigen Restaurant serviert, und im Sommer wird im Freien diniert. Im Garten, in der Bar, dem Aufenthaltsraum und auf der Terrasse entspannt man sich mit Blick auf die herrliche Umgebung.

Our inspector loved: *The newly renovated suites with views of the river.*

Directions: A7 > exit Condrieu > follow signs.

Web: www.johansens.com/beaurivage
E-mail: infos@hotel-beaurivage.com
Tel: +33 4 74 56 82 82
Fax: +33 4 74 59 59 36

Price Guide: (including VAT)
double €90-125
suite €135-210

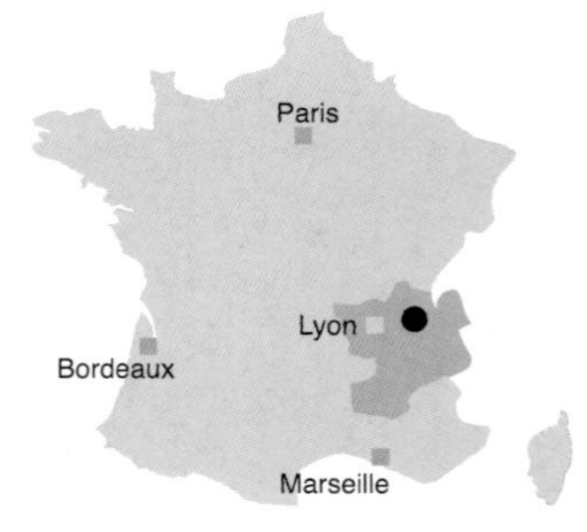

La Sivolière

73120 COURCHEVEL 1850, FRANCE

Set amidst stunning landscape right next to a forest with direct access to the slopes of Courchevel, this hotel consists of a group of typical Savoy stone and wood chalets. The individually decorated rooms, suites and flats are extremely comfortable; some have fireplaces and balconies. Delicious regional dishes are served in the welcoming restaurant, with large windows overlooking the snow-covered pine trees. There is a special ski room to warm ski shoes, rent equipment and book courses, and after a day on the slopes guests can relax in the fitness centre with sauna and massage service.

Situé au cœur de superbes paysages, à l'orée d'une forêt et avec un accès direct aux pistes de Courchevel, cet hôtel est composé de plusieurs chalets savoyards en pierres et en bois. Les chambres, suites et appartements individuellement décorées sont extrêmement confortables et certaines ont cheminées et balcons. De délicieux plats régionaux sont servis dans l'accueillant restaurant d'où l'on peut admirer les sapins enneigés à travers les grandes baies vitrées. Il y a un ski room pour réchauffer ses chaussures, louer son équipement et réserver des cours. Après une journée sur les skis, les hôtes peuvent se relaxer au centre de remise en forme avec sauna ou se faire masser.

Dieses inmitten herrlicher Landschaft neben einem Wald mit direktem Zugang zu den Pisten von Courchevel gelegene Hotel besteht aus regionstypischen Chalets aus Holz und Stein. Die unterschiedlich gestalteten Zimmer, Suiten und Appartements, einige mit Kamin und Balkon, sind sehr komfortabel. Im Restaurant mit Blick auf schneebedeckte Kiefern werden regionale Köstlichkeiten serviert. Es gibt einen Skiraum, wo man seine Stiefel wämen, Ausrüstung leihen und Kurse buchen kann, und nach einem Tag auf der Piste bietet das Fitness-Zentrum mit Sauna und Massagen Entspannung.

Our inspector loved: *The games room and dining room dedicated to children.*

Directions: Located on the border of a forest near the centre of Courchevel.

Web: www.johansens.com/silvoliere
E-mail: lasivoliere@wanadoo.com
Tel: +33 4 79 08 08 33
Fax: +33 4 79 08 15 73

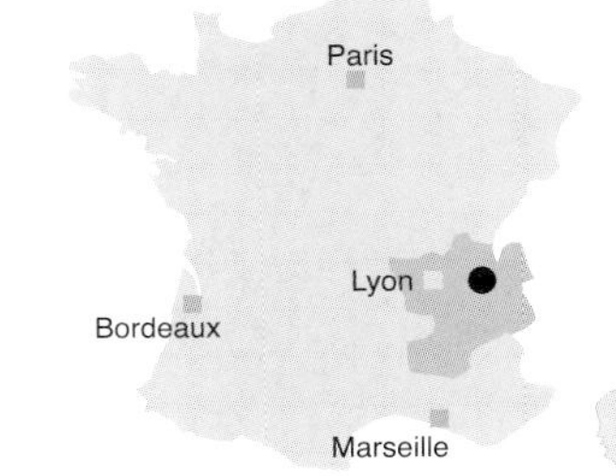

Price Guide: (room only, excluding VAT)
double €250-660
suite €900-1,700
flat €2,200

  40    20      

CHÂTEAU DE DIVONNE

01220 DIVONNE~LES~BAINS, FRANCE

Directions: A6 > A40 > exit Bellegarde > Gex / Divonne.

Web: www.johansens.com/chateaudedivonne
E-mail: divonne@grandesetapes.fr
Tel: +33 4 50 20 00 32
Fax: +33 4 50 20 03 73

Price Guide:
single €140–310
double €140–310
suite €380–430

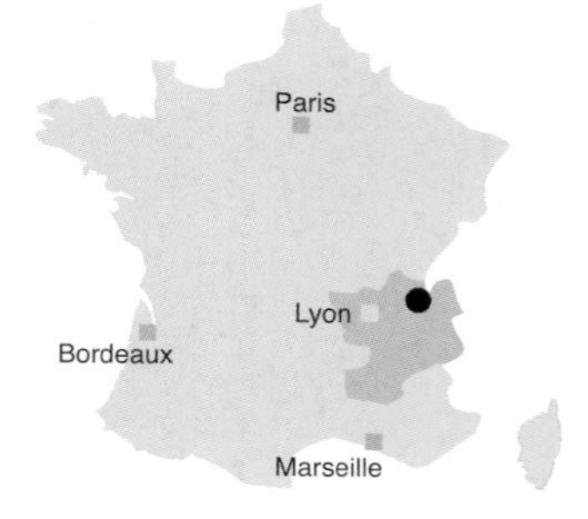

Standing proudly on a small hill and surrounded by 22 hectares of lush parkland, this is a luxurious and welcoming 19th-century gourmet hotel that offers peace, tranquillity and spectacular lake and mountain views. Delightfully fusing the traditional and the modern, the interior is appointed in stylish décor, fabrics and furniture, with each bright and spacious guest room individually and elegantly furnished to the highest standard.

Ce luxueux et accueillant hôtel gastronomique du XIXe siècle qui se tient fièrement sur une petite colline et est entouré de 22 hectares de parc luxuriant, offre paix, tranquillité et des vues spectaculaires sur le lac et la montagne. Mélangeant de manière délicieuse le traditionnel et le moderne, la décoration intérieure, les tissus et meubles sont élégants et les chambres lumineuses et spacieuses sont individuellement décorées selon les plus hauts standards.

In stolzer Lage auf einer Anhöhe und umgeben von 22ha üppiger Parklandschaft, bietet dieses einladende und luxuriöse Gourmethotel aus dem 19. Jahrhundert absolute Ruhe und atemberaubende Blicke auf See und Berge. Das Interieur, eine attraktive Mischung aus traditionell und modern, ist mit stilvollen Stoffen und Möbeln gestaltet, und jedes der hellen und geräumigen Zimmer ist individuell und elegant eingerichtet und bietet höchsten Komfort.

Our inspector loved: *The large terrace with amazing views over the French Alps and Mont Blanc.*

LE DOMAINE DE DIVONNE CASINO, GOLF & SPA RESORT

AVENUE DES THERMES, 01220 DIVONNE-LES-BAINS, FRANCE

The Domaine de Divonne is one of the most exclusive French resorts, the nearest to Geneva and the Swiss border. The magnificent estate consists of a 1930 art deco residence, the Grand Hotel, an 18-hole golf course, a casino and a night club. The elegant guest rooms offer balconies overlooking the Alps or Jura mountains and state-of-the-art technology. 5 restaurants, including the 1 Michelin star La Terrasse, offer a diversity of cuisine. The Atelier de Beauté Anne Sémonin offers a wide range of treatments.

Le Domaine de Divonne est un resort unique en France. C'est également le plus proche de Genève et de la frontière suisse. Cet éstablissement de grand luxe, dans un style art déco des anées 30, réunit Le Grand Hôtel, un golf 18 trous, un casino et une discothèque. Les chambres luxueuses disposent de balcons avec vue sur les Alpes et le Jura et un équipement technique trés complet. Il y a 5 restaurants, dont La Terrasse a l'étoile Michelin. L'Ateleir de Beaute Anne Sémonin offre des soins personnalisés et relaxants.

Domaine de Divonne, eines der exklusivsten Resorts in Frankreich, nahe bei Genf und der Schweizer Grenze. Das luxuriöse Anwesen im 30er Jahre Art-Déco-Stil besteht aus dem Grand Hotel, einem 18-Loch Golfplatz, Casino und einem Nightclub. Die eleganten Zimmer bieten Balkon mit Blick auf die Alpen und modernste Technologie. 5 Restaurants stehen zur Auswahl, darunter das mit 1 Michelin-Stern ausgezeichnete La Terrasse. Zahlreiche Behandlungen sind im Atelier de Beauté Anne Sémonin geboten.

Our inspector loved: *The wide range of activities available especially the spa.*

Directions: N1 from Geneva > Coppet/Divonne exit.

Web: www.johansens.com/domainededivonne
E-mail: info@domaine-de-divonne.com
Tel: +33 4 50 40 34 34
Fax: +33 4 50 40 34 24

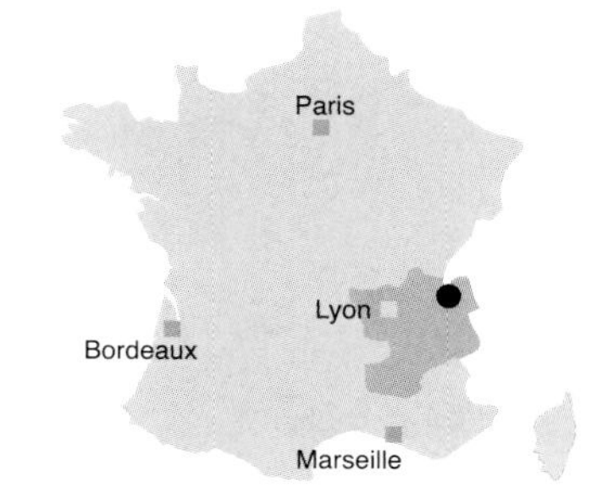

Price Guide:
single €195–275
double/twin €270–360
suite €485–2,850

Chalet Hôtel La Marmotte

61 RUE DU CHÊNE, 74260 LES GÊTS, FRANCE

Situated amidst the beautiful alpine trails and ski slopes of the French Alps, the very family-orientated La Marmotte is friendly and cosy and the perfect base from which to explore this exciting region. Guests of all ages will appreciate the range of activities, including on-site gym, indoor swimming pool, spa and beauty facilities. Exhilarating ski slopes, golf courses and Lac de Baignade are nearby, and lively Les Gets with its shops and restaurants is within easy reach of other "Portes du Soleil" ski resorts.

Au pied des pistes de ski et des sentiers pédestres des Alpes, vous attend un grand chalet convivial et confortable, la base parfaite pour explorer une région fascinante. Idéal pour les familles, cet hôtel offre des activités aux visiteurs de tout âge, qui peuvent profiter notamment du gymnase, de la piscine couverte, du spa et du centre de beauté. Pistes grisantes, golfs et lac de baignade ne sont qu'à deux pas. Et si l'animation des Gets, avec ses restaurants et ses magasins, ne vous suffit pas, vous pouvez facilement accéder aux autres stations des "Portes du Soleil".

Umgeben von herrlichen Wanderwegen und Skipisten der französischen Alpen bietet das freundliche, familienorientierte Hotel La Marmotte den perfekten Ausgangspunkt, um diese faszinierende Gegend zu erforschen. Gäste aller Altersstufen nutzen das umfassende Freizeitangebot, wie Fitnessraum, Hallenbad, Spa und Schönheitsfarm. Traumhafte Abfahrten, Golfplätze und der Lac de Baignade sind in der Nähe, und vom lebhaften Les Gets mit seinen Restaurants und Geschäften sind auch andere "Portes du Soleil" Skigebiete leicht erreichbar.

Our inspector loved: *The indoor swimming pool overlooking the ski slopes.*

Directions: Leave the A40 and exit at Cluses.

Web: www.johansens.com/chaletlamarmotte
E-mail: info@hotel-marmotte.com
Tel: + 33 4 50 75 80 33
Fax: +33 4 50 75 83 26

Price Guide: (half-board, excluding VAT)
double/twin €99–185

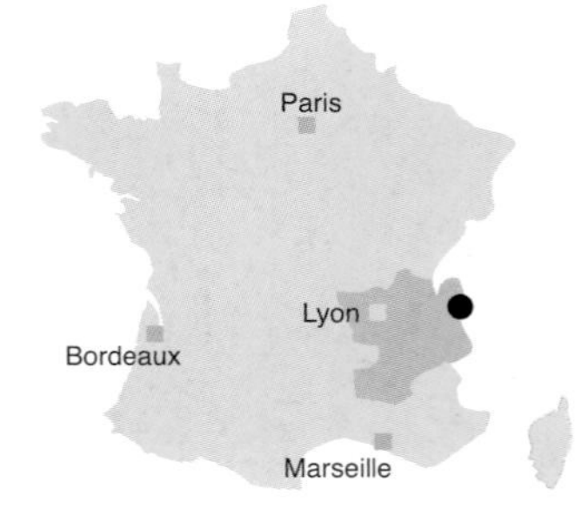

La Tour Rose

22 RUE DU BOEUF, 69005 LYON, FRANCE

Boasting a Tuscan garden with terraces, waterfalls and ornamental pools, this striking collection of 3 Renaissance buildings is perhaps Lyon's most luxurious hotel. Each of the suites has been designed by one of Lyon's most famous silk manufacturers. A former chapel, leading onto a terrace, the restaurant serves classically-inspired nouvelle cuisine. Afterwards, visitors can relax in the stylish bar or one of the sun-lit gardens.

La Tour Rose a pour cadre un jardin toscan avec terrasses, cascades et bassins d'agrément. Ses 3 bâtiments Renaissance composent probablement l'un des hôtels les plus luxueux de Lyon. Chaque suite a été décorée par de célèbres fabricants de soie. Le restaurant, jadis une chapelle, mène à la terrasse et sert une cuisine nouvelle teintée de classicisme. Les visiteurs pourront également se relaxer dans le bar stylé ou dans un des jardins ensoleillés.

Mit seinem toskanischen Garten, herrlichen Terrassen, Wasserfällen und farbenfrohen Teichen ist dieser eindrucksvolle Komplex aus 3 Renaissancebauten das wohl luxuriöseste Hotel in Lyon. Jede der Suiten wurde von einem bekannten Lyoner Seidenfabrikanten entworfen. Das Restaurant, eine ehemalige Kapelle, führt auf eine Terrasse und serviert moderne und doch klassisch inspirierte Gerichte, und die Gäste können sich in der eleganten Bar oder in einem der sonnigen Gärten vergnügen.

Our inspector loved: *Its ideal location in the heart of the old town, perfect to explore Lyon's historic treasures.*

Directions: Vieux-Lyon.

Web: www.johansens.com/tourrose
E-mail: contact@tour-rose.com
Tel: +33 4 78 92 69 10
Fax: +33 4 78 42 26 02

Price Guide: (breakfast €18)
double/twin €230–290
suite €335–540

FRANCE / RHÔNE~ALPES (MEGÈVE)

Le Fer à Cheval

36 ROUTE DU CRÊT D'ARBOIS, 74120 MEGÈVE, FRANCE

This stunning hotel is composed of 4 traditional chalets that form a tiny village within the heart of Megève Ski Resort. The warm timber interior, with magnificent beams and roaring fireplaces, creates a cosy haven after a day on the slopes. Friendly staff, who are dedicated to the well-being of their guests, give a hearty welcome from the moment guests step in the door, and 2 superb restaurants offer a fantastic gastronomic experience featuring local dishes and sophisticated flavours.

Ce superbe hôtel, au cœur de la station de Megève, est composé de 4 chalets traditionnels formant un petit village. L'intérieur tout en bois est chaleureux, de magnifiques poutres et de beaux feux de bois créent un refuge confortable après une journée sur les pistes. Un personnel aimable et attentif au bien être des clients accueille chaleureusement les hôtes dés leur arrivée. Les 2 superbes restaurants proposent une réelle expérience gastronomique à partir de mets locaux et de saveurs raffinées.

Dieses herrliche Hotel besteht aus 4 traditionellen Chalets, die ein eigenes kleines Dorf innerhalb des Skiresorts von Megève bilden. Das gemütliche Holzinterieur schafft mit seinen wundervollen Holzbalken und offenen Kaminen eine erholsame Oase am Ende eines langen Tages auf der Piste, und das freundliche Personal erfüllt den Gästen vom Betreten des Hotels an jeden erdenklichen Wunsch. 2 hervorragende Restaurants sorgen mit einheimischen Zutaten und raffinierten Beigaben für exquisiten kulinarischen Genuss.

Our inspector loved: *Suite 52, with 2 bedrooms and private fireplace.*

Directions: Take the A40 or A43 to Megève.

Web: www.johansens.com/cheval
E-mail: fer-a-cheval@wanadoo.fr
Tel: +33 4 50 21 30 39
Fax: +33 4 50 93 07 60

Price Guide: (excluding VAT)
single €152-230
double €115-198
suite upon request

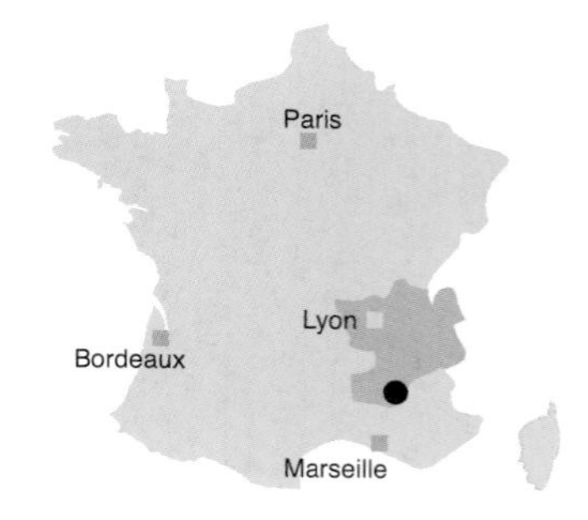

DOMAINE DE FONTANELLE

CHEMIN DE LA ROSE, 01480 SAVIGNEUX, FRANCE

This beautifully renovated 17th-century manor house, with its tree-like roof, long shaded balcony and luxurious rural interior, nestles in the heart of a 20-acre estate close to the gastronomical city of Lyon and the vineyards of Beaujolais and Burgundy. An ideal retreat for the discerning traveller seeking tranquillity, classical charm and the utmost comfort. 5 individually themed suites have every amenity from Jacuzzi to personal computer. There is a heated outdoor swimming pool, tennis court and superb wine cellar.

Cette superbe métairie restaurée du XVIIe siècle, dont les balcons ombragés sont soutenus par de majestueuses poutres, offre luxe et charme rural. Niché au cœur d'un domaine de 8 hectares, proche de la gastronomie de Lyon et des vignobles du Beaujolais et de la Bourgogne, c'est un refuge idéal pour le voyageur averti en quête de tranquillité et de charme dans le plus grand confort. Les 5 suites aux décors et thèmes différents offrent le must de l'équipement du jacuzzi à l'ordinateur personnel. Il y a également une piscine extérieure chauffée, court de tennis et une magnifique cave à vins.

Dieses traumhaft restaurierte Herrenhaus aus dem 17. Jahrhundert mit seinem hohen, baumartigen Dach, langem schattigen Balkon und luxuriösem ländlichen Interieur liegt inmitten eines 8ha großen Grundstücks nahe der gastronomisch bekannten Stadt Lyon und der Beaujolais- und Burgunder Weinberge. Der ideale Ort für den anspruchsvollen Gast, der Ruhe, klassischen Charme und höchsten Komfort sucht. Die 5 individuell gestalteten Suiten bieten alles vom Jacuzzi bis hin zum PC. Ein beheiztes Freibad, ein Tennisplatz und ein herausragender Weinkeller stehen zur Verfügung.

Our inspector loved: *The feeling of being in a private house whilst being treated like a VIP.*

Directions: A6 > exit Villefranches/Saône > signs to Jassans > D904 to Savigneux. Limousine transfer is available.

Web: www.johansens.com/fontanelle
E-mail: fontanelle@theclementcollection.com
Tel: +33 4 74 08 12 15
Fax: +33 4 74 08 12 16

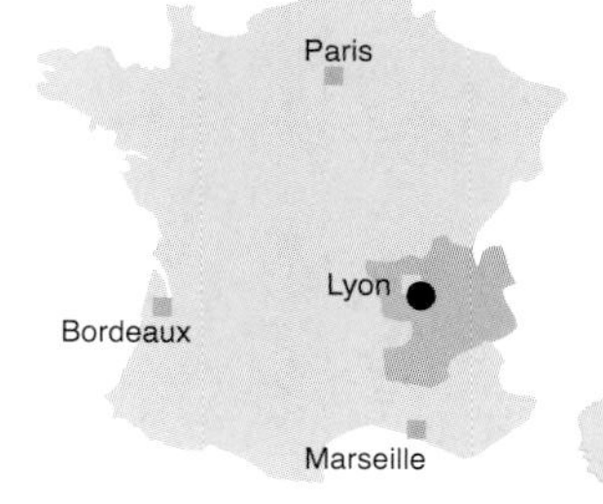

Price Guide:
suite €400-1,200

Château de Coudrée

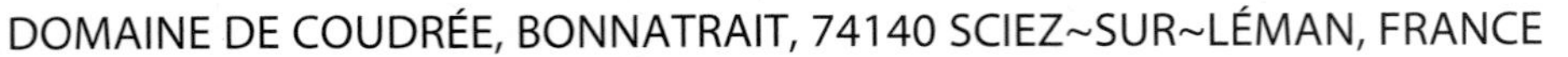

DOMAINE DE COUDRÉE, BONNATRAIT, 74140 SCIEZ~SUR~LÉMAN, FRANCE

Perched on the edge of Lake Geneva, this 12th-century château with its turrets and pinnacles offers a truly fairy tale experience. With a mere 19 guest rooms, all furnished with antiques, this is an elite hotel. Exquisite salons, and a big terrace overlooking the pool and gardens down to the water's edge all contribute to the visitors' overall pleasure. A memorable gastronomic experience is also guaranteed.

Niché sur les bords du Lac de Genève, ce château du XIIe siècle avec ses 19 chambres meublées d'antiquités, offre une vision de conte de fée, avec ses tourelles et ses donjons. Des salons raffinés, un bar accueillant, une grande terrasse avec vue sur la piscine et le jardin descendant jusqu'au bord du lac rendent les séjours encore plus agréables. Une mémorable expérience gastronomique est également garantie.

Am Ufer des Genfer Sees gelegen bietet dieses Château aus dem 12. Jahrhundert mit seinen Türmen und Zinnen einen märchenhaften Aufenthalt. Mit nur 19 Zimmern, alle mit erlesenen Antiquitäten möbliert, ist Exklusivität garantiert. Herrliche Salons, eine große Terrasse mit Blick über den Pool und ein Garten bis zum Seeufer schaffen ein Gefühl der totalen Entspannung. Die Küche verspricht gastronomischen Hochgenuss.

Our inspector loved: *Its fantastic location on the shore of Lake Geneva, with its private boating stage and amazing views.*

Directions: A40 > Annemasse/Thonon/Evian > Sciez Bonnatrait.

Web: www.johansens.com/decoudree
E-mail: chcoudree@coudree.com
Tel: +33 4 50 72 62 33
Fax: +33 4 50 72 57 28

Price Guide:
single/double/twin €120.45–327.80
apartment €280.55–344.55

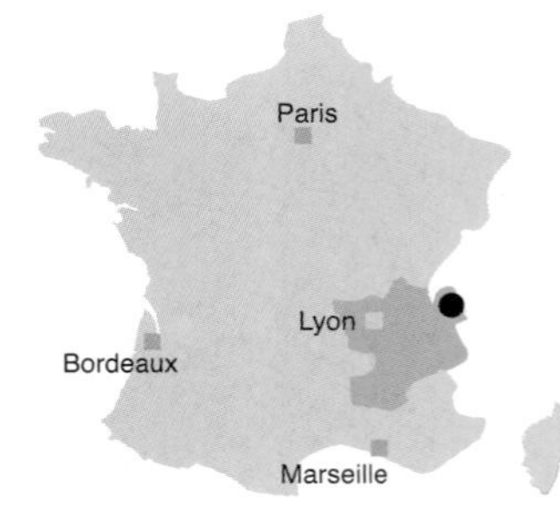

L'Auberge du Choucas

05220 MONÊTIER~LES~BAINS, SERRE~CHEVALIER, HAUTES~ALPES, FRANCE

This 17th-century mountain farmhouse is situated in an old Alpine village, on the edge of the Écrins National Park, in the Serre-Chevalier skiing area and offers many activities both in winter and summer. It is a warm and charming family-run hotel just a few minutes' walk from the foot of the ski slopes. The friendly ambience is enhanced by big log fires in the winter and the aroma of high living – herbs, flowers, wines and cooking. Many of the light and airy bedrooms, with their Alpine-style décor, have balconies. The Auberge restaurant serves inventive and delicious cuisine.

Cette ferme de montagne du XVIIe siècle est située dans un vieux village alpin, sur les bords du Parc National des Ecrins, au cœur du domaine skiable de Serre Chevalier. De nombreuses activités y sont proposées été comme hiver. Ce charmant et accueillant hôtel de famille n'est qu'à quelques minutes à pieds des pistes de ski. L'ambiance amicale est accrue par les grands feux de cheminée en hiver et par les arômes d'herbes, de fleurs, de vins et de cuisine. Les chambres claires et douillettes sont décorées dans un style montagnard et possèdent pour la plupart des balcons. Une cuisine délicieuse et inventive est servie à l'auberge.

Dieses Bergbauernhaus aus dem 17. Jahrhundert liegt in einem alten Alpendorf am Rande des Écrins Nationalparks. Das im Skigebiet von Serre-Chevalier gelegene herzliche familiengeführte Haus bietet sommers wie winters zahlreiche Aktivitäten und ist nur ein paar Minuten von den Skipisten entfernt. Die freundliche Atmosphäre wird durch offene Kaminfeuer im Winter und den herrlichen Duft von Kräutern, Blumen, Wein und Kochen noch verstärkt. Viele der hellen und luftigen im Alpenstil eingerichteten Zimmer bieten einen eigenen Balkon. Im Auberge werden einfallsreiche Köstlichkeiten serviert.

Our inspector loved: *The family atmosphere, very warm welcome, and the gastronomic cooking.*

Directions: Between Grenoble and Briançon. Follow signs for Monêtier-les-Bains and the farmhouse is behind the church opposite the town hall.

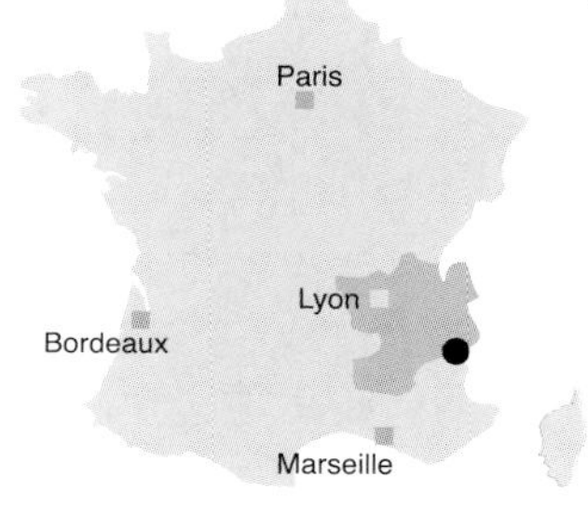

Web: www.johansens.com/laubergeduchoucas
E-mail: auberge.du.choucas@wanadoo.fr
Tel: +33 4 92 24 42 73
Fax: +33 4 92 24 51 60

Price Guide:
single €116–166
double/twin €130–190
suite €190–270

HÔTEL DU PALAIS

1 AVENUE DE L'IMPÉRATRICE, 64200 BIARRITZ, FRANCE

Directions: The hotel is situated in the centre of Biarritz. The nearest airport is Biarritz. Biarritz TGV station and Bordeaux Airport are 2 hours away. Bilbao, Spain is 2 hours away. San Sebastian is 30 minutes away.

Web: www.johansens.com/palais
E-mail: manager@hotel-du-palais.com
Tel: +33 5 59 41 64 00
Fax: +33 5 59 41 67 99

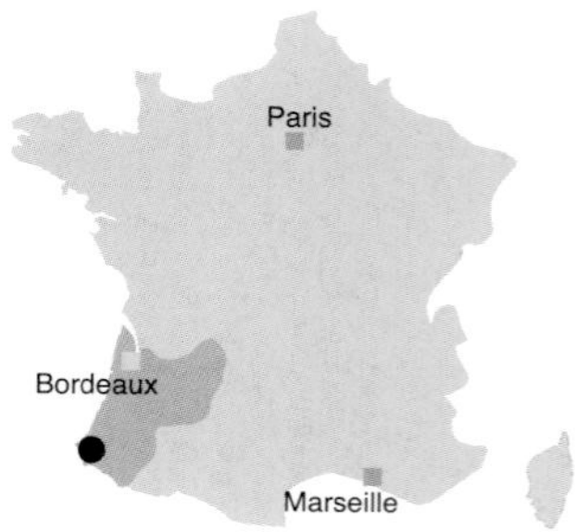

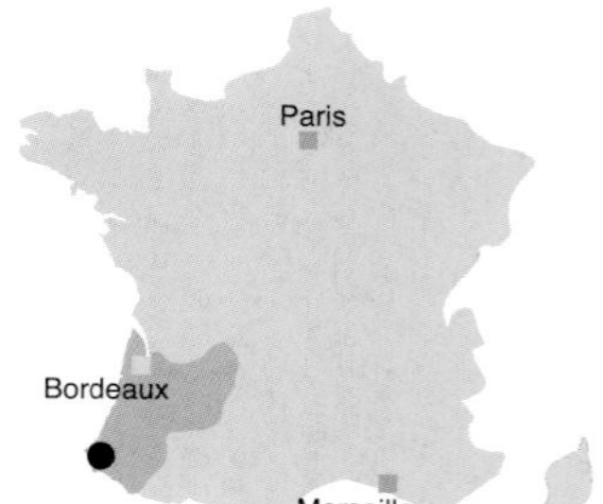

Price Guide: (room only, excluding VAT)
single €260–435
double/twin €370–520
suite €520–1,370
royal suite upon application

The auspicious history of this exceptional waterfront residence echoes proudly today. Marble pillars and glistening chandeliers adorn its palatial foyer and exquisite antique furniture is set throughout the sophisticated bars and luxurious bedrooms. One of the 2 new opulent Royal Suites also boasts an ocean view. Built by request of Napoleon III for his wife Eugénie in 1855, the hotel offers a dazzling range of entertainment. The elegance of its 1 Michelin Star restaurant is worthy of the many notable guests who have chosen this magnificent hotel as their summer retreat.

Cadeau impérial de Napoléon III à son épouse Eugénie, cette somptueuse demeure, construite sur le front de mer en 1855, témoigne d'un riche passé. Des colonnes de marbre et des lustres scintillants ornent le hall grandiose, et des meubles anciens raffinés agrémentent les bars élégants et les chambres luxueuses. Une des nouvelles suites royales luxueuses s'enorgueillit d'une vue sur la mer. L'hôtel offre en outre un choix impressionnant de loisirs. Quant à l'élégant restaurant une étoile Michelin, il est digne des nombreux hôtes prestigieux qui ont fait de ce palais leur résidence d'été.

Dieses prächtige, direkt am Wasser gelegene Anwesen ist reich an Geschichte – Napoleon III. baute es 1855 für seine Gemahlin Eugénie. Marmorsäulen und glänzende Lüster zieren das palastartige Foyer, und die eleganten Bars und luxuriösen Schlafzimmer sind mit erlesenen antiken Möbeln gefüllt. Eine der neuen Royal Luxussuiten bietet Blick auf das Meer. Umfassende Freizeitmöglichkeiten stehen zur Verfügung, und das elegante 1 Michelin Stern Restaurant begeistert die zahlreichen Gäste, die sich dieses superbe Hotel als "Sommerresidenz" ausgewählt haben.

Our inspector loved: *The grandeur of this palatial hotel.*

Château de Sanse

33350 SAINTE~RADEGONDE, FRANCE

Situated in the Bordeaux region, only 20 minutes from the famous vineyards of Saint-Emilion, this charming château is surrounded by a 5-ha estate. Bright and airy living rooms create a wonderfully comfortable ambience. The extremely spacious bedrooms are decorated with simple, light colours and many have direct access to a private balcony or terrace with views over Gensac or the Dordogne valley. In the new air-conditioned terrace restaurant guests can enjoy local specialities featuring fresh produce, much of which is grown in the private garden.

Situé dans le Bordelais, à seulement 20 minutes des célèbres vignobles de Saint-Emilion, cet établissement de charme est entouré d'un parc de 5ha. Ses pièces lumineuses et aérées créent une ambiance merveilleusement confortable. Les chambres spacieuses à la décoration raffinée et personnalisée ont pour la plupart un accès direct à un balcon privé ou une terrasse avec vue sur Gensac et la vallée de la Dordogne. L'espace restaurant climatisé et sa terrasse permettront aux hôtes d'apprécier les spécialités locales cuisinées avec les produits frais, la plupart provenant du jardin potager.

Dieses charmante, von 5ha Land umgebene Château befindet sich in Bordeaux, nur 20 Minuten von den berühmten Saint-Emilion Weinbergen entfernt. Helle, luftige Aufenthaltsräume schaffen eine entspannende Atmosphäre, und die geräumigen Zimmer sind in einfachen, sanften Farben gehalten; einige haben direkten Zugang auf einen eigenen Balkon oder Terrasse mit Blick auf Gensac oder das Dordognetal. Im neuen, klimatisierten Restaurant mit Terrasse werden einheimische Spezialitäten serviert, für die frische, meist im eigenen Garten angebaute Zutaten verwendet werden.

Our inspector loved: *The beautiful suites with their open-plan bathrooms.*

Directions: Bordeaux > N89 > Libourne > D936 > Castillon La Bataille > D17 > Pujols > D18 > Gensac.

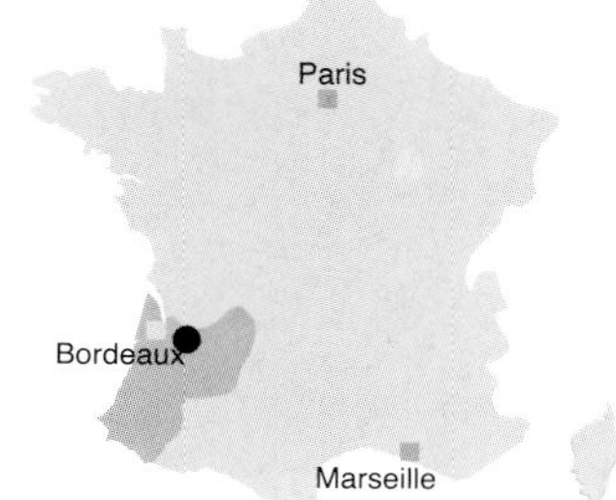

Web: www.johansens.com/chateaudesanse
E-mail: contact@chateaudesanse.com
Tel: +33 5 57 56 41 10
Fax: +33 5 57 56 41 29

Price Guide: (breakfast €12)
double/twin €100-135
suite €165-195

Château des Briottières

49330 CHAMPIGNÉ, FRANCE

Surrounded by 360 acres of parkland "à l'anglaise", this magnificent family-owned stately home is set in the heart of peaceful Anjou. The luxurious interior, with its pervading air of serenity, features Louis XV antiques and quirky memorabilia. The immaculately presented bedrooms have windows overlooking the estate, inviting the rich perfumes of herbs and flowers. Traditional Anjou meals are served in the impressive period dining room.

Entouré d'un jardin anglais de 150ha, cette magnifique maison familiale est en plein coeur de la paisible région d'Anjou. L'intérieur luxueux dégage une ambiance sereine et présente des pièces Louis XV et des objets de collection. Les chambres immaculées donnent sur le domaine et laissent entrer le doux parfum des herbes aromatiques et des fleurs. Les repas traditionnels d'Anjou sont servis dans l'ancienne salle à manger impressionnante.

Umgeben von 150 ha Parklandschaft „à l'anglaise" liegt dieses prächtige, im Familienbesitz befindliche Herrenhaus im Herzen des friedlichen Anjou. Die luxuriöse Inneneinrichtung mit Antiquitäten aus der Zeit Louis XV. schafft eine ruhige Atmosphäre. Die perfekt gestalteten Zimmer bieten einen Blick über das Gut und durch die Fenster strömt der Duft von Kräutern und Blumen. Die traditionsreiche Küche des Anjou wird im eindrucksvollen Speisezimmer serviert.

Our inspector loved: *"La Chambre Rose", an elegant suite with stunning views over the park.*

Directions: A11 > exit 11 > D859 > Champigné > 4km.

Web: www.johansens.com/chateaudesbriottieres
E-mail: briottieres@wanadoo.fr
Tel: +33 2 41 42 00 02
Fax: +33 2 41 42 01 55

Price Guide: (room only)
single €140–230
double/twin €120–240
suites €275–320

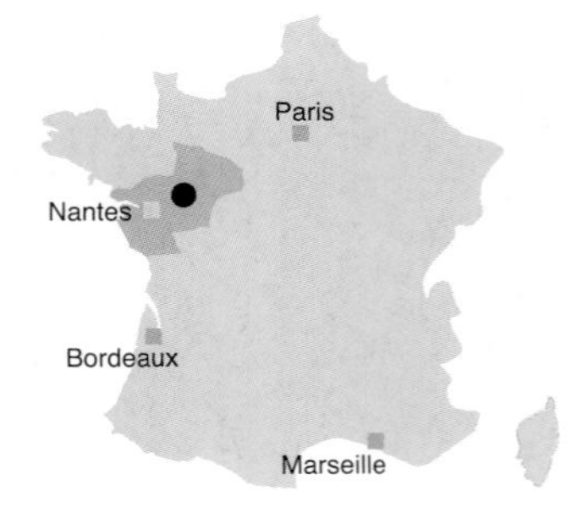

Great Britain & Ireland

Hotel location shown in red (hotel) or purple (spa hotel) with page number

AMBERLEY CASTLE

AMBERLEY, NEAR ARUNDEL, WEST SUSSEX BN18 9LT, ENGLAND

Winner of the Johansens Award for Outstanding Excellence and Innovation 2003, this medieval fortress is over 900 years old and boasts a fascinating history. Today it offers a warm welcome and the ultimate in contemporary yet timeless luxury. Distinctive new suites have been added, and each room is individually designed with its own Jacuzzi bath. The exquisite 12th-century Queen's Room makes the perfect setting for the hotel's creative cuisine, whilst nearby, Roman ruins, antiques, horse-racing and stately homes are found in abundance.

Le gagnant du prix Johansens Award for Outstanding Excellence and Innovation en 2003 a plus de 900 ans et un passé fascinant. Aujourd'hui, il réserve un accueil chaleureux à ses visiteurs qui y découvrent un luxe à la fois moderne et hors du temps. L'hôtel comprend de nouvelles suites et des chambres avec jacuzzi décorées de manière individuelle. Datant du XIIe siècle, la ravissante chambre de la reine forme un cadre parfait pour la cuisine de l'hôtel, situé dans une région où abondent les ruines romaines, les antiquaires, les champs de courses et les demeures ancestrales.

Diese mittelalterliche Festung wurde 2003 mit dem Johansens Award for Outstanding Excellence and Innovation ausgezeichnet. Das über 900 Jahr alte Anwesen ist heute ein einladendes Hotel, das das Beste an zeitgemäßem und doch zeitlosen Luxus bietet. Hervorragende neue Suiten wurden eingerichtet, und jedes Zimmer ist individuell gestaltet und hat ein Jacuzzi-Bad. Der Queen's Room aus dem 12. Jahrhundert ist das ideale Umfeld, um die Küche des Hotels zu genießen, und in der Nähe kann man zahlreiche Ruinen und Landsitze erkunden, Antiquitäten kaufen oder zum Pferderennen gehen.

Our inspector loved: *The castle walls, black swans and white peacocks.*

Directions: A29 - B2139 between Bury and Storrington.

Web: www.johansens.com/amberleycastleeuro
E-mail: info@amberleycastle.co.uk
Tel: +44 1798 831 992
Fax: +44 1798 831 998

Price Guide: (room only)
double/twin £155–375
suite £285–375

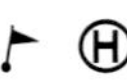

THE CRANLEY

10 BINA GARDENS, SOUTH KENSINGTON, LONDON SW5 0LA, ENGLAND

Standing in the heart of Kensington, this charming and sophisticated town house blends traditional style and service with 21st-century technology. Beautiful antiques, hand-embroidered fabrics, striking colour combinations and stone are used throughout. Some of the delightful bedrooms feature four-poster beds and all benefit from luxurious bathrooms. Copious continental breakfasts, English afternoon tea and evening apéritifs are served. Many of London's restaurants and attractions are within walking distance.

Charmant et raffiné, cet hôtel particulier au coeur de Kensington allie un style et un service traditionnels à un confort moderne. L'intérieur est rehaussé par de belles antiquités, des tissus brodés à la main, des combinaisons de couleurs remarquables et l'usage de la pierre. Des lits à baldaquin trônent dans certaines des chambres, toutes équipées de salles de bains luxueuses. L'hôtel sert de copieux petits déjeuners continentaux, le thé de cinq heures et l'apéritif avant le dîner. Nombre des restaurants et des attractions de la capitale ne sont qu'à deux pas.

Dieses charmante und elegante mitten in Kensington gelegene Stadthaus verbindet traditionellen Stil und Service mit der Technologie des 21. Jahrhunderts. Herrliche Antiquitäten, handbestickte Stoffe, auffällige Farbkombinationen und Stein zieren das Interieur. Einige der hübschen Zimmer haben Himmelbetten und alle besitzen luxuriöse Bäder. Gäste genießen ein üppiges Frühstück, englischen Nachmittagstee und Apéritifs am Abend. Zahlreiche Restaurants und Attraktionen befinden sich in nächster Nähe.

Our inspector loved: *This beautifully decorated rooms and gorgeous antique furniture.*

Directions: The nearest underground stations are Gloucester Road and South Kensington.

Web: www.johansens.com/cranleyeuro
E-mail: info@thecranley.com
Tel: +44 20 7373 0123
Fax: +44 20 7373 9497

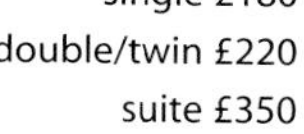

Price Guide:
single £180
double/twin £220
suite £350

THE DORCHESTER

The Leading Hotels of the World®

PARK LANE, MAYFAIR, LONDON W1A 2HJ, ENGLAND

Recently completely refurbished in a multi-million pound project, The Dorchester is one of the finest hotels in the world. Each of the bedrooms and suites has been luxuriously designed and individually decorated in traditional English country style, and benefits from marble bathrooms and state-of-the-art entertainment and business systems. Service is outstanding, with three members of staff per guest room. Apart from the acclaimed Grill Room, there is an exquisite Chinese restaurant. Specialised health and beauty treatments are available in the gloriously impressive Spa.

Ayant juste subi une rénovation de plusieurs millions de Livres Sterling, le Dorchester est l'un des plus beaux hôtels au monde. Chacune des chambres et suites a été luxueusement conçue et décorée dans un style individuel et traditionnel de la campagne anglaise et possède des salles de bains en marbre ainsi que des équipements de pointe pour les affaires ou le divertissement. Le service est exceptionnel avec 3 employés par chambre. Outre le fameux Grill Room, il existe un délicieux restaurant chinois. Des traitements et soins spécialisés de santé et de beauté sont dispensés au magnifique et impressionnant Spa.

Vor kurzem in einem mehre Millionen Pfund kostenden Projekt rundum erneuert, ist das Dorchester eines der besten Hotels der Welt. Alle Zimmer und Suiten sind luxuriös und individuell in traditionell englischem Stil gestaltet und verfügen über Marmorbäder sowie hochmoderne Unterhaltungs- und Bürosysteme. Der Service ist einzigartig, auf ein Zimmer kommen drei Bedienstete. Außer dem renommierten Grill Room gibt es auch ein herrliches kantonesisches Restaurant. Besondere Schönheits- und Gesundheitsbehandlungen werden im fantastischen Spa angeboten.

Directions: Hyde Park Corner end of Park Lane.

Web: www.johansens.com/thedorchestereuro
E-mail: reservations@dorchesterhotel.com
Tel: +44 (0)20 7629 8888
Fax: + 44 (0)20 7409 0114

Price Guide: (excluding VAT)
single £275–365
double/twin £355–465
suite £550–2,125

Our inspector loved: *This superb example of English elegance, charm and service.*

Draycott House Apartments

10 Draycott Avenue, Chelsea, London SW3 3AA, England

Draycott House stands in a quiet tree-lined avenue in the heart of Chelsea and offers luxury accommodation in 1, 2 or 3-bedroomed apartments. Combining comfort, privacy and security, the apartments are spacious, luxurious and well-equipped. Draycott House will organise cars, airport transfers, catering and theatre arrangements etc., as well as an introduction to an exclusive health club. There is 5-day maid service, in-house laundry facilities and garage parking.

Draycott House s'élève dans une rue paisible bordée d'arbres en plein coeur de Chelsea et offre un logement luxueux. Les appartements avec 1, 2 ou 3 lits allient confort, intimité et sécurité. Ils sont spacieux, luxueux et bien équipés. Draycott House organise sur demande des taxis, des transferts aéroport, des services de restauration, des places de théâtre, etc. Il offre également son club de remise en forme prestigieux. Le service de femmes de chambre est tous les cinq jours, et des services de blanchisserie ainsi qu'un garage sont disponibles.

Die großzügigen Zimmer 1-, 2- und 3-Appartements des Draycott House liegen in einer ruhigen Allee im Herzen von Chelsea. Geräumig, luxuriös und bestens ausgestattet bieten sie eine Mischung aus Komfort, Abgeschiedenheit und Sicherheit. Taxis, Flughafentransfer, Verpflegung, Theaterkarten etc. können organisiert werden, ebenso wie die Einführung in einen exklusiven Fitnessclub. Ausserdem stehen 5-Tages-Zimmerservice, Waschmaschine und Trockner wie auch überdachte Parkplätze zur Verfügung.

Our inspector loved: *These well appointed apartments, which are perfect for a long stay in London.*

Directions: Close to Sloane Square.

Web: www.johansens.com/draycotthouseapartmentseuro
E-mail: sales@draycotthouse.co.uk
Tel: +44 20 7584 4659
Fax: +44 20 7225 3694

Edinburgh
Dublin
Cardiff
London

Price Guide: (excluding VAT)
£188–235 per night
£1178–2948 per week

GREAT BRITAIN & IRELAND / ENGLAND (LONDON)

THE LOWNDES HOTEL

21 LOWNDES STREET, KNIGHTSBRIDGE, LONDON SW1X 9ES, ENGLAND

Directions: The nearest underground tube stations are Knightsbridge, Hyde Park Corner and Sloane Square.

Web: www.johansens.com/lowndeseuro
E-mail: contact@lowndeshotel.com
Tel: +44 20 7823 1234
Fax: +44 20 7235 1154

Price Guide: (room only, excluding VAT)
double £260-£280
suite £360-£460

This stylish hotel lies in the exclusive area of Belgravia – just minutes from the sophisticated shopping areas of Knightsbridge and Chelsea, and within a short taxi ride of the West End, the City and London's major attractions. Designed in boutique style, the hotel offers a blend of classic and contemporary features to create a chic yet welcoming environment, with Citronelle Restaurant offering Mediterranean cuisine and including a terrace for al fresco dining, "The Library" for social gatherings or business meetings and first-class leisure & spa facilities.

Cet élégant hôtel se situe dans le quartier prestigieux de Belgravia – à quelques minutes des boutiques chics de Knightsbridge et de Chelsea, et proche en taxi du West End, de la City et des attractions londoniennes. Conçu dans le style boutique, cet hôtel marie les styles classiques et contemporains créant ainsi un environnement stylé mais accueillant. Le Citronelle offre une cuisine méditerranéenne et une terrasse pour les dîners al fresco. L'hôtel dispose d'une bibliothèque pour les réceptions et les réunions et d'équipements de loisirs et d'un spa de premier ordre.

Dieses elegante Hotel befindet sich im exklusiven Stadtteil Belgravia, nur ein paar Minuten von den berühmten Einkaufsstraßen von Knightsbridge und Chelsea, und eine kurze Taxifahrt vom West End, der City und vielen anderen Attraktionen entfernt. Das im Boutique-Stil gestaltete Hotel bietet eine Mischung aus klassisch und modern und ein edles und doch herzliches Ambiente. Das Citronelle serviert Mittelmeerküche, und auf einer Terrasse kann man al fresco dinieren. Eine Bibliothek für private Feierlichkeiten oder Geschäftstreffen steht zur Verfügung, ebenso wie erstklassige Spa- und Freizeiteinrichtungen.

Our inspector loved: *The outdoor dining terrace overlooking Lowndes Square.*

Mayflower Hotel

26-28 TREBOVIR ROAD, LONDON SW5 9NJ, ENGLAND

This recently renovated hotel offers an intriguing blend of eastern influences and modern luxury. Vibrant fabrics and Indian and oriental antiques abound in the individually decorated bedrooms, 4 of which have balconies. High ceilings and hand-carved wardrobes and bedside tables are complemented by stylish bathrooms and state-of-the-art technology with Internet access and wide-screen televisions. Knightsbridge and Chelsea, the V&A and the Natural History and Science Museum are close by, whilst Earls Court Exhibition Centre is on the doorstep.

Cet hôtel récemment remis à neuf offre un mélange fascinant d'influences de l'Est et de luxe moderne. Des tissus vifs et objets d'art de l'Orient et de l'Inde ornent les chambres décorées de façon individuelle, dont 4 ont des balcons. Des plafonds hauts, armoires et tables de chevet sculptées à la main sont complétés par des salles de bains élégantes et équipements du dernier cri, comprenant accès Internet et des grands télévisions. Knightsbridge et Chelsea, les musées V&A et Natural History and Science sont tout proches, alors que le centre d'expositions Earls Court n'est pas loin.

Dieses kürzlich renovierte Hotel bietet eine interessante Mischung aus östlichen Einflüssen und modernem Luxus. Farbenfrohe Stoffe und indische und asiatische Antiquitäten füllen die unterschiedlichen Zimmer (4 mit Balkon), und hohe Decken, handgeschnitzte Schränke und Nachttische, edle Bäder und modernste Technologie mit Internetzugang und Widescreen-Fernsehen sorgen für das gewisse Extra. Knightsbridge und Chelsea, das V&A, das Natural History and Science Museum sowie das Ausstellungszentrum Earls Court liegen in nächster Nähe.

Our inspector loved: *The Eastern influence in all the bedrooms.*

48

25

Directions: Situated between Earls Court Road and Warwick Road. The nearest underground station is Earls Court.

Web: www.johansens.com/mayflowereuro
E-mail: info@mayflower-group.co.uk
Tel: +44 20 7370 0991
Fax: +44 20 7370 0994

Price Guide:
single £79
double £109
family room £130

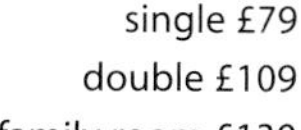

Pembridge Court Hotel

34 PEMBRIDGE GARDENS, LONDON W2 4DX, ENGLAND

Directions: The hotel is 2 minutes from Portobello Road.

Web: www.johansens.com/pembridgecourteuro
E-mail: reservations@pemct.co.uk
Tel: +44 20 7229 9977
Fax: +44 20 7727 4982

Price Guide:
single £130–170
double/twin £190–200

Beautifully restored to its 19-century origins, this gracious Victorian town house offers the high level of service demanded by today's discerning traveller. The well-appointed bedrooms are individually decorated with pretty fabrics and the walls are adorned with a collection of framed Victorian fans. It is situated in the heart of Notting Hill, renowned for its vibrant nightlife and one of the largest antiques markets in the world.

Superbement restauré en fonction de ses origines du XIXe siècle, cette jolie maison de ville victorienne offre un grand standing de service. Les jolies chambres sont toutes individuellement décorées avec des superbes tissus et les murs sont ornés d'une collection d'évantails victoriens. Il est situé au coeur de Notting Hill, renommé pour sa vie nocturne animée et pour être un des plus grands marchés aux puces du monde.

Dieses elegante viktorianische Herrenhaus aus dem 19. Jahrhundert wurde perfekt restauriert und bietet dem anspruchsvollen Gast von heute höchsten Standard an Service. Die gutausgestatteten Zimmer sind individuell mit hübschen Stoffen gestaltet, und eine Sammlung von viktorianischen Fächern ziert die Wände. Das Pembridge Court liegt im Herzen von Notting Hill, das für sein reges Nachtleben und einen der weltgrößten Antiquitätenmärkte bekannt ist.

Our inspector loved: *The cosy "at home" feel of the sitting room and the collection of Victorian fans.*

GREAT BRITAIN & IRELAND / ENGLAND (LONDON)

THE ROYAL PARK

3 WESTBOURNE TERRACE, LANCASTER GATE, HYDE PARK, LONDON W2 3UL, ENGLAND

Three stately Georgian town houses have been gracefully combined to create this little gem of a hotel. Beautifully designed, the style is very sympathetic to the building's heritage, combining deep colours, Regency stripes and rich furnishings. The delightful bedrooms exude timeless elegance, with magnificent beds and handmade mattresses. The hotel is ideally situated on the doorstep of Hyde Park and Kensington Palace Gardens and is within walking distance of Oxford Street and Notting Hill.

Trois majestueuses maisons datant du règne de George V ont été réunies afin de créer ce petit joyau hôtelier. Magnifiquement conçu, le style reflète l'histoire du bâtiment associant des couleurs sombres, des tissus Régence et de somptueux meubles. Les ravissantes chambres respirent l'élégance intemporelle avec leurs superbes lits et les matelas faits main. L'hôtel est idéalement situé aux portes de Hyde Park, des jardins de Kensington Palace et n'est qu'à quelques minutes à pied d'Oxford Street et de Notting Hill.

Drei eindrucksvolle Stadthäuser aus der Zeit Georges V. bilden dieses wahre Juwel von einem Hotel. Das mit viel Liebe und Gefühl für sein kostbares Erbe eingerichtete Haus ist mit kräftigen Farben, Regency-Streifen und prächtigem Mobiliar eingerichtet, und die herrlichen, zeitlos eleganten Zimmer bieten traumhafte Betten mit handgefertigten Matratzen. Das Hotel liegt ideal ganz in der Nähe des Hyde Park und der Kensington Palace Gardens, und nur ein paar Gehminuten von der Oxford Street und Notting Hill entfernt.

Our inspector loved: *The beautifully designed bedrooms with their handmade four-poster beds and exquisite linens.*

Directions: The nearest underground station is Lancaster Gate. The hotel is a 2-minute walk from the Heathrow Express at Paddington Station.

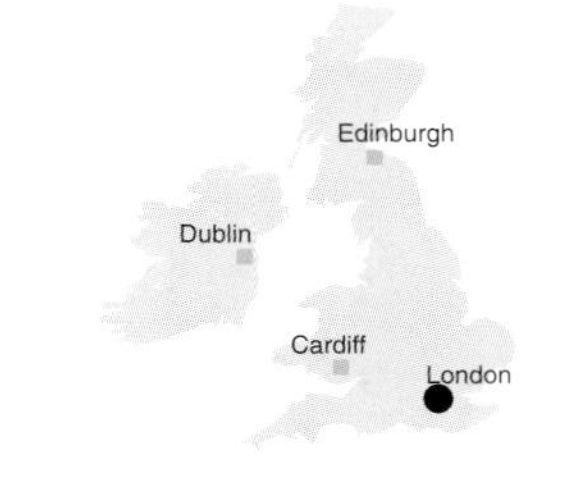

Web: www.johansens.com/royalparkeuro
E-mail: info@theroyalpark.com
Tel: +44 20 7479 6600
Fax: +44 20 7479 6601

Price Guide: (weekend rates)
single £110–165
double £135–190

Twenty Nevern Square

20 NEVERN SQUARE, LONDON SW5 9PD, ENGLAND

Directions: 2 minutes from Earl's Court underground station.

Web: www.johansens.com/twentynevernsquareeuro
E-mail: hotel@twentynevernsquare.co.uk
Tel: +44 20 7565 9555
Fax: +44 20 7565 9444

Price Guide:
single £99-130
double £130–165
suite £275

This elegant town house has been sumptuously restored with an emphasis on natural materials – linen, cotton and silks – and beautiful hand-carved beds and furniture. Each of the 20 intimate bedrooms is individually designed echoing both Asian and European influences. The hotel overlooks a tranquil garden square and has its own delightful restaurant, Café Twenty, serving modern European food. Guests are a mere 10 minutes from London's most fashionable shopping areas, restaurants, theatres and cultural attractions.

Restauré avec faste, cet élégant hôtel particulier privilégie aujourd'hui les matières naturelles – lin, coton et soie – et les beaux lits et autres meubles artisanaux. Chacune des 20 chambres intimes est décorée dans un style individuel aux influences asiatiques et européennes. L'hôtel donne sur un square paisible et dispose d'un restaurant raffiné, le Café Twenty, qui sert une cuisine européenne moderne. Les restaurants, les théâtres, les attractions culturelles et les rues commerçantes les plus chics de Londres ne sont qu'à 10 minutes.

Dieses elegante Stadthaus wurde im großen Stil renoviert, wobei man vornehmlich natürliche Materialien wir Leinen, Baumwolle und Seide sowie herrliche handgeschnitzte Betten und Möbel verwendete. Jedes der 20 gemütlichen Zimmer ist individuell gestaltet und von asiatischen und europäischen Einflüssen geprägt. Das Hotel blickt auf einen ruhigen Garten, und das eigene Restaurant Café Twenty serviert moderne europäische Küche. Londons beliebteste Einkaufsstraßen, Restaurants, Theater und kulturelle Attraktionen sind nur 10 Minuten entfernt.

Our inspector loved: *This very friendly town house hotel with its luxurious Eastern fabrics and furniture in all the rooms.*

The Peacock at Rowsley

ROWSLEY, NEAR MATLOCK, DERBYSHIRE DE4 2EB, ENGLAND

This superb 17th-century country house has been refurbished to reflect its wonderful ambience. Numerous antiques have been exquisitely restored, and the comfortable en-suite bedrooms, 1 of which has a four-poster, are equipped with all modern amenities. Guests enjoy contemporary English cuisine based on local produce and game from the estate. Conference and banqueting facilities for up to 20 are available. The hotel is a paradise for fishing enthusiasts, whilst the Peak District National Park, Haddon Hall and Chatsworth are all within easy reach.

Cette maison de campagne datant du XVIIe siècle a été remis à neuf pour refléter son ambiance superbe. De nombreux objets d'art ont été finement restaurés et les chambres attenantes confortables, dont 1 a un lit à baldaquin, offrent toutes les facilités modernes. Les hôtes peuvent savourer la cuisine anglaise contemporaine créée avec des ingrédients locaux et du gibier de la propriété. Les facilités de conférence et banquet sont disponibles pour jusqu'à 20 personnes. L'hôtel est un paradis pour les passionnés de la pêche, alors que le Peak District National Park, Haddon Hall et Chatsworth sont tous d'accès facile.

Dieses herrliche Landhaus aus dem 17. Jahrhundert wurde im Einklang mit dem Ambiente des Hauses komplett neu hergerichtet. Wundervolle Antiquitäten wurden hervorragend restauriert, und die komfortablen Zimmer (1 mit Himmelbett) bieten jeglichen modernen Komfort. Serviert wird moderne englische Küche mit einheimischen Zutaten und eigenem Wild. Konferenz- und Banketteinrichtungen für bis zu 20 Personen sind vorhanden. Das Hotel ist ein Anglerparadies, und der Peak District Nationalpark, Haddon Hall und Chatsworth liegen in nächster Nähe.

Our inspector loved: *The sensitive modernization to this ancient property.*

Directions: M1 > exit 28 > towards A6 > midway between Matlock and Bakewell.

Web: www.johansens.com/peacockeuro
E-mail: office@thepeacockatrowsley.com
Tel: +44 1629 733518
Fax: +44 1629 732671

Edinburgh
Dublin
Cardiff
London

Price Guide:
single £55
double £125

THE FRENCH HORN

SONNING ON THAMES, BERKSHIRE RG4 6TN, ENGLAND

Directions: M4 > exit junction 8/9 > follow A404 > at Thickets roundabout turn left > A4 towards Reading for 8 miles > Sonning > cross Thames on B478 > hotel is on the right.

Web: www.johansens.com/frenchhorneuro
E-mail: info@thefrenchhorn.com
Tel: +44 1189 692204
Fax: +44 1189 442210

Price Guide:
single £110–165
double/twin £140–205

This luxurious, charming hotel and gourmet restaurant is the epitome of the quaint, quintessential English riverside village retreat. Set near Windsor and the historic village of Sonning, there are 4 riverside cottages, alongside 4 riverside rooms, and 12 suites and en-suite double rooms to choose from. The family-run restaurant looks out onto the Thames and serves classic French cuisine alongside traditional English dishes, and the wine list is reputed to be amongst the finest in Europe. Meeting facilities for up to 16 delegates are available.

Ce charmant hôtel luxueux avec son restaurant gastronome est la quintessence d'un village retrait au charme vieillot au bord de la rivière. Situé près de Windsor et le village historique de Sonning, l'hôtel propose 4 petites maisons et 4 chambres près de la rivière, ainsi que 12 suites et chambres attenantes. Le restaurant familial donne sur le Thames et sert une cuisine française classique ainsi que des plats traditionnels anglais et les vins sont réputés être parmi les meilleurs en Europe. Des facilités de conférence pour jusqu'à 16 personnes sont disponibles.

Dieses zauberhafte, luxuriöse Hotel und Gourmetrestaurant ist der Inbegriff eines typischen englischen, an einem Fluss gelegenen Dorfhotels. Das Hotel befindet sich in der Nähe von Windsor und dem historischen Ort Sonning und umfasst 4 Cottages und 4 Zimmer direkt an der Themse sowie 12 Suiten und Doppelzimmer mit eigenem Bad. Das familiengeführte Restaurant blickt ebenfalls auf den Fluss und serviert klassische französische Küche und traditionelle englische Gerichte, und die Weinkarte ist eine der besten in ganz Europa. Konferenzeinrichtungen für bis zu 16 Personen vorhanden.

Our inspector loved: *The glorious riverside setting and the Old World charm.*

Aberdeen Lodge

53-55 PARK AVENUE, BALLSBRIDGE, DUBLIN 4, IRELAND

Located in the south city centre, set within formal gardens on a serene tree-lined avenue, this classic example of Edwardian architecture prides itself on ensuring that the needs of its guests are met wholeheartedly. Elegant bedrooms are furnished in complete harmony with the house, spacious suites feature Jacuzzis and period furniture, whilst the award-winning intimate dining room serves a special menu and good selection of fine wines. The hotel provides an ideal base from which to enjoy Dublin's sights and shopping in the famous Grafton Street. Private car park.

Situé au centre sud de la ville, ce bel exemple d'architecture édouardienne se dresse au milieu d'un jardin à la française, dans une paisible avenue bordée d'arbres, et met un point d'honneur à satisfaire tous les besoins des visiteurs. Les chambres élégantes sont en harmonie avec le reste de l'hôtel et les suites spacieuses comportent des jacuzzis et des meubles d'époque. La petite salle à manger primée propose un menu exceptionnel et un excellent choix de vins fins. L'hôtel est idéal pour visiter Dublin et faire du shopping dans la célèbre Grafton Street. Parking privé.

Dieses inmitten formeller Gärten an einer Allee gelegene Hotel im sudlichen Zentrum der Stadt ist ein klassisches Beispiel Edwardischer Architektur. Kein Wunsch bleibt hier unerfüllt. Die eleganten Zimmer sind im Einklang mit der Umgebung gestaltet, und die geräumigen Suiten bieten Jacuzzis und Stilmöbel. Im preisgekrönten Speisesaal wird ein Sondermenü und eine gute Auswahl an erlesenen Weinen serviert. Das Hotel liegt ideal, um Dublin zu erkunden und in der berühmten Grafton Street einkaufen zu gehen. Privatparkplatz vorhanden.

Our inspector loved: *The quiet seclusion so close to the city centre.*

Directions: Off Ailesbury Road, 7 minutes from the city centre by D.A.R.T.

Web: www.johansens.com/aberdeenlodge
E-mail: aberdeen@iol.ie
Tel: +353 1 283 8155
Fax: +353 1 283 7877

Price Guide:
single €106–139
double/twin €139–189
four poster €169-229
suite €190–299

Royal Marine Hotel

GOLF ROAD, BRORA, SUTHERLAND KW9 6QS, SCOTLAND

Directions: Inverness > A9 north > follow signs for Wick > at Brora cross over bridge > turn right.

Web: www.johansens.com/royalmarineeuro
E-mail: info@highlandescape.com
Tel: +44 1408 621252
Fax: +44 1408 621181

Price Guide:
single £75-95
double £120-138
suite £158

Standing midway between Inverness and John O'Groats, this former private home has been refurbished to provide all modern amenities, whilst still retaining original features such as the wooden arches of the entrance hall, carved wood fireplaces and the grand staircase. Particular emphasis is placed on quality and service, complementing the pleasing décor and comfort throughout. Many of the attractive guest rooms offer splendid scenic views. Guests can use the facilities of the leisure club, play golf, go fishing on Loch Brora, or explore the numerous attractions nearby.

Situé entre Inverness et John O'Groats, cette ancienne résidence privée a été rénovée pour offrir tout le confort moderne, alors qu'elle garde ses détails originaux comme les voûtes en bois de l'entrée, les cheminées en bois et le splendide escalier. Une importance particulière est accordée à la qualité, le service, le confort et le décor agréable. Plusieurs chambres offrent des vues scéniques spectaculaires. Les hôtes peuvent profiter du club de remise en forme, jouer au golf, aller à la pêche sur Loch Brora ou découvrir les nombreuses attractions dans les alentours.

Dieses einstige Privathaus auf halber Strecke zwischen Inverness und John O'Groats wurde renoviert und mit modernsten Einrichtungen versehen, wobei einige ursprüngliche Details wie z.B. die Holzbögen in der Eingangshalle, geschnitzte offene Kamine und das herrliche Treppenhaus erhalten blieben. Die Betonung liegt hier auf Qualität, Service, Komfort und angenehmem Décor. Einige Zimmer bieten eine traumhafte Sicht auf das Umland. Ein Freizeitkomplex steht zur Verfügung, man kann Golf spielen, auf dem Loch Brora angeln oder die Umgebung erkunden.

Our inspector loved: *The excellent facilities; great golf on the doorstep, and proximity to Inverness.*

Muckrach Lodge Hotel & Restaurant

DULNAIN BRIDGE, BY GRANTOWN~ON~SPEY, INVERNESS-SHIRE PH26 3LY, SCOTLAND

With its welcoming log fires, fresh flowers, comfortable sofas and country house charm this former sporting lodge has a relaxed, informal ambience. It is surrounded by 10 acres of landscaped grounds and amazing scenery featuring the Cairngorms National Park and its River Spey, lochs and moors. Muckrach's bedrooms are spacious, and imaginative cuisine is served in the 2 AA Rosette awarded Fanlarig Restaurant complemented by fine wines and rare malts. Guests can explore nearby ancient ruined castles, forts, Culloden battlefied and the famous Malt Whisky Trail.

Avec ses feux de bois, ses fleurs coupées, ses canapés confortables et son charme de maison de campagne, cet ancien pavillon de chasse a une ambiance détendue et sans façons. Il est entouré de 4 ha de terres aménagées et la beauté du parc national de Cairngorm avec la rivière Spey, des lochs et des landes. Les chambres sont spacieuses et une cuisine inventive est servie au restaurant Fanlarig à 2 Rosettes AA, complétée par des vins fins et des malts rares. On peut explorer des ruines de châteaux et forts, le champ de bataille de Culloden et le célèbre chemin du malt.

Mit seinen Kaminfeuern, frischen Blumen, bequemen Sofas und Landhauscharme bietet dieses einstige Jagdhaus eine entspannte, informelle Atmosphäre. Muckrach ist umgeben von 4ha gepflegtem Garten und der traumhaften Landschaft des Cairngorm-Nationalparks mit dem Fluss Spey und mehreren Lochs und Mooren. Die Zimmer sind geräumig und im mit 2 AA Rosetten ausgezeichneten Fanlarig Restaurant werden einfallsreiche Speisen, edle Weine und seltene Whiskys serviert. Gäste können Burgruinen, Festungen und das Schlachtfeld von Culloden besichtigen und dem berühmten Whiskypfad folgen.

Our inspector loved: *The relaxed style and the abscence of pretentiousness.*

Directions: Muckrach Lodge is 3 miles South West of Grantown-on-Spey on the B9102 and A95, through Dulnain Bridge Village on the A938. Inverness Airport is 36 miles away.

Web: www.johansens.com/muckrachlodgeeuro
E-mail: stay@muckrach.co.uk
Tel: +44 1479 851257
Fax: +44 1479 851325

Price Guide:
single £60
double/twin £120–160
special short breaks available

Skeabost Country House

SKEABOST BRIDGE, PORTREE IV51 9NP, SCOTLAND

Recently refurbished with style and opulent good taste, Skeabost Country House stands at the edge of Loch Snizort and is amongst the best of Highland retreats. Open fires and elegant public rooms exceed all expectations and ensure a wonderful, restful getaway. Individually decorated bedrooms are the ultimate in comfort and there are 3 rooms adjacent to the hotel, perfect for a self-catering holiday. Activities include fishing, golf and exploring the breathtaking mountains of the island.

Récemment remis à neuf dans un style élégant et opulent, Skeabost Country House situé sur les bords du lac Snizort, est l'un des meilleurs refuges des Highlands. Cheminées et salons élégants dépassent toutes les attentes et assurent un séjour agréable et reposant. Les chambres individuellement décorées offrent le summum du confort et les 3 chambres adjacentes à l'hôtel sont parfaites pour les plus indépendants. De nombreuses activités sont disponibles telles que la pêche, le golf ainsi que la découverte des extraordinaires montagnes de l'île.

Das kürzlich mit viel Stil und gutem Geschmack renovierte Skeabost Country House liegt am Rande des Loch Snizort und ist eines der besten Hotels in den schottischen Highlands. Offene Kamine und elegante Aufenthaltsräume übertreffen alle Erwartungen und garantieren einen erholsamen Besuch. Die individuell gestalteten Zimmer bieten höchsten Komfort, und 3 Nebengebäude sind ideal für einen Aufenthalt mit Selbstverpflegung. Aktivitäten sind Angeln, Golf und Ausflüge in die atemberaubende Berglandschaft der Insel.

Our inspector loved: *The new stylish bedroom with splendid drapes and décor.*

Directions: A87 towards Uig > after 4 miles turn left > A850 towards Dunvegan > the hotel is on the right. The nearest airport is Inverness.

Web: www.johansens.com/skeabosteuro
E-mail: reception@skeabostcountryhouse.com
Tel: +44 1470 532202
Fax: +44 1470 532454

Price Guide:
single £110
double £170-300

GREAT BRITAIN & IRELAND / SCOTLAND (SCOTTISH BORDERS)

Castle Venlaw Hotel

EDINBURGH ROAD, PEEBLES, SCOTLAND EH45 8QG

Overlooking the ancient town of Peebles in the peaceful Borders countryside, yet only 40 minutes from Edinburgh, this majestic hotel has an air of elegance and relaxed informality. Great care has been taken to preserve the charm and character of the castle and the restaurant, with its 2 AA-Rosettes, provides fresh, locally produced meals of superb quality with an international flavour. Acres of beautiful woodlands can be explored or there is golf, fishing and many historic buildings in the area.

Donnant sur l'ancienne ville de Peebles dans la campagne paisible de Borders, mais seulement à 40 minutes d,Edimbourgcet, cet hôtel majestueux a une ambiance également élégante et détendue. Le charme et le caractère du château ont été soigneusement préservés. Le restaurant, attribué 2 rosettes AA, sert des plats frais avec une influence internationale, utilisant des produits locaux de très bonne qualité. Les hôtes peuvent explorer les bois, jouer au golf, aller à la pêche ou visiter les nombreux bâtiments historiques dans les alentours.

Dieses majestätische Hotel mit Blick auf die alte Stadt Peebles inmitten der Borders-Region, doch nur 40 Minuten von Edinburgh entfernt, besitzt eine Aura der Eleganz kombiniert mit entspannter Atmosphäre. Der Charme und Charakter des Hotels wurde sehr sorgfältig beibehalten, und im mit einer AA-Rosetten ausgezeichneten Restaurant werden hervorragende, aus frischen, einheimischen Zutaten zubereitete Gerichte mit internationaler Note serviert. Die Gäste können die herrliche umliegende Waldlandschaft erkunden, Golf spielen, angeln oder die zahlreichen historischen Stätten der Region besichtigen.

Our inspector loved: *The exceptionally large rooms, the peace and quiet and the proximity to Edinburgh.*

Directions: Edinburgh > A703 to Peebles > the hotel is then signposted on the left just after the 30mph sign.

Web: www.johansens.com/venlaweuro
E-mail: enquiries@venlaw.co.uk
Tel: +44 1721 720384
Fax: +44 1721 724066

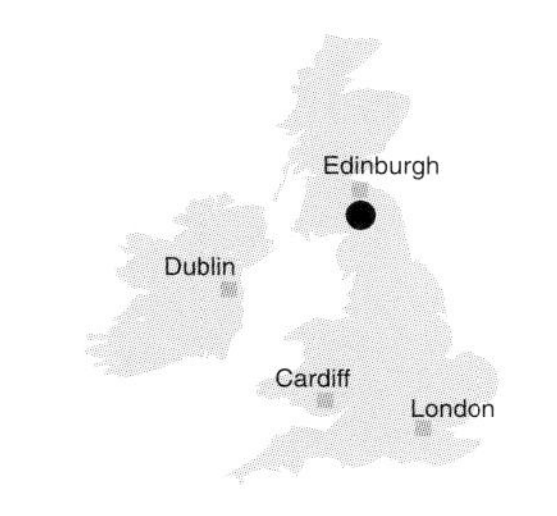

Price Guide:
single £60-85
double/twin £120-180

GREECE

Hotel location shown in red (hotel) or purple (spa hotel) with page number

ASTIR PALACE VOULIAGMENI

40 APOLLONOS STREET, 166 71 VOULIAGMENI, ATHENS, GREECE

Astir Palace Vouliagmeni is an impressive luxury resort sprawling across an 80-acre, private peninsula just a 40-minute drive from Athens. 3 exclusive hotels, surrounded by pine forests and colourful gardens, are spectacularly set with panoramic sea views towards neighbouring isles. The hotels offer 420 elegant, spacious, comfortably furnished guest rooms, 30 suites, stylish restaurants, outdoor swimming pools and private beaches. There are also 75 bungalows at the resort, as well as extensive leisure and meeting facilities.

Astir Palace Vouliagmeni est un impressionnant resort de luxe qui s'étend sur une péninsule privée de plus de 32 hectares à 40 minutes en voiture d'Athènes. 3 hôtels uniques, entourés de forêts de pins et de jardins colorés sont situés de façon spectaculaire avec des vues panoramiques sur les îles voisines. Les hôtels offrent 420 chambres élégantes, spacieuses et confortablement meublées, 30 suites, des restaurants de style, piscines extérieures et plages privées. Le resort offre également 75 bungalows ainsi que des équipements pour les loisirs et les affaires.

Das Astir Palace Vouliagmeni ist ein eindrucksvolles Luxusresort, das sich über 32ha auf einer privaten Halbinsel nur 40 Minuten Autofahrt von Athen befindet. 3 exklusive, von Pinienwäldern und bunten Gärten umgebene Hotels bieten eine fantastische Lage mit Panoramablick aufs Meer und die Nachbarinseln. 420 elegante, geräumige Zimmer sind komfortabel eingerichtet, außerdem gibt es 30 Suiten, edle Restaurants, Swimmingpools und Privatstrände. 75 Bungalows sowie umfassende Freizeit- und Konferenzeinrichtungen sind ebenfalls vorhanden.

Our inspector loved: *The endless view to the deep blue sea.*

Directions: E Venizelos Airport is 25km away.

Web: www.johansens.com/astirpalace
E-mail: marketing-sales@astir.gr
Tel: +30 210 890 2000
Fax: +30 210 896 2582

Price Guide:
single €230-530
double €330-1,100
suite €650-7,000

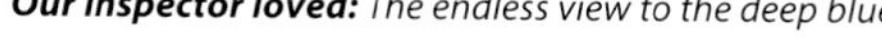

Hotel Pentelikon

66 DILIGIANNI STREET, 14562 ATHENS, GREECE

Set in a peaceful residential area of Athens, this impressive, discreet de luxe 5-star small hotel is the essence of style. Fine antiques, silk curtains and immaculate staff contribute to its select ambience. The luxurious bedrooms are individually decorated in English fabrics with harmonising wall coverings. Cuisine is a delight with the informal La Terrasse and the gourmet Vardis restaurant, the only restaurant in Greece that has been awarded a Michelin Star for 6 consecutive years.

Situé dans un quartier calme d'Athènes, ce petit hôtel impressionnant et discret de luxe 5* est une figure de style. Des antiquités raffinées, des rideaux de soie et un personnel impeccable contribuent à son ambiance sélective. Les chambres luxueuses sont décorées individuellement avec des tissus anglais coordonnés aux papiers muraux. La table est divine tant sur la Terrace détendue qu'au restaurant gastronomique le Vardis, le seul restaurant en Grèce à avoir gagnée une étoile Michelin pendant 6 années consécutives.

In einer ruhigen Wohngegend von Athen gelegen bietet dieses vortreffliche kleine 5-Sterne Luxushotel Diskretion und einzigartigen Stil. Kostbare Antiquitäten, seidene Vorhänge und tadelloses Personal tragen zu diesem exklusiven Ambiente bei. Die luxuriösen Zimmer sind individuell mit englischen Stoffen und damit harmonisierenden Tapeten gestaltet. Köstliche Gerichte werden im informellen La Terrasse oder im Gourmetrestaurant Vardis serviert, das einzige Restaurant in Griechenland, das 6 Jahre hintereinander einen Michelinstern bekam.

Our inspector loved: *The delicious dinner at Vardis Restaurant and its lovely setting.*

Directions: Set in the suburb of Kifissia. Venizelos Airport is 30 minutes away.

Web: www.johansens.com/pentelikon
E-mail: pentelik@otenet.gr and reservations@hotelpentelikon.gr
Tel: +30 2 10 62 30 650
Fax: +30 2 10 62 81 400

Price Guide:
single €270-360
double/twin €285-440
suite €560-2,500

Athens
Rhodes
Iráklion - *Crete*

Athina Suites

KSAMOUDOCHORI, PLATANIAS, 73014 CHANIA, CRETE, GREECE

Nestling in 8 acres of pure Mediterranean landscape, Athina Suites is a complex of luxurious villas, located surprisingly close to the beach and resort town of Platanias. Each villa accommodates up to 6 people and offers spacious living rooms, fully equipped kitchens and Jacuzzis in the bathrooms. Private swimming pools, expensive pieces of locally crafted furniture and home cooked local delicacies create a feeling of character mixed with luxury that makes these suites a haven for the discerning guest.

Niché dans 4ha d'un paysage typiquement méditerranéen, Athina Suites est un complexe de villas luxueuses, situées incroyablement près de la plage et de la station balnéaire de Platanias. Chaque villa peut loger 6 personnes et bénéficie d'un salon spacieux, d'une cuisine toute équipée et d'un jacuzzi dans la salle de bain. Piscines privées, mobilier artisanal local luxueux et mets délicats fait maison créent une atmosphère de caractère et de luxe qui fait de ces suites un havre pour les hôtes les plus exigeants.

Athina Suites ist ein Kompex aus Luxusvillas inmitten von 4ha herrlicher Mittelmeerlandschaft, überraschend nahe am Strand und der Resortstadt Platanias. Jede Villa beherbergt bis zu 6 Personen und bietet einen geräumigen Wohnbereich, voll ausgestattete Küche und Jacuzzi im Bad, sowie einen privaten Swimmingpool. Erlesene, am Ort gefertigte Möbel und köstliche einheimische Speisen schaffen eine Mischung aus ortstypischem Charakter und Luxus und lassen den anspruchsvollen Gast einen ganz besonderen Aufenthalt genießen.

Our inspector loved: *The peaceful atmosphere by the swimming pool at night.*

Directions: National Road > exit Platanias > left onto Ksamoudochori > follow signs. The nearest airport is Chania.

Web: www.johansens.com/athinasuites
E-mail: info@athina-suites.gr
Tel: +30 28210 20960
Fax: +30 28210 20970

Price Guide: (excluding VAT)
villa €200-350

Athens
Rhodes
Iráklion - *Crete*

The Peninsula at Porto Elounda De Luxe Resort

72053 ELOUNDA, CRETE, GREECE

Located on a peninsula, within the famous Porto Elounda De Luxe Resort, this hotel boasts spectacular views over the bay. Large, airy suites are decorated with Greek marble and teak floors and have access to either a shared or private heated seawater pool. There is a private beach, tennis, 9-hole par-3 golf course with academy, water sports, wellness, indoor pool, gym, a home cinema and a children's club. A wine cellar, several restaurants, the "Playiada" square with its boutiques, jeweller, an art gallery and an orthodox chapel complete the resort.

Situé sur une péninsule, au sein du célèbre Porto Elounda De Luxe Resort, cet hôtel s'enorgueillit de vues spectaculaires sur la baie. Les grandes suites sont décorées de marbre grec et de planchers en teck et ont accès à des piscines d'eau de mer chauffées partagées avec d'autres suites ou privées. Le resort dispose de sa plage privée, tennis, golf à 9 trous par-3 avec école, centre de remise en forme, piscine couverte, cinéma, club pour les enfants, une cave à vins et plusieurs restaurants, ainsi que d'une place centrale "Playiada" avec boutiques, bijouterie, galérie d'art et une chapelle orthodoxe.

Dieses Hotel auf einer Halbinsel innerhalb des berühmten Porto Elounda De Luxe Resorts bietet eine herrliche Sicht auf die Bucht. Die großen Suiten sind mit griechischem Marmor und Teakböden gestaltet und haben Zugang zu einem Gemeinschafts- oder eigenem beheizten Salzwasserpool. Es gibt einen privaten Strand, Tennis, 9-Loch par-3 Golfplatz mit Golfakademie, Wellness-Centre, Hallenbad, Hauskino, Kinderclub, Weinkeller und mehrere Restaurants, sowie den "Playiada"-Platz mit seinen Boutiquen, Juwelierladen, einer Kunstgalerie und einer orthodoxen Kappelle.

Our inspector loved: *The luxury in this refined environment.*

Directions: Available on request. The nearest airport is Heraklion.

Web: www.johansens.com/peninsulacrete
E-mail: porto@elounda-sa.com
Tel: +30 28410 68000
Fax: +30 28410 41889

Price Guide:
suite €300–8,500

Athens
Rhodes
Iráklion - *Crete*

PLEIADES LUXURIOUS VILLAS

PLAKES, 72100 AGHIOS NIKOLAOS, CRETE, GREECE

Set in a quiet location with beautiful views over the Mirabello gulf, just 2km from Aghios Nikolaos, this new complex consists of 7 individually designed villas sleeping 4-6 persons. Each villa has a spacious living area, fireplace, fully equipped kitchen and dining room as well as its own swimming pool and offers all modern amenities including Internet access. Upon arrival, guests receive a complimentary bottle of champagne and a fruit basket. A daily maid service and cook are available upon request. Activities include water skiing, windsurfing, diving, horse riding and tennis.

Situé dans une position tranquille avec de belles vues sur le golfe de Mirabello et à 2 km de Aghios Nikolaos, ce nouveau complexe comprend 7 villas décorées de façon individuelle pour 4-6 personnes. Chaque villa a un espace vital spacieux, une cheminée, une cuisine et salle à manger bien équipées, ainsi que sa propre piscine. Elles offrent toute facilité moderne, comprenant accès Internet. En arrivant, les hôtes sont offerts une bouteille de champagne et une corbeille de fruits. Femme de ménage et chef de cuisine disponibles sur demande. Loisirs: ski nautique, planche à voile, plongée, équitation et tennis.

In ruhiger Lage mit herrlicher Sicht auf den Golf von Mirabello, nur 2km von Aghios Nikolaos entfernt, liegt dieser neue Komplex, der aus 7 unterschiedlich gestalteten Villen für 4-6 Personen besteht. Jede Villa ist geräumig, hat einen Kamin, vollausgestattete Küche und Esszimmer sowie einen eigenen Pool und moderne Einrichtungen wie z.B. Internetzugang. Bei der Ankunft wartet eine Flasche Champagner und ein Obstkorb auf die Gäste. Täglicher Reinigungsdienst und Koch auf Anfrage. Aktivitäten: Wasserski, Windsurfen, Tauchen, Reiten und Tennis.

Our inspector loved: *The charming unique details in each villa.*

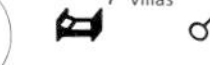

7 villas

Directions: Heraklion Airport > Elounda. Hotel is located before Aghios Nikolaos on the left.

Web: www.johansens.com/pleiades
E-mail: pleia@otenet.gr
Tel: +30 28410 90450
Fax: +30 28410 90479

Price Guide: (self-catering)
2-bedroom villa €240-680
3-bedroom villa €350-950

St Nicolas Bay Hotel

PO BOX 47, 72100 AGHIOS NIKOLAOS, CRETE, GREECE

Directions: Heraklion > Aghios Nikolas.

Web: www.johansens.com/stnicolasbay
E-mail: stnicolas@otenet.gr
Tel: +30 2841 025041
Fax: +30 2841 024556

Price Guide:
single €90-280
double/twin €130–300
suite €180–415
suite with private pool €400–1,656

Flower-filled gardens with olive, lemon and orange trees surround this bungalow hotel. With its own quiet sandy beach, it offers excellent accommodation, mouth-watering cuisine and superb service. All rooms and suites enjoy stunning views from their balconies or terraces, whilst the suites have marble bathrooms with Jacuzzi; some boast a private heated pool. Facilities include water sports, scuba diving, boats for sea excursions, gym, sauna, steam bath, Jacuzzi, massage, hydromassage, aromatherapy and beauty treatments. Member of the Charming Hotels Consortium.

Des jardins remplis de fleurs et d'oliviers, de citronniers et d'orangers entourent cet hôtel formé de pavillons. Outre sa plage privée tranquille, l'hôtel offre un excellent logement, une table savoureuse et un service impeccable. Les chambres et suites possèdent des balcons ou des terrasses avec une vue imprenable. Les suites, certaines avec piscine privée chauffée, ont des salles de bain en marbre avec jacuzzi. Loisirs: sports nautiques, plongée, excursions en bateau, gymnase, sauna, hammam, jacuzzi, massage, hydro-massage, aromathérapie et traitements de beauté. Membre de Charming Hotels.

Mit Blumen und Oliven-, Zitronen- und Orangenbäumen gefüllte Gärten umgeben dieses Bungalow-Hotel mit eigenem ruhigen Sandstrand. Küche, Service und Unterkunft sind hervorragend; die Zimmer und Suiten bieten vom Balkon oder der Terrasse traumhafte Ausblicke. Die Suiten, einige mit beheiztem Pool, haben Marmorbad mit Jacuzzi. Aktivitäten: Wassersport, Tauchen, Bootsexkursionen aufs Meer, Fitness, Sauna, Dampfbad, Whirlpool, Massage, Hydromassage, Aromatherapie und Schönheitsbehandlungen. Mitglied der Charming Hotels.

***Our inspector loved:** Enjoying a drink at the poolside bar at sunset.*

APANEMA

TAGOO, MYKONOS, GREECE

This elegant boutique hotel is set on the waterfront, just a 10-minute walk from Mykonos town. Built in 2000 and partially refurbished every year, the hotel has only 17 large rooms with balcony or terrace, thus providing a cosy and relaxed retreat from the island's vibrant lifestyle. Offering all the amenities of a large hotel, it is particularly suited for those who wish to relax and enjoy a private environment, with a choice between a soft or hard mattress, Hermès or Molton Brown bath products and breakfast until 2pm. Johansens guests are welcomed with fruit salad and a bottle of Chablis.

Cet élégant boutique hôtel est situé au bord de la mer, à 10 minutes à pied de la ville de Mykonos. Construit en 2000 et partiellement remis à neuf chaque année, l'hôtel ne dispose que de 17 grandes chambres avec balcon ou terrasse et donc offre un refuge intime pour échapper la vie trépidante de l'île. Offrant toutes les facilités d'un grand hôtel, il est idéal pour ceux qui veulent se dérouler dans un environnement privé. Il offre un choix de matelas forts et doux et des produits de bains Hermès ou Molton Brown. Le petit déjeuner est servi jusqu'à 14 h. En arrivant, les clients de Johansens reçoivent une salade de fruits et une bouteille de Chablis.

Dieses elegante Boutique-Hotel liegt direkt am Meer, nur 10 Minuten zu Fuß von Mykonos-Stadt entfernt. Das 2000 erbaute und jährlich weiter erneuerte Hotel hat nur 17 große Zimmer mit Balkon oder Terrasse und bietet so ein gemütliches Versteck vor dem regen Inseltreiben. Alle Annehmlichkeiten eines großen Hotels sind geboten, ideal um in familiärer Atmosphäre zu entspannen. Man hat die Wahl zwischen harter oder weicher Matratze und Hermès oder Molton Brown-Badeartikeln, Frühstück bis 14 Uhr. Johansens-Gäste bekommen frischen Obstsalat und eine Flasche Chablis.

Our inspector loved: *The tranquillity of the hotel during sunset.*

Directions: Mykonos Airport > across the main sea port > 800m towards Tagoo on the right.

Web: www.johansens.com/apanema
E-mail: mail@apanemaresort.com
Tel: +30 22890 28590
Fax: +30 22890 79250

Price Guide:
single €135-240
double €170-330
suite €260-385

THARROE OF MYKONOS

ANGELIKA, 84600 MYKONOS, GREECE

Directions: The hotel is 800m from Mykonos town centre.

Web: www.johansens.com/tharroe
E-mail: tharroe@myk.forthnet.gr
Tel: +30 22890 27370
Fax: +30 22890 27375

Price Guide:
single €100-460
double €120-600
suite €180-2,000

This hilltop location enjoys breathtaking sunsets and glorious views over the Aegean Sea. Mykonos town centre is just 15 minutes away and Ornos beach is within walking distance. Décor is modern and minimalist, and the en-suite bedrooms have a balcony or terrace. Traditional Greek and Mediterranean cuisine, organic and vegetarian menus are served in the Barbarossa restaurant, fine wines, organic beers and cocktails, in the Colors of the Sunset Bar. The Princess Shanhaz Ayurvedic natural herbal centre offers hair and body spa treatments.

Sa location au sommet d'une colline offre des couchers de soleil à couper le souffle et des vues splendides sur la mer Egée. Le centre de la ville de Mykonos n'est qu'à 15 minutes et la plage Ornos est accessible à pied. Le décor est moderne et minimaliste, et les chambres avec salle de bain ont un balcon ou une terrasse. Une cuisine grecque et méditerranéenne et des menus biologiques et végétariens sont servis au restaurant Barbarossa; des vins fins, des bières biologiques et des cocktails sont servis au Colors of the Sunset Bar. Le Princess Shanhaz centre ayurvédique offre des traitements bains et soins de beauté.

Von seiner Hügellage bietet dieses Hotel herrliche Sonnenuntergänge und Ausblicke auf die Ägäis. Mykonos Stadtzentrum ist nur 15 Minuten entfernt, und der Ornos-Strand ist zu Fuß erreichbar. Das Décor ist modern und minimalistisch, die Zimmer haben eigenes Bad und Terrasse oder Balkon. Das Barbarossa serviert traditionelle griechische und Mittelmeerküche und vegetarische und Bio-Menüs, in der Colors of the Sunset Bar gibt es edle Weine, Bier aus biologischem Anbau und Cocktails. Das Princess Shanhaz Ayurveda-Zentrum bietet Kur- und Schönheitsbehandlungen.

Our inspector loved: *The view of Mykonos Bay and town from the poolside.*

GREECE (PARAS)

Acquamarina Resort

NEW GOLDEN BEACH, 84400 PAROS, GREECE

This intimate, family-run resort is situated directly on the seafront and offers every guest individual care and attention in a relaxed atmosphere. The whitewashed bungalow villas are built in traditional Cycladian design, with spacious marble floored rooms and either a balcony or veranda. The outdoor pool is one of the largest in the Cycladic islands and is complemented by a poolside bar, whilst the alluring gardens reflect the tranquillity of the resort. Guests can enjoy mouth-watering cuisine in the taverna or the à la carte restaurant.

Cet ensemble balnéaire familial intime est situé directement en bordure de mer et offre à ses hôtes une attention individualisée dans une atmosphère détendue. Les bungalows aux murs blanchis sont construits dans le style traditionnel des Cyclades, avec de grandes pièces aux sols en marbre et soit un balcon soit une véranda. La piscine extérieure est la plus grande des Cyclades avec bar au bord, alors que des jardins émane la tranquillité de la station. Les hôtes peuvent déguster une cuisine savoureuse à la taverne ou au restaurant à la carte.

Dieses kleine, familiengeführte Resort befindet sich direkt am Meer und bietet jedem Gast höchst individuelle Aufmerksamkeit in entspannter Atmosphäre. Die weißgetünchten Bungalow-Villen sind in traditionellem kykladischen Design gestaltet und haben geräumige Zimmer mit Marmorböden und entweder Balkon oder Veranda. Der Swimmingpool – komplett mit Bar – ist einer der größten der Kykladischen Inseln und die hübschen Gärten spiegeln die Beschaulichkeit des Resorts wider. In der Taverne oder im à la carte Restaurant wird köstliche Küche serviert.

Our inspector loved: *The charming restaurant by the seaside.*

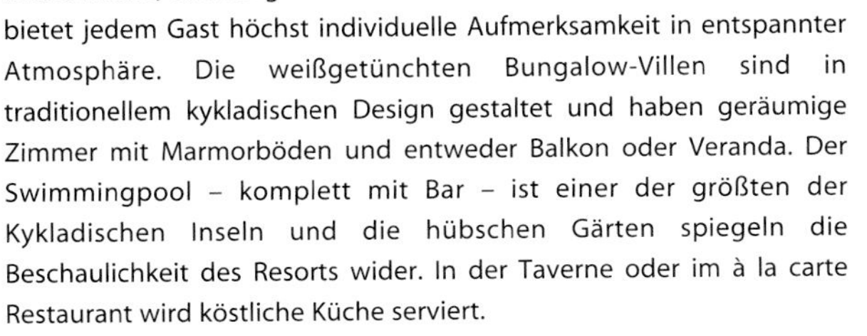

Directions: Paros Airport > Paros Port > towards New Golden Beach Road (Neachrisiakti) > at the beach the hotel is signposted.

Web: www.johansens.com/acquamarina
E-mail: acquamarina@cybex.gr
Tel: +30 228404 3281
Fax: +30 228404 3236

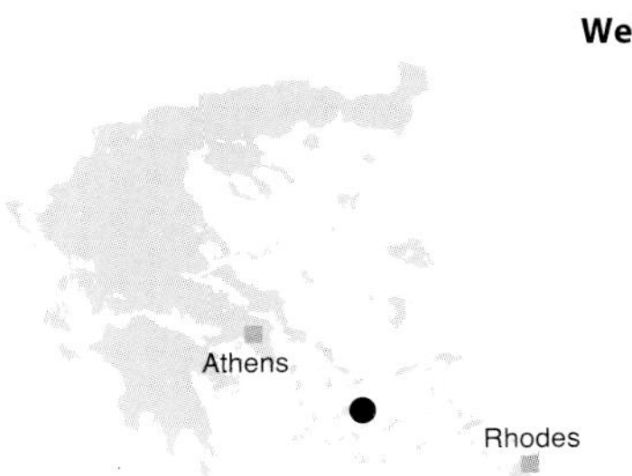

Price Guide:
single €98-140
double €140-200
suite €180-300

ITALY

Hotel location shown in red (hotel) or purple (spa hotel) with page number

ALTAFIUMARA HOTEL

SANTA TRADA DI CANNITELLO, 89010 VILLA SAN GIOVANNI (REGGIO CALABRIA), ITALY

Situated in one of the most beautiful areas of Calabria, along the purple coast, Altafiumara is built around an ancient Bourbon fortress dating back to the 18th century, and today is an elegant hotel focusing on the total wellbeing of its guests. A delight to the senses, there are spectacular views with sweeping horizons, and Mediterranean fragrances abound. The castle has been carefully integrated into a 7-hectare park looking out to the sea, and an impressive well-being centre takes a holistic approach to its treatments.

Situé dans l'une des plus belles parties de Calabria, le long de la côte, Altafiumara est construit autour d'une ancienne forteresse Bourbon datant du XVIIIe siècle. C'est aujourd'hui un élégant hôtel dédié au bien-être de ses hôtes. Pour le bonheur des sens, il y a de spectaculaires vues qui balayent l'horizon et les senteurs méditerranéennes abondent. Le château a été soigneusement intégré dans un parc de 7 hectares avec vue sur la mer. L'impressionnant centre de bien-êtrespa utilise une approche holistique dans les soins.

In einem der schönsten Teile Kalabriens, entlang der Costa Viola, befindet sich Altafiumara, um eine alte bourbonische Festung aus dem 18. Jahrhundert herum gebaut, und heute ein elegantes Hotel, das sich ganz dem Wohlergehen seiner Gäste widmet. Das Hotel ist ein Genuss für die Sinne, man kann spektakuläre Ausblicke bewundern, und mediterrane Aromen erfüllen die Luft. Die Burg wurde sorgfältig in einen 7ha großen Park mit Blick aufs Meer eingegliedert, und ein eindrucksvolles Wellness-Zentrum bietet Behandlungen mit holistischem Ansatz.

***Our inspector loved:** The spa; among the best in southern Italy.*

Directions: Airport > Reggio Calabria > Salerno > exit S. Trada.

Web: www.johansens.com/altafiumara
E-mail: info@altafiumarahotel.it
Tel: +39 096 575 9804
Fax: +39 096 575 9566

Milan
Venice
Rome

Price Guide:
single €125-230
double €200-310
suite €235-395

Hotel Villa Maria

VIA S. CHIARA 2, 84010 RAVELLO (SA), ITALY

Situated with a unique and breathtaking view of the Amalfi coast and the hills that gently slope down to it lies this family-owned hotel, which has a romantic and intimate ambience, as if staying in a private villa. The rooms are large and spacious overlooking the orchard that provides ingredients for the elegant dinner table. Guests also have use of the swimming pool at the nearby sister hotel, Hotel Giordano.

Cet hôtel familial à l'ambiance romantique et intime comme celle d'une villa privée, a des vues uniques et à couper le souffle sur la côte d'Amalfi et sur les collines qui descendent doucement vers celle-ci. Les chambres sont grandes et spacieuses et s'ouvrent sur les vergers d'où viennent certains ingrédients utilisés pour l'élégante table du dîner. Les hôtes peuvent également utiliser la piscine de l'hôtel partenaire tout proche, l'hôtel Giordano.

In einzigartiger Lage mit atemberaubender Sicht auf die Amalfiküste und die sanft bis zur Küste hinunterführenden Hügel liegt dieses familiengeführte Hotel, das ein romantisches und familiäres Ambiente besitzt, so dass man sich wie in einer privaten Villa fühlt. Die Zimmer sind groß und geräumig und blicken auf den Garten, der stets für frische Zutaten für ein elegantes Abendessen sorgt. Gäste können den Swimmingpool des nahegelegenen Schwesterhotels Giordano benutzen.

Our inspector loved: *The organic orchard, and stunning view.*

Directions: A3 (Naples – Salerno) > exit Angri > Costa Amalfitana > Ravello.

Web: www.johansens.com/villamaria
Email: villamaria@villamaria.it
Tel: +39 089 857255
Fax: +39 089 857071

Price Guide:
single €150–180
double €180–280
suite €400–440

Grand Hotel Cocumella

VIA COCUMELLA 7, 80065 SANT'AGNELLO, SORRENTO, ITALY

This former Jesuit monastery was transformed into a hotel in 1822. Traces of the past remain; the elegant hall was once the cloisters and the chapel is still used for weddings and concerts. Many of the guest rooms have magnificent antique furnishings and the bridal suite has an exquisite painted ceiling. Guests feast on aromatic Mediterranean dishes, and in summer, light buffet lunches are enjoyed by the pool.

Cet ancien monastère jésuite a été transformé en hôtel en 1822. Les traces du passé sont encore présentes, le hall élégant occupe l'ancien cloître et la chapelle continue d'être utilisée pour des mariages ou des concerts. De magnifiques meubles anciens agrémentent les chambres et une peinture raffinée orne le plafond de la suite nuptiale. Les visiteurs dégustent des plats méditerranéens aux saveurs aromatiques l'été et des buffets légers sont proposés au bord de la piscine.

Dieses ehemalige Jesuitenkloster wurde 1822 zu einem Hotel umgebaut, und Spuren der Vergangenheit sind immer noch vorhanden. Die elegante Halle war einst der Kreuzgang und die Kapelle wird noch heute für Hochzeiten und Konzerte genutzt. Viele der Zimmer sind mit prächtigen Antikmöbeln eingerichtet und die Hochzeitssuite ziert eine beeindruckend bemalte Decke. Die Gäste erfreuen sich an köstlichen mediterranen Gerichten, und in den Sommermonaten sind leichte Buffetlunches am Pool zu genießen.

Our inspector loved: *The scent of the garden: a revitalising experience.*

Directions: Naples > Castellammare di Stabia > Sorrento.

Web: www.johansens.com/grandcocumella
E-mail: info@cocumella.com
Tel: +39 081 878 2933
Fax: +39 081 878 3712

Price Guide:
single €215–305
double/twin €330–460
suite €470–760

54

Monte del Re

40050 DOZZA (BOLOGNA), ITALY

Directions: From the A1 > A14 towards Ancona > exit Castel San Pietro Terme > follow directions to Imola - Dozza SS9 (Via Emilia).

Web: www.johansens.com/montedelre
E-mail: montedelre@tiscali.it
Tel: +39 0542 678400
Fax: +39 0542 678444

Price Guide:
single €97-170
double €125-230
junior suite €175-260

This ancient convent, which enjoys a prestigious location within a park overlooking the hills, offers the perfect combination of tranquillity and comfort needed in today's hectic world. Guests at Monte del Re are immediately surrounded by its magical, romantic atmosphere, enhanced by the charming surroundings. Superb culinary delights are served in the restaurant, and guests will appreciate the richly elegant furnishings, the panoramic swimming pool and the beautiful garden. The ancient church is now used as a conference centre or for banquets.

Ce couvent très ancien, qui jouit d'une position prestigieuse au sein d'un parc donnant sur les collines, offre la combinaison parfaite de tranquillité et confort, dont nous avons tellement besoin dans la vie trépidante de nos jours. Les hôtes sont immédiatement entourés par une ambiance romantique, mise en valeur par les environs charmants. Des délices culinaires superbes sont servies dans le restaurant, et les hôtes apprécieront les mobiliers élégants, la piscine panoramique et le beau jardin. L'église ancienne a été transformée en centre de conférences et banquets.

Dieses einstige Kloster in seiner herrlichen Lage inmitten eines Parks mit Blick auf die Hügellandschaft bietet die perfekte Verbindung von Ruhe und Komfort, so dringend nötig in unserer hektischen Welt. Man ist hier sofort von einer magischen, romantischen Atmosphäre umgeben, die durch die zauberhafte Umgebung noch verstärkt wird. Im Restaurant wird hervorragende Küche serviert, und die üppig-elegante Einrichtung, der Panorama-Swimmingpool und der hübsche Garten runden das Ganze wunderbar ab. Die alte Kirche dient nun als Konferenz- oder Bankettsaal.

Our inspector loved: *The magical atmosphere and the superb restaurant.*

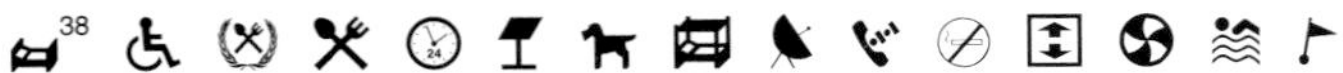

Ripagrande Hotel

VIA RIPAGRANDE 21, 44100 FERRARA, ITALY

This superbly restored 15th-century palace features a Renaissance interior, appropriate to the history of the hotel. The entrance hall is spectacular with its marble staircase and pillars, wrought-iron banisters and beamed ceiling. The attractive Ripa restaurant serves many traditional Ferrarese specialities. 2 enchanting courtyards make wonderful settings for banquets. Guests relax in the cool salons or upon terraces, some of which are privately adjoined to the spacious bedrooms, which have been recently refurbished.

Ce palais du XVe siècle superbement restauré est agrémenté d'un intérieur Renaissance. Le hall d'entrée est spectaculaire en raison de sa cage d'escalier orné d'une rampe en fer forgé, de ses colonnes en marbre et de son plafond orné de poutres. Le charmant restaurant Ripa sert nombre de spécialités traditionnelles de Ferrare. Enfin, 2 délicieuses cours forment un cadre idéal pour les banquets. Les hôtes peuvent se relaxer dans les salons ou sur les terrasses, dont certaines privées rejoignent les chambres spacieuses et récemment renovées.

Das Interieur dieses perfekt restaurierten Palais aus dem 15. Jahrhundert ist im Renaissance-Stil gehalten und passt somit zur Geschichte des Hotels. Die Eingangshalle beeindruckt mit Marmortreppe und -säulen, schmiedeeisernen Geländern und Balkendecke. Das Restaurant Ripa serviert traditionelle Spezialitäten aus Ferrara, und 2 zauberhafte Innenhöfe sind perfekt für Bankette. Entspannen kann man in den kühlen Salons oder auf den Terrassen, von denen einige zum Privatgebrauch direkt an die geräumigen, kürzlich renovierten Zimmer angrenzen.

Our inspector loved: *The 2 magnificent Renaissance courtyards and the exquisite cuisine.*

Directions: The hotel is halfway between Venice and Florence. A13 > Ferrara.

Web: www.johansens.com/ripagrande
E-mail: ripahotel@mbox.4net.it
Tel: +39 0532 765250
Fax: +39 0532 764377

Price Guide:
single €125
double/twin €195
suite €175–190

Hotel Posta (Historical Residence)

PIAZZA DEL MONTE, 2, 42100 REGGIO EMILIA, ITALY

Directions: A1 (Milano/Roma) > exit at Reggio Emilia > town centre.

Web: www.johansens.com/posta
E-mail: info@hotelposta.re.it
Tel: +39 05 22 43 29 44
Fax: +39 05 22 45 26 02

Price Guide:
single €135-150
double €180
suite €210-250

Located in the town's historic centre, this imposing medieval building was built in 1280 as Palazzo del Capitano (Magistrate's House) and has a long tradition of hospitality. The influence of the different centuries can be appreciated in the charming blend of styles throughout the hotel. The bar with its refined and unusual atmosphere is particularly delightful, whilst the splendid Salone del Capitano is available for meetings and banquets. Excursions in and out of town can be organised, including a visit to a cheese factory, where the legendary Parmigiano Reggiano (parmesan cheese) is produced.

Situé au cœur de la ville historique, cette maison médiévale imposante fut construite en 1280 comme Palazzo del Capitano (la maison du magistrat) et possède une longue tradition d'hospitalité. L'influence des siècles passés se montre dans le mélange de styles dans tout l'hôtel. Le bar avec son atmosphère élégante et exceptionnelle est splendide, alors que le Salone del Capitano est l'endroit idéal pour des conférences ou des banquets. Des excursions peuvent être organisées, comprenant une visite à une fromagerie produisant le Parmigiano Reggiano légendaire.

Dieses eindrucksvolle mittelalterliche Haus befindet sich im Zentrum der Altstadt und erfreut sich einer langen Tradition der Gastfreundschaft. 1280 als Palazzo del Capitano (Haus des Stadtverwalters) erbaut, zeigen sich auch heute noch die Einflüsse der Jahrhunderte in einer zauberhaften Stilmischung. Besonders die Bar mit ihrer einmaligen Atmosphäre ist ein Genuss. Der Salone del Capitano bietet sich sowohl für Konferenzen als auch Bankette an. Exkursionen werden organisiert, darunter der Besuch einer Käserei, in der der berühmt Parmigiano Reggiano hergestellt wird.

Our inspector loved: *The magnificent medieval style façade.*

Hotel des Nations

LUNGOMARE COSTITUZIONE 2, 47838 RICCIONE (RN), ITALY

Situated on the beach, this quiet, charming hotel was conceived according to the wellness philosophy. Stunning sea views and beautiful antique furniture enhance the elegant bedrooms. Natural organic food and local delicacies are served in the harmoniously decorated breakfast room, and guests can make reservations at the adjacent restaurant. Health treatments such as massage, reflexology and mud therapy are available; outdoor pursuits include tennis, excursions and fishing.

Situé sur la plage, ce charmant hôtel a été conçu suivant les principes du bien-être. Une vue imprenable sur la mer et de beaux meubles anciens mettent en valeur les chambres élégantes. Une nourriture naturelle et biologique et des spécialités locales sont servies dans la salle du petit-déjeuner. Les repas peuvent être pris dans le restaurant adjacent à l'hôtel. Les hôtes peuvent profiter de traitements tels que massage, réflexologie et bains de boue, alors que les activités incluent tennis, voile, excursions et pêche.

Dieses ruhige, am Strand gelegene Hotel wurde gemäß der Wellness-Philosophie erbaut. Traumhafte Meeresblicke und schöne antike Möbel verstärken das elegante Ambiente der Zimmer. Im harmonisch gestalteten Frühstücksraum werden biologische Kost und einheimische Köstlichkeiten serviert, und die Gäste können das Restaurant nebenan besuchen. Behandlungen wie Massage, Reflexologie und Schlammtherapie werden angeboten; Tennis, Exkursionen und Angeln sind ebenfalls möglich.

Our inspector loved: *The emphasis on well-being, from the natural delicacies at breakfast to the therapies for body and mind.*

Directions: A14 > exit Riccione > follow directions to Riccione Mare.

Web: www.johansens.com/hoteldesnations
E-mail: info@desnations.it
Tel: +39 0541 647878
Fax: +39 0541 645154

Price Guide:
single €140–175
double €210–270
suite €306–545

Ciasa de Gahja

VIA ANZOLET 13, 33070 BUDOIA (PN), ITALY

Directions: A4 > A27 towards Belluno/Vittorio Veneto > exit Conegliano > follow signs to Salile Pordenone.

Web: www.johansens.com/ciasadegahja
E-mail: info@ciasadegahja.com
Tel: +39 0434 654 897
Fax: +39 0434 654 815

Price Guide:
single €80
double €110
suite €150

The combination of its unique location in the heart of a small, medieval village at the foot of a lovely mountain range with surroundings of peaceful parks and woodland provides this charming hotel with a sense of total tranquillity and relaxation. Family run, Ciasa de Gahja offers a historic atmosphere with modern-day home comforts and individually designed bedrooms furnished to the highest standard. Excellent Italian cuisine is attentively served in the homely restaurant, complemented by an extensive selection of fine wines exclusive to the region.

La combinaison de sa situation unique au cœur d'un petit village médiéval situé au pied d'une belle chaîne de montagnes et entouré de parcs et de bois paisibles donne à ce charmant hôtel un sentiment de tranquillité et de relaxation totale. Géré en famille, Ciasa de Gahja, offre une atmosphère historique avec tout le confort moderne et de ravissantes chambres décorées individuellement et meublées avec soin. Une délicieuse cuisine italienne est servie dans l'accueillant restaurant accompagné d'une excellente sélection de vins exclusifs à cette région.

Dieses charmante familiengeführte Hotel befindet sich in einzigartiger Lage im Herzen eines mittelalterlichen Dörfchens am Fuße einer herrlichen Bergkette und umgeben von friedlicher Park- und Waldlandschaft. Ein Gefühl von kompletter Ruhe und Erholung verbindet sich hier mit historischem Ambiente und modernem Komfort. Die individuell gestalteten Zimmer sind hervorragend ausgestattet, und im gemütlichen Restaurant wird köstliche italienische Küche mit einer umfassenden Auswahl an edlen Weinen, die es nur in dieser Region gibt, serviert.

Our inspector loved: *The joyful atmosphere.*

ITALY / LAZIO (PALO LAZIALE – ROME)

La Posta Vecchia Hotel Spa

PALO LAZIALE, 00055 LADISPOLI, ROME, ITALY

Overlooking the sea and surrounded by natural parkland, the sumptuous Posta Vecchia, built on ancient Roman foundations, has a quiet luxuriousness. Many of the original structures such as stone doorways and fireplaces are preserved whilst stunning mosaics and antiques have been carefully restored and displayed in the hotel's museum. Exquisite décor and warm colour schemes create a welcoming atmosphere and the Italian cooking is simply delicious. There is a private beach and excellent leisure facilities inlcuding a beauty salon.

Surplombant la mer et entouré d'un parc naturel, le somptueux Posta Vecchia, construit sur d'anciennes fondations romaines, bénéficie d'un luxe tranquille. La plupart des installations originelles telles qu'encadrements de porte en pierre et cheminées a été préservée alors que d'étonnantes mosaïques et antiquités ont été restaurées avec soin et sont présentées dans le musée de l'hôtel. Le décor raffiné et les couleurs chaudes créent une atmosphère accueillante; la cuisine italienne est tout simplement délicieuse. L'hôtel dispose d'une plage privée et d'excellentes installations de loisirs, incluant un salon de beauté.

Dieses auf römischen Fundamenten erbaute, von Parklandschaft umgebene Hotel mit Meerblick bietet Eleganz und unaufdringlichen Luxus. Viele ursprüngliche Strukturen wie steinerne Torbögen und Kamine blieben erhalten, zauberhafte Mosaiken und Antiquitäten wurden sorgfältig restauriert und im Hotelmuseum ausgestellt. Exquisites Décor und warme Farben schaffen eine einladende Atmosphäre, und die italienische Küche ist einfach unübertroffen. Ein Privatstrand sowie Freizeiteinrichtungen sind vorhanden, darunter ein Beautysalon.

Our inspector loved: *The many Roman antiques displayed around the hotel.*

Directions: A12 > Cerveteri - Ladispoli > follow SSI south > exit Palo Laziale.

Web: www.johansens.com/postavecchia
E-mail: info@lapostavecchia.com
Tel: +39 0699 49501
Fax: +39 0699 49507

Price Guide: (double occupancy)
superior room €570
junior suite €920
master suite €1,400

THE DUKE HOTEL

VIA ARCHIMEDE 69, 00197 ROME, ITALY

Located in the prestigious and elegant residential district of Parioli, The Duke is a peaceful and stylish 4-star hotel that offers attentive and personal service for the most exacting guest. The style is a winning combination of classic Italian bourgeois design and the ambience of an English Gentleman's Club, creating a warmth of atmosphere that is mirrored by the attitude of its staff. The hotel is set between the parks of Villa Borghese and Villa Glori, and numerous sights are within easy reach. A complimentary limousine service to Via Veneto is available.

Situé dans le prestigieux et élégant quartier résidentiel de Parioli, le Duke est un hôtel 4 étoiles chic et paisible qui offre un service personnel et attentif pour les hôtels les plus exigeants. Le style est une combinaison gagnante de style italien bourgeois classique et d'ambiance de Club de gentleman anglais, créant ainsi une atmosphère chaleureuse reflétée dans l'attitude du personnel. Cet hôtel est situé entre les parcs de la Villa Borghèse et de la Villa Glori, et proche de nombreuses curiosités touristiques. Un service de limousine à Via Veneto est disponible.

Das inmitten des vornehmen, edlen Wohnviertels Parioli gelegene Duke Hotel ist ein friedliches und elegantes 4-Sterne-Hotel, dessen aufmerksamer, persönlicher Service selbst den anspruchsvollsten Gast zufrieden stellt. Der Stil ist eine attraktive Mischung aus klassischem italienischen bürgerlichem Design und dem Ambiente eines englischen Gentlemen Clubs, dessen herzliche Atmosphäre sich in der Freundlichkeit des Personals widerspiegelt. Das Hotel befindet sich zwischen den Parks der Villa Borghese und der Villa Glori, und zahlreiche Sehenswürdigkeiten liegen in nächster Nähe. Limousinenservice zur Via Veneto ist vorhanden.

Directions: 40 minutes from Ciampino and Fiumicino Airports.

Web: www.johansens.com/dukehotel
E-mail: rvisocchi@thedukehotel.com
Tel: +39 06 367221
Fax: +39 06 36004104

Price Guide:
single €222-269
double €320-430
suite €528-1,005

Our inspector loved: *The Polo Lounge, designed by Busiri Vici's studio.*

Hotel Aventino

VIA SAN DOMENICO 10, 00153 ROME, ITALY

Newly restored with care and respect for the district's historic past this charming city centre hotel enjoys an atmosphere of refined and innovative tranquillity. Décor and furnishings evoke a world of genteel and traditional relaxation, which radiates out from elegant public rooms and spacious guest rooms with all modern facilities to the attractive shady garden. The lounge boasts an antique fireplace, which during the colder months creates a very romantic and charming atmosphere. An ideal base for exploring Rome's treasures.

Récemment restauré avec soin et respect de l'histoire du quartier, cet hôtel charmant du centre ville bénéficie d'une atmosphère tranquille et raffinée. Le décor et le mobilier évoquent un monde de distinction associé à une détente traditionnelle, qui irradient des élégantes salles communes et des chambres spacieuses disposant de tout le confort moderne, jusqu'au beau jardin ombragé. Le salon a une cheminée antique, qui pendant des moins plus froids, crée une atmosphére romantique et charmante. Une base idéale pour explorer les trésors de Rome.

Dieses zauberhafte, erst kürzlich mit viel Liebe und Respekt für die historische Vergangenheit dieses Bezirks restaurierte Hotel im Stadtzentrum besitzt eine Atmosphäre der Eleganz und Ruhe. Décor und Einrichtung sorgen für ein Gefühl der Entspannung, das in den eleganten Aufenthaltsräumen, großen Gästezimmern mit jeglichem modernem Komfort und dem attraktiven, schattenspendenden Garten zu spüren ist. Der Aufenthaltsraum hat einen antiken Kamin, der während der kälteren Monate eine romantische und bezaubernde Atmosphäre erstellt. Der ideale Ausgangspunkt, um Roms Schätze zu erkunden.

Our inspector loved: *This wonderful oasis amidst the hustle and bustle of Rome.*

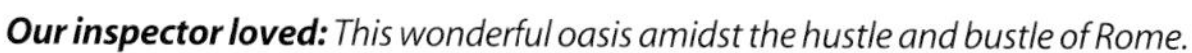

Directions: Located in the heart of the city.

Web: www.johansens.com/aventino
E-mail: info@aventinohotels.com
Tel: +39 06 5745 231
Fax: +39 06 5745 174

Price Guide:
single €109
double €180-200
suite €210

HOTEL DEI BORGOGNONI

VIA DEL BUFALO 126 (PIAZZA DI SPAGNA), 00187 ROME, ITALY

Directions: The hotel is a short walk from Piazza di Spagna metro station. Private parking is available.

Web: www.johansens.com/borgognoni
E-mail: info@hotelborgognoni.it
Tel: +39 06 6994 1505
Fax: +39 06 6994 1501

Price Guide:
single €218-255
double €305-395
suite upon request

Hidden in a "vicolo", within the surrounding area of the Trevi Fountain, stands this charming hotel. Recently refurbished, the hall and common area have been enhanced to reflect the exquisite elegance of its ambience. In an ideal location, the hotel is a short walk from the Trevi Fountain and the Spanish Steps as well as many cultural delights. Each of the en-suite bedrooms overlooks the hotel's enclosed garden, featuring an abundance of flowers. The refined lounge offers a relaxing place to take a drink. Conference rooms are also available.

Ce charmant hôtel se cache dans un « vicolo » au quartier de la fontaine de Trévi. Récemment renovés, le hall et le salon reflètent l'élégance exquisite des environs. Situé dans un endroit idéal, l'hôtel est tout près de la fontaine de Trévi, la Piazza di Spagna ainsi que d'autres délices culturelles. Toutes les chambres, avec salle de bains attenante, donnent sur le jardin enclos de l'hôtel avec son abondance de fleurs, et le salon raffiné offre un environnement relaxant pour prendre un verre. Des salles de conférence sont aussi disponibles.

Dieses bezaubernde Hotel liegt versteckt in einem vicolo im Viertel um den Trevibrunnen. Eingangshalle und Aufenthaltsbereich wurden kürzlich neu gestaltet und spiegeln perfekt die exquisite Eleganz der Umgebung wider. Das Hotel liegt ideal nur einen kurzen Spaziergang vom Trevibrunnen, der Spanischen Treppe und vielen anderen kulturellen Attraktionen entfernt. Alle Zimmer haben ein eigenes Bad und blicken auf das Blumenmeer im von außen abgeschirmten Hotelgarten, und in der eleganten Lounge kann man bei einem Drink wunderbar entspannen. Konferenzräume sind ebenfalls vorhanden.

Our inspector loved: *Its location in the heart of the city's historic centre.*

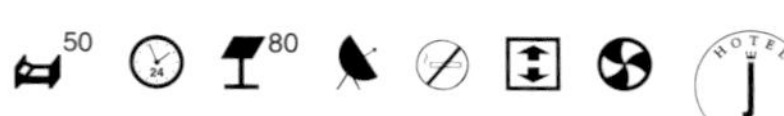

Hotel dei Consoli

VIA VARRONE 2/D, 00193 ROMA, ITALY

In the heart of town, near the Tiber river and close to the Vatican, this charming hotel welcomes guests into a peaceful retreat. Its history dates back to the 19th century and ornate public rooms feature soaring stucco decorations, Murano chandeliers, antique furniture, fresh flowers and excellent paintings. Guest rooms and suites, many of which overlook St Peter's dome, are beautifully appointed with period style furniture, rich fabrics, objets d'art and spacious bathrooms. The hotel boasts a superb location for the business and leisure traveller alike and takes great pride in its impeccable level of service.

Situé en plein centre ville, près du fleuve de Tibre et du Vatican, cet hôtel charmant offre à ses hôtes un refuge de paix. L'hôtel date du XIXe siècle et les salles publiques fleuries sont ornées de grandes décorations de stuc, lustres de Murano, des meubles antiques, des belles peintures et des fleurs. Les chambres et les suites, dont plusieurs donnent sur le Dôme Saint Pierre, sont meublées dans le style de l'époque et décorées avec des tissus de luxe et des objets d'art. Les salles de bains sont toutes spacieuses. L'hôtel revendique un endroit superbe pour le voyageur d'affaires ainsi que pour le voyageur de loisirs et le personnel est fier de son niveau impeccable de service.

Dieses zauberhafte, nahe am Tiber und am Vatikan gelegene Hotel bietet seinen Gästen ein ruhiges Versteck mitten im Herzen der Stadt. Seine Geschichte geht bis ins 19. Jahrhundert zurück, und in den Aufenthaltsräumen kann man Stuckverzierungen, Muranolüster, antikes Mobiliar, frische Blumen und herrliche Gemälde bewundern. Die Zimmer und Suiten - zahlreiche mit Blick auf den Petersdom - sind wundervoll mit Stilmöbeln, üppigen Stoffen, Kunstgegenständen und geräumigen Badezimmern eingerichtet. Das Hotel liegt ideal sowohl für Geschäftsreisende als auch Touristen und ist zurecht stolz auf seinen tadellosen Service.

Our inspector loved: *This real gem! A wonderfully peaceful haven.*

Directions: The hotel is a 2-minute walk from the Vatican and 15 minutes from the Spanish Steps.

Web: www.johansens.com/deiconsoli
E-mail: info@hoteldeiconsoli.com
Tel: +39 0668 892972
Fax: +39 0668 212274

Price Guide:
single €100-220
double €150-300
junior suite €200-480

HOTEL FENIX

VIALE GORIZIA 5/7, 00198 ROME, ITALY

Directions: The hotel is situated in the city centre. 50km from Fiumicino Airport and 30km from Ciampino Airport.

Web: www.johansens.com/fenix
E-mail: info@fenixhotel.it
Tel: +39 06 8540 741
Fax: +39 06 8543 632

Price Guide:
single €130
double €140-180

Opened in 1960, this elegant hotel is situated in Rome's Trieste district, just 20 minutes from the famous shopping area around Via Veneto and close to numerous historical and cultural attractions. Some of the comfortable bedrooms and suites are furnished in neo-classical style; many have private terraces, and the suites offer Jacuzzi bathtubs. Traditional Mediterranean and Roman dishes are served in the subtly lit restaurant or in the bedrooms (Mon-Fri). The meeting room accommodates up to 25 people. Guided tours can be arranged by the hotel.

Ouvert en 1960, cet élégant hôtel est situé dans le quartier Trieste de Rome, à seulement 20 minutes des boutiques autour de Via Veneto et proche de nombreuses attractions culturelles et historiques. Certaines des chambres et suites confortables sont meublées dans un style néoclassique, beaucoup ont des terrasses privées et les suites possèdent un jacuzzi. Des plats traditionnels, méditerranéens et romains sont servis dans le restaurant à l'éclairage subtil ou dans les chambres (du lundi au vendredi). Les salles de réunion accueillent jusqu'à 25 personnes. Des visites guidées peuvent être organisées par l'hôtel.

Dieses elegante, 1960 eröffnete Hotel liegt im Trieste-Viertel, nur 20 Minuten von der berühmten Einkaufsstraße Via Veneto und nicht weit von zahlreichen kulturellen und historischen Attraktionen entfernt. Einige der komfortablen Zimmer und Suiten sind neoklassizistisch gestaltet, einige haben eine eigene Terrasse, die Suiten bieten Jacuzzibadewannen. Traditionelle Mittelmeerküche und römische Speisen werden im sanft beleuchteten Restaurant oder (Mo-Fr) auf im Zimmer serviert. Der Konferenzraum faßt 25 Personen. Exkursionen können arrangiert werden.

Our inspector loved: *The relaxed atmosphere and great location.*

Hotel Giulio Cesare

VIA DEGLI SCIPIONI 287, 00192 ROME, ITALY

The Giulio Cesare, situated close to some of the most glorious streets in Rome, is the essence of comfort. Offering its guests a unique blend of hospitality, relaxation and excellent service, this 18th-century neo-classical hotel is ideal for either business or pleasure. The intimate bar is delightful with a fine collection of wines. Whilst there is no restaurant, sumptuous dishes are served at all times of the day in the bar and garden.

Le Giulio Cesare, proche des rues les plus prestigieuses de Rome, est la quintessence du confort. Offrant un degré exceptionnel d'hospitalité, de détente et de qualité de service, cet hôtel néo-classique est idéal pour les voyageurs d'affaires comme pour les touristes. Le bar intime est charmant et offre une palette de grands vins exceptionnelle. Bien qu'il n'y ait pas de restaurant, de succulents plats sont servis à toute heure de la journée dans le bar ou dans le jardin.

Das Giulio Cesare liegt in der Nähe einiger der prachtvollsten Straßen Roms und ist der Inbegriff von Komfort. Mit seiner einzigartigen Mischung aus Gastfreundschaft, Entspannung und exzellentem Service ist dieses neoklassizistische Hotel aus dem 18. Jahrhundert ideal sowohl für Urlauber als auch Geschäftsreisende. Die intime Bar wartet mit einer erlesenen Auswahl an Weinen auf. Zwar besitzt das Hotel kein Restaurant, doch in der Bar oder im Garten werden rund um die Uhr verlockende Speisen serviert.

Our inspector loved: *Enjoying breakfast in the garden to the song of birds.*

Directions: Lepanto tube.

Web: www.johansens.com/giuliocesare
E-mail: giulioce@uni.net
Tel: +39 06 321 0751
Fax: +39 06 321 1736

Price Guide:
single €250
double/twin €300-376

HOTEL PIRANESI

VIA DEL BABUINO 196, 00187 ROME, ITALY

With a favourable central location between the Spanish Steps and Vanvitelli's masterpiece, the Piazza del Popolo, this prestigious, historical residence has been carefully renovated into a luxury boutique hotel. Retaining its early Baroque style and heritage, the classic, elegant rooms and warm welcoming lounges provide exclusive comfort. A small gym and an amazing roof garden overlook the rooftops of Rome and Pincio Hill, and the lobby bar provides a relaxing retreat. City and shopping excursions and tours to the coast can be arranged upon request.

Doté d'un emplacement central à deux pas du chef d'œuvre de Vanvitelli, la Piazza del Popolo, cette demeure historique vient juste d'être soigneusement rénové et transformé en un boutique hôtel de luxe. Gardant son héritage et son style Baroque, les chambres classiques mais élégantes et les salons chaleureux sont de tout confort. Une petite salle de gymnastique et le petit jardin sur le toit offrent des vues sur Rome et sur le Pincio, et le bar est l'endroit idéal pour la détente. Découverte de la ville, shopping et excursions sur la côte peuvent être organisées sur demande.

Diese prestigereiche, historische Residenz, die günstig zwischen der Spanischen Treppe und Vanvitellis Meisterwerk, der Piazza del Popolo gelegenist, wurde sorgfältig renoviert und in ein luxuriöses Boutique-Hotel umgewandelt. Die deutlich vom Barockstil geprägten klassischen, eleganten Zimmer und einladenden Aufenthaltsräume bieten exklusiven Komfort. Ein kleiner Fitnessraum und ein atemberaubender Dachgarten blicken auf die Dächer von Rom und den Pincio-Hügel, und der Barbereich ist der ideale Ort zur Entspannung. Stadtrundfahrten, Einkaufstrips und Ausflüge an die Küste können arrangiert werden.

Our inspector loved: *The feeling of belonging to an exclusive club.*

Directions: The hotel is situated within the heart of the city.

Web: www.johansens.com/piranesi
E-mail: info@hotelpiranesi.com
Tel: +39 06328041
Fax: +39 063610597

Price Guide:
double (single occupancy) €240-270
double €320-360
junior suite €420
piranesi suite €520

Grand Hotel Diana Majestic

VIA OLEANDRI 15, 18013 DIANO MARINA (IM), ITALY

This small resort hotel has a great position just by the sea with its own private sandy beach, and is set in delightful ancient olive groves. The comfortable bedrooms all have a balcony and sea view, whilst the new suites have the added temptation of a large terrace with outdoor Jacuzzi. Excellent Mediterranean cuisine is served nightly, whilst the terrace by the sea provides a stunning backdrop for candle-lit dining. The hotel's bar boasts 60 brands of whisky and 100 bottles of the finest liqueurs and spirits from the 1920s.

Cette petite station de vacances se trouve tout près de la mer avec sa propre plage de sable et parmi des anciennes oliveraies merveilleuses. Toutes les chambres confortables ont un balcon avec vue sur la mer, et les nouvelles suites offrent une grande terrasse avec Jacuzzi en plein air. Une cuisine excellente méditerranéenne est servie chaque soir, alors que la terrasse près de la mer est l'endroit parfait pour des dîners aux chandelles. Le bar offre 60 marques de whisky ainsi que 100 bouteilles de liqueurs et de spiritueux des années 1920.

Dieses kleine Resort-Hotel befindet sich in bevorzugter Lage inmitten alter Olivenhaine direkt am Meer und hat einen eigenen Sandstrand. Die komfortablen Zimmer haben alle Balkon und Meerblick, und die neuen Suiten bieten zudem noch eine große Terrasse mit Jacuzzi im Freien. Jeden Abend wird exzellente Mittelmeerküche serviert, die man bei Kerzenschein auf der Terrasse direkt am Meer genießen kann. Die Bar bietet 60 Sorten Whisky sowie 100 Flaschen feinster Liköre und Spirituosen der 20er Jahre.

Our inspector loved: *The romantic atmosphere of the terrace overlooking the sea.*

Directions: Exit A10 at San Bartolomeo Al Mare, then follow signs for Diano Marina. Easy access from Genoa and Nice Airports.

Web: www.johansens.com/dianamajestic
E-mail: grandhotel@dianamajestic.com
Tel: +39 0183 402 727
Fax: +39 0183 403 040

Price Guide:
single €110-200
double €160-220
suite €260-750

Hotel Punta Est

VIA AURELIA 1, 17024 FINALE LIGURE (SV) ITALY

This elegant 18th-century villa was once a private summer residence. Today, it is a unique hotel, nestled in its own park with shaded pathways and olive groves, and fabulous panoramic views over the Ligurian Sea. Relaxation is guaranteed both by the swimming pool and the private beach, and the Aladdin's Cave with its stalagmites and stalactites provides a unique setting for musical events, weddings and parties.

Cette élégante villa du XVIIIe siècle fût une résidence priveé. Aujourd'hui, c'est un hôtel unique, niché dans son propre parc aux allées ombragées et oliveraies, et aux vues panoramiques fabuleuses sur la Mer Ligurienne. La détente est garantie tout aussi bien grâce à la piscine et aux plages privées, mais aussi aux caves d'Aladin avec ses stalagmites et stalactites qui procure un décor unique pour des évènements musicaux, mariages et fêtes diverses.

Diese elegante Villa aus dem 18. Jahrhundert war einst eine private Sommerresidenz. Heute ist sie ein einzigartiges Hotel inmitten eines eigenen Parks mit schattigen Wegen, Olivenhainen und herrlichem Panoramablick auf das Ligurische Meer. Swimmingpool und Privatstrand sorgen für Entspannung, und die Aladdinhöhle mit ihren Stalagmiten und Stalaktiten bietet eine einmalige Bühne für Musikveranstaltungen, Hochzeiten und andere Feste.

Our inspector loved: *The amazing view and the magnificent "Aladdin's Cave".*

Directions: Genoa > Autostrada > A10 Savona > Finale Ligure.

Web: www.johansens.com/puntaest
E-mail: info@puntaest.com
Tel: +39 019 600611
Fax: +39 019 600611

Price Guide:
single €120-150
double/twin €220-260
suite €270–470

Romantik Hotel Villa Pagoda

VIA CAPOLUNGO 15, 16167 GENOA NERVI, ITALY

Located directly on the coast and with private access to the beach, this early 19th-century Oriental-style villa was originally built for a wealthy merchant who fell in love with a local girl on one of his voyages to China. The interior is lavishly decorated with period furniture and fabrics, and antique Carrara marble floors. The tower rooms particularly enjoy spectacular panoramic views of the Mediterranean all the way to Portofino. The restaurant serves fine traditional Ligurian cuisine.

Situé sur la côte avec un accès privé à la plage, cette villa du début du XIXe siècle de style oriental fut à l'origine construite pour un marchand fortuné qui tomba amoureux d'une jeune chinoise lors de l'un de ses voyages en Chine. L'intérieur est somptueusement décoré avec des meubles et des tissus d'époque et des sols anciens en marbre de Carrare. Les chambres situées dans les tours offrent plus particulièrement de superbes vues panoramiques sur la Méditerranée jusqu'à Portofino. Le restaurant propose une excellente cuisine traditionnelle.

Direkt an der Küste gelegen und mit privatem Zugang zu einem Strand, war diese Anfang des 19. Jahrhunderts im fernöstlichen Stil erbaute Villa einst das Anwesen eines wohlhabenden Kaufmanns, der sich bei einer Reise nach China in eine Einheimische verliebte. Das Interieur ist üppig mit Stilmöbeln, Stoffen und antikem Carrara-Marmorboden ausgestattet. Ganz besonders die Turmzimmer genießen einen spektakulären Panoramablick auf das Mittelmeer bis hin nach Portofino. Im Restaurant wird erlesene ligurische Küche serviert.

Our inspector loved: *The huge precious Murano chandeliers and the circular balcony of the first floor.*

Directions: A12 > exit Genoa Nervi.

Web: www.johansens.com/pagoda
E-mail: info@villapagoda.it
Tel: +39 010 372 6161
Fax: +39 010 321 218

Price Guide: (buffet breakfast included when staying for 3 nights or more)
single €114-195
double €145-255
suite €320-560

Grand Hotel Miramare

VIA MILITE IGNOTO, 30, 16038 SANTA MARGHERITA LIGURE, LIGURIA, ITALY

Directions: A12 Genoa-Livorno road > turn off towards Rapallo and Santa Margherita (approximately a 40-minute drive from Genoa International Airport). Transport to and from the airport can be arranged.

Web: www.johansens.com/grandmiramare
E-mail: miramare@grandhotelmiramare.it
Tel: +39 0185 287013
Fax: +39 0185 284651

Price Guide:
single €149-195
double/twin €230-320
suite €370-700

This historic hotel stands in an idyllic location between lush green hillside and deep blue sea in the heart of the Italian Riviera. Overlooking the promenade to the beautiful village of Portofino, the 100-year-old, family-owned Grand Hotel Miramare is one of the region's most exclusive venues. Its rich and elegant ambience, impeccable service and gourmet culinary delights attract an international clientele who appreciate a comfortable blend of traditional style and modern amenities. Entrance to the fully-equipped beach is complimentary for hotel guests.

Cet hôtel chargé d'histoire est idéalement situé au c'ur de la Riviera Italienne entre la végétation verdoyante des collines et le bleu profond de la mer. Surplombant le front de mer menant au superbe village de Portofino, le Grand Hotel Miramare, demeure centenaire familiale, est l'un des sites les plus exclusifs de la région. Son atmosphère riche et élégante, son service impeccable et ses délices culinaires attirent une clientèle internationale qui apprécie le mariage subtil du style traditionnel et des techniques modernes. L'entrée à la plage bien approvisionnée est gratuite pour les résidents de l'hôtel.

Dieses historische Hotel liegt idyllisch zwischen üppig grüner Hügellandschaft und tiefblauem Meer im Herzen der italienischen Riviera und blickt auf die Promenade des hübschen Ortes Portofino. Das 100 Jahre alte, familiengeführte Hotel ist eines der exklusivsten Häuser der Region. Mit seinem prunkvollen, eleganten Ambiente, tadellosem Service und kulinarischen Genüssen zieht es eine internationale Kundschaft an, die eine komfortable Mischung aus traditionellem Stil und modernen Einrichtungen schätzt. Der Zugang zum voll ausgerüsteten Strand ist für Hotelgäste gratis.

Our inspector loved: *The contrast between the blue sea and tropical garden.*

Hotel Vis à Vis & Ristorante Olimpo

VIA DELLA CHIUSA 28, 16039 SESTRI LEVANTE (GE), ITALY

Set on an idyllic hillside overlooking Sestri Levante and 2 spectacular bays, this family-run hotel is surrounded by olive trees and is an enchanting place to stay. Guests will be mesmerised by the breathtaking view from the hotel's elegant restaurant Olimpo, which serves delicious food complemented by the finest regional wines. There is an open-air barbecue on the terrace and a magnificent roof garden, Ponte Zeus. An outside lift links the hotel to the centre of town.

Situé sur les flancs idylliques d'une colline avec vue sur le Sestri Levante et 2 baies superbes, cet hôtel familial entouré d'oliviers est un endroit enchanteur où séjourner. Les hôtes seront ébahis par la vue à couper le souffle qu'ils auront à partir de l'élégant restaurant Olimpo, qui sert une cuisine délicieuse accompagnée des meilleurs vins régionaux. Il y a un barbecue en plein air sur la terrasse et un jardin sur le toit magnifique, Ponte Zeus. Un ascenseur extérieur relie l'hôtel au centre-ville.

Dieses auf einem idyllischen Hügel mit Blick auf Sestri Levante und 2 herrliche Buchten gelegene und von Olivenbäumen umgebene familiengeführte Hotel ist ein zauberhafter Aufenthaltsort. Eine atemberaubende Sicht genießt man auch aus dem eleganten Restaurant Olimpo, in dem köstliche Speisen und erlesene Weine der Region serviert werden. Es gibt einen offenen Grill auf der Terrasse und einen herrlichen Dachgarten, Ponte Zeus. Ein Lift verbindet das Hotel mit dem Stadtzentrum.

Our inspector loved: *The spectacular view of the 2 bays from the restaurant and terrace.*

Directions: A12 > Genoa > Livorno > Sestri Levante > follow the signs to Centro > the hotel is signposted.

Milan
Venice
Genoa
Rome

Web: www.johansens.com/visavis
E-mail: visavis@hotelvisavis.com
Tel: +39 0185 42661
Fax: +39 0185 480853

Price Guide:
single €115–150
double €155–220
suite €220–330

GRAND HOTEL VILLA SERBELLONI

VIA ROMA 1, 22021 BELLAGIO, LAKE COMO, ITALY

Built in the early 19th century, this majestic villa stands in a beautiful and sunny position on a promontory between the two halves of Lake Como, and has an air of grandeur and luxury that few can rival. Elegantly frescoed ceilings, stunning crystal chandeliers and lush carpeting are complemented by stylish antique pieces, whilst 2 restaurants serve the very best in international cuisine. 2 swimming pools, a private beach and a luxury health spa complete the feeling of total relaxation.

Cette villa majestueuse fut construite au début du XIXe siècle et se trouve dans un endroit ensoleillé sur un promontoire entre les deux parties du lac Como. Son air de grandeur et de luxe est incomparable. L'hôtel est pourvu de plafonds ornés de fresques élégantes, de lustres magnifiques de cristal, de tapis somptueux et de pièces antiques raffinées. Les 2 restaurants servent des plats délicieux internationaux, alors que les 2 piscines, une plage privée et un centre de remise en forme luxueux créent une ambiance de détente absolue.

Diese Anfang des 19. Jahrhunderts erbaute majestätische Villa befindet sich in herrlicher, sonnenbeschienener Lage auf einer Landzunge zwischen den beiden Hälften des Comer Sees und besitzt eine unvergleichliche Aura von Eleganz und Luxus. Mit wundervollen Fresken verzierte Decken, traumhafte Kristalllüster und üppige Teppiche wechseln sich mit edlen antiken Stücken ab, und in 2 Restaurants wird hervorragende internationale Küche serviert. 2 Swimmingpools, ein Privatstrand und ein luxuriöses Wellnesszentrum sorgen für Entspannung pur.

Our inspector loved: *The private beach, landing stage and dock.*

Directions: A9 > exit Como Sud > follow directions to Bellagio.

Web: www.johansens.com/serbelloni
E-mail: inforequest@villaserbelloni.it
Tel: +39 031 950 216
Fax: +39 031 951 529

Price Guide:
single €165-245
double €250-475
suite €495-805

Grand Hotel Gardone Riviera

VIA ZANARDELLI 84, 25083 GARDONE RIVIERA (BS), LAGO DI GARDA, ITALY

This magnificent hotel, built in 1884, exudes a refined atmosphere of a bygone era. Beyond the ivy-clad, rose-covered façade the elegantly decorated guest rooms and suites boast beautiful lakeside views. During summer a lunch buffet is served on the garden terrace and a romantic dinner, complete with stunning backdrop, can be enjoyed at the Veranda Restaurant. Winnies Piano Bar offers a relaxed environment with live music and dancing. Guests receive a 10-20% discount when using 2 local golf courses and have exclusive use of the hotel's private beach.

De cet hôtel magnifique construit en 1884, émane l'atmosphère raffinée des temps passés. Derrière la façade rose couverte de lierre, les chambres et suites élégamment décorées s'enorgueillissent de vues splendides sur le lac. L'été, un buffet est servi pour le déjeuner dans le jardin en terrasse et un dîner romantique, sur une toile de fond superbe, peut être dégusté au restaurant Veranda. Le piano-bar Winnies offre un environnement détendu, avec musique live et danse. Les hôtes ont l'accès exclusif à la plage privée de l'hôtel alors que 2 cours de golf locaux offrent une réduction de 10-20%.

Dieses wundervolle, 1884 erbaute Hotel verströmt die Atmosphäre einer längst vergangenen Zeit. Hinter der mit Efeu bewachsenen und von Rosen bedeckten Fassade verstecken sich elegante Zimmer und Suiten mit herrlicher Sicht auf den See. Im Sommer wird auf der Gartenterrasse ein Mittagsbuffet serviert und abends genießt man das romantische Ambiente des Veranda Restaurants. Winnies Piano Bar bietet das perfekte Umfeld für Live-Musik und Tanz. Die Gäste können den Privatstrand exklusiv nutzen, und 2 örtliche Golfplätze bieten einen Rabatt von 10-20%.

Our inspector loved: *The enchanting position and landscape.*

Directions: A4 > exit Desenzano towards Salò-Gardone.

Web: www.johansens.com/gardoneriviera
E-mail: ghg@grangardone.it
Tel: +39 0365 20261
Fax: +39 0365 22695

Price Guide:
single €96-118
double €166-220
junior suite €206-260

PARK HOTEL

VIA LUNGOLAGO CESARE BATTISTI 19, 25015 DESENZANO DEL GARDA, LAKE GARDA, (BS) ITALY

Directions: A4 > exit Desenzano del Garda > follow signs to Centro. 20km from Brescia and Verona. 110km from Milan. 150km from Venice.

Web: www.johansens.com/parkhotel
E-mail: park@cerinihotels.it
Tel: +39 030 914 3494
Fax: +39 030 914 2280

Price Guide:
double €110-175
junior suite €160-210

Located on the lake promenade, just minutes from the ancient town centre of Desenzano, this delightful hotel has a warmth and intimacy that is reminiscent of a bygone era. There is a classical flavour among the elegant rooms, each finished with a perfect mix of style and comfort, and the service and attention to detail are second to none. The restaurant, Due Colombe, serves a spectacular gourmet breakfast and some excellent local dishes accompanied by a great wine selection.

Situé en bord de lac, à quelques minutes du centre de la veille ville de Desenzano, ce ravissant hôtel offre le charme et l'intimité d'autrefois. Il y a une atmosphère classique dans les chambres élégantes et toutes ont un parfait mélange de style et de confort. Le service et l'attention au détail sont irréprochables. Le restaurant, Due Colombe, sert un somptueux petit-déjeuner gastronomique ainsi que de délicieux plats locaux accompagnés d'excellents vins.

Dieses entzückende Hotel an der Uferpromenade ist nur ein paar Minuten vom alten Stadtzentrum von Desenzano entfernt und besitzt eine warme, familiäre Atmosphäre, die an längst vergangene Zeiten erinnert. Die eleganten Zimmer haben eine klassische Note, jedes ist eine perfekte Mischung aus Stil und Komfort, und der Service und die Liebe zum Detail sind unübertroffen. Im Due Colombe werden ein spektakuläres Gourmetfrühstück sowie köstliche Speisen und hervorragende Weine serviert.

Our inspector loved: *The traditional style of hospitality.*

50 100

HOTEL DE LA VILLE

VIALE REGINA MARGHERITA 15, 20052 MONZA (MI), ITALY

Within a quiet residential town, a short distance from Milan and the Formula One race track, Hotel de la Ville stands opposite the former summer palace of the Royal House of Savoy. Warm hospitality, exquisitely furnished public rooms and attentive staff ensure a stress-free stay. Each bedroom is individually decorated and La Villa, originally an aristocratic home, offers 7 exclusively private bedrooms and suites. Guests may enjoy an apéritif in the American Bar before savouring the regional specialities served in the highly regarded Derby Grill.

Au cœur d'une ville résidentielle tranquille, proche de Milan et du circuit de Formule 1, Hôtel de la Ville fait face à l'ancienne résidence d'été de la famille Royale de Savoy. Accueil chaleureux, décoration extrêmement soignée et personnel attentif sont les garants d'un séjour sans stress. Chaque chambre est décorée de manière individuelle et La Villa, une ancienne maison de maître, offre 7 chambres et suites exclusives. Les clients peuvent prendre l'apéritif à l'American Bar avant de déguster les spécialités régionales au fameux Derby Grill.

Dieses Hotel befindet sich in einer ruhigen Wohngegend, nahe bei Mailand und der Formel Eins Rennstrecke, und gegenüber des einstigen Sommer palastes des Königshauses von Savoyen. Herzliche Gastfreundschaft, exquisit eingerichtete Aufenthaltsräume und aufmerksames Personal sorgen für einen stressfreien Aufenthalt. Jedes Zimmer ist individuell gestaltet und La Villa, einst ein Adelshaus, bietet 7 exklusive Privatzimmer und -suiten. Man trifft sich in der Amerikanischen Bar zum Apéritif bevor man im vielgerühmten Derby Grill regionale Spezialitäten genießt.

Our inspector loved: *The private collections of carefully selected antiques and objets d'art, and the excellent restaurant; worth a visit!*

Directions: A4 > exit Sesto San Giovanni Cinisello Balsamo.

Web: www.johansens.com/hoteldelaville
E-mail: info@hoteldelaville.com
Tel: +39 039 382 581
Fax: +39 039 367 647

Price Guide:
single €121-190
double €191-250
suite €310-490

62 200

Hotel Bellerive

VIA PIETRO DA SALÒ 11, 25087 SALÒ (BS), ITALY

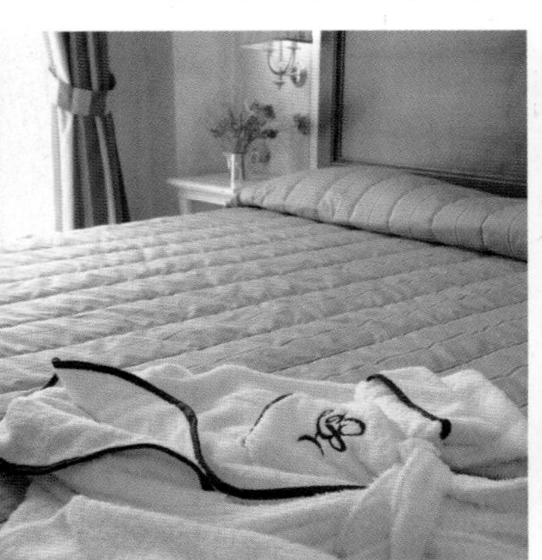

Directions: A4 > exit Desenzano or Brescia est > follow directions to Salò.

Web: www.johansens.com/bellerive
E-mail: info@hotelbellerive.it
Tel: +39 0365 520 410
Fax: +39 0365 290 709

Price Guide:
single €125-200
double €155-215
suite €250-350

Located on the shores of glistening Lake Garda, this beautiful venue offers professional service and an inviting ambience that reflects the mesmerising colours of the lake and lights of the charming harbour nearby. The stylish bedrooms have been carefully decorated with fresh tones and comfortable furnishings. The hotel's 100km restaurant serves delicious Gardenese delicacies, whose ingredients are locally sourced and always fresh. The historical Salò quarter is nearby, where guests will delight in exploring the atmospheric narrow streets and gardens.

Situé sur les bords du miroitant lac de Garde, ce magnifique hôtel propose un service professionnel dans une ambiance accueillante qui reflète les fascinantes couleurs du lac et des lumières du port voisin. Les chambres stylées ont été soigneusement décorées de tons frais et de mobilier confortable. Le restaurant 100KM de l'hôtel sert de délicieux plats de la région de Garde à partir d'ingrédients frais et locaux. Le quartier historique Salò est proche et les hôtes prendront plaisir à en parcourir les rues étroites et les jardins.

Dieses schöne Hotel am Ufer des glitzernden Gardasee bietet professionellen Service und ein einladendes Ambiente, das die Farben des Sees und die Lichter des nahegelegenen zauberhaften Hafens widerspiegelt. Die eleganten Zimmer sind sorgfältig mit frischen Farben dekoriert und mit bequemen Möbeln eingerichtet. Im Restaurant 100km werden Köstlichkeiten der Region serviert, deren stets frische Zutaten aus einheimischen Quellen stammen. Ganz in der Nähe befindet sich das historische Salò-Viertel, in dem man romantische enge Gassen und kleine Gärten bewundern kann.

Our inspector loved: *The soothing colour scheme and beautiful lamps.*

ITALY / PIEMONTE (BELGIRATE - LAKE MAGGIORE)

Villa Dal Pozzo d'Annone

STRADA STATALE DEL SEMPIONE 5, 28832 BELGIRATE (VB), LAKE MAGGIORE, ITALY

Idyllically located on the shores of Lake Maggiore, this exclusive villa stands within beautiful gardens and park. Reminiscent of a Victorian stately home, featuring original 15th-19th-century furnishings, guests may stay in one of 6 suites within the main villa or one of 12 luxurious rooms located in Borgo Ottocentesco, the restored former homes of gardeners and naval men. Enjoy an apéritif by the pool or in the cosy bar before dinner in the Bistrot-Wine Bar, accompanied by fine Italian wines. Sailing and water skiing can be arranged.

Idéalement situé sur les rives du Lac Majeur, cette villa prestigieuse se dresse au milieu de superbes jardins dans un parc. Evoquant toute sa splendeur de l'époque victorienne et agrémentée de meubles originaux du XVe au XIXe siècle, la villa accueille ses hôtes dans l'une des 6 suites du bâtiment principal ou l'une des 12 chambres luxueuses dans l'annexe située à Borgo Ottocentesco, anciennes maisons rénovées du personnel. L'apéritif pourra être apprécié près de la piscine ou au bar confortable avant de dîner au Bistrot-Bar à Vins en dégustant de délicieux vins italiens. Voile et ski nautique peuvent être organisés.

Diese exklusive, idyllisch am Ufer des Lago Maggiore gelegene Villa befindet sich inmitten herrlicher Gärten und Parklandschaft. Einrichtungsgegenstände des 15. – 19. Jahrhunderts betonen die Ähnlichkeit mit einem Herrenhaus aus dem 19. Jahrhundert. Gäste haben die Wahl zwischen 6 Suiten im Hauptgebäude und einem der 12 luxuriösen Zimmer im Borgo Ottocentesco, der restaurierten einstigen Unterkunft der Gärtner und Seeleute. Ein Apéritif am Pool ist der ideale Auftakt zum Diner mit erlesenen italienischen Weinen in der Bistrot-Weinbar. Segeln und Wasserski können arrangiert werden.

Our inspector loved: *The amazingly spacious bathrooms in the main villa.*

Directions: A26 > exit Meina. 35km from Mapensa Airport. Open from Easter to October.

Web: www.johansens.com/dalpozzodannone
E-mail: info@villadalpozzodannone.com
Tel: +39 0322 7255
Fax: +39 0322 772021

Price Guide:
suite €250-620

Hotel Villa Aminta

VIA SEMPIONE NORD 123, 28838 STRESA (VB), ITALY

Directions: A8 motorway from Milan towards Lago Maggiore > exit Carpugnino > follow signs to Stresa.

Web: www.johansens.com/aminta
E-mail: booking@villa-aminta.it
Tel: +39 0323 933 818
Fax: +39 0323 933 955

Price Guide: (room only)
double €233-280
junior suite €357
suite €464-620

This recently renovated 5-star de luxe hotel is a charming villa situated on the shores of Lake Maggiore, one of the most enchanting lakes in Italy. All bedrooms have a romantic décor, stucco works, precious furniture and look out over the gorgeous lake. Gastronomic delights are served in the Le Isole restaurant, and in summer, romantic dinners can be enjoyed on the terrace. Sightseeing tours, lake cruises and water-skiing are just some of the activities guests may enjoy, whilst nearby places of interest include Isola Bella, Villa Pallavicino and Locarno.

Ce charmant et luxueux hôtel à 5 étoiles récemment rénové est située sur les bords du Lac Maggiore, l'un des lacs les plus enchanteurs d'Italie. Les chambres ont un décor romantique, des ornements en stuc, un meublier de valeur et vue sur le lac. Les plaisirs gastronomiques sont servis au restaurant Le Isole, et la terrasse est l'endroit idéal l'été, pour un dîner romantique. De nombreuses activités sont disponibles, telles qu'excursions, croisières sur le lac et ski nautique; parmi les sites proches à visiter, on compte Isola Bella, Villa Pallavicino et Locarno.

Diese neu renovierte Villa ist ein luxuriöses 5-Sterne Hotel am Ufer des Lago Maggiore, eines der bezauberndsten Seen Italiens. Die Zimmer sind romantisch mit kostbaren Möbeln eingerichtet und haben Stuckdecken und herrliche Sicht auf den See. Kulinarische Köstlichkeiten werden im Le Isole serviert, und im Sommer kann man romantisch auf der Terrasse dinieren. Gäste können Besichtigungstouren und Fahrten auf dem See machen, Wasserski fahren oder Sehenswürdigkeiten in der Nähe, wie z.B. Isola Bella, Villa Pallavicino und Locarno besuchen.

Our inspector loved: *The enchanting views of the islands on Lake Maggiore.*

ITALY / PIEMONTE (VERBANIA - LAKE MAGGIORE)

Grand Hotel Majestic

VIA VITTORIO VENETO 32, PALLANZA, 28922 VERBANIA (LAKE MAGGIORE), ITALY

This tranquil 19th-century hotel is set on a promontory jutting out onto Lake Maggiore, a 5-minute walk from Pallanza. Airy, light rooms are decorated with La Belle Epoque influence and some bedrooms have marble bathrooms, Jacuzzis and a lakeside view. Gourmet regional and local specialities are served in the romantic La Beola restaurant, whilst La Terrazza enjoys panoramic views of the mountains and Borronnee Islands. Guests have access to their very own waterfront and tiny beach, sailing can be organised and the Balneotherapy Spa (opening in spring 2005) will offer relaxing treatments.

Cet hôtel calme du XIXe siècle se trouve sur un promontoire avançant dans le lac Maggiore, 5 minutes à pied de Pallanza. Les pièces claires et spacieuses sont meublées en style Belle Epoque, et certaines chambres possèdent des salles de bain en marbre, jacuzzi et vue sur le lac. Une cuisine gastronomique régionale et locale est servie dans le romantique La Beola, alors que La Terrazza offre des vues panoramiques sur les montagnes et les îles Borronnées. Les clients ont accès à une petite plage privée; la voile peut être arrangée. Le centre de balnéothérapie (s'ouvrant en printemps 2005) offrera de nombreux soins relaxants.

Dieses ruhige Hotel aus dem 19. Jahrhundert liegt auf einer Halbinsel im Lago Maggiore, nur 5 Minuten zu Fuß von Pallanza entfernt. Die Räume sind hell, luftig und im Belle Epoque-Stil gehalten, und einige der Zimmer bieten Marmorbad, Jacuzzi und Seeblick. Im romantischen La Beola werden regionale und einheimische Gourmetspeisen serviert, und das La Terrazza bietet einen Panoramablick auf die Berge und die Borronnee-Inseln. Ein eigener kleiner Strand ist vorhanden, Segeln kann arrangiert werden, und im Balneotherapie-Spa (Eröffnung Frühling 2005) kann man herrlich entspannen.

Our inspector loved: *The fantastic view of the lake from the hall.*

Directions: A26 towards Gravellona-Toce > exit Baveno > Verbania. 45 minutes from Malpensa International Airport.

Web: www.johansens.com/majesticmaggiore
E-mail: info@grandhotelmajestic.it
Tel: +39 0323 504305
Fax: +39 0323 556379

Price Guide:
double (single occupancy) €155-300
double €175-320
suite €500

ITALY / PUGLIA (FASANO)

MASSERIA MARZALOSSA

C.DA PEZZE VICINE 65, 72015 FASANO (BR), ITALY

Built in the 16th century on the site of a former palace, this traditional fortified farmhouse sits amidst grounds strewn with aged olive trees. Today, its rustic yet elegant guest apartments are located in different wings, each with a private entrance. Visitors can enjoy the gardens, terraces and swimming pool, as well as the restaurant's local cuisine, which incorporates produce from the estate, such as jams and olive oil. The Mediterranean ocean is just a few kilometres away.

Construit au XVIe siècle sur le site d'un ancien palace, cette métairie traditionnelle fortifiée trône au cœur de terres jonchées de vieux oliviers. Aujourd'hui, ses appartements rustiques mais élégants sont situés dans différentes ailes, chacun avec sa propre entrée. Les clients peuvent profiter des jardins, des terrasses et de la piscine ainsi que de la cuisine locale servie au restaurant où les produits issus du domaine, tels que la confiture et l'huile d'olive, sont utilisés. La Méditerranée n'est qu'à quelques kilomètres.

Dieses im 16. Jahrhundert an der Stätte eines einstigen Palastes erbaute traditionelle Bauernhaus liegt inmitten von uralten Olivenbäumen. Heute sind die rustikalen und doch eleganten Gästezimmer in verschiedenen Flügeln des Hauses untergebracht, und haben alle einen eigenen Eingang. Man kann die Gärten, Terrassen und den Swimmingpool genießen, und natürlich die einheimische Küche, für die Zutaten aus eigenem Anbau verwendet werden, wie z.B. Marmelade aus eigenem Obst und Olivenöl. Das Mittelmeer ist nur ein paar Kilometer entfernt.

Our inspector loved: *The shaded porch; pure serenity.*

Directions: Bari Airport > SS379 towards Fasaho > Pezze di Greco > follow directions.

Web: www.johansens.com/marzalossa
E-mail: masseriamarzalossa@marzalossa.it
Tel: +39 080 4413 780
Fax: +39 080 4413 024

Price Guide:
single €154-179
double €109-200

VILLA SAN MARTINO

VIA TARANTO, ZONA G - 59, 74015 MARTINA FRANCA (TA), ITALY

Idyllically set in a natural park surrounded by oak, eucalyptus, pine and olive trees, Villa San Martino was built on the site of a 19th-century villa. From the grandest to the smallest, all rooms are elegant, inviting and comfortable with a warm, unpretentious atmosphere. The restaurant, Duca di Martina, serves exquisite Mediterranean cuisine featuring local seafood. The nearby Apulian towns and villages are delightful, with sandy, deserted beaches. Enjoy the range of treatments available at the Spa and Beauty Centre.

Situé dans un parc naturel entouré de chênes, d'eucalyptus, de pins et d'oliviers, Villa San Martino fut construite au site d'une villa du XIXe siècle. De la plus grande à la plus petite, toutes les pièces sont élégantes, accueillantes et confortables et l'atmosphère est chaleureuse et sans prétentions. Le restaurant, Duca di Martina, sert une délicieuse cuisine méditerranéenne à base de fruits de mer locaux. Les proches villes et villages des Pouilles sont ravissants avec de belles plages de sables désertes. Le Spa et centre de beauté offre une variété des soins et traitements.

Die idyllisch in einem Park umgeben von Eichen, Pinien, Eukalyptus- und Olivenbäumen gelegene Villa San Martino wurde an der Stelle einer Villa aus dem 19. Jahrhundert erbaut. Alle Zimmer sind elegant, einladend und komfortabel mit warmer, einfacher Atmosphäre. Im Duca di Martina werden exquisite mediterrane Speisen serviert, vor allem Fisch und Meeresfrüchte. Die umliegenden Städte, Dörfer und menschenleeren Sandstrände Apuliens sind einen Besuch wert. Im Spa und Beauty-Zentrum wird eine Vielzahl von Behandlungen angeboten.

Our inspector loved: *The lessons in restoring works of art given by experts.*

Directions: Bari Airport is 75km away. Brindisi Airport is 60km away. The hotel is closed from 7th January - 9th February.

Web: www.johansens.com/martino
E-mail: info@relaisvillasanmartino.com
Tel: +39 080 480 5152
Fax: +39 080 480 1026

Price Guide:
single €180-220
double €220-320
suite €350-650

Masseria San Domenico

A member of The Leading Small Hotels of the World

LITORANEA 379, 72010 SAVELLETRI DI FASANO (BRINDISI) ITALY

The Masseria is an ancient watchtower dating from the 15th century, built overlooking the Adriatic by the knights of Malta to ward off attacks by the Ottomans. Surrounded by more than 3,700 acres of olive groves and vineyards, its architectural glory has been restored and its facilities include a spectacular outdoor seawater pool, tennis courts, Thalassotherapy Spa, and a brand new 18-hole golf course. Places of historic interest nearby include Egnazia, Alberobello and Castellana.

La Masseria est une ancienne tour de garde du XVe siècle, surplombant l'Adriatique et construite par les Chevaliers de Malte pour prévenir les attaques des ottomans. Entourée de plus de 1500ha d'oliveraies et vignobles, sa gloire architecturale a été restaurée et ses installations incluent une spectaculaire piscine d'eau de mer, en plein air, des courts de tennis, un centre de thalassothérapie et un tout nouveau golf 18 trous. D'un point de vue historique, Egnazia, Alberobello et Castellana sont à visiter.

Dieser alte Wachturm aus dem 15. Jahrhundert mit Blick auf die Adria wurde von den maltesischen Rittern erbaut, um Angriffe der Ottomanen abzuwehren. Die architektonische Pracht der inmitten von über 1500ha Olivenhainen und Weinbergen gelegenen Masseria wurde komplett restauriert. Zu den Einrichtungen gehören ein spektakulärer Salzwasserpool, Tennisplätze, ein Thalassotherapie-Spa und ein brandneuer 18-Loch-Golfplatz. Ausflugsziele sind Egnazia, Alberobello und Castellana.

Our inspector loved: *The amazing treatments on offer in the spa and the golf course; one of the loveliest in Europe, on a breathtaking spot by the coast.*

Directions: Bari YSS16 > Brindisi > Litoranea 379 > Fasano Savelletri.

Web: www.johansens.com/masseriasandomenico
E-mail: info@masseriasandomenico.com
Tel: +39 080 482 7769
Fax: +39 080 482 7978

Price Guide: (excluding VAT)
single €195–260
double €300–470
suite €385–2,200

Domina Palumbalza Sporting

GOLFO DI MARINELLA, 52 PORTO ROTONDO, 07026 OLBIA (SASSARI), ITALY

Located in an enchanting and peaceful bay in the Marinella Gulf, this hotel delightfully combines attentive service with simple décor to create a warm and comfortable ambience. The staff exude kindness and the hotel prides itself on its versatility, with children having their own dedicated space. An ideal spot in which to relax and enjoy watersports, the wonderful sandy beach is fully equipped and the small private harbour is a great base from which to explore the many coves of this beautiful piece of coastline.

Situé dans la tranquille baie du Golfe de Marinella, ce ravissant hôtel associe un service attentif à un décor simple créant ainsi une ambiance chaleureuse et confortable. Le personnel respire la gentillesse et l'hôtel peut s'enorgueillir de sa faculté d'adaptation, les enfants ayant leur propre espace. La superbe plage de sable possède tout l'équipement nécessaire et est parfaite pour se relaxer ou pratiquer les sports nautiques. Le petit port privé est la base idéale pour partir explorer les nombreuses criques de cette magnifique côte.

Dieses in einer zauberhaften, ruhigen Bucht am Golf von Marinella gelegene Hotel verbindet aufmerksamen Service mit einfachem Décor und herzlichem, gemütlichen Ambiente. Das Personal ist sehr freundlich, und das Hotel ist zu Recht stolz auf seine Vielseitigkeit, es gibt sogar spezielle Bereiche nur für Kinder. Der herrliche Sandstrand ist ideal zum Entspannen und für Wassersport, und vom kleinen privaten Hafen aus kann man wunderbar die vielen Buchten dieser traumhaften Küste erkunden.

Our inspector loved: *The natural beauty and elegance.*

Directions: 16km from Olbia Airport. Olbia SS 125 > follow signs to Costa Smeralda.

Web: www.johansens.com/dominapalumbalza
E-mail: palumbalza@domina.it
Tel: +39 0789 32005
Fax: +39 0789 32009

Price Guide:
single €70-238
double €71-430
suite €144-546

HOTEL DES ETRANGERS ET MIRAMARE

PASSEGGIO ADORNO 10/12, 96100 SIRACUSA, ITALY

Just reopened after 30 years, this prestigious hotel lies in the heart of the unique city of Ortigia. Facing directly onto the fine sandy beach, it is a haven of simple elegance and luxury, with just 80 rooms, many of which have sea views. There are 2 restaurants – the stunning Medusa boasts dramatic panoramic views over the coastline, whilst the Roof Garden has a wonderful terrace for outdoor dining – both of which offer some of the finest Italian dishes.

Réouvert après 30 ans de fermeture, cet hôtel renommé est situé au cœur de la ville unique d'Ortigia. L'hôtel donne sur la plage de sable et offre un havre d'élégance et de luxe avec 80 chambres, dont plusieurs ont une vue sur la mer. Il y a 2 restaurants – l'excellent Medusa qui offre des vues panoramiques dramatiques sur la côte et le jardin sur le toit avec sa terrasse parfaite pour manger au frais – ils offrent tous les deux des meilleurs plats italiens.

Dieses prestigereiche, nach 30 Jahren neueröffnete Hotel befindet sich im Herzen der einzigartigen Stadt Ortigia und blickt direkt auf einen herrlichen Sandstrand. Das Haus ist eine Oase der einfachen Eleganz und des Luxus, mit nur 80 Zimmern, viele davon mit Blick aufs Meer. Es gibt 2 Restaurants – das eindrucksvolle Medusa mit Panoramablick auf die Küste und den Dachgarten mit seiner traumhaften Terrasse – in denen feinste italienische Küche serviert wird.

Our inspector loved: *The modern design.*

Directions: Catania Airport > highway to Siracusa > exit Siracusa Centro > direction Ortigia.

Web: www.johansens.com/etrangersetmiramare
E-mail: desetrangers@medeahotels.com
Tel: +39 0931 62671
Fax: +39 0931 65124

Price Guide: (half board rates available, €60 supplement charge for sea view)
single €101-174
double €90-174
junior suite €150-235
de luxe suite €180-295

Grand Hotel Atlantis Bay

VIA NAZIONALE 161, TAORMINA MARE, ITALY

The toast of Taormina beach, this newly opened hotel has already become home to many celebrities and international guests. Entering the hotel is like walking into an enchanted cave and its lavishly decorated stone walls, carved out of the stone of the bay, hold a huge aquarium of colourful tropical fish. Guest rooms are decorated with cool white washed walls and simple, delicate fabrics. From the candle-lit restaurant to the terraces and panoramic views, it is impossible not to be swept away by the hotel's exotic ambience.

La coqueluche de la baie de Taormina, cet hôtel récemment ouvert est déjà devenu la nouvelle base de nombreuses célébrités et hôtes internationaux. Entrer dans cet hôtel est comme pénétrer dans une cave enchantée et sur ses murs de pierre somptueusement décorés, sculptés dans le roc de la baie, se tient un immense aquarium de poissons tropicaux. Les chambres sont décorées de murs lessivés blancs et d'étoffes simples et délicates. Du restaurant éclairé aux chandelles, aux terrasses et vues panoramiques, il est impossible de ne pas être ensorcelé par l'ambiance exotique de l'hôtel.

Dieses fantastische neueröffnete Hotel am Strand von Taormina ist bereits ein beliebter Zweitwohnsitz zahlreicher Prominenter und Gäste aus aller Welt. Man betritt das Hotel wie eine verzauberte Höhle, und die üppig dekorierten, in den Fels gehauenen Steinwände bergen ein riesiges Aquarium voller tropischer Fische. Die Gästezimmer haben kühle weiße Wände und mit einfachen, feinen Stoffen bezogene Betten. Vom mit Kerzen beleuchteten Restaurant bis hin zu den Terrassen und Panoramablicken – das exotische Ambiente des Hotels raubt einem den Atem.

Our inspector loved: *This truly unique hotel for the discerning traveller.*

Directions: Located on Taormina's seafront. Catania is the nearest airport.

Web: www.johansens.com/atlantis
E-mail: info@atlantisbay.it
Tel: +39 0942 618011
Fax: +39 0942 23194

Price Guide:
single €252-400
double €304-480
suite €504-720

GRAND HOTEL MAZZARÒ SEA PALACE

VIA NAZIONALE 147, 98030 TAORMINA (ME), ITALY

The Grand Hotel stands in one of Taormina's most enchanting spots right on the beach of a small bay and offers breathtaking views. The bedrooms are exquisitely furnished and have amazing terraces; some even boast private pools. Large windows look out onto the pool terrace and beyond to the sea. Guests can enjoy the private beach and the attention of exclusive and outstanding service provided by the extremely friendly staff. Taormina is easily reached by cable car.

L'hôtel se trouve dans un des endroits les plus enchanteurs de Taormina, sur la plage d'une petite baie, offrant des vues à couper le souffle. Les chambres meublées avec beaucoup de goût, ont des terrasses incroyables, et certaines ont des piscines privées. De grandes fenêtres ouvrent sur la terrasse autour de la piscine et le golfe. Les hôtes peuvent profiter de la plage privée et d'un service exclusif et impeccable d'un personal amical. Taormina est facilement accessible par téléphérique.

Dieses Hotel befindet sich an einem der schönsten Orte Taorminas, direkt am Strand einer kleinen Bucht mit atemberaubenden Ausblicken. Die Zimmer sind wundervoll gestaltet und bieten herrliche Terrassen, einige haben sogar einen eigenen Pool. Große Fenster geben den Blick frei auf die Poolterrasse und das Meer im Hintergrund. Die Gäste können den Privatstrand genießen und sich voll und ganz dem exklusiven, hervorragenden freundlichen Service hingeben. Taormina ist leicht mit der Gondelbahn zu erreichen.

Our inspector loved: *The sea, the silence, and the view of beautiful Sicily.*

Directions: Easily accessed from A18 ME - CT, exit Taormina towards Taormina mare-Mazzarò.

Web: www.johansens.com/mazzeroseapalace
E-mail: info@mazzaroseapalace.it
Tel: +39 0942 612111
Fax: +39 0942 626237

Price Guide:
single €252-400
double €304-480
suite €504-780

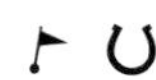

Baia Taormina Hotel & Spa

STATALE DELLO IONIO 39, 98030 MARINA D'AGRO (ME), ITALY

Moulded into rocky cliffs leading down to Taormina Bay, views of the sea from each of the double rooms, with private terrace, are magical. International and local cuisine is served in the elegant Solemoro restaurant where the view is savoured through large glass windows. The health and beauty centre features a Turkish bath, massage service and gym. Courses in deep-sea diving, hang gliding, surfing and paragliding can be arranged. Alternatively, enjoy the hotel's private beach or take the shuttle service to the nearby city centre.

Construit sur les falaises rocheuses menant à la baie de Taormina, les vues offertes de chaque chambres et de leur terrasse privée sont magiques. Une cuisine internationale et locale est servie à l'élégant restaurant Solemoro où la vue peut-être appréciée au travers de grandes baies vitrées. Le centre de beauté et de remise en forme propose un bain turc, un service de massage et une salle de gym. Des cours de plongée sous-marine, de deltaplane, de surf et de parapente peuvent être organisés. Les clients peuvent également profiter de la plage privée de l'hôtel ou prendre la navette pour se rendre en ville.

In die Felswände geschmiegt, die sich bis hinunter zur Bucht von Taormina erstrecken, bietet dieses Hotel von seinen Doppelzimmern mit eigener Terrasse eine herrliche Sicht. Internationale und einheimische Küche wird im eleganten Solemoro mit seinen großen Fenstern serviert, und im Health- und Beauty-Zentrum gibt es Dampfbad, Massagen und Fitnessraum. Kurse für Tiefseetauchen, Hanggliden, Surfen und Paragliden können arrangiert werden, ein Privatstrand steht zur Verfügung und ein Shuttle bringt Gäste ins nahe Stadtzentrum.

Our inspector loved: *The most elegant and amazing view of Taormina Bay.*

Directions: Catania > A18 towards Messina > exit Taormina > Letojanni > Forza d'Agrò.

Web: www.johansens.com/baiataormina
E-mail: info@baiataormina.com
Tel: +39 0942 756292
Fax: +39 0942 756603

Price Guide:
single €121–214
double/twin €162–288
de luxe €180-304

Hotel Dominik am Park

UNTERDRITTELGASSE 13, VIA TERZO DI SOTTO, I-39042 BRIXEN/BRESSANONE, ITALY

Delightfully situated in the centre of the pretty Dolomite town of Bressanone, this friendly, family-run bed and breakfast Alpine chalet hotel offers pure relaxation, modern comfort, a sense of elegance and is an excellent base for exploring the countryside, mountain walking and skiing. At the heart of the hotel is the large, classically decorated lounge hung with family portraits. Bedrooms provide every home-from-home facility; most have balconies overlooking the lovely, lawned garden. Large indoor pool and sauna. Dinner for groups by arrangement.

Joliment situé au sein de la jolie ville des Dolomites Bressanone, cet établissement alpin, chalet familial de chambres d'hôtes offre dans un confort moderne, élégant, et une atmosphère de détente et de gentillesse, une base idéale pour la découverte du pays, la randonnée en montagne et le ski. Au cœur de l'hôtel se trouve le grand salon meublé de manière classique où pendent des portraits de famille. Les chambres procurent le confort de la maison ; la plupart ont des balcons donnant sur l'adorable jardin gazonné. Egalement disponibles, une grande piscine intérieure et un sauna. Les dîners pour groupes sont possibles sur arrangement préalable.

Dieses im Zentrum der Dolomitenstadt Brixen gelegene freundliche, familiengeführte Alpen-Chalethotel bietet Entspannung pur, modernen Komfort, ein Gefühl von Eleganz, und ist der ideale Ausgangspunkt, um die Umgebung zu erkunden und Wandern und Skifahren zu gehen. Das Herz des Hotels bildet der klassisch gestaltete, mit Familienportraits geschmückte Aufenthaltsraum. Die Zimmer sind mit jeglichem Komfort ausgestattet, die meisten haben Balkon mit Blick auf den hübschen Garten. Großes Hallenbad und Sauna. Abendessen für Gruppen auf Anfrage.

Directions: Verona > A22 Bolzano > Bressanone > exit Brixen Bressanone. The nearest airports are Verona, Bolzano and Innsbruck.

Web: www.johansens.com/dominik
E-mail: info@hoteldominik.com
Tel: +39 0472 830 144
Fax: +39 0472 836 554

Price Guide:
single €95
double €146
suite €220

Our inspector loved: *The Safari Suite.*

ART HOTEL CAPPELLA

STR. PECEI 17, ALTA BADIA - DOLOMITES, 39030 COLFOSCO/CORVARA (BZ), ITALY

Dating back to 1912, this hotel has a long tradition of hospitality. The owner, an artist and photographer, has utilised her extensive cultural knowledge and travel experiences to create a warm and inviting atmosphere, carefully blending modern art, rare ethnic pieces and hand-crafted furnishings. 2 restaurants provide casual dining. Many sports activities make for an action packed holiday, whilst there is a spa for those in search of a more relaxed break. Starting right at the doorstep, guests are connected to the ski slopes of Sella Ronda and Alta Badia.

Datant de 1912, cet hôtel a une longue tradition d'hospitalité. La propriétaire, artiste et photographe, a utilisé ses connaissances artistiques et ses expériences de voyages pour créer une atmosphère chaleureuse, mélangeant art moderne, pièces ethniques et mobilier fait main. 2 restaurants offrent des dîners simples. On peut choisir parmi de nombreuses activités sportives alors que ceux qui sont à la recherche d'un séjour plus reposant peuvent profiter du spa. Depuis la porte les hôtes ont accès aux pistes de Sella Ronda et Alta Badia.

Seit 1912 bietet dieses Hotel seine Gastfreundschaft an. Die Eigentümerin, eine Künstlerin und Fotografin, nutzte ihr umfassendes kulturelles Wissen und ihre Reiseerfahrungen für die Mischung aus moderner Kunst, ethnischen Stücken und handgefertigten Einrichtungen, die eine einladende Atmosphäre schafft. In 2 Restaurants kann man in informeller Atmosphäre essen. Zahlreiche sportliche Aktivitäten werden angeboten, es gibt aber auch ein Spa für einen etwas entspannteren Urlaub. Man ist direkt ab der Haustür mit den Pisten der Sella Ronda und Alta Badia-Skigebiete verbunden.

Our inspector loved: *The entire experience; feeding the mind, body and soul.*

Directions: Enquire at hotel; ask for Renata Kostner.

Web: www.johansens.com/cappella
E-mail: info@hotelcappella.com
Tel: +39 0471 836183
Fax: +39 0471 836561

Price Guide:
single €93-295
double €136-410
suite €238-470

HOTEL LORENZETTI

VIA DOLOMITI DI BRENTA 119, 38084 MADONNA DI CAMPIGLIO (TN) ITALY

Directions: A4 > exit Brescia Est > SS. 45 bis SS. 237 > follow directions to Lago Idro > Madonna di Campiglio.

Web: www.johansens.com/lorenzetti
E-mail: hotellorenzetti@hotellorenzetti.com
Tel: +39 0465 44 14 04
Fax: +39 0465 44 06 88

Price Guide:
single €60–175
double/twin €95–325
suite €118–400

This enchanting chalet-style hotel, with its flower-bedecked balconies, stands apart from the main ski lifts and village centre, offering tranquillity and spectacular views over the mountains. The interior is very elegant, and some of the superb suites have hydromassage facilities. Winter sports enthusiasts appreciate the fine skiing and the ice rink. In summer, residents stroll in the gardens, walk in the mountains and play golf. The hotel's new wellness centre boasts beauty facilities such as massage, sauna, steam bath and solarium.

Ce charmant hôtel de style chalet, avec ses balcons ornés de fleurs, se dresse à l'écart des remontée-mécaniques et du centre du village, offrant tranquillité et des vues spectaculaires sur les montagnes. L'intérieur est très élégant, et certaines des superbes suites ont des hydro-masseurs. Les mordus des sports d'hiver apprécieront les belles pistes et la patinoire. En été, les clients se prélassent dans les jardins, font des randonnées en montagne ou peuvent jouer au golf. Le nouveau centre de beauté comprend massage, sauna, bain turc et solarium.

Dieses hübsche Hotel im Chaletstil steht mit seinen blumengeschmückten Balkonen abseits der Skilifte und des Dorfzentrums und ermöglicht Ruhe, Entspannung und atemberaubende Aussichten. Das Interieur ist elegant und in einigen der einzigartigen Suiten gibt es Wassermassage. Anspruchsvolle Skipisten und eine Schlittschuhbahn begeistern die Wintersportler, und im Sommer kann man Spaziergänge in den Gärten und Wanderungen in den Bergen unternehmen oder Golf spielen. Das Wellness-Centre bietet Massage, Sauna, Türkisches Bad und Solarium.

***Our inspector loved:** The hotel's excellent location and the cosy atmosphere.*

ROMANTIK HOTEL OBERWIRT

ST FELIXWEG 2, 39020 MARLING – MERAN, ITALY

Owned by the Waldner family since 1749, this hotel has been offering hospitality since the 15th century. The extensive gardens, culinary delights and the cosy Tyrolean bar are reason enough to come and visit this historic house. A special highlight is the wellness and beauty residence Amadea. Sports enthusiasts will enjoy the fitness area, indoor and outdoor swimming pools and the hotel's own tennis school.

Propriété de la famille Waldner depuis 1749, cet hôtel offre de l'hospitalité depuis le XVe siècle. Les grands jardins, délices culinaires et le bar intime tyrolien sont parmi les attractions et une bonne raison de visiter cette maison historique. Une attraction particulière est le centre de bien-être et beauté Amadea. Les personnes sportives apprécieront la zone fitness, la piscine couverte et la piscine en plein air ainsi que l'école de tennis de l'hôtel.

Dieses Hotel bietet seine Gastfreundschaft bereits seit dem 15. Jahrhundert an und befindet sich seit 1749 im Besitz der Familie Waldner. Der großzügige Gastgarten, die kulinarischen Genüsse sowie die gemütliche Tiroler Bar sind Grund genug, dieses historische Haus zu besuchen. Ein besonderes Highlight ist die Wellness- und Beutyresidenz Amadea. Für alle Sportlichen gibt es einen Fitnessbereich, ein Hallenbad, ein Freischwimmbad und das hauseigene Tenniscamp.

Our inspector loved: *The view over Meran and its famous racecourse from the top floor suites.*

Directions: Innsbruck Verona road > Bozen Sud > Meran > Marling.

Web: www.johansens.com/oberwirt
E-mail: info@oberwirt.com
Tel: +39 0473 22 20 20
Fax: +39 0473 44 71 30

Price Guide:
double €120–200
suite €150-240

44 SPA

Park Hotel Mignon

VIA GRABMAYR 5, 39012 MERAN (BZ), ITALY

Close to the famous promenades of Merano and surrounded by its own green park, lies the family-run Park Hotel Mignon. The hotel is bright and harmoniously decorated with a relaxing and regenerating atmosphere. For those whishing to be pampered, the health and beauty centre offers personalised programmes and treatments. The excellent cuisine includes South Tyrolean and Italian dishes. In the evenings, guests may enjoy live music at the piano bar or in the garden by the swimming pool.

A proximité des célèbres promenades de Merano, cet hôtel familial entouré d'un parc verdoyant invite à se détendre dans un cadre lumineux et harmonieux. Qui souhaite se faire dorloter sera comblé par les programmes et les traitements personnalisés offerts par le centre de beauté et de remise en forme. Le menu savoureux est composé de spécialités du Haut-Adige et de plats italiens. Le soir, les visiteurs se laissent bercer par la musique dans le piano-bar ou dans le jardin, au bord de la piscine.

In der Nähe der berühmten Meraner Promenaden und umgeben von seinem eigenen Park liegt das familiengeführte Park Hotel Mignon. Es ist hell und harmonisch eingerichtet und besitzt eine entspannende Atmosphäre. Wer sich verwöhnen lassen will, findet im wellness und Schönheitszentrum eine Reihe von individuellen Programmen und Behandlungen. Für kulinarischen Genuss sorgen köstliche Südtiroler und italienische Gerichte, und abends erfreuen sich die Gäste an Live-Musik in der Pianobar oder im Garten am Pool.

Our inspector loved: *The beautiful garden and the superb hospitality.*

Directions: Brennero > exit Bolzano Sud > Meran Sud > Maia Alta.

Web: www.johansens.com/parkhotelmignon
E-mail: info@hotelmignon.com
Tel: +39 0473 230353
Fax: +39 0473 230644

Price Guide:
single €80–110
double/twin €160–220
suite €210–280

Relais della Rovere

VIA PIEMONTE 10, LOC BADIA, 53034 COLLE VAL D'ELSA (SI), ITALY

Midway between Florence and Siena, this delightful Tuscan retreat epitomises the simple rustic elegance of the area. Formerly an abbey dating back to the 11th century, it cleverly combines old and modern styles, with elegant and spacious bedrooms and delightful cloistered dining. The restaurant serves a fantastic menu of local cuisine and wines, and the swimming pool is the ideal place from which to relax and enjoy the stunning Tuscan scenery.

A mi-chemin entre Florence et Sienne, cette ravissante retraite toscane incarne la simple élégance rustique de la région. Autrefois une abbaye construite au XIe siècle, elle combine des styles modernes et anciens, avec de belles chambres spacieuses et une délicieuse salle de restaurant cloîtrée. Le restaurant offre un menu superbe de cuisine et de vins locaux, et la piscine est l'endroit idéal où se détendre et apprécier la vue incroyable sur les paysages toscans.

Dieses wundervolle toskanische Hotel auf halber Strecke zwischen Florenz und Siena verkörpert perfekt die einfache, rustikale Eleganz der Region. Die einstige Abtei aus dem 11. Jahrhundert kombiniert geschickt alten und modernen Stil. Die Zimmer sind elegant und geräumig und man diniert in klösterlicher Atmosphäre. Im Restaurant wird eine verlockende Auswahl toskanischer Köstlichkeiten und Weine serviert, und der Swimmingpool ist der ideale Ort, um zu entspannen und die traumhafte Landschaft zu bewundern.

Our inspector loved: *The hotel's simple beauty.*

Directions: A1 > exit Firenze Certosa > motorway to Siena > exit Colle Val D'Elsa Nord.

Web: www.johansens.com/dellarovere
E-mail: dellarovere@chiantiturismo.it
Tel: +39 0577 924696
Fax: +39 0577 924489

Price Guide:
rooms €176–290
suite €262–428

Relais Villa Baldelli

SAN PIETRO A CEGLIOLO 420, 52044 CORTONA (AR), ITALY

Meticulously converted into a 4-star hotel, this charming 17th-century villa stands in 12 acres of peaceful Arezzo parkland overlooking Cortona, the oldest and one of the most enchanting cities in Italy. A cool, pastel interior is complemented by original features, elegant furnishings, splendid antiques, pastoral frescoes and fine original paintings. Old and modern décor combine delightfully in the stylish guest rooms whose comforts include four-poster bed and Jacuzzi. Dining in the restaurant can be arranged upon request.

Méticuleusement transformée en hôtel 4 étoiles, cette superbe villa du 17XVIIe siècle se situe au cœur du paisible domaine de 5 hectares d'Arezzo, surplombant Cortona, la plus ancienne et plus enchanteresse ville d'Italie. Les tons pastels de l'intérieur sont complétés par des caractéristiques d'origine, d'élégants ameublements, de superbes antiquités, des fresques pastorales et de magnifiques tableaux. L'ancien et le moderne se marient délicatement dans les chambres élégantes dont le confort comprend lit à baldaquin et jacuzzi. Les repas peuvent être pris au restaurant sur demande.

Diese perfekt in ein 4-Sterne-Hotel umgewandelte charmante Villa aus dem 17. Jahrhundert liegt inmitten von fast 5ha friedlicher Parklandschaft in Arezzo, mit Blick auf Cortona, die älteste und eine der bezauberndsten Städte Italiens. Das kühle, in Pastelltönen gehaltene Interieur ist mit originalgetreuen Details, eleganter Einrichtung, herrlichen Antiquitäten, ländlichen Fresken und edlen Originalgemälden gefüllt. Alt und Neu verbinden sich perfekt in den eleganten Zimmern, die mit Himmelbett und Jacuzzi ausgestattet sind. Im Restaurant kann man auf Anfrage dinieren.

Our inspector loved: *The reception desk, which is an ancient altar, and room 33 with its twin four-poster beds.*

Directions: The nearest airports are Florence and Rome. The nearest train station is Camcia. Take the A1 from Florence > exit Valdichiana > SS75 towards Perugia > exit Cortona > follow signs to Arezzo SS71.

Web: www.johansens.com/villabaldelli
E-mail: info@villabaldelli.com
Tel: +39 0575 612406
Fax: +39 0575 612 407

Price Guide:
single €180
double €200
de luxe €250
senior suite €300

HOTEL LORENZO IL MAGNIFICO

VIA LORENZO IL MAGNIFICO 25, 50129 FLORENCE, ITALY

This newly opened villa, located just a few steps from the heart of Florence, is the epitome of refined, simple elegance. The emphasis is on comfort and exceptional hospitality, provided by the wonderful staff. Each room is equipped with Jacuzzi bath or shower, whilst particular care has been taken in the selection of the superb bath and bed linens. A pretty garden, private garage and meeting room for up to 30 delegates complete the villa's amenities. Guests' cats and dogs are welcome.

Cette villa récemment ouverte et à deux pas du cœur de Florence est la quintessence d'élégance raffinée et simple. Une importance particulière est accordée au confort et à l'hospitalité exceptionnelle, offert par le personnel magnifique. Chaque chambre dispose d'un bain ou douche jacuzzi, alors qu'un soin particulier a été apporté à la sélection de linge, qui est superbe. La villa dispose aussi d'un beau jardin, garage privé et salle de conférences pour jusqu'à 30 délégués. Les chats et les chiens des hôtes sont accueillis.

Diese neu eröffnete Villa ist nur ein paar Schritte vom Stadtzentrum entfernt und der Inbegriff von edler, einfacher Eleganz. Die Betonung liegt hier auf Komfort und außergewöhnlichem Service. Jedes Zimmer bietet Jacuzzibad oder -dusche, und besondere Sorgfalt wurde auf die Auswahl der Bettwäsche und Handtücher gelegt. Ein hübscher Garten, eine Garage und ein Konferenzzimmer für bis zu 30 Personen vervollkommnen das Angebot. Auch die Hunde und Katzen der Gäste sind hier sehr willkommen.

Our inspector loved: *The simple elegance demonstrated by the fresh flowers and beautiful linens.*

Directions: A1 > any exit to Florence, then follow directions to Viali di Circonvallazione and Piazza della Libertà.

Web: www.johansens.com/lorenzomagnifico
E-mail: booking@lorenzoilmagnifico.net
Tel: +39 055 4630878
Fax: +39 055 4630878

Price Guide:
double (single occupancy) €130-240
double €140-280
suite €320-500

J AND J HISTORIC HOUSE HOTEL

VIA DI MEZZO 20, 50121 FLORENCE, ITALY

Directions: Borgo Pinti > city centre.

Web: www.johansens.com/jandj
E-mail: jandj@dada.it
Tel: +39 055 26312
Fax: +39 055 240282

Price Guide:
double/twin €282-315
suite €370-460

This is a veritable retreat for travellers, a charming transformation from a convent to a delightful small hotel, far from the bustle of the commercial world despite its central location. The individual bedrooms look out over the rooftops or down onto concealed cloister and are furnished with antiques and hand-woven fabrics. The lounge is very elegant and a small bar leads into a courtyard which is a pleasant spot for drinks in fine weather.

Cet ancien couvent a été converti en un ravissant petit hôtel et constitue un vrai refuge pour le voyageur. Tout en étant situé de façon centrale, il reste protégé de l'agitation du monde extérieur. Les chambres individuelles donnent sur les toits de la ville ou sur un cloître caché, et sont garnies de meubles anciens et d'étoffes tissées à la main. Le salon est très élégant et un petit bar mène à une cour intérieure, endroit fort agréable pour prendre un verre lorsque le temps le permet.

Dieses charmante kleine Hotel war ursprünglich ein Kloster und ist nun ein wahrer Erholungsort für Reisende, fernab von der Hektik der modernen Welt und doch zentral gelegen. Die individuell gestalteten Zimmer blicken über die Dächer der Stadt oder auf einen versteckte Säulengang und sind mit Antiquitäten und handgewebten Stoffen geschmückt. Der Aufenthaltsraum ist äußerst elegant, und eine kleine Bar führt in einen Hof – ein beliebter Ort, um einen Drink zu genießen.

Our inspector loved: *The view of the rooftops and the hidden courtyards, characteristic of the region.*

Marignolle Relais & Charme

VIA DI S QUIRICHINO A MARIGNOLLE 16, 50124 FLORENCE, ITALY

Situated midway between the Ponte Vecchio and Certosa convent, this little gem of a hotel overlooks the beautiful hillside countryside around Florence. The 7 spacious rooms are immaculately styled reflecting the owners' impeccable taste and attention to detail, whilst the panoramic terrace and quiet gardens are the perfect locations for a drink. The hotel is ideally positioned for exploring the historical city centre as well as enjoying some great golf courses and numerous Tuscan attractions in the vicinity.

Situé à mi-chemin entre Ponte Vecchio et le couvent de Certosa, ce petit joyau d'hôtel offre des vues sur la magnifique campagne entourant Florence. Les 7 chambres spacieuses sont meublées avec soin et reflètent le raffinement et le goût impeccable du propriétaire ainsi que l'attention qu'il porte au détail. La terrasse panoramique et les magnifiques jardins sont des lieux parfaits pour boire un verre. L'hôtel est idéalement situé pour visiter le centre ville historique, les nombreuses attractions de la région ou pour découvrir de superbes terrains de golf.

Das auf halber Strecke zwischen der Ponte Vecchio und dem Certosa-Kloster gelegene Hotel ist ein wahres Juwel mit Blick auf die herrliche Hügellandschaft um Florenz. Die 7 geräumigen Zimmer sind makellos eingerichtet und spiegeln den exquisiten Geschmack und Liebe zum Detail der Besitzer wider, und auf der Panoramaterrasse und im Garten kann man Drinks genießen. Ideal gelegen, um das historische Stadtzentrum sowie einige fantastische Golfplätze und zahlreiche Attraktionen der Toskana zu erkunden.

Our inspector loved: *The elegant surroundings.*

Directions: A1 > exit Firenze Certosa > Via Senese > Via Delle Bagnese.

Web: www.johansens.com/marignolle
E-mail: info@marignolle.com
Tel: +39 055 228 6910
Fax: +39 055 204 7396

Milan
Venice
Florence
Rome

Price Guide:
double (single occupancy) €165-225
double €195-255
suite €255-345

Villa Montartino

VIA GHERARDO SILVANI 151, 50125 FLORENCE, ITALY

Directions: A1 > exit Firenze-Certosa > SS2 to Galluzzo > Via Gherardo Silvani.

Web: www.johansens.com/villamontartino
E-mail: info@montartino.com
Tel: +39 055 223520
Fax: +39 055 223495

Price Guide:
double/twin €290
suite €335
(weekly rate) apartment €1,000–1,800

Set 3km from the heart of Florence, above the beautiful Ema Valley and surrounded by stone walls, olive trees and vineyards, Villa Montartino & Residence Le Piazzole offer quality service in a peaceful setting. The luxurious, spacious rooms have views of the hills and contain original antiques and modern conveniences. Dinner can be arranged in the beautiful Loggia; wine and extra virgin olive oil produced here, can be tasted in the old cellars, with prior notice. Private chapel and meeting room for or up to 30 guests, 2 heated swimming pools, Jacuzzi, steam bath, 2 private car parks.

S,élevant au dessus de la belle vallée de l'Ema, à 3 km du centre de Florence et entourée de murs de pierre, d'oliviers et de vignobles, la paisible Villa Montartino & Residence Le Piazzole offrent un service irréprochable. Les chambres luxueuses ont vue sur les collines et sont spacieuses, contenant des antiquités originales et tout le confort moderne. Le dîner peut être servi dans la belle loggia, et on peut déguster des vins et l'huile d'olives faite à la maison aux vieilles caves. Chapelle et salle de réunions pour 30 personnes, 2 piscines chauffées, jacuzzi, bain turc, 2 parkings privés.

3km von Florenz entfernt, hoch über dem Ema-Tal und von Steinmauern, Olivenbäumen und Weinbergen umgeben, bieten die Villa Montartino & Residence Le Piazzole exzellenten Service in ruhiger Lage. Die luxuriösen, großen Zimmer haben Blick auf die Hügel und sind mit Original-Antiquitäten und modernem Komfort ausgestattet. Abendessen kann in der hübschen Loggia serviert werden. Weine und selbstgemachtes Olivenöl kann man auf Anfrage im alten Kellergewölbe kosten. Eine Kapelle und ein Konferenzraum bieten Platz für bis zu 30 Personen. 2 beheizte Swimmingpools, Jacuzzi, Dampfbad und 2 private Parkplätze.

***Our inspector loved:** The view of the hills and countryside surrounding Florence.*

ITALY / TUSCANY (FORTE DEI MARMI - LUCCA)

HOTEL BYRON

VIALE A MORIN 46, 55042 FORTE DEI MARMI (LU), ITALY

Comprising 2 Liberty-style villas overlooking the seafront, Hotel Byron is situated in one of the most exclusive areas on the Versilian coast. Recent renovations have restored the house to its original elegance, and it is now a refined hotel with the ambience of a private residence. Interior decorations have been personally chosen by the owners and give the hotel a fresh, crisp style, with a profusion of plants and flowers. The restaurant, La Magnolia, has an excellent reputation for its fine cuisine and wine selection.

Composé de 2 villas dans le style Liberty surplombant le bord de mer, Hôtel Byron est situé sur l'une des plus belles parties de la côte de Versilia. De récentes rénovations ont rendues à la maison son élégance d'origine et c'est maintenant un hôtel raffiné avec l'atmosphère d'une résidence privée. La décoration d'intérieure à été choisie par les propriétaires et donne à l'hôtel un style frais et croustillant avec une profusion de plantes et de fleurs. Le restaurant La Magnolia à une excellente réputation pour sa délicieuse cuisine et sa sélection de vins.

Das aus 2 Villen im Liberty-Stil bestehende Hotel Byron blickt direkt aufs Meer und liegt in einer der exklusivsten Gegenden an der Küste der Versilia. Kürzliche Renovierungen brachten die einstige Eleganz des Hauses zum Vorschein, das nun ein edles Hotel mit der Atmosphäre einer privaten Residenz ist. Das von den Besitzern persönlich ausgewählte Décor im Interieur gibt dem Hotel einen frischen, klaren Stil mit einer Unmenge an Pflanzen und Blumen. Das Restaurant La Magnolia besitzt einen hervorragenden Ruf für seine raffinierten Gerichte und guten Weine.

***Our inspector loved:** The sparkling white walls and shining marble floor.*

Directions: A12 > exit Versilia.

Web: www.johansens.com/byron
E-mail: info@hotelbyron.net
Tel: +39 0584 787 052
Fax: +39 0584 787 152

Price Guide:
single €186-268
double €255-551
apartment €386-814
suite €412-1,066

Country House Casa Cornacchi

LOC. MONTEBENICHI, 52021 AREZZO, TUSCANY, ITALY

Directions: From Rome: take A1 > exit at Valdichiana > Siena exit at Colonna del Grillo > Bucine Montebenichi > exit at Montebenichi. From Florence: take A1 > eixit at Valdarno > Siena > Bucine > Ambra > Montebenichi.

Web: www.johansens.com/cornacchi
E-mail: info@cornacchi.com
Tel: +39 055 998229
Fax: +39 055 9983863

Price Guide:
single €120
double €160
suite €180
apartment €220

After an exhilarating drive through the breathtaking countryside between Siena and Arezzo, guests receive a warm welcome at this relaxing and tranquil country residence. Casa Cornacchi consists of fully restored stone buildings dating back to the 16th century and offers exquisitely furnished bedrooms, a panoramic swimming pool and Jacuzzi as well as some fine Tuscan wines. Guests can explore this enchanting Chianti region with its wonderful treasures of art, history and nature.

Après une promenade en voiture vivifiante à travers la belle campagne de Siena et Arezzo, les hôtes reçoivent le bon accueil à cette résidence de campagne tranquille et relaxante. Les bâtiments en pierre datant du XVIe siècle ont été restaurés et offrent des chambres exquisément ornées, une piscine panoramique et jacuzzi ainsi que de fins vins toscans. La région enchanteresse de Chianti avec son art, son histoire et sa nature fascinants, est à découvrir.

Nach einer wundervollen Fahrt durch die atemberaubende Landschaft zwischen Siena und Arezzo wird man in diesem entspannten, ruhigen Landsitz mit offenen Armen empfangen. Casa Cornacchi besteht aus Steingebäuden aus dem 16. Jahrhundert und bietet exquisit eingerichtete Gästezimmer, einen Panorama-Swimmingpool und Jacuzzi sowie einige ausgezeichnete toskanische Weine. Die zauberhafte Chianti-Region mit ihren zahlreichen Kunstschätzen, geschichtsträchtigen Stätten und herrlicher Natur bietet etwas für jeden Geschmack.

Our inspector loved: *The feeling of joy and serenity of the hotel and surrounding area.*

DIONORA

VIA VICINALE DI POGGIANO, 53040 MONTEPULCIANO (SIENA), ITALY

Dionora is an enchanting pearl amidst the magical scenery of Tuscany, immersed within nature and the scent of flowers and herbs. Cool interiors have stunning timber beams and rich, luxurious furnishings that are extremely stylish and captivate the traditional elegance of the area. Most bedrooms have a private Jacuzzi and sauna. Breakfast is served in the Lemon House by the swimming pool, which offers gorgeous views over the surrounding countryside.

Dionora est une véritable perle plongée dans la nature et les senteurs d'herbes et de fleurs, au cœur des paysages magnifiques de Toscane. A l'intérieur, de magnifiques poutres en bois et un ameublement luxueux et très stylé reflètent l'élégance traditionnelle de la région. La plupart des chambres possèdent un sauna et un jacuzzi privés. Le petit-déjeuner est servi dans la maison aux citrons près de la piscine et offre de superbes vues sur la campagne avoisinante.

Dionora ist ein bezauberndes Anwesen inmitten traumhafter toskanischer Landschaft, erfüllt von Natur und dem Duft von Blumen und Kräutern. Das kühle Interieur bietet herrliche Holzbalken und üppige, luxuriöse, extrem stilvolle Einrichtung, die die traditionelle Eleganz der Region perfekt einfängt. Die meisten Zimmer haben einen eigenen Jacuzzi und eine Sauna. Frühstück wird im Zitronenhaus am Swimmingpool serviert, von dem man eine herrliche Sicht auf die Umgebung hat.

Our inspector loved: *The enchanting surroundings.*

Directions: From the north: A1 > exit Bettolle/Valdichiana > follow signs to Montepulciano. From the south: A1 > Chiusi/Chianciano Terme > follow signs to Montepulciano.

Web: www.johansens.com/dionora
E-mail: info@dionora.it
Tel: +39 0578 717 496
Fax: +39 0578 717 498

Price Guide:
double €230-350

Hotel Monteriggioni

VIA 1 MAGGIO 4, 53035 MONTERIGGIONI (SI), ITALY

Directions: A1 Florence–Siena road > exit at Monteriggioni > pass Colonna di Monteriggioni > SS2 Cassia for 1km > Siena > left.

Web: www.johansens.com/monteriggioni
E-mail: info@hotelmonteriggioni.net
Tel: +39 0577 305009
Fax: +39 0577 305011

Price Guide:
single €100-130
double/twin €200-230
suite €300-400

Set within the walls of the fortified village of Monteriggioni, with its 14 towers and parish church still preserved, this charming hotel has maintained its original character by sympathetic restoration and scrupulous interior design. The atmosphere is one of discreet luxury, with each of the bedrooms being individually dressed with elegant fabrics and antique furniture that are in perfect harmony with the Tuscan stone exterior. The beautiful gardens encourage relaxation, with an elegant swimming pool and shady olive groves.

À l'abri des remparts du village fortifié de Monteriggioni, dont les 14 tours et l'église paroissiale sont restées intactes, cet hôtel de charme a gardé son cachet d'origine tout en bénéficiant d'une restauration harmonieuse et d'une décoration soignée. Il y règne un luxe discret, distillé par les étoffes élégantes et le mobilier raffiné, en parfait accord avec la façade en pierre toscane, qui parent les chambres apprêtées de manière individuelle. Le superbe jardin, avec sa belle piscine et ses olivaies ombragées, est une invitation à la détente.

Dieses charmante, innerhalb der Festungsmauern des Dorfes Monteriggioni gelegene Hotel, dessen 14 Türme und die Kirche noch intakt sind, behielt während seiner Renovierung und Umgestaltung seinen ursprünglichen Charakter bei. Unaufdringlicher Luxus ist überall spürbar, und die individuell gestalteten Zimmer sind mit feinen Stoffen und antiken Möbeln eingerichtet, die perfekt mit dem toskanischen Steinmauern harmonieren. Der herrliche Garten mit seinem eleganten Swimmingpool und schattenspendenden Olivenbäumen ist ideal zum Entspannen.

Our inspector loved: *The fascinating fortified medieval village of Monteriggioni.*

Castel Pietraio

STRADA DI STROVE 33, 53035 MONTERIGGIONI, ITALY

With even its later additions dating back to the 15th century, Castel Pietraio is steeped in local history and today is the centre of a strong wine-growing estate. Whilst marble bathrooms and Jacuzzi baths have been added to ensure every comfort, there is still a definite and enchanting medieval ambience. Considerately planned to accommodate guests' every requirement, there is an elegant swimming pool and playground on site, whilst the tower is lit by torches for grand banquets in the Capacci hall. There are 2 golf courses nearby.

Ce château imprégné d'histoire, dont même les agrandissements les plus récents remontent au XVe siècle, est aujourd'hui le noyau d'un important domaine viticole. L'installation de salles de bains en marbre et de jacuzzis pour le plus grand confort du visiteur n'a rien ôté au charme médiéval de l'endroit. Conçu de manière à satisfaire tous les besoins des visiteurs, cet hôtel dispose d'une élégante piscine et d'un terrain de jeu. La tour est illuminée par des torches lors des grands banquets organisés dans la salle Capacci. 2 parcours de golf se situent à proximité.

Diese geschichtsträchtige Burg, deren neueste Erweiterungen aus dem 15. Jahrhundert stammen, ist heute das Zentrum eines erfolgreichen Weinanbaugebietes. Zwar wurde mit Marmorbädern und Jacuzzis für modernen Komfort gesorgt, doch die herrliche mittelalterliche Atmosphäre ist noch deutlich spürbar. Alles wurde perfekt auf die Bedürfnisse heutiger Gäste abgestimmt. Es gibt einen eleganten Swimmingpool und einen Spielplatz, und der Turm wird für prunkvolle Bankette im Capacci-Saal mit Fackeln beleuchtet. 2 Golfplätze liegen in der Nähe.

Our inspector loved: *The Tuscan combination of nature, wine and modern comforts.*

Directions: A1Florence – Siena road, exit at Monteriggioni > SS541 towards Badia Isola.

Web: www.johansens.com/castelpietraio
E-mail: monteriggioni@interfree.it
Tel: +39 0577 300020
Fax: +39 0577 300977

Milan
Venice
Florence
Rome

Price Guide:
single/double/twin €150–160
junior suite €180

VILLA SASSOLINI

LARGO MONCIONI 85-88, 52020 MONCIONI MONTEVARCHI (AREZZO), ITALY

Directions: A1 motorway > exit 5 Valdarno > follow signs to Montevarchi. The Villa Sassolini is in the little square of Moncioni.

Web: www.johansens.com/sassolini
E-mail: info@villasassolini.it
Tel: +39 055 9702246
Fax: +39 055 9702943

Price Guide:
standard double €200–€240
deluxe double €200–€240
suite €280–€350

Sympathetic renovation has transformed this 18th-century villa into a charming hotel of character. Situated at the border of the Arno Valley and Chianti hills, Sassolini is a gem of elegance and splendour to gratify the most discerning visitor. A simplistic exterior is matched by cool, relaxing rooms inside. Many original features have been retained, principally the beamed ceilings, which blend harmoniously with delicate pale décor and exquisite furniture. A gourmet restaurant with summer dining is situated around the swimming pool.

Une belle rénovation a transformée cette villa du XVIIIe en un charmant hôtel de caractère. Situé sur les bords de la vallée de l'Arno et les collines du Chianti, Sassolini est un bijou d 'élégance et de splendeur. L'extérieur simpliste est assorti aux chambres relaxantes à l'intérieur. De nombreux éléments d'origine ont été gardés tels que les plafonds aux poutres apparentes qui se marient harmonieusement au décor pâle et au superbe mobilier. Le restaurant gastronomique sert à dîner en été autour de la piscine.

Durch sorgfältige Renovierung wurde aus dieser Villa aus dem 18. Jahrhundert ein charmantes, charaktervolles Hotel. Am Rande des Arno-Tales und der Chianti-Hügel gelegen, verzaubert dieses wahre Kleinod an Eleganz und Pracht selbst den anspruchsvollsten Gast. Das einfache Exterieur wird durch kühle, ruhige Räume ergänzt, und viele ursprüngliche Details blieben erhalten, vor allem Holzbalkendecken, die perfekt mit dem zarten pastellfarbenen Décor und exquisitem Mobiliar harmonisieren. Ein Gourmetrestaurant mit Sitzgelegenheit im Freien liegt direkt am Swimmingpool.

Our inspector loved: *The fine, sober elegance.*

Albergo Pietrasanta - Palazzo Barsanti Bonetti

VIA GARIBALDI 35, 55045 PIETRASANTA (LUCCA), ITALY

An authentic 17th-century palace in true Renaissance style, the hotel has been restored and maintained in a unique fashion. Its main hall combines abstract paintings with antique furniture, marble chip floors and beautiful moulded stucco and fresco ceilings. The covered courtyard has been transformed into a bar, and the enchanting waterfall in one corner completes its evocative charm. Bedrooms feature attractive fabrics and antique décor, and many bistros and brasseries, including one of the most renowned restaurants of Versilia, are nearby.

Ce palais authentique du XVIe siècle en style de la Renaissance a été restauré et maintenu de manière unique. Sa salle principale marie à merveille des peintures abstraites avec des meubles antiques, un sol en marbre et des plafonds magnifiques de stuc et de fresques. La cour couverte a été transformée en bar et la fontaine au coin complète son charme évocateur. Les chambres sont décorées de manière antique avec des tissus attractifs. De nombreux bistrots et brasseries, comprenant une des plus célèbres de Versilia, sont à proximité.

Dieses echte Renaissance-Palais aus dem 17. Jahrhundert wurde auf einzigartige Weise restauriert und erhalten. In der Haupthalle mischen sich abstrakte Gemälde mit Antiquitäten, Marmorböden und wundervollen Stuck- und Freskodecken. Der überdachte Innenhof wurde in eine Bar umgewandelt, und der zauberhafte Wasserfall in der Ecke sorgt für ganz besonderen Charme. Die Zimmer sind mit hübschen Stoffen und antikem Décor ausgestattet, und zahlreiche Bistros und Brasserien, darunter eines der bekanntesten Restaurants von Versilia, liegen in nächster Nähe.

Our inspector loved: *The harmonious blend of abstract paintings (from their private collection) with the antique furniture.*

Directions: A12 (Genova-Livorno) > exit at Versilia > Pietrasanta > Viale Apua > historical centre > Vicolo Lavatoi.

Web: www.johansens.com/pietrasanta
E-mail: info@albergopietrasanta.com
Tel: +39 0584 793 727
Fax: +39 0584 793 728

Price Guide:
double €220-380
junior suite €320-500
suite €380-700

RELAIS LA SUVERA

53030 PIEVESCOLA – SIENA, ITALY

In 1989 the Marchess Ricci and his wife Principessa Eleonora Massimo created this elite and luxurious hotel composed of 4 beautifully restored houses surrounding a courtyard. The elegant reception has a welcoming ambience, enhanced by a display of wines from their own vineyard. The exquisite salons are bedecked with antiques and the family art collection. Guests feast on Tuscan dishes served in the hotel's restaurant.

C'est en 1989 que le marquis Ricci et son épouse la princesse Eleonora Massimo ont créé cet hôtel luxueux de grand standing formé de 4 maisons superbement restaurées autour d'une cour. L'élégante réception se caractérise par une ambiance chaleureuse, accentuée par une série de bouteilles de vins provenant du vignoble du Relais. Les salons ravissants sont agrémentés de belles pièces anciennes et d'une collection d'oeuvres d'art de la famille. Les hôtes se régalent de succulents plats toscans servis au restaurant de l'hôtel.

1989 schufen der Marquis Ricci und seine Gemahlin Principessa Eleonora Massimo dieses elitäre Luxushotel, das aus 4 wunderschön restaurierten Häusern besteht. Schon der elegante Empfangsraum, in dem einige der Weine aus dem eigenen Weinberg ausgestellt werden, strahlt warme Herzlichkeit aus. Die prachtvollen Aufenthaltsräume sind mit Antiquitäten und einer von der Familie zusammengestellten Kunstsammlung gefüllt. Für kulinarischen Genuss im Hotelrestaurant sorgen köstliche toskanische Speisen.

Our inspector loved: *The family's collection of antiques and the hotel's cultural heritage.*

Directions: Superstrada Siena-Florence > Colle Val d'Elsa > Grosseto.

Web: www.johansens.com/relaislasuvera
E-mail: lasuvera@lasuvera.it
Tel: +39 0577 960300
Fax: +39 0577 960220

Price Guide:
double/twin €360–560
suite €480–980

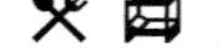

Hotel Relais Dell'Orologio

VIA DELLA FAGGIOLA 12/14, 56126 PISA, ITALY

In the centre of Pisa, a short distance from Piazza dei Miracoli and Piazza dei Cavalieri, stands this carefully restored 14th-century tower house. Soothing colour schemes and period pieces furnish the spacious guest rooms that feature exposed beams and provide every modern comfort; each has Internet and PC connections. The Hallet's Bar restaurant oozes romance, and breakfast may be enjoyed in the Italian garden whilst drinks are served on the veranda. Nearby sites include the local church, monastery and Natural Reserve of San Rossore, which leads down to the sea.

Au centre de Pise, tout près de la Piazza dei Miracoli et de la Piazza dei Cavalieri, se tient cette tour soigneusement restaurée datant du XIVe siècle. Des couleurs apaisantes et des meubles d'époque habillent les chambres spacieuses aux poutres apparentes et au confort le plus moderne ; toutes ont des prises ordinateur et connexion internet. Le restaurant Hallet's Bar invite à la romance, le petit déjeuner peut être pris dans le jardin italien, et des boissons dégustées sur la véranda. A visiter tout proche l'église locale, le monastère et la Réserve Naturelle de San Rossore qui mène tout droit à la mer.

Im Herzen von Pisa, nur wenige Minuten von der Piazza dei Miracoli und der Piazza dei Cavalieri entfernt, befindet sich dieses sorgfältig restaurierte Turmhaus aus dem 14. Jahrhundert. Ruhige Farben, Stilmöbel und freiliegende Balken zieren die geräumigen, komfortablen Zimmer, jedes mit PC und Internetzugang. Das Hallet's Bar Restaurant hat eine romantische Atmosphäre, Frühstück wird im italienischen Garten serviert, und Drinks genießt man auf der Veranda. Attraktionen sind die Kirche, ein Kloster und das Naturreservat von San Rossore, das bis zum Meer führt.

Our inspector loved: *The romantic, intimate atmosphere.*

Directions: Pisa Airport > taxi to hotel. Situated in the centre of Pisa. If driving, full directions are given on request.

Web: www.johansens.com/relaisorologio
E-mail: info@hotelrelaisorologio.com
Tel: +39 050 830 361
Fax: +39 050 551 869

Price Guide:
single €225
double (single occupancy) €286
double €326
junior suite €440
suite €620

ITALY / TUSCANY (PORTO ERCOLE)

Il Pellicano Hotel & Spa

LOC. SBARCATELLO, 58018 PORTO ERCOLE (GR), TUSCANY, ITALY

Directions: Rome > A12 > Civitavecchia > Orbetello > Porto Ercole.

Web: www.johansens.com/ilpellicano
E-mail: info@pellicanohotel.com
Tel: +39 0564 858111
Fax: +39 0564 833418

Price Guide:
double from €432
suite from €787
(half board)
double from €470
suite from €929

This ivy-clad villa, surrounded by a cluster of cottages is set amongst old olive trees in spectacular gardens and situated on the breathtaking Argentario Peninsula; a real paradise. Each room and suite is uniquely decorated and guests can enjoy exquisite local and international cuisine and wine at The Pelican Point Restaurant or al fresco at La Terrazza. After a day of water skiing, tennis or swimming in the heated seawater pool guests can take advantage of the Paradise Spa and relax with a massage. The hotel boasts its very own private cove which can be reached by lift.

Cette villa recouverte de lierre et entourée de charmants cottages, est située parmi de vieux oliviers dans de spectaculaires jardins sur la péninsule Argentario: un vrai paradis. Chacune des chambres et suites est décorée de manière unique et les clients peuvent déguster une délicieuse cuisine locale et internationale au restaurant Pelican Point ou à l'extérieur à La Terrazza. Après une journée de ski nautique, de tennis ou au bord de la piscine d'eau de mer chauffée, les clients peuvent se rendre au Paradise Spa et apprécier un massage. L'hôtel possède sa propre anse que l'on rejoint en ascenseur.

Diese efeubewachsene, von Cottages umgebene Villa liegt inmitten von Olivenbäumen in einem Garten auf der paradiesischen Argentario-Halbinsel. Alle Zimmer und Suiten sind unterschiedlich eingerichtet, und im The Pelican Point Restaurant oder al fresco im La Terrazza werden exquisite einheimische und internationale Gerichte und Weine serviert. Man kann Wasserski fahren, Tennis spielen oder im beheizten Salzwasserpool schwimmen und danach bei einer Massage im Paradise Spa entspannen. Das Hotel bietet eine eigene kleine Bucht, die mit einem Lift zu erreichen ist.

***Our inspector loved:** This magical place where life is a dream from which you never want to wake.*

Relais Fattoria Vignale

VIA PANIGIANI 9, 53017 RADDA IN CHIANTI (SIENA), ITALY

Located in the heart of the Chianti Classico region, just outside the medieval village of Radda, this 18th-century manor house was formerly a family-run wine estate. Bedrooms and public rooms feature antiques and some guest rooms have a Jacuzzi, terrace and panoramic view. Meals may be taken on the wisteria and jasmine-covered terrace. Alternatively, Vignale Restaurant, 300m away, serves seasonal cuisine complemented by Fattoria Vignale, national and Tuscan wines. The original wine cellars host wine tastings and the rustic-style Taverna.

Situé au cœur de la région de Chianti Classico, juste à l'extérieur du village médiéval de Radda, ce manoir du XVIIIe siècle était autrefois un domaine viticole familial. Des antiquités habillent ses pièces communes et chambres, certaines de ses dernières bénéficiant de jacuzzi et vues panoramiques. Les repas peuvent être pris sur la terrasse couverte de jasmin et glycine. Autrement, le restaurant Vignale, à 300 m, sert une cuisine de saison complétée par Fattoria Vignale, des vins nationaux et toscans. Les celliers originaux abritent un atelier de dégustation et une taverne de style rustique.

Im Herzen der Chianti Classico Region, außerhalb des mittelalterlichen Dorfes Radda befindet sich dieser Herrensitz aus dem 18. Jahrhundert, einst ein familiengeführtes Weingut. Die Zimmer sind mit Antiquitäten eingerichtet, einige haben Jacuzzi, Terrasse und Panoramablick. Gegessen wird auf der mit Blauregen und Jasmin umrankten Terrasse, oder im 300m entfernten Vignale, wo man saisonbedingte Küche und italienische, toskanische oder Weine der Fattoria Vignale genießt. In den alten Weinkellern, wo sich auch die rustikale Taverne befindet, finden Weinproben statt.

Our inspector loved: *The sweet scented flower-covered terrace with splendid views.*

40

Directions: From north: A1 (north) > exit Florence Certosa 7 > main road to Siena for 22km > exit San Donato > Castellina > Radda. From south: A1 (south) > exit Valdarno 7 (Montevarchi) > country road 408 towards Gaide Siena > Radda.

Web: www.johansens.com/vignale
E-mail: vignale@vignale.it
Tel: +39 0577 738300
Fax: +39 0577 738592

Price Guide:
single €150
double €180-320
suite €380

Pieve di Caminino (Historical Residence)

VIA PROV. DI PERUZZO, 58028 ROCCATEDERIGHI (GROSSETO), ITALY

This small hamlet is set within the walls of the historical 11th-century monastery, built on Paleo-Christian ruins. Caminino lies in a large amphitheatre with views of the sea and the lush hills that are adorned with fortresses and castles from medieval times. Each apartment has an open fireplace and terrace and is individually decorated with antique furniture and paintings that enhance the authenticity of the ancient architecture. The extensive landscaped gardens are beautiful.

Ce petit hameau est situé entre les murs du monastère du XIe siècle, construit sur les ruines paléo-chrétiennes. Caminino se trouve dans un large amphithéâtre et a vue sur la mer et sur les collines luxuriantes couvertes de châteaux et de forteresses datant du Moyen-Age. Chaque appartement possède cheminée et terrasse et est individuellement décoré de meubles anciens et de peintures qui soulignent l'authenticité de l'architecture ancienne. Les vastes jardins paysagers sont superbes.

Dieses kleine Dörfchen liegt innerhalb der Mauern eines historischen Klosters aus dem 11. Jahrhundert, das auf paleo-christlichen Ruinen erbaut wurde. Caminino befindet sich in einem großen Amphitheater mit Blick auf das Meer und die grünen, von Festungen und Burgen aus dem Mittelalter gezierten umliegenden Hügel. Die Appartements bieten offene Kamine und eigene Terrassen und sind individuell mit Antiquitäten und Malereien eingerichtet, die die authentische Wirkung der alten Architektur unterstreichen. Der große, herrlich gestaltete Garten ist einfach ein Traum.

Our inspector loved: *The beautiful pond.*

Directions: Aurelia Road towards Livorno and Grosseto > exit Braccagni > follow directions to Montemassi - Sassofortino. Or Siena - Grosseto freeway > exit Civitella Marittima > Follonica > Montemassi > Sassofortino.

Web: www.johansens.com/caminino
E-mail: caminino@caminino.com
Tel: +39 0564 569 737
Fax: +39 0564 568 756

Price Guide: (excluding breakfast)
apartment 2 people (per night) €110-140
apartment 2 people (per week) €700-900
apartment 4-5 people (per night) €220-250
apartment 4-5 people (per week) €1,300-1,550

8 70

Hotel Plaza e de Russie

PIAZZA D'AZEGLIO 1, 55049 VIAREGGIO (LU), ITALY

This splendid hotel was the first built in Viareggio in 1871 and retains a stately magnificence that is today combined with modern comfort and luxury. Tall and elegantly proportioned rooms are all individually decorated with rich antiques, Italian marble and classic Murano chandeliers. The gourmet restaurant, La Terrazza, offers Mediterranean inspired high cuisine and the terrace has outstanding views of the Versilia coast climbing up towards the Apuan Alps and is a stunning place to enjoy some spectacular sunsets.

Ce splendide hôtel fut le premier construit à Viareggio en 1871 et garde une imposante magnificence qui est aujourd'hui combinée au luxe et au confort moderne. Les chambres, grandes et en élégante harmonie sont individuellement décorées avec de somptueuses antiquités, du marbre italien et des chandeliers de Murano. Le restaurant gastronomique La Terrazza sert une délicate cuisine d'inspiration méditerranéenne et la terrasse offre non seulement de superbes vues sur la côte de Versilia jusqu'aux Alpes Apuanes mais est également l'endroit idéal pour admirer de magnifiques couchers de soleil.

Dieses 1871 erbaute fantastische Hotel war das erste in Viareggio und besitzt auch heute noch eine ehrwürdige Pracht, die sich perfekt mit modernem Komfort und Luxus verbindet. Die hohen, eleganten Zimmer sind alle individuell mit üppigen Antiquitäten, italienischem Marmor und klassischen Murano-Lüstern eingerichtet. Im Gourmetrestaurant La Terrazza wird exzellente Mittelmeerküche serviert, und von der Terrasse hat man eine herrliche Sicht auf die Küste von Versilia bis hin zu den Apuanischen Alpen. Ein wundervoller Ort für spektakuläre Sonnenuntergänge.

Our inspector loved: *The roof terrace with its splendid view of the Versilia river.*

Directions: A12 > exit Viareggio - Camaiore.

Web: www.johansens.com/russie
E-mail: info@plazaederussie.com
Tel: +39 0584 44449
Fax: +39 0584 44031

Price Guide:
single €113-159
double €167-272
suite €251-324

ROMANTIK HOTEL LE SILVE DI ARMENZANO

06081 LOC ARMENZANO, ASSISI (PG), ITALY

This small hotel dates back to before the birth of St Francis of Assisi, the patron saint of animals. Le Silve is 700 metres above sea level, built on a plateau at the foot of the Subasio mountains. The air is scented by olive groves, and deer and horses ramble through the beautiful countryside. Umbrian cooking is delicious and here, the bread is baked traditionally in the fireplace. A charming sense of unspoilt rural simplicity is created by touches such as alfresco dining and country furniture.

Ce petit hôtel dâte d'avant la naissance de Saint François d'Assise, le saint patron des animaux. Le Silve se situe à 700 mètres au dessus du niveau de la mer. Il a été construit sur un plateau, au pied des montagnes du Subasio. L'air y est parfumé par les oliveraies et des biches et des chevaux gambadent dans le magnifique parc. La cuisine ombrienne est délicieuse et le pain proposé est cuit de façon traditionnelle dans la cheminée. Le diner servi à l'extérieur et le mobilier de style campagnard dégagent un agréable sentiment de simplicité rurale.

Dieses kleine Hotel existierte bereits vor der Geburt von Franz von Assisi, dem Schutzpatron der Tiere. Es liegt 700 Meter über dem Meeresspiegel auf einem Plateau am Fuße der Subasio-Berge und vom Duft der Olivenhaine umgeben. Wild und Pferde durchstreifen die herrliche Landschaft. Die Küche Umbriens ist einfach köstlich, und das Brot wird traditionell im Holzofen gebacken. Man spürt ein unbeschwertes Gefühl von ländlicher Schlichtheit, das durch rustikales Mobiliar und Essen unter freiem Himmel noch betont wird.

Our inspector loved: *The elegance of this charming retreat which offers you traditional dishes and homemade delicacies.*

Directions: Perugia > Assisi> S 75 > Armenzano.

Web: www.johansens.com/silvediarmenzano
E-mail: hotellesilve@tin.it
Tel: +39 075 801 9000
Fax: +39 075 801 9005

Price Guide:
single €83–91
double/twin €166–182

Romantik Hotel Villa di Monte Solare

VIA MONTALI 7, 06070 COLLE SAN PAOLO - PANICALE (PG), ITALY

The combination of its elegant Italian gardens, chapel and beautiful surroundings of woods and vineyards provide this elegant hotel with its sense of total tranquillity. The authenticity of the building has been painstakingly preserved in its restoration and today it offers individually designed bedrooms, some with their original frescoes and terracotta floors. Chef, Antonio Bondi, prepares high-quality Italian food (guests have the opportunity to join the cooking school) and more than 360 Umbrian wines are on offer.

La combinaison de ses beaux jardins italiens, de sa chapelle et des superbes bois et vignobles qui l'entourent, procure à cet élégant hôtel son sentiment de tranquillité absolue. L'authenticité du bâtiment a été préservée avec soin lors de sa restauration et il offre aujourd'hui des chambres individuellement décorées, certaines ayant gardé leurs fresques et sols en terre cuite d'origine. Le restaurant sert une cuisine italienne de grande qualité, préparée par Antonio Bondi (et aussi la chance de s'enrôler dans l'école de cuisine), et plus de 360 vins ombriens.

Die Kombination aus eleganten italienischen Gärten, einer Kapelle und der wunderschönen Umgebung aus Wäldern und Weinbergen gibt diesem eleganten Hotel eine Aura von Ruhe und Frieden. Die Authentizität des Gebäudes wurde bei der Restaurierung sorgfältig bewahrt, und heute findet man hier unterschiedlich gestaltete Zimmer, von denen einige noch die ursprünglichen Fresken und Terrakottaböden aufweisen. Chefkoch Antonio Bondi bereitet köstliche italienische Speisen zu (Gäste können hier auch einen Kochkurs machen), und über 360 umbrische Weine stehen zur Auswahl.

Our inspector loved: *The superb hospitality and the fabulous cuisine.*

Directions: A1 > exit Chiusi towards Tavernelle - Colle San Paolo.

Web: www.johansens.com/montesolare
E-mail: info@villamontesolare.it
Tel: +39 075 832376
Fax: +39 075 8355818

Milan
Venice
Perugia
Rome

Price Guide:
single €90–105
classic double €150–180
superior double €170-200

Castello di Petroia

LOCALITÀ PETROIA, 06020 GUBBIO (PG), ITALY

Directions: E45 (Orte–Cesena) > exit at Bosco > the castle is on the SS298.

Web: www.johansens.com/castellodipetroia
E-mail: castellodipetroia@castellodipetroia.com
Tel: +39 075 92 02 87
Fax: +39 075 92 01 08

Price Guide:
double/twin €115–135
tower €120–140
suite €155–190

Steeped in Italian history and the birthplace of Count Federico da Montefeltro, Duke of Urbino, Castello di Petroia is a beautiful collection of buildings housed within castle walls. The duke played a key part in the Italian Renaissance and the castle has been restored today in complete sympathy with its origins. Guests at the castle are assured of a quite unique experience. The common rooms are beautiful, and the swimming pool a truly relaxing haven overlooking the peaceful woods and grounds that surround the estate.

Imprégnée d'histoire italienne, et le lieu de naissance du Comte Federico da Montefeltro, Duc d'Urbino, Castello di Petroia est un ensemble de bâtiments situés au sein des murs du château. Le Duc joua un rôle important pendant la renaissance italienne et le château a maintenant été restauré en accord avec ses particularités d'origine; ses hôtes peuvent donc jouir d'une expérience unique. Les pièces communes sont superbes et la piscine, avec sa vue sur les bois et le parc entourant la propriété, est l'endroit idéal où se détendre.

Das geschichtsträchtige Castello di Petroia war Geburtsort des Grafen Federico da Montefeltro, Herzog von Urbino, der eine bedeutende Rolle in der italienischen Renaissance spielte. Es besteht aus mehreren herrlichen Gebäuden innerhalb der Burgmauern und wurde in völliger Harmonie mit seinen Ursprüngen restauriert. Gäste erwartet eine wahrhaft einzigartige Erfahrung. Die Aufenthaltsräume sind wunderschön gestaltet, und der Swimmingpool ist eine Oase der Ruhe mit Blick auf die friedliche Umgebung.

Our inspector loved: *The fascinating history behind this authentic castle.*

Palazzo Terranova

LOC. RONTI MORRA, 06010 MORRA (PG), ITALY

Palazzo Terranova is quite simply a stunning hotel; both in its location at the top of a hill overlooking the rolling Umbrian landscape, and in terms of its style. Each of the 10 rooms and 3 suites has been immaculately designed featuring wrought-iron beds, antique pieces and creative use of colour. The new Bar and Enoteca serves delicious food including homemade salamis, cheese and olive oil as well as excellent wines. There is a stunning pool, a spa, Il Tempio, and for guests wishing to get away from it all, the hotel is available for exclusive use.

Palazzo Terranova est tout simplement un hôtel magnifique; sur le plan de sa position privilégiée donnant sur les collines onduleuses d'Ombrie et sur le plan de son style. Chacune des 10 chambres et 3 suites a un design impeccable avec des lits en fer forgé, des objets d'art et l'emploi créatif de couleur. Des salamis, fromages et huile d'olive faits à la maison ainsi que des vins excellents sont servis dans le nouveau bar et Enoteca. Il y a une piscine superbe et le spa Il Tempio, et pour les hôtes souhaitant laisser tous leurs ennuis derrière eux, l'hôtel est disponible pour l'utilisation exclusive.

Dieses Hotel ist einfach einmalig, sowohl was seine Lage auf einem Hügel mit Blick auf die umbrische Landschaft als auch seine Eleganz betrifft. Jedes der 10 Zimmer und 3 Suiten wurde mit schmiedeeisernen Betten, Antiquitäten und kreativen Farben gestaltet. In der neuen Bar und Enoteca gibt es köstliches Essen, darunter selbstgemachte Salami, Käse und Olivenöl und hervorragende Weine. Ein herrlicher Swimmingpool und das Il Tempio Spa stehen zur Verfügung, und wer sich nach völliger Abgeschiedenheit sehnt, kann das Hotel exklusiv mieten.

Our inspector loved: *The stunning views and gardens - a true haven away from chaotic daily life.*

Directions: A1 towards Rome > exit Monte San Savino > Castiglion Fiorentino > over bridge > right at crossroads > right at traffic lights > left at third set of lights > Citta di Castello > Ronti > left before Cyprus trees > dirt track 2km.

Web: www.johansens.com/terranova
E-mail: bookings@palazzoterranova.com
Tel: +39 075 857 0083
Fax: +39 075 857 0014

Price Guide: (based on 2 persons, per night)
double €300-500
suite €550-775

Villa Ciconia

VIA DEI TIGLI 69, LOC CICONIA, 05018 ORVIETO (TR), ITALY

Directions: Approximately 85km south of Perugia. From Orvieto Scalo follow directions towards Arezzo (SS71).

Web: www.johansens.com/villaciconia
E-mail: villaciconia@libero.it
Tel: +39 0763 305582/3
Fax: +39 0763 302077

Price Guide: (lunch €18, dinner €18)
single €120-145
double €130-155

This 16th-century villa located near the town of Orvieto is an elegant haven of tranquillity set amidst a beautiful park. Newly renovated, the villa has maintained its original character, apparent in its thick walls, large beams and terracotta flooring. 12 comfortable guest rooms look onto the park. Guests can enjoy traditional Umbrian delicacies complemented by fine wines from the well-stocked cellar. Villa Ciconia is the ideal base from which to explore the enchanting Umbrian countryside and picturesque villages.

Cette villa datant du XVIe siècle près de la ville d'Orvieto est un élégant havre de tranquillité au sein d'un beau parc. Récemment rénovée, la villa a gardé son caractère original, évident dans ses murs épais, ses grandes poutres apparentes et ses sols en terracotta. Les 12 chambres donnent sur le parc. Les hôtes peuvent savourer des spécialités ombriennes accompagnées de bons vins de la cave bien équipée. Villa Ciconia est la base idéale pour découvrir la campagne enchanteresse d'Ombrie et ses villages pittoresques.

Diese Villa aus dem 16. Jahrhundert nahe der Stadt Orvieto ist eine Oase der Ruhe und Eleganz inmitten eines herrlichen Parks. Die kürzlich renovierte Villa besitzt immer noch ihren ursprünglichen Charakter, sichtbar an den dicken Wänden, großen Holzbalken und Terrakottaböden. Die 12 komfortablen Zimmer blicken auf den Park. Die Gäste genießen traditionelle Köstlichkeiten Umbriens und erlesene Weine aus dem gutbestückten Weinkeller. Dies ist der ideale Ausgangspunkt für Ausflüge in die zauberhafte umbrische Landschaft mit ihren malerischen Dörfern.

Our inspector loved: *The simple elegance.*

Alla Corte del Sole Relais

LOC. I GIORGI, 06061 PETRIGNANO DEL LAGO (PG), ITALY

This delightful, 15th-century monastic village with its renovated, rebuilt and refurbished accommodation stands near Lake Trasimeno, midway between Cortona and Montepulciano. It is the ideal retreat for anyone seeking to be pampered and enjoy the region's cultural centres. Each guest room is charmingly elegant, air-conditioned and has every home comfort. The beautifully maintained grounds feature a large swimming pool.

Ce charmant village monastique datant du XVe siècle avec des logements rénovés, reconstruit et remis à neuf, est situé près du lac Trasimeno, entre Cortona et Montepulciano. Il est l'endroit parfait pour des personnes cherchant à se dorloter et profiter des centres culturels de la région. Chaque chambre est élégante, climatisée et dispose de tout le confort moderne. Il y a une grande piscine dans le parc superbement entretenu.

Dieses wundervolle klösterliche Dorf aus dem 15. Jahrhundert in der Nähe des Trasimener Sees auf halber Strecke zwischen Cortona und Montepulciano bietet komplett renovierte und neu gestaltete Unterkunft und ist der ideale Ort, um sich total zu entspannen und das kulturelle Angebot der Region zu nutzen. Jedes der eleganten, zauberhaften Zimmer bietet Klimaanlage und jeglichen Komfort. Ein großer Swimmingpool befindet sich ebenfalls auf dem herrlichen Gelände.

Our inspector loved: *The mouthwatering breakfast and the attention to detail.*

Directions: A1 > exit Valdichiana/Bettolle > take Superstrada to Perugia > second exit for Cortona > follow signs for Monte Pulciano.

Web: www.johansens.com/cortedelsole
E-mail: info@cortedelsole.com
Tel: +39 075 9689008
Fax: +39 075 9689070

Price Guide:
single €110-120
double €173-203
suite €203-303

LE TORRI DI BAGNARA

STRADA DELLA BRUNA 8, 06080 PIEVE SAN QUIRICO, PERUGIA, ITALY

High on a hill overlooking the Tiber Valley, this historic complex offers guests a peaceful refuge. Le Torri di Bagnara consists of 3 main buildings surrounded by a 1,300-acre estate, which includes tobacco and beet plantations, a nature reserve, gardens and swimming pool. A 13th-century tower houses 4 superb apartments, the 11th-century abbey offers luxury bedrooms, suites and restaurant and the Quirico House is the welcoming reception and lounge venue. Bed and breakfast accommodation and a restaurant will open in winter 2004/5.

Haut perché sur une colline surplombant la vallée du Tibre, Le Torri di Bagnara offre à ses hôtes un refuge tranquille. Ce complexe historique est composé de 4 bâtiments principaux entourés d'un domaine de plus de 500 hectares comprenant des plantations de tabac et de betteraves, une réserve naturelle, des jardins et une piscine. Une tour du XIIIe siècle abrite 3 superbes appartements, l'abbaye du XIe siècle abrite de luxueuses chambres, suites et le restaurant et la Maison Quirico accueille la réception et le salon. Logement avec petit-déjeuner et un restaurant sont envisagés pour l'hiver de 2004/5.

Hoch auf einem Hügel mit Blick auf das Tibertal gelegen, garantiert das Le Torri di Bagnara einen ruhigen Aufenthalt. Dieser historische Komplex besteht aus 4 Gebäuden inmitten eines 526ha großen Geländes mit Tabak- und Rübenplantage, Naturreservat, Gärten und Swimmingpool. Im Turm aus dem 13. Jahrhundert liegen 3 fantastische Appartements, die Abtei aus dem 11. Jahrhundert bietet Luxuszimmer, Suiten und ein Restaurant, und das Quirico Haus bildet die einladende Rezeption mit Aufenthaltsbereich. Zimmer mit Frühstück und ein Restaurant sind für Winter 2004/5 geplant.

Our inspector loved: *The outstanding natural beauty.*

Directions: E45 (Orte - Ravenna) > exit Resina > SS Tiberina (towards north) > turn left at Km89.7 > Pieve S Quirico - Bagnara.

Web: www.johansens.com/bagnara
E-mail: info@letorridibagnara.it
Tel: +39 075 604 136 and +39 335 6408 549
Fax: +39 075 5792 105

Price Guide: (room only)
apartment (2 beds) €70-90
apartments (4-5 beds) €120-156
double/twin €100-140
suite €120-190

CONVENTO DI AGGHIELLI

FRAZIONE POMPAGNANO, LOCALITÀ AGGHIELLI, 06049 SPOLETO (PG), ITALY

Guests are guaranteed a truly unique experience at this 13th-century Country Resort for Wellness and Cooking, a remarkable retreat from the world. Everything here is designed in total harmony with nature, from the eco-friendly building materials to the ingredients used in the kitchen, which are all organically grown or raised on the property. Guests can attend cookery classes, explore the beautiful Umbrian countryside or simply relax and enjoy some well-deserved pampering sessions, including hydromassage, reflexology and ayurvedic treatments.

Les hôtes sont assurés d'une expérience unique dans ce lieu de vacances datant du XIIIe siècle et situé à la campagne, qui se spécialise dans le bien-être et l'art culinaire; une superbe retraite loin du monde. Tout a été créé en harmonie avec la nature, des matériaux de construction écologiques aux ingrédients utilisés dans la cuisine, issus de l'agriculture et de l'élevage biologiques de la propriété. Les hôtes peuvent assister à des cours de cuisine, explorer la belle campagne ombrienne ou simplement se détendre et se faire choyer lors de séances bien méritées d'hydrothérapie, réflexologie et traitements ayur-védiques.

Ein Aufenthalt in diesem Country Resort for Wellness and Cooking aus dem 13. Jahrhundert ist ein unvergleichliches Erlebnis. Alles in diesem wahrhaften Versteck vor der Welt ist in Harmonie mit der Natur gestaltet, von den Baumaterialien bis hin zu den Speisen, deren Zutaten ausschließlich aus eigenem biologischen Anbau oder eigener Aufzucht stammen. Man kann Kochkurse machen, die herrliche Landschaft Umbriens erkunden oder sich einfach mit Hydromassage, Reflexologie, Ayurweda-Behandlungen und vielem mehr verwöhnen lassen.

Directions: Approximately 66km south-east of Perugia and 2km south of Spoleto on the S3.

Web: www.johansens.com/agghielli
E-mail: info@agghielli.it
Tel: +39 0743 225 010
Fax: +39 0743 225 010

Price Guide:
double €124-155
suite €140-230

Our inspector loved: *The plunge into 100ha of pure nature.*

HOTEL SAN LUCA

VIA INTERNA DELLE MURA 21, 06049 SPOLETO, ITALY

This delightful, family-run hotel is set in a restored 19th-century tannery in the heart of the medieval hilltop town of Spoleto, whose origins date back to Roman times. Family antiques decorate the impressive public rooms and fresh flowers from the garden are used throughout. The spacious guest rooms are individually decorated and well equipped with all modern comforts and extremely luxurious bathrooms. There is a lovely fountain courtyard and a pretty garden in which to enjoy a delicious homemade breakfast or an apéritif.

Ce charmant hôtel de famille est situé dans une tannerie restaurée du XIXe siècle, au cœur de la ville médiévale de Spoleto, dont les origines remontent à l'ère romaine. Des meubles anciens de la famille décorent les impressionnantes pièces communes et l'on trouve partout des bouquets de fleurs fraîches du jardin. Les chambres spacieuses et bien-équipées sont décorées de manière individuelle avec tout le confort moderne ainsi que de très luxueuses salles de bains. Le petit-déjeuner et l'apéritif peuvent être dégustés dans le jardin ou dans la cour intérieure avec fontaine.

Dieses bezaubernde, familiengeführte Hotel liegt in einer restaurierten Gerberei aus dem 19. Jahrhundert im Herzen der mittelalterlichen Bergstadt Spoleto, deren Ursprünge bis zur Zeit der Römer zurüchgehen. Antiquitäten der Familie zieren die eindrucksvollen Aufenthaltsräume, und überall findet man frische Blumen aus dem Garten. Die individuell gestalteten Zimmer sind geräumig und gut ausgestattet und bieten jeglichen modernen Komfort und extrem luxuriöse Bäder. Der hübsche Innenhof mit Springbrunnen und der Garten sind ideal für ein hausgemachtes Frühstück oder einen Apéritif.

Our inspector loved: *The fountain courtyard.*

Directions: From Florence > A1 towards Rome > exit Valdichiana > Spoleto. From Rome > A1 towards Florence > exit Orte > Spoleto.

Web: www.johansens.com/sanluca
E-mail: sanluca@hotelsanluca.com
Tel: +39 0743 223 399
Fax: +39 0743 223 800

Price Guide:
single €85-130
double €110-240
suite €210-300

Romantik Hotel Villa Novecento

VIALE MONTE BIANCO 64, 11013 COURMAYEUR, AOSTA, ITALY

At the foot of the icy mountain, Mont Blanc, this former noble house, with its antique furnishings and precious fabrics, provides cosy and elegant accommodation. Novecento serves traditional dishes created from ancient recipes, to be savoured following the many activities on offer nearby. Cross-country skiing, trekking, ice-skating, kayaking and nature trails can all be arranged. The fitness centre features a sauna, Jacuzzi, Turkish bath and techno-gym, and a private shuttle takes guests to and from the ski slope.

Au pied du Mont Blanc cette maison majestueuse remplie d'antiquités et de tissus raffinés, offre un hébergement confortable et élégant. Novecento sert des plats traditionnels inspirés de recettes anciennes à déguster après les nombreuses activités disponibles dans les environs. Ski de fond, randonnée, patinage sur glace, kayak et sentiers dans la nature peuvent être organisés. Le centre de remise en forme offre sauna, hammam, jacuzzi et appareils de techno-gym. Une navette privée emmène les clients sur les pistes de ski.

Am Fuße des Mont Blanc gelegen, ist dieses einstige Adelshaus mit seinen antiken Einrichtungen und wertvollen Stoffen eine gemütliche und elegante Bleibe. Im Novecento werden traditionelle, nach alten Rezepten zubereitete Gerichte serviert, die man sich nach einem aktiven Tag redlich verdient hat. Langlaufen, Wandern, Schlittschuhlaufen, Kayaken und Naturwanderungen können arrangiert werden. Das Fitnesszentrum bietet Sauna, Jacuzzi, Türkisches Bad und Techno-Gym, und ein privates Shuttle bringt die Gäste an die Skipiste und holt sie wieder ab.

Our inspector loved: *The cosy and refined atmosphere, and the view of Mont Blanc from the bedrooms.*

Directions: A5 (Torino - Aosta) > exit Courmayeur > follow directions to the centre.

Web: www.johansens.com/novecento
E-mail: info@villanovecento.it
Tel: +39 0165 843 000
Fax: +39 0165 844 030

Price Guide:
single €136-256
double €170-320
suite €250-460

ALBERGO AL SOLE

VIA COLLEGIO 33, 31011 ASOLO, TREVISO, ITALY

Nestled in the heart of the medieval village of Asolo, this beautiful, timeless hotel has a warm atmosphere and is surrounded by a rich diversity of art and culture. Elegant bedrooms are luxuriously decorated with authentic furniture whilst antique-style baths live in perfect harmony with Jacuzzi showers and other modern comforts. La Terrazza Bar and Restaurant has breathtaking views over the castle and is the ideal place for delicious culinary treats.

Tapi au cœur du village médiéval d'Asolo, ce magnifique, intemporel hôtel à l'atmosphère chaleureuse est entouré d'une grande diversité culturelle et artistique. Les chambres élégantes sont luxueusement décorées de meubles authentiques et les baignoires de style ancien se marient parfaitement avec les douches jacuzzis et autres équipements modernes. Le bar et restaurant La Terrazza offre des vues à couper le souffle sur le château et est l'endroit idéal pour déguster de véritables plaisirs culinaires.

Dieses im Herzen des mittelalterlichen Dorfes Asolo gelegene zeitlos schöne Hotel besitzt eine herzliche Atmosphäre und ist von einer Vielfalt an Kunst und Kultur umgeben. Die eleganten Zimmer sind luxuriös mit echten alten Möbeln eingerichtet, und die antik gestalteten Bäder harmonisieren mit Jacuzzi-Duschen und anderem modernen Komfort. La Terrazza Bar und Restaurant bietet atemberaubende Blicke auf die Burg und ist der ideale Ort, um sich von kulinarischen Köstlichkeiten verwöhnen zu lassen.

Our inspector loved: *The 16th-century Cave of Bacco where guests can enjoy gourmet dinners.*

Directions: In the historical centre of the medieval village of Asolo.
From Milan > A4 Vicenza > A31 Dueville > s.s. 248 Bassano del Grappa > Asolo.
From Venice > A27 Treviso > s.s. 348 Montebelluna > Asolo.

Web: www.johansens.com/alsole
E-mail: info@albergoalsole.com
Tel: +39 0423 951 332
Fax: +39 0423 951 007

Price Guide:
single €110-150
standard double €170-205
superior double/suite €205-255

ITALY / VENETIA (BARDOLINO - LAKE GARDA)

COLOR HOTEL

VIA SANTA CRISTINA 5, 37011 BARDOLINO (VR), ITALY

The recent renovation of this hotel has been inspired by colour, the essence of life and wellbeing. Chromatherapy transforms the interior into a relaxing, cheerful and stimulating environment, which features innovative decorations and furnishings as well as unique pieces of art. Each space is perfectly harmonious and superb hospitality enhances the vitality and warmth of the hotel. Mountain biking down Mount Baldo is a must and there is a specially designed cable car that guests can board with their bike.

La couleur, essence de la vie, a inspiré la récente rénovation de cet hôtel. La Chromothérapie métamorphose l'intérieur en un environnement relaxant, gai et stimulant, où sont présentés mobiliers et décorations innovants ainsi que d'uniques pièces d'art. Les espaces sont en parfaite harmonie et le fantastique accueil met en valeur l'énergie et la chaleur de l'hôtel. VTT sur le mont Baldo est absolument à faire et il y a un téléphérique spécialement conçu pour les clients avec leur vélo.

Die kürzliche Renovierung dieses Hotels wurde nach dem Farbprinzip, der Grundlage des Lebens und Wohlbefindens gestaltet. Chromatherapie schafft hier ein entspanntes, heiteres und stimulierendes Umfeld, mit innovativem Décor und Einrichtungen sowie einzigartigen Kunstwerken. Jeder Winkel befindet sich in perfekter Harmonie mir der Umgebung, und die wundervolle Gastfreundschaft unterstreicht die Vitalität und Wärme des Hotels. Mit dem Mountainbike den Monte Baldo hinunterzufahren ist ein Muss, und eine spezielle Gondelbahn bringt die Gäste und ihr Bike wieder hinauf.

Our inspector loved: *The cheerful, colourful atmosphere.*

Directions: A22 > exit Affi > follow signs to Lago di Garda.

Web: www.johansens.com/color
E-mail: info@colorhotel.it
Tel: +39 045 621 0857
Fax: +39 045 621 2697

Price Guide:
single €70-155
double/twin €110-165
junior suite €150-285
suite €180-360

HOTEL CA' SETTE

VIA CUNIZZA DA ROMANO 4, 36061 BASSANO DEL GRAPPA, ITALY

Directions: A4 > A31 towards Valdastico > exit at Dueville > take the main road to Bassano del Grappa.

Web: www.johansens.com/ca-sette
E-mail: info@ca-sette.it
Tel: +39 0424 383350
Fax: +39 0424 393287

Price Guide:
single €110–130
double €170–210
suite €250–400

The Hotel Ca' Sette takes its name from a Venetian family who built the villa as a summer residence in the 18th century and is a truly stylish home from home. An atmosphere of quiet elegance is created by immaculate style and harmonious use of space whilst original local furniture and antiques create an authentic feel. Delicious food can be enjoyed in the award-winning restaurant or in the lovely manicured Italian garden. Bassano has a rich cultural life, stunning Venetian architecture, museums and a number of frescoed palazzi.

L' hôtel Ca' Sette tient son nom d'une famille vénitienne qui construit la villa comme résidence d'été au XVIIIe siècle. On se sent vraiment chez soi dans cet hôtel élégant. Une atmosphère d'élégance discrète est créée par le style immaculé et l'utilisation harmonieuse de l'espace, renforcée par un mobilier local original et des antiquités ajoutant au caractère authentique. Une cuisine délicieuse est servie dans le restaurant renommé ou le beau jardin dessiné au style italien. Bassano a une riche vie culturelle, une architecture vénitienne superbe, des musées et des palais ornés de fresques.

Dieses heimelige Hotel erhielt seinen Namen von einer venezianischen Familie, die die Villa im 18. Jahrhundert als Sommerresidenz erbaute. Makelloser Stil und harmonische Raumaufteilung schaffen eine ruhige Eleganz, während einheimisches Mobiliar und Antiquitäten für ein authentisches Flair sorgen. Im preisgekrönten Restaurant oder im hübschen, italienisch gestalteten Garten werden köstliche Speisen serviert. Bassano ist reich an Kultur, venezianischer Architektur, Museen und einer Anzahl von mit Fresken geschmückten Palazzi.

Our inspector loved: *This stylish home away from home.*

CASTELBRANDO

VIA BRANDOLINI 29, 31030 CISON DI VALMARINO (TV), ITALY

A visit to Castelbrando is like a step back in time. Dating back to Roman times, this fortress at the foothills of the Alps of Treviso offers an unforgettable experience. Situated on 9 levels, this medieval "village" boasts 2 restaurants for casual or elegant dining, 8 bars, a spa and gym, 3 theatres, 4 museums, 4 conference halls and 47 tastefully furnished bedrooms. Guests may enjoy the magnificent views from the cable cars and take advantage of the extensive cultural entertainment, including guest performances by well-known musicians and theatre companies.

Un séjour à Castelbrando vous replonge dans le passé. Datant du temps des romains, ce château-fort dans les contreforts des alpes de Treviso offre une expérience inoubliable. Avec 9 niveaux, ce «village médiéval» s'enorgueillit de 2 restaurants pour des dîners élégants ou détendus, 8 bars, un spa et centre de remise en forme, 3 théâtres, 4 musées, 4 salles de conférences et 47 chambres ornées avec goût. Les hôtes peuvent apprécier les vues magnifiques depuis les téléphériques et profiter des divertissements culturels, comprenant des représentations et soirées musicales avec des artistes bien-connus.

Ein Aufenthalt hier ist wie eine Reise in die Vergangenheit. Diese am Fuße der Treviser Alpen gelegene Festung aus römischer Zeit ist ein ganz besonderer Ort. Das mittelalterliche „Dorf" liegt auf 9 Ebenen und besitzt 2 Restaurants (ein elegantes und ein eher legeres), 8 Bars, ein Kur- und Fitnesszentrum, 3 Theater, 4 Museen, 4 Konferenzsäle und 47 geschmackvoll eingerichtete Zimmer. Die Gondelbahnen bieten eine herrliche Sicht auf die Umgebung, und das umfassende kulturelle Angebot wird durch Gastspiele bekannter Musiker und Theatergruppen bereichert.

Directions: A27 > exit Vittorio Veneto Nord > follow directions to Follina Valdobbiadene > signposted.

Milan
Venice
Rome

Web: www.johansens.com/castelbrando
E-mail: hotel@castelbrando.it and info@castelbrando.it
Tel: +39 0438 9761
Fax: +39 0438 916020

Price Guide:
single €126
double €177
suite €329-385

Our inspector loved: *The combination of a hotel with museums and theatres.*

VILLA MADRINA

VIA PAOLO VERONESE, 37016 GARDA (VR), ITALY

Directions: A4 > A22 towards Brennero > exit Affi > follow signs to Garda.

Web: www.johansens.com/villamadrina
E-mail: villamadrina@villamadrina.it
Tel: +39 045 6270 144
Fax: +39 045 7256 716

Price Guide: (per person)
double from €64-95.50

Peacefully situated in a panoramic setting, Villa Madrina is 200m from the centre of Garda. A homely atmosphere welcomes guests into this carefully furnished hotel reflecting local traditional style. Each of the junior suites has a hydromassage bath and view of the lake from a private terrace. Lounge in the bar with an apéritif before dinner in the pretty restaurant where Mediterranean and regional dishes are served. Stroll around the gardens or enjoy the solarium; guests receive a 20% discount off their green fee for courses within the Lake Garda area.

Tranquillement située dans un cadre panoramique, Villa Madrina est à 200 mètres du centre ville de Garda. Les hôtes sont reçus dans une atmosphère accueillante dans cet hôtel meublé avec soin et reflétant le style traditionnel local. Chacune des juniors suites possède une baignoire hydromassante et a vue sur le lac depuis sa terrasse privée. Les clients peuvent prendre l'apéritif au bar avant de dîner au charmant restaurant où une cuisine méditerranéenne et régionale est servie. Les hôtes peuvent flâner dans les jardins ou profiter du solarium, et tous les parcours de golf dans la région de Garda offrent une remise de 20 % aux résidents de l'hôtel.

In friedlicher Lage mit herrlichem Panorama liegt die Villa Madrina, nur 200m vom Zentrum von Garda entfernt. Eine heimelige, herzliche Atmosphäre liegt über diesem liebevoll im traditionellen Stil eingerichteten Haus. Jede der Juniorsuiten bietet ein Hydromassage-Bad und Blick auf den See von der eigenen Terrasse. In der Bar entspannt man mit einem Apéritif, bevor man sich im hübschen Restaurant zu mediterraner und regionaler Küche niederläßt. Der Garten lädt zum Spaziergang ein, es gibt ein Solarium und alle Green-Gebühren in der Umgebung sind um 20% reduziert.

Our inspector loved: *The lovely garden.*

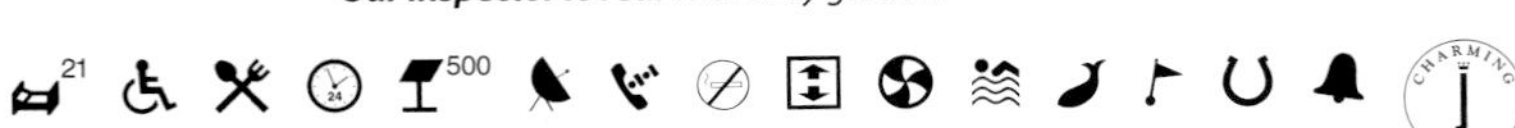

HOTEL MADRIGALE

VIA GHIANDARE 1, 37010 MARCIAGA, LAKE GARDA (VR), ITALY

Set close to a golf course in the hills overlooking Lake Garda, this charming hotel is a haven of peace and tranquillity. All bedrooms have been recently renovated, offer great comfort and afford wonderful views of the lake from a pretty balcony. Excellent local and international cuisine is served in the panoramic restaurant, complemented by a great selection of wines. Guests can enjoy the 2 swimming pools, one of which is heated, in the grounds, whilst staff are happy to organise excursions to the lake and surrounding vineyards.

Situé près d'un parcours de golf parmi des collines surplombant le lac Garda, cet hôtel charmant est un havre de paix et de tranquillité. Les chambres récemment rénovées, offrent tout le confort et des balcons jolis avec vue sur le lac. Une excellente cuisine locale et internationale est servie au restaurant panoramique, accompagnée par une grande sélection de vins. L'hôtel dispose de 2 piscines, dont une chauffée,et des excursions au lac et aux vignobles des alentours peuvent être organisées.

Dieses zauberhafte Hotel nahe eines Golfplatzes in den Hügeln oberhalb des Gardasees ist eine wahre Oase der Ruhe. Alle Zimmer wurden kürzlich renoviert und bieten jeglichen Komfort, alle haben einen hübschen Balkon mit Blick auf den See. Im Panoramarestaurant werden hervorragende einheimische und internationale Gerichte sowie eine große Auswahl an Weinen serviert. Das Hotel besitzt 2 Swimmingpools (einer ist beheizt), und Exkursionen zum See und den umliegenden Weinbergen können organisiert werden.

Our inspector loved: *The peacefulness and the panoramic views, especially from the swimming pool.*

Directions: A22 > direction Brenner > exit at Affi > follow signs to Garda.

Web: www.johansens.com/madrigale
E-mail: madrigale@madrigale.it
Tel: +39 045 627 9001
Fax: +39 045 627 9125

Price Guide:
single €75-100
double €117-170
suite €160-220

PARK HOTEL BRASILIA

VIA LEVANTINA, 30017 LIDO DI JESOLO, ITALY

Directions: A4 motorway > Quarto D'Altino > Lido Di Jesolo > "Zona Est".

Web: www.johansens.com/parkhotelbrasilia
E-mail: info@parkhotelbrasilia.com
Tel: +39 0421 380851
Fax: +39 0421 92244

Price guide:
double (single occupancy) €95–155
double €118–194
suite €192–230

Located on the eastern side of the Lido di Jesolo across the lagoon from Venice, the hotel boasts a quiet position, a private sandy beach and 2 swimming pools. Recently refurbished in soft, elegant shades and fabrics, all bedrooms are comfortable and boast terraces and sea views. At the Ipanema Restaurant guests can enjoy candle-lit dinners of local and international cuisine and exquisite wines from the cellar. Lunch is served either on the veranda or alongside the pool.

Situé côté Est du Lido di Jesolo en face de Venise sur l'autre rive du lagon, l'hôtel bénéficie d'une position tranquille, d'une plage de sable privée et de 2 piscines. Récemment redécorées dans des tons et tissus doux et élégants, toutes les chambres sont confortables avec terrasses et vue sur la mer. Au restaurant Ipanema, les hôtes peuvent dîner aux chandelles une cuisine locale et internationale accompagnée de vins fins du cellier. Le déjeuner est servi soit sous la véranda soit au bord de la piscine.

Dieses Hotel am Ostende des Lido di Jesolo gegenüber der Lagune von Venedig bietet eine ruhige Lage mit privatem Sandstrand und 2 Swimmingpools. Alle Zimmer wurden kürzlich mit sanften, eleganten Farben und Stoffen neu gestaltet und haben Balkons oder Terrassen mit Meerblick. Im Ipanema Restaurant kann man bei Kerzenschein einheimische und internationale Gerichte sowie erlesene Weine genießen. Das Mittagessen wird entweder auf der Veranda oder am Pool serviert.

Our inspector loved: *The hotel's lovely position by the sea and its beautiful private sandy beach.*

Relais La Magioca

VIA MORON 3, 37024 VALPOLICELLA (VERONA), ITALY

Set in an immaculate park, this charming relais offers breathtaking views, a romantic atmosphere and total peace and tranquillity. An ancient stone-built farmhouse, it has been furnished with refined taste and attention to detail. The 6 individually designed bedrooms are charming and comfortable, lounge and delightful breakfast room create a typical country house ambience. Sample local wines in the fabulous cellar and visit nearby attractions including Verona, the vineyards of Valpolicella and Soave and Lake Garda. Venice is also within easy reach.

Situé dans un parc splendide, ce relais charmant, havre de paix, offre une vue à couper le souffle et une atmosphère romantique. Un ancien corps de ferme en pierre, il a été restauré et meublé avec raffinement jusque dans ses moindres détails. Les 6 chambres, décorées différemment, sont charmantes et confortables, et avec le salon et la ravissante salle du petit déjeuner, créent une ambiance typique de maison de campagne. Des vins locaux peuvent être dégustés dans la cave excellente, et Vérone, les vignobles de Valpolicella et de Soave et le Lac Garda sont des attractions touristiques très proches. Venise est également facile d'accès.

In einem gepflegten Park liegt dieses bezaubernde Relais, das eine herrliche Sicht, romantische Atmosphäre und völlige Ruhe bietet. Das alte, aus Stein gebaute Farmhaus wurde geschmackvoll und mit Liebe zum Detail eingerichtet. Die 6 individuell gestalteten Zimmer sind komfortabel und schaffen zusammen mit dem Aufenthalts- und dem Frühstücksraum ein typisches Landhausambiente. Der eindrucksvolle Keller lädt zur Weinprobe ein, und Verona, die Weinberge von Valpolicella und Soave und der Gardasee sowie Venedig sind nicht weit entfernt.

Our inspector loved: *The romantic atmosphere and great attention to detail.*

Directions: A4 > exit Verona Sud > Negrar–Valpolicella > A22 > exit Verona Nord > Valpolicella–Negrar.

Web: www.johansens.com/lamagioca
E-mail: info@magioca.it
Tel: +39 045 600 0167
Fax: +39 045 600 0840

Price Guide:
single €150–200
double/twin €170–240
suites €195–390

Domina Prestige Giudecca

CORTE FERRANDO 409/C, GIUDECCA, 30133 VENICE (VE), ITALY

Built right in the heart of Venice, this new hotel enjoys a wonderful canal location on Giudecca Island, only 10 minutes from Piazza San Marco. Comfortable bedrooms have marvellous beamed ceilings and are furnished in a modern, luxurious style, whilst cool public rooms are enhanced by stunning marble and tiles. A delicious breakfast is served in the Veranda Ferrando, and views over the canal and surrounding architecture can be seen from the reception area.

Construit au cœur de Venise, ce nouvel hôtel profite d'un emplacement au bord du canal sur l'île de Giudecca, à 10 minutes de la Place Saint-Marc. Les chambres confortables ont de superbes plafonds à poutres apparentes et sont meublées dans un style moderne et luxueux. Les pièces communes sont mises en valeur par de somptueux marbres et carrelages. Un délicieux petit-déjeuner est servi dans la Veranda Ferrando, et la réception offre des vues sur le canal et les architectures voisines.

Dieses neue Hotel befindet sich im Herzen Venedigs auf der hübschen kleinen Kanalinsel Giudecca, nur 10 Minuten vom Markusplatz entfernt. Die komfortablen Zimmer haben herrliche Holzbalkendecken und sind modern und luxuriös gestaltet, während die Aufenthaltsräume atemberaubenden Marmor und traumhafte Fliesen bieten. Im Veranda Ferrando genießt man ein köstliches Frühstück, und von der Rezeption aus hat man eine gute Sicht auf den Kanal und die faszinierende umliegende Architektur.

Our inspector loved: *The fresh style and cosy atmosphere.*

Directions: 10 minutes by boat from Piazza San Marco.

Web: www.johansens.com/dominaprestige
E-mail: giudecca@domina.it
Tel: +39 041 2960 168
Fax: +39 041 5289 520

Price Guide:
single €115-264
double €150-405
de luxe €180-557

Hotel Giorgione

SS APOSTOLI 4587, 30131 VENICE, ITALY

A 15th-century building houses this charming hotel, which is set in a quiet location in the centre of the old town, close to the Rialto bridge and a few minutes from Piazza San Marco. The recently renovated hotel provides all modern comforts whilst retaining its original charm. All rooms are decorated in a romantic and refined style with antique Venetian pieces of furniture. Breakfast is served inside or outside in the beautiful garden. At the adjacent Osteria-Enoteca Giorgione guests can enjoy a great variety of wines and local dishes.

Un bâtiment du XVe siècle abrite ce charmant hôtel, situé dans un endroit calme au centre de la vieille ville, à proximité du pont Rialto et de la Piazza San Marco. Récemment rénové, l'hôtel est équipé de toutes les commodités modernes tout en conservant son charme d'origine. Les chambres sont décorées dans un style romantique et raffiné avec des meubles vénitiens antiques. Le petit-déjeuner est servi à l'intérieur ou à l'extérieur dans le jardin. Dans la Osteria-Enoteca Giorgione voisine, les clients peuvent goûter à une variété de vins et de plats locaux.

Ein Gebäude aus dem 15. Jahrhundert beherbergt dieses zauberhafte Hotel, das sich in ruhiger Lage im Zentrum der Altstadt nahe der Rialto-Brücke und dem Markusplatz befindet. Das kürzlich renovierte Hotel bietet jeglichen modernen Komfort, hat jedoch seinen ursprünglichen Charme beibehalten. Die Zimmer sind romantisch und elegant mit alten venezianischen Möbeln eingerichtet. Frühstück wird drinnen oder draußen im Garten serviert, und die Osteria-Enoteca Giorgione bietet eine große Auswahl an Weinen und hiesigen Gerichten.

Our inspector loved: *The warm welcome and the romantic Venetian courtyard with lovely fountain.*

Directions: Airport > bus to Piazzale Roma > Vaporetto to Cà d'Oro. Railway station > Vaporetto to Cà d'Oro.

Web: www.johansens.com/giorgione
E-mail: giorgione@hotelgiorgione.com
Tel: +39 041 522 5810
Fax: +39 041 523 9092

Price Guide:
rooms €105–400

Hotel Londra Palace

RIVA DEGLI SCHIAVONI, 4171, 30122 VENICE, ITALY

Directions: Located in the city centre, near Piazza S Marco.

Web: www.johansens.com/londrapalace
E-mail: info@hotelondra.it
Tel: +39 041 5200533
Fax: +39 041 5225032

Price Guide:
double/twin (single occupancy) €265-475
double/twin €380-585
junior suite €485-790

Just a few steps from the Piazza San Marco and the Grand Canal, this exclusive boutique hotel offers guests a feeling of unforgettable glamour and a romantic atmosphere. Each of the spacious, richly decorated bedrooms and suites, most of which afford stunning views of the lagoon, is a unique experience in itself, evoking a sense of discreet luxury. Guests can enjoy refined cuisine in a sophisticated setting at the hotel's restaurant, Do Leoni, and during the warmer months, lunch or drinks are served on the veranda.

A deux pas de la Place San Marco et le Grand Canal, cet hôtel exclusif propose aux visiteurs un sens de prestige inoubliable dans une atmosphère romantique. Chacune des chambres et suites spacieuses et somptueusement décorées, dont la plupart offrent une vue imprenable sur la lagune, est une expérience unique en soi, évoquant un sens de luxe discrète. Une cuisine raffinée est servie dans un cadre sophistiqué au restaurant Do Leoni, et pendant les mois plus chauds, les hôtes peuvent prendre un verre ou déjeuner sur la véranda.

Dieses exklusive Boutique-Hotel liegt nur ein paar Schritte vom Markusplatz und dem Canal Grande entfernt und bietet seinen Gästen unvergleichlichen Glamour und eine romantische Atmosphäre. Jedes der geräumigen, üppig dekorierten Zimmer und Suiten, von denen die meisten auf die Lagune blicken, ist ein Erlebnis für sich und weckt ein Gefühl von zurückhaltendem Luxus. Im edlen Hotelrestaurant Do Leoni werden raffinierte Gerichte serviert, und in den wärmeren Monaten kann man auf der Terrasse Mittag essen oder einen Drink zu sich nehmen.

Our inspector loved: *The superb location and the view of the lagoon.*

53       

ALBERGO QUATTRO FONTANE - RESIDENZA D'EPOCA

30126 LIDO DI VENEZIA, VENICE, ITALY

A distinctive country house set in an idyllic garden on the Lido amongst orchards and productive vineyards, away from the hustle and bustle of Venice, the Albergo is only 10 minutes by water-bus from San Marco square. Signore Bevilacqua, whose family has owned the property for over 50 years, has collected some very unusual antique furniture, art and artefacts from all over the world. Venetian specialities complement wine from local vineyards.

Maison de campagne raffinée dans un jardin idyllique sur le Lido, l'Albergo, avec ses vergers et ses vignobles, est à seuleument 10 minutes en navette-bateau de la place Saint Marc. Le Signore Bevilacqua, dont la famille est propriétaire depuis 50 ans, a collectionné des meubles, de l'art et des objets façonnés originaux provenant du monde entier. Des spécialités vénitiennes complètent la carte de vins des producteurs locaux

Dieses herrliche Landhaus liegt in einem idyllischen Garten am Lido, umgeben von Obstplantagen und Weinbergen und fernab vom geschäftigen Treiben Venedigs, aber innerhalb von 10 Minuten per Boot vom Markusplatz zu erreichen. Signore Bevilacqua, dessen Familie das Hotel seit über 50 Jahren besitzt, hat eine Sammlung ungewöhnlicher Antiquitäten, Gemälde und Kunstgegenstände aus aller Welt. Für kulinarischen Genuss sorgen venezianische Spezialitäten und Weine aus einheimischen Weinbergen.

Our inspector loved: *The hotel's originality and the precious collection of objets d'art from each corner of the world.*

Directions: Lido via San Marco > Albergo.

Web: www.johansens.com/albergoquattrofontane
E-mail: info@quattrofontane.com
Tel: +39 041 526 0227
Fax: +39 041 526 0726

Price Guide:
single €130–270
double/twin €160–420
apartment €300-600

Hotel Gabbia d'Oro (Historical Residence)

CORSO PORTA BORSARI 4A, 37121 VERONA, ITALY

Set in the historical centre of Verona, this very special small luxury hotel is housed in a 18th-century palazzo. Wooden ceilings, frescoes and precious paintings abound, whilst in the bedrooms antique furniture, oriental carpets, rich accessories, beautiful fabrics and lace create a romantic ambience. The Orangerie, a charming winter garden, is the perfect place to enjoy a cup of coffee or a light snack. The vineyards of Valpolicella and Lake Garda are all within easy reach, whilst Venice is a popular destination for a day trip.

Au cœur historique de Vérone, ce petit hôtel de luxe très spécial se situe au sein d'un palais du XVIIIe siècle. Les plafonds en bois, fresques et peintures précieuses, ainsi que le mobilier ancien des chambres, les tapis orientaux, les accessoires luxueux, les beaux tissus et dentelles créent une atmosphère particulièrement romantique. L'Orangerie, un charmant jardin d'hiver, est l'endroit idéal pour déguster une tasse de café ou un repas léger. Les vignobles de Valpolicella et le Lac Garda sont faciles d'accès et Venise est une destination populaire pour une journée de sortie.

Dieses kleine Luxushotel befindet sich im historischen Zentrum Veronas in einem Palazzo aus dem 18. Jahrhundert. Hölzerne Decken, Fresken und kostbare Malereien zieren das Interieur, und in den Schlafzimmern schaffen antike Möbel, orientalische Teppiche, schmuckvolle Accessoires, herrliche Stoffe und Spitze ein romantisches Ambiente. Die Orangerie, ein zauberhafter Wintergarten, ist der perfekte Ort für eine Tasse Kaffee oder einen Snack. Die Valpolicella-Weinberge und der Gardasee sind leicht erreichbar; Venedig ist eine beliebte Tagestour.

Our inspector loved: *The joyful Orangerie and the collection of fine silverware.*

Directions: In historical centre of Verona, near Piazza delle Erbe.

Web: www.johansens.com/gabbiadoro
E-mail: gabbiadoro@easyasp.it
Tel: +39 045 8003060
Fax: +39 045 590293

Price Guide:
single €160–284
double €232–351
suite €284–826

PALAZZO SAN FERMO

STRADA SAN FERMO 8, 37121 VERONA, ITALY

A unique alternative to a typical hotel experience, this wonderful 17th-century palazzo in the centre of Verona offers 5 stunning luxury apartments serviced by the Hotel Gabbia d'Oro. Guests may take advantage of all facilities offered by the hotel, which is just a few minutes' walk away. The beautifully decorated apartments range in size from 115 to 125m² and are fully equipped to provide all modern comforts. Guests also have a cellular phone at their disposal.

Une alternative unique à l'expérience typique d'hôtel, ce palais magnifique du XVIIe siècle au sein de Vérone consiste en 5 appartements de luxe fantastiques qui font partie de l'hôtel Gabbia d'Oro. Les hôtes peuvent profiter de toutes les facilités de l'hôtel, qui est à quelques minutes à pied. Les appartements, ornés à la perfection, sont de 115m² à 125m² en taille et offrent tout le confort moderne. Un téléphone portable est à la disposition des clients.

Dieses herrliche Palazzo aus dem 17. Jahrhundert im Herzen von Verona ist eine einzigartige Alternative zu einem typischen Hotelaufenthalt. Die 5 Luxusappartements gehören zum nur ein paar Minuten Fußmarsch entfernten Hotel Gabbia d'Oro, dessen Einrichtungen die Gäste selbstverständlich benutzen können. Die wunderschön eingerichteten Appartements sind 115m² bis 125m² groß und mit jeglichen modernen Annehmlichkeiten ausgestattet. Alle Gäste bekommen ein Mobiltelefon zur Verfügung gestellt.

Our inspector loved: *The opportunity to feel and live like a true noble citizen of Verona.*

Directions: From A4 > exit Verona Sud. From A22 > exit Verona Ovest. The hotel is in the centre of historic Verona.

Milan
Venice
Rome

Web: www.johansens.com/sanfermo
E-mail: info@palazzosanfermo.com
Tel: +39 045 800 3060
Fax: +39 045 590 293

Price Guide: (apartment only, minimum stay 2 nights)
1-4 people €350-550
5-6 people €500-800

LUXEMBOURG

Hotel location shown in red (hotel) or purple (spa hotel) with page number

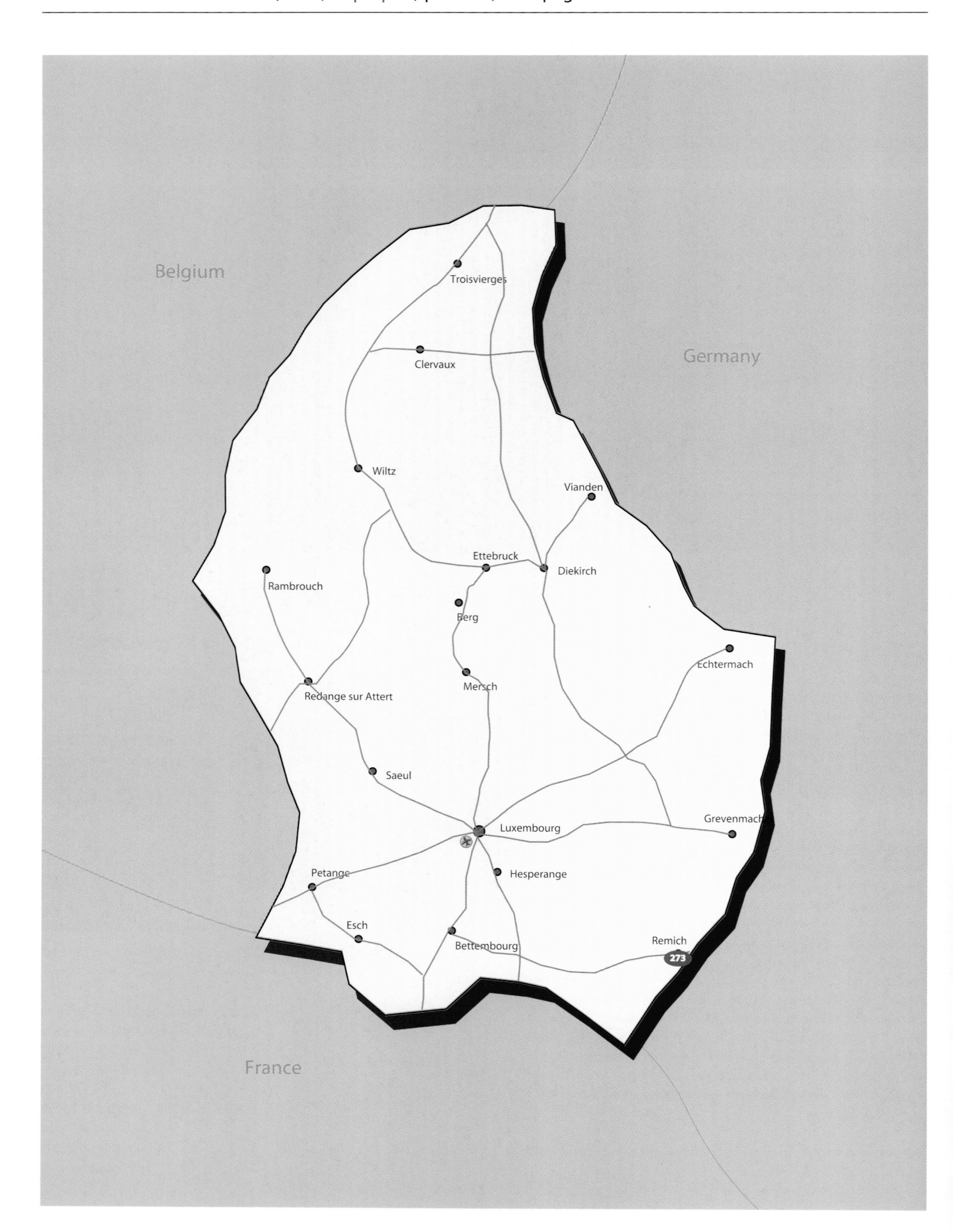

HOTEL SAINT~NICOLAS

31 ESPLANADE, 5533 REMICH, LUXEMBOURG

Set in the picturesque town of Remich, this family-run hotel affords fantastic views across the esplanade and lush vineyards as it lies on the banks of the river Moselle. The eclectic hotel features unusual public rooms adorned with interesting paintings. The hotel's Lohengrin Restaurant serves traditional French cuisine; a true gastronomic delight. Complimentary broadband Internet access is available.

Situé dans la ville pittoresque de Remich, cet hôtel familial offre des vues fantastiques sur l'esplanade et les vignobles étant situé sur les berges de la rivière Moselle. Cet hôtel éclectique a des salles communes originales décorées de peintures uniques. Le restaurant de l'hôtel, le Lohengrin est un délice gastronomique proposant une cuisine traditionnelle française. Un service Internet ASDL gratuit est disponible.

Das familiengeführte Hotel Saint Nicolas, das an der Mosel mitten in der malerischen Stadt Remich gelegen ist, bietet spektakuläre Ausblicke auf die Uferpromenade und die üppigen Weainberge. Die Aufenthaltsräume sind originell und mit interessanten Bildern geschmückt. Das Restaurant Lohengrin mit seiner traditionellen französischen Küche bietet einen gastronomischen Hochgenuss. Gratis ADSL-Internetzugang ist vorhanden.

Our inspector loved: *Its promenade location and the wonderful service.*

Directions: Luxembourg > E29 > Remich or A13 > exit 13 Schengen.

Web: www.johansens.com/saintnicolas
E-mail: hotel@pt.lu
Tel: +352 2666 3
Fax: +352 2666 3666

Clervaux
Echternach
Luxembourg

Price Guide:
single €79–104
double/twin €101–126
gastronomic offer (incl 2-night stay) €174–199

MONACO

Hotel location shown in red (hotel) or purple (spa hotel) with page number

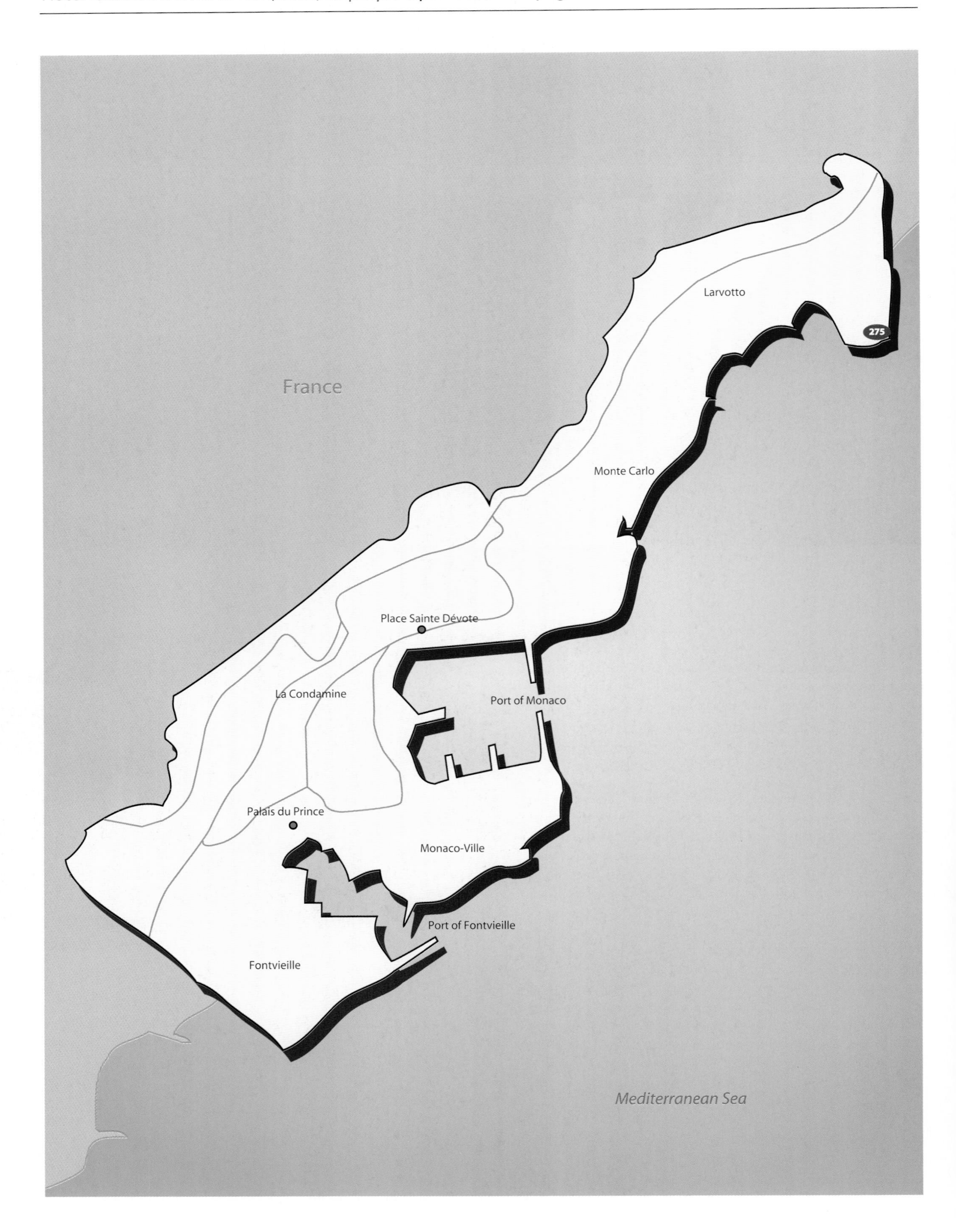

MONTE~CARLO BEACH HOTEL

AVENUE PRINCESSE GRACE, 06190 ROQUEBRUNE – CAP~MARTIN, FRANCE

Decorated throughout in Italian Riviera style, this charming yet lavish property has been a resting place for the glitterati since the 1930s, and its popularity remains to day. Bright colours adorn the bedrooms, and 4 excellent restaurants serve different flavours. The private beach and the olympic-sized swimming pool add to the appeal. Through the Société des Bains de Mer Resort, guests can enjoy tennis at the Country Club, golf at the 18-hole Golf Club, the famous Spa centre "Les Thermes Marins" as well as entertainment at the Sporting Monte-Carlo.

Ce petit palace de charme, empreint d'un air de Riviera italienne reçoit le beau monde depuis 1930, et sa popularité se perpétue aujourd'hui. Des couleurs vives égayent les chambres, et les 4 restaurants proposent des cuisines aux saveurs différentes. Sa plage privée et la piscine olympique rendent cet endroit magique encore plus irrésistible. Grâce au Resort de la Société des Bains de Mer, les hôtes profiteront également du Country Club et de ses 23 courts de tennis, du Golf Club (parcours à 18 trous), des Thermes Marins ainsi que du Sporting Monte-Carlo.

Dieses im Stil der italienischen Riviera eingerichtete Hotel beherbergt seit 1930 die Reichen und Schönen dieser Welt, und sein Charme ist bis heute ungebrochen. Einzigartige Farbkombinationen zieren die Zimmer und jedes der 4 vorzüglichen Restaurants bietet eine andere Geschmacksrichtung. Der Privatstrand und der olympische Pool machen diesen Ort unwiderstehlich. Dank des Resorts der Société des Bains de Mer können die Gäste im Country Club Tennis spielen und den Golf Club, die "Thermes Marins" und den Sportclub Monte-Carlo benutzen.

Our inspector loved: *The bedrooms, which all overlook the Mediterranean Sea with panoramic views.*

Directions: Nice Airport > 25km.

Web: www.johansens.com/montecarlo
E-mail: resort@sbm.mc
Tel: +377 92 16 25 25
Fax: +377 92 16 26 26

Price Guide: (Continental breakfast €26)
single/double/twin €255–610
junior suite €390–765
suite €715–1,835

The Netherlands

Hotel location shown in red (hotel) or purple (spa hotel) with page number

AMBASSADE HOTEL

HERENGRACHT 341, 1016 AZ AMSTERDAM, THE NETHERLANDS

The Ambassade is a most attractive hotel in the heart of Amsterdam. Originally 10 separate houses, each the home of a wealthy merchant on the Herengracht ("the Gentlemen's Canal"), the hotel has been converted into one building which retains all the erstwhile interior architecture and the external façades. Over the years, numerous authors have stayed at this hotel; an extensive collection of signed books can be found in the library. A special Internet office is available free of charge. The hotel's luxurious float and massage centre Koan Float, is situated further along the street.

L'Ambassade est un hôtel très attrayant dans le coeur d'Amsterdam. Originellement 10 maisons séparées, chacune étant la maison d'un riche marchand de Herengracht (Le "Canal des Messieurs"), l'hôtel a été converti en un bâtiment qui comprend toute l'architecture intérieure ancienne et les façades extérieures d'époque. De nombreux auteurs ont visité cet hôtel, et on peut admirer une collection de livres signés dans la bibliothèque. Un bureau avec service Internet gratuit est disponible. Le centre de massage luxueux Koan Float, appartenant à l'hôtel, est situé à proximité.

Dieses attraktive Hotel im Herzen von Amsterdam bestand ursprünglich aus 10 separaten Häusern, jedes im Besitz eines reichen Kaufmanns auf der Herengracht ("Herrenkanal"). Das Hotel wurde zu einem einzigen Gebäude umgebaut, wobei das ehemalige Interieur sowie die Architektur und die Außenfassaden erhalten blieben. Viele Schriftsteller waren hier zu Gast, und in der Bibliothek findet man eine Sammlung signierter Bücher. Ein Büro mit gratis Internetzugang steht zur Verfügung. Das hoteleigene, luxuriöse Float- und Massagezentrum Koan Float befindet sich ein paar Häuser weiter.

Our inspector loved: *Breakfast in the elegant dining room overlooking the canal.*

Directions: Schiphol Airport > take a taxi, train or car to the centre of the city.

Web: www.johansens.com/ambassade
E-mail: info@ambassade-hotel.nl
Tel: +31 20 5550222
Fax: +31 20 5550277

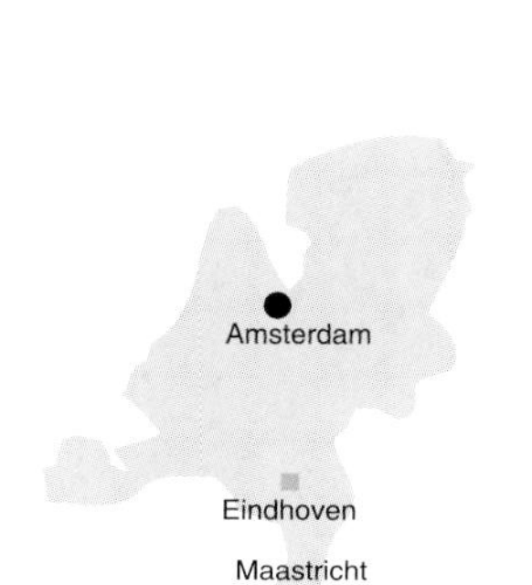

Price Guide: (breakfast €16)
single €165
double €195
suite €245-340

Norway

Hotel location shown in red (hotel) or purple (spa hotel) with page number

Fleischers Hotel

5700 VOSS, NORWAY

This grand hotel is set in a superb position, overlooking the lake. The façade, with its towers and pointed dormer windows, is reminiscent of Switzerland. Built in 1889 and still run by the same family, the hotel has been discreetly modernised without losing its original charm. There is a warm ambience in the foyer with its convivial and elegant salons. Delicious food including local fish and Norwegian specialities is served in the restaurant with its warm colour scheme.

Ce grand hôtel est situé idéalement au dessus du lac. La façade, avec ses tours et ses lucarnes pointues qui sont des reminiscences suisses. Construit en 1889 et toujours tenu par la même famille, l'hôtel a été modernisé intelligemment sans perdre son charme originel. Il y a une ambiance chaleureuse dans le salon avec ses salons amicaux et élégants. Le restaurant, qui se caractérise par des couleurs chaudes, propose une cuisine délicieuse, avec notamment du poisson de la région et des spécialités norvégiennes.

Dieses Grand Hotel hat eine herrliche Lage mit Aussicht über den See. Die Fassade mit ihren Türmen und spitzen Giebelfenstern erinnert an die Schweiz. 1889 erbaut und immer noch von der gleichen Familie geführt, wurde das Hotel umsichtig renoviert, ohne seinen ursprünglichen Charme zu verlieren. Das Foyer strahlt mit seinen freundlichen und eleganten Salons ein gemütliches Ambiente aus. Das Restaurant ist in warmen Farben gehalten und serviert köstliche norwegische Spezialitäten und Fisch der Region.

Our inspector loved: *Fleischers' fabulous breakfast buffet enjoyed at a window table with views of the fjord.*

Directions: Bergen > E16 > Voss.

Web: www.johansens.com/fleischers
E-mail: hotel@fleischers.no
Tel: +47 56 52 05 00
Fax: +47 56 52 05 01

Price Guide:
single NOK1,125
double/twin NOK1,490–1,690

PORTUGAL

Hotel location shown in red (hotel) or purple (spa hotel) with page number

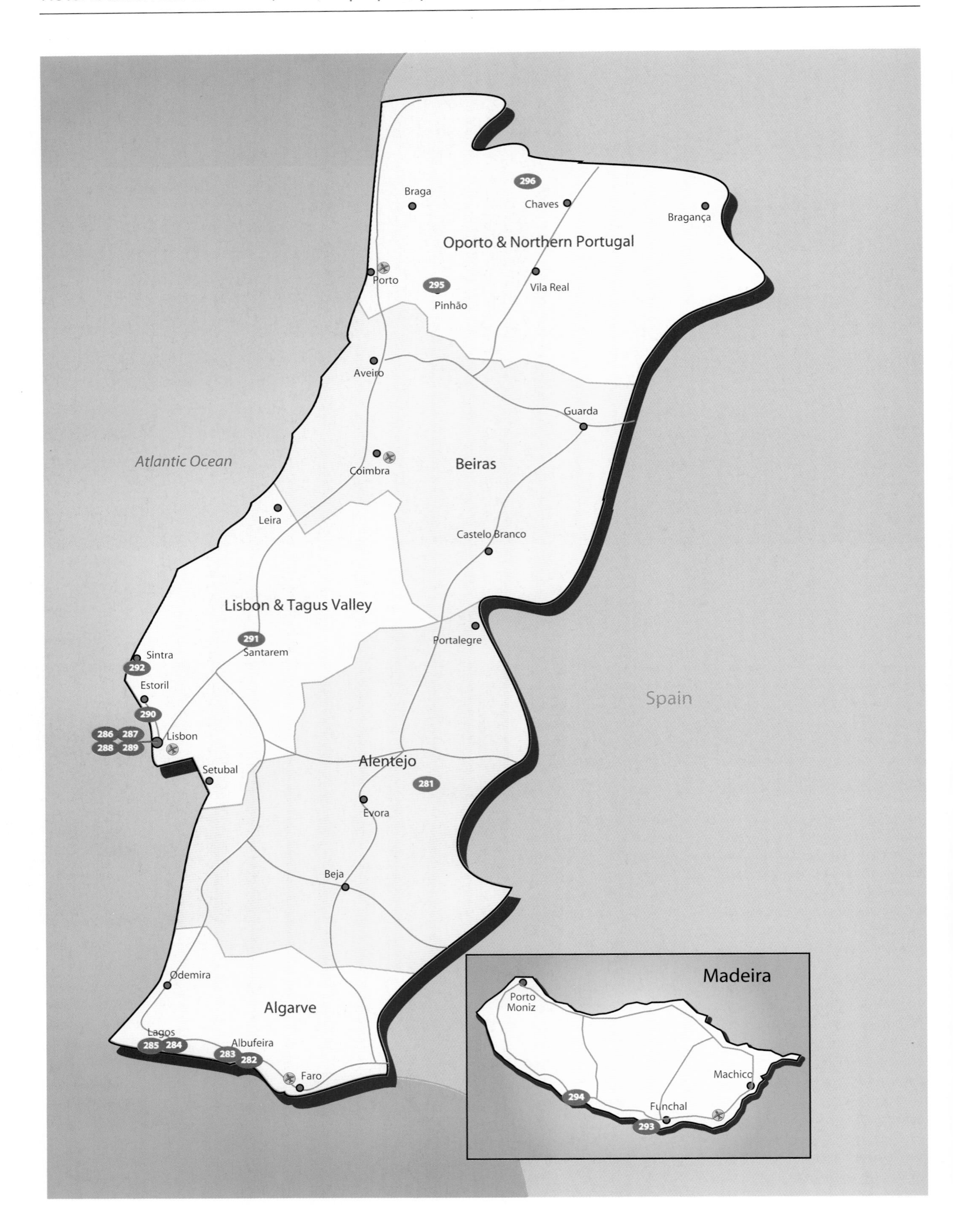

Convento de São Paulo

ALDEIA DA SERRA, 7170 –120 REDONDO, PORTUGAL

Situated between Estremoz and Redondo in the Alentejo, Convento de São Paulo, "the Monastery of Saint Paul", was constructed in 1182 by monks seeking a tranquil location to pray. Many vestiges of the 12th century have remained; the original chapel and church are popular venues for weddings and special events, whilst the bedrooms are the old chambers of the monks. Guests dine beneath the splendour of 18th-century fresco paintings in the stylish restaurant. The convent also has a collection of 50,000 tiles.

Situé dans l'Alentejo, entre Estremoz et Redondo, le Convento de São Paulo fût construit en 1182 par des moines en quête d'endroit tranquille pour prier. De nombreux vestiges du XIIe siècle ont été conservés; la chapelle et l'église originales sont des endroits populaires pour les mariages ou les occasions spéciales, et les anciennes cellules des moines servent aujourd'hui de chambres. Les hôtes dînent sous de somptueuses fresques du XVIIIe siècle, dans l'élégante salle à manger. Le couvent aussi dispose d'une collection de 50 000 carreaux.

Convento de São Paulo, "das Kloster des Heiligen Paulus", liegt zwischen Estremoz und Redondo und wurde 1182 von Mönchen erbaut – sie suchten einen ruhigen Platz, um zu beten. Viele Spuren aus dem 12. Jahrhundert sind hier erhalten geblieben: Die ursprüngliche Kapelle und die Kirche sind bei Hochzeiten und feierlichen Anlässen sehr begehrt, und die alten Kammern der Mönche sind die heutigen Gästezimmer. Im eleganten Restaurant diniert man unter herrlichen Fresken aus dem 18. Jahrhundert. Das Kloster besitzt auch eine Sammlung von 50.000 Kacheln.

Our inspector loved: *The absolute beauty and tranquillity.*

Directions: Lisbon > A6 > Evora/Estremoz > Redondo.

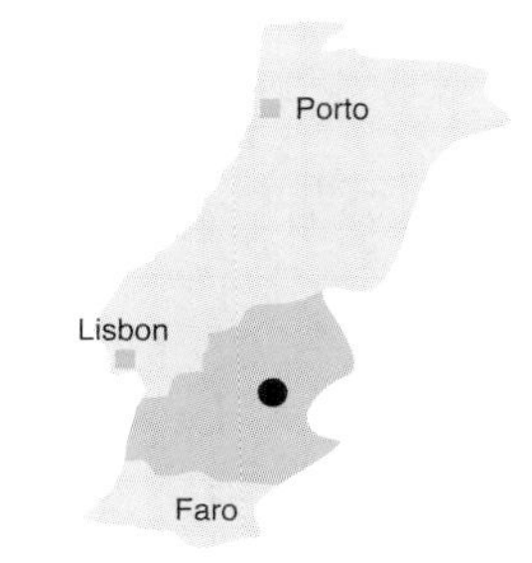

Web: www.johansens.com/conventodesaopaulo
E-mail: hotelconvspaulo@mail.telepac.pt
Tel: +351 266 989 160
Fax: +351 266 989 167

Price Guide:
single €115–175
double/twin €130–190
suite €180–250

Grande Real Santa Eulália Resort & Hotel Spa

PRAIA DE SANTA EULÁLIA, PO BOX 2445, 8200-916 ALBUFEIRA, PORTUGAL

Located moments from Santa Eulália beach and close to the town of Albufeira, this impressive hotel stands next to a wonderful spa, amidst a spectacular resort. The spacious guest rooms are fitted with local network connections and decorated in bright colours; some have sea or garden views and some have Jacuzzis. There are 6 bars and 5 restaurants to choose from, 3 of which are outside the resort. The 1,000m² spa features 16 treatment rooms, a sauna, thalasso therapy and a beauty centre. Rea & Lito's Kids Club provides supervised care.

Situé à deux pas de la plage de Eulálıá et proche de la ville de Albufeira, cet impressionnant hôtel se dresse à côté d'un merveilleux Spa au cœur d'un resort spectaculaire. Les chambres spacieuses sont équipées d'une connection internet locale et décorées de couleurs vives. Certaines ont vues mer ou jardin et certaines ont un jacuzzi. Il y a 6 bars et 5 restaurants, dont 3 au dehors du resort. Le spa de 1000 m² propose 16 salles de traitements, un sauna et un centre de thalassothérapie et de beauté. Les enfants sont sous bonne surveillance au Club Rea & Lito.

Das nur ein paar Schritte vom Strand von Santa Eulália entfernte und nahe der Stadt Albufeira gelegene eindrucksvolle Hotel befindet sich neben einem Spa inmitten eines fantastischen Resorts. Die geräumigen, bunt gestalteten Zimmer bieten örtliche Internet-Verbindung, einige haben Blick auf den Garten oder das Meer und einige bieten Jacuzzis. Es gibt 6 Bars und 5 Restaurants, 3 davon außerhalb des Resorts. Im 1.000m² großen Spa findet man 16 Behandlungsräume, Sauna und ein Thalassotherapie- und Beauty-Zentrum. In Rea & Lito's Kids Club sind auch die kleinen Gäste gut aufgehoben.

Our inspector loved: *The spacious lobby with its pyramid-style ceilings.*

Directions: Faro Airport > N125 > Albufeira > the hotel is signposted.

Web: www.johansens.com/eulaliaresort
E-mail: info.gse@grandereal.com
Tel: +351 289 598 000
Fax: +351 289 598 001

Price Guide: (excluding VAT)
single €150-385
double €170-405
resort suite €130-510
hotel suite €250-1,180

VILA JOYA

PRAIA DA GALÉ, PO BOX 120, P-8200 ALBUFEIRA, ALGARVE, PORTUGAL

A true gem, hidden amongst beautiful Algarve scenery, Vila Joya is built in Moorish style and welcomes guests into a world of sheer indulgence and relaxation. All bedrooms and luxurious suites are generously sized and individually decorated and have a balcony or terrace with access to the immaculate subtropical gardens and panoramic views of the Atlantic Sea. Delicious daily changing menus are served in the smart and relaxed restaurant, the only one in Portugal to be awarded 2 Michelin stars. There are 2 heated pools and a 4-mile beach is close by, whilst golf is just 5 minutes away.

Véritable joyau caché au coeur des superbes paysages de l'Algarve, Villa Joya construit dans un style mauresque accueille ses hôtes dans un monde de totale indulgence. Toutes les chambres et suites sont spacieuses, individuellement décorées et ont balcon ou terrasse avec accès aux jardins immaculés ainsi que vues panoramiques sur l'Atlantique. De délicieux menus, changés tous les jours sont servis dans l'élégant restaurant, le seul au Portugal à posséder 2 étoiles Michelin. Il y a 2 piscines chauffées, une plage de 7 kilomètres à proximité et golf à 5 minutes.

Dieses im maurischen Stil erbaute Hotel ist ein wahres Juwel und liegt inmitten herrlichster Algarve-Landschaft. Den Gast erwartet hier eine Welt völliger Entspannung. Alle Zimmer und Suiten sind großzügig und individuell gestaltet und haben Balkon oder Terrasse mit Zugang zum makellosen Garten sowie Panorama-Blick auf den Atlantik. Köstliche Speisen werden im eleganten Restaurant serviert, dem einzigen in Portugal mit 2 Michelinsternen. Es gibt 2 beheizte Swimmingpools, ein 7km langer Strand ist nicht weit, und Golf ist nur 5 Minuten entfernt.

Our inspector loved: *The huge star-lit bath with views to the ocean.*

Directions: Faro Airport > N125 > Galé Beach.

Web: www.johansens.com/joya
E-mail: info@vilajoya.com
Tel: +351 289 59 1795
Fax: +351 289 59 1201

Price Guide: (excluding VAT)
double €370-585
suite €510-1,030

ROMANTIK HOTEL VIVENDA MIRANDA

PORTO DE MÓS, 8600 LAGOS, PORTUGAL

Vivenda Miranda is a delightful hotel, with Moorish influences evident in its architecture. It is nestled on a bluff above the sea, surrounded by a subtropical garden, and with captivating views from the terrace. Hearty breakfasts and light lunches anticipate the fantastic gourmet meal served in the evening, accompanied by fine wines. Tennis facilities are nearby, mountain bikes are available and water sports can be practised at the Marina. The hotel has its own PGA Golf Professional and the 8 golf courses in the vicinity offer superb green fee reductions.

Le Vivenda Miranda est un hôtel délicieux, avec, dans son architecture, une influence maure évidente. Il est niché sur une avancée au dessus de la mer, entouré d'un jardin subtropical, et bénéficie de vues captivantes de la terrasse. Des petits-déjeuners copieux et des déjeuners légers sont un préambule au fantastique repas gastronomique accompagné de vins fins servi le soir. Des courts de tennis sont tout proches, des VTT sont disponibles et les sports aquatiques peuvent être pratiqués à la marina. L'hôtel a sa propre PGA Golf Professional (Association des Professionnels du Golf) et les 8 parcours de golf du voisinage offrent de très bonnes réductions.

Dieses auf einer Klippe über dem Meer gelegene einladende Hotel ist von einem subtropischen Garten umgeben und bietet eine atemberaubende Sicht von der Terrasse. Maurische Einflüsse zeigen sich deutlich in der Architektur. Ein herzhaftes Frühstück und leichtes Mittagessen bereiten auf ein Feinschmeckermahl und erlesene Weine am Abend vor. Gäste können Tennis spielen, Mountainbiken und Wassersport betreiben. Das Hotel verfügt über seinen eigenen PGA Golf Professional, und 8 nahegelegene Golfplätze bieten reduzierte Green-Gebühren.

Our inspector loved: *Relaxing on the terrace, enjoying the view over the ocean.*

Directions: Faro Airport > N125 > Lagos > singposted.

Web: www.johansens.com/vivendamiranda
E-mail: reservations@vivendamiranda.pt
Tel: +351 282 763222
Fax: +351 282 760342

Price Guide:
single €77–130
double €57–92
suite €64–145

Villa Esmeralda

PORTO DE MÓS, 8600 LAGOS, PORTUGAL

This charming hotel stands within a subtropical palm garden above the bay of Porto de Mós, near the historical town of Lagos. A special home-from-home comfort features throughout the hotel and in the spacious guest rooms, which include 2 junior suites. Each room boasts views of the ocean, terrace or garden. Guests may take breakfast or tea on the terrace and savour the fresh fish of the day in the beach restaurant. The hotel has a private entrance to the beach.

Cette hôtel de charme se dresse au cœur d'un jardin subtropical de palmiers au-dessus de la baie de Porto de Mós, près de la ville historique de Lagos. Le sentiment particulier d'être comme à la maison se ressent à travers tout l'hôtel ainsi que dans les chambres spacieuses, qui comprennent 2 junior suites. Chaque chambre offre une vue sur l'océan, la terrasse ou le jardin. Les clients peuvent apprécier leur petit-déjeuner ou le thé sur la terrasse et déguster le poisson frais du jour au restaurant de la plage. L'hôtel à un accès privé à la plage.

Dieses zauberhafte Hotel liegt inmitten eines suptropischen Palmengartens über der Bucht von Porto de Mós, nahe der historischen Stadt Lagos. Ein Gefühl von Behaglichkeit liegt über dem Hotel, und besonderen Komfort bieten die geräumigen Zimmer, darunter 2 Juniorsuiten, alle mit Blick auf das Meer, die Terrasse oder den Garten. Frühstück und Nachmittagskaffee werden auf der Terrasse serviert, und im Strandrestaurant genießt man fangfrischen Fisch. Das Hotel hat einen eigenen Zugang zum Strand.

Our inspector loved: *The location, so close to the sea.*

Directions: Faro Airport > IPI > Lagos.

Web: www.johansens.com/esmeralda
E-mail: villa@lagos.cc
Tel: +351 282 760 430
Fax: +351 282 760 433

Price Guide:
double €130-170
junior suite €140-210

As Janelas Verdes

RUA DAS JANELAS VERDES 47, 1200-690 LISBON, PORTUGAL

Directions: Lisbon Airport > taxi to As Janelas.

Web: www.johansens.com/janelasverdes
E-mail: janelas.verdes@heritage.pt
Tel: +351 21 39 68 143
Fax: +351 21 39 68 144

Price Guide: (breakfast €14)
single €210-260
double €218-290

This small 18th-century palace offers a romantic atmosphere in the heart of Lisbon, next to the National Art Museum. The home-from-home ambience is enhanced by the friendly staff and inviting neo-classical décor fitted with objets d'art, paintings and mementoes of a bygone era. Bedrooms are individually decorated and the ivy-covered patio is a peaceful haven. Drinks may be taken on the panelled library's balcony overlooking the River Tagus, and breakfast savoured in the garden during warmer months.

Ce petit palais du XVIIIe siècle offre une atmosphère romantique au cœur de Lisbonne, à deux pas du Musée National d'Arts. Le personnel amical et l'attrayante décoration néoclassique avec ses objets d'art, peintures et souvenirs d'autrefois créent une atmosphère chaleureuse où l'on se sent comme chez soi. Les chambres sont décorées de manière individuelle et le patio couvert de lierre est un refuge tranquille. L'apéritif peut-être dégusté sur le balcon de la bibliothèque en bois surplombant le Tage et le petit-déjeuner peut-être pris dans le jardin pendant les mois les plus chauds.

Dieses kleine Palais aus dem 18. Jahrhundert bietet romantische Atmosphäre im Herzen Lissabons, neben dem Museum nationaler Kunst. Verstärkt wird das heimelige Ambiente durch das freundliche Personal und das einladende neoklassizistische Décor, mit Objets d,art, Gemälden und Memorabilia vergangener Zeiten. Die Zimmer sind individuell gestaltet, und die mit Efeu bewachsene Terrasse ist eine friedliche Oase. Der Balkon der holzverschalten Bibliothek mit Blick auf den Fluss Tagus lädt zum Drink ein, und Frühstück wird in den wärmeren Monaten im Garten serviert.

Our inspector loved: *Watching the River Tagus from the library terrace.*

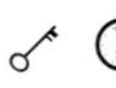

Hotel Britania

RUA RODRIGUES SAMPAIO 17, 1150-278 LISBON, PORTUGAL

Opened in 1944 and designed by the famous Portuguese modernist architect Cassiano Branco, this prestigious, family-run hotel is the only surviving original Art Deco hotel in Lisbon. It has been lovingly restored to regain its 1940s ambience and is now classified as a historic building. Service is simply outstanding. Beautiful photographs of Lisbon adorn the walls of the welcoming lounge with its fireplace and small library, and the 30 very spacious bedrooms feature a relaxing décor and marble bathrooms.

Ouvert en 1944 et conçu par le fameux architecte moderne portugais Cassiano Branco, ce prestigieux hôtel de famille est le seul hôtel art déco d'origine à Lisbonne. Il a été soigneusement restauré afin de garder son ambiance des années 1940 et est maintenant un monument classé. Le service est tout simplement parfait. De superbes photographies de Lisbonne décorent les murs ainsi que l'accueillant salon avec sa cheminée et petite bibliothèque. Les 30 chambres spacieuses ont une décoration relaxante et des salles de bain en marbre.

1944 eröffnet und von dem modernistischen portugiesischen Architekten Cassiano Franco gestaltet, ist dieses prestigereiche, familiengeführte Hotel das einzige überlebende Art-Deco Hotel der Stadt. Nach sorgfältiger Renovierung erlangte es sein typisches 1940er Ambiente wieder und ist nun als historisches Gebäude klassifiziert. Der Service hier ist einfach unvergleichlich. Herrliche Fotografien von Lissabon zieren die Wände des einladenden Aufenthaltsraumes mit Kamin und kleiner Bibliothek, und die 30 sehr geräumigen Zimmer bieten ruhiges Décor und Marmorbäder.

Our inspector loved: *The relaxing lounge and excellent service.*

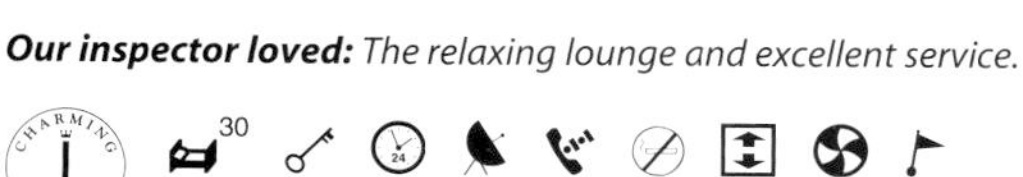

Directions: Lisbon Airport > city centre.

Web: www.johansens.com/britania
E-mail: britania.hotel@heritage.pt
Tel: +351 21 31 55 016
Fax: +351 21 31 55 021

Price Guide: (breakfast €14)
single €183-210
double €195-230

Porto
Lisbon
Faro

Lisboa Plaza Hotel

TV. SALITRE / AV. LIBERDADE, 1269-066 LISBON, PORTUGAL

This elegant, family-owned hotel is centrally based and located just off from the famous Avenida da Liberdade. Originally built in 1953, recent refurbishments have created a contemporary boutique-style hotel with interior décor by Portuguese designer Graca Viberto. The atmosphere throughout is relaxed and informal with attentive staff providing guests with an efficient and personal service. The property is an ideal base for exploring the streets, ancient buildings and stunning scenery of old Lisbon.

Cet élégant hôtel de famille est situé en centre ville, seulement quelques pas de la fameuse Avenida da Liberdade. Originellement construit en 1953, de récentes rénovations l'ont transformé en un boutique hôtel contemporain dont l'architecture d'intérieure revient à la designer portugaise Graca Viberto. Dans tout l'hôtel l'atmosphère est décontractée et informelle et le personnel attentif offre aux clients un service efficace et personnel. Cet établissement est une base idéale pour explorer les rues, anciens bâtiments et superbes décors de Lisbonne.

Dieses elegante, familiengeführte Hotel liegt zentral nur wenige Meter von der berühmten Avenida da Liberdade entfernt. Das ursprünglich 1953 erbaute Haus wurde durch kürzliche Erneuerungen in ein zeitgenössisches Boutique-Hotel umgewandelt, dessen Interieur die berühmte portugiesische Designerin Graca Viberto gestaltete. Die Atmosphäre ist entspannt und informell, und das aufmerksame Personal bietet effizienten, persönlichen Service. Der ideale Ausgangspunkt, um die Straßen, alten Gebäude und herrliche Kulisse des alten Lissabon zu erkunden.

Directions: Lisbon Airport > city centre.

Web: www.johansens.com/lisboa
E-mail: plaza.hotels@heritage.pt
Tel: +351 213 218 218
Fax: +351 213 471 630

Price Guide: (breakfast €14)
single €183-210
double €195-230
suite €320-380

Our inspector loved: *The sincere welcome upon entering this lovely hotel.*

Solar do Castelo

RUA DAS COZINHAS 2, 1100–181 LISBON, PORTUGAL

Surrounded by the walls of Lisbon's St George's Castle, this historic building has been carefully transformed into a charming, contemporary hotel. Many of the original features have been brought back to life by architect Vasco Massapina, such as the elaborate design of the main façade and typical Portuguese Pombal tiling with its star and flower pattern. Guests can explore the castle grounds and visit numerous restaurants, shops and historical sites in the vicinity.

A Lisbonne, cerné par les murs du château de San Jorge, ce monument historique a été soigneusement transformé en un charmant hôtel contemporain. Pour la plupart, ses caractéristiques originelles, telles que la façade principale raffinée et ses céramiques Pombal si typiquement portugaises aux motifs floraux et d'étoiles, ont été "ranimées" par l'architecte Vasco Massapina. Les hôtes peuvent visiter les terres du château ainsi que les nombreux restaurants, magasins et sites historiques du voisinage.

Dieses von den Mauern der St.-Georgs-Burg umgebene historische Gebäude wurde sorgfältig in ein freundliches, zeitgenössisches Hotel umgewandelt, wobei der Architekt Vasco Massapina viele der Originalmerkmale zum Leben erweckte, so z.B. die kunstvoll verzierte Fassade und die typischen portugiesischen Fliesen im Pombal-Muster mit Sternen und Blumen. Die Gäste können das Schlossgelände erkunden und zahlreiche Restaurants, Geschäfte und historische Stätten in der Umgebung besuchen.

Our inspector loved: *Stepping out of this lovely hotel into the "Olde Worlde" charm of Lisbon.*

Directions: Lisbon Airport > taxi to hotel.

Web: www.johansens.com/solardocastelo
E-mail: solar.castelo@heritage.pt
Tel: +351 218 870 909
Fax: +351 218 870 907

Price Guide: (breakfast €14)
single €210-260
double €218–290

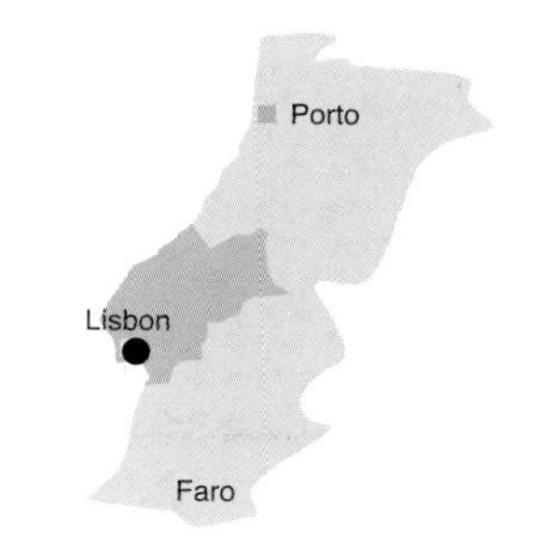

14

ALBATROZ PALACE, LUXURY SUITES

A member of The Leading Small Hotels of the World

RUA FREDERICO AROUCA 100, 2750-353 CASCAIS, LISBON, PORTUGAL

This carefully restored former royal summer retreat is situated on the cliffs above Conceição beach in the charming fishing village of Cascais. Sheer indulgence is reflected by the elegant décor featuring antique and modern furnishings. The 4 luxurious rooms and 2 suites boast sea views and with Albatroz Hotel a few metres away guests may dine in the locally renowned restaurant and swim in the hotel's pool with panoramic views of the bay below. Golf and sightseeing can be arranged. Guests can be picked up from the airport in a private taxi with English-speaking driver (€55).

Cet ancien retrait royal restauré est situé sur les falaises au-dessus de la plage de Conceição au village de Cascais. Une ambiance d'indulgence est reflétée dans le décor élégant avec des ameublements anciens et modernes exquis. Les 4 chambres et les 2 suites s'enorgueillissent d'une vue sur la mer, et Albatroz Hotel étant à quelques mètres, les hôtes peuvent passer des soirées dans son restaurant renommé et nager dans sa piscine avec des vues panoramiques. Golf et visites touristiques peuvent être organisés. Un service de taxi avec un chauffeur qui parle l'anglais, est disponible pour chercher les hotes de l'aéroport (€55).

Diese restaurierte ehemalige königliche Sommerresidenz liegt in den Klippen über dem Strand von Conceição im Fischerdorf Cascais. Das elegante Interieur ist mit herrlichen Antiquitäten und exquisitem modernen Mobiliar gestaltete. Die 4 luxuriösen Zimmer und 2 Suiten haben Meerblick, und das nur ein paar Meter entfernte Albatroz Hotel bietet ein beliebtes Restaurant und einen Swimmingpool mit Panoramablick auf die Bucht. Golf und Besichtigungstouren können arrangiert werden. Gäste können im Privattaxi mit englischsprachigem Fahrer vom Flughafen abgeholt werden (€55).

Our inspector loved: *The sheer comfort of the rooms.*

Directions: 24km from the centre of Lisbon. 15km from Sintra. 4km from Estoril. 24km from Lisbon. From the airport take the A5 towards Cascais.

Web: www.johansens.com/albatroz
E-mail: albatroz@albatrozhotels.com
Tel: +351 21 484 73 80
Fax: +351 21 484 48 27

Price Guide: (excluding VAT, breakfast €15)
single €150-322
double €180-355
suite €275-510

Casa da Alcáçova

LARGO DA ALCÁÇOVA 3, PORTAS DO SOL, 2000 SANTARÉM, PORTUGAL

In the heart of Santarém, within the medieval ramparts of a 12th-century castle, this family-run hotel provides romance, charm and luxurious comfort in spectacular surroundings by the River Tagus. Each en-suite guest room, with Jacuzzi, is adorned with works of art, antiques and exquisite linen and lace. Paintings created by local artists hang in the little art gallery and medieval relics are on display throughout the property. Full English breakfast is served in guests' bedrooms or in the dining room; dinner is served by prior arrangement.

Au cœur de Santarém, à l'intérieur des remparts datant du Moyen-Age d'un château du XIIe siècle, cet hôtel familial offre charme, romance et confort luxueux dans un environnement spectaculaire à proximité du fleuve Tage. Chaque chambre, avec jacuzzis, est décorée d'œuvres d'arts, d'antiquités, de lins et de dentelles raffinés. Des tableaux d'artistes locaux sont accrochés dans la petite galerie d'art et des vestiges du Moyen-Age sont exposés dans tout l'établissement. Un copieux petit-déjeuner anglais est servi en chambre ou dans la salle à manger et le dîner est servi sur demande.

Im Herzen von Santarém innerhalb der mittelalterlichen Ruinen einer Burg aus dem 12. Jahrhundert befindet sich dieses familiengeführte Hotel, das Romantik, Charme und luxuriösen Komfort in herrlicher Lage am Fluss Tagus verspricht. Jedes der Zimmer bietet ein eigenes Bad, Jacuzzi, Kunstwerke, Antiquitäten und exquisite Bettwäsche mit Spitze. Malereien einheimischer Künstler zieren die kleine Galerie, und mittelalterliche Reste können überall bewundert werden. Ein volles englisches Frühstück wird auf dem Zimmer oder im Speisesaal serviert, Abendessen gibt es auf Anfrage.

Our inspector loved: *The beautiful linen in the bedrooms.*

Directions: Lisbon Airport > A1 > Santarém.

Web: www.johansens.com/alcacova
E-mail: info@alcacova.com
Tel: +351 243 304 030
Fax: +351 243 304 035

Price Guide: (dinner, including wine €40)
double €109-169

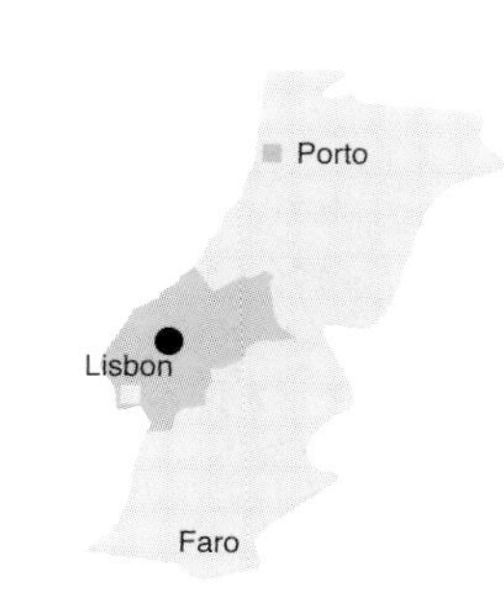

8 30

Convento De São Saturnino

2705-001 AZOIA - SINTRA, PORTUGAL

Within the centre of a 5,800-acre ocean-side nature reserve, this exclusive hotel was originally a 12th-century monastery. Standing in a fertile valley at the foot of the wooded Sintra Hills, numerous tourist, cultural and sporting attractions are nearby. Paintings, wooden beams, antique furniture and canopied beds tastefully decorate each guest room to create refined havens of comfort. Formerly the monastery's water tank, the pool looks out to the sea; many beaches are close by. Dinner can be prepared by arrangement.

Au cœur d'une réserve naturelle de 2300 hectares en bord de mer, cet hôtel unique était à l'origine un monastère du XIIe siècle. Situé dans une vallée fertile au pied du mont boisé de Cintra, de nombreuses activités touristiques, culturelles et sportives sont à proximité. Tableaux, poutres, meubles anciens et lits à baldaquins décorent avec goût chacune des chambres, créant ainsi un havre de confort. Anciennement le réservoir d'eau du monastère, la piscine offre des vues sur la mer et de nombreuses plages sont proches. Le dîner peut-être servi sur demande.

Dieses exklusive, im Zentrum eines 2.300ha großen Naturreservates am Meer gelegene Hotel war im 12. Jahrhundert ein Kloster. Zahlreiche touristische, kulturelle und Sportattraktionen befinden sich in der Nähe dieses fruchtbaren Tales am Fuße der Sintra-Hügel. Malereien, Holzbalken, Antiquitäten und Himmelbetten sorgen für Behaglichkeit in den geschmackvoll gestalteten Zimmern. Der einstige Wassertank des Klosters ist heute ein Swimmingpool mit Blick aufs Meer, und einige Strände liegen in nächster Nähe. Abendessen kann auf Anfrage zubereitet werden.

Our inspector loved: *The sheer silence and peace.*

Directions: A5 towards Cascais > exit Malveira da Serra > continue for 10 minutes > Azoia > follow hotel signs. The hotel is a 40-minute drive from Lisbon Airport.

Web: www.johansens.com/saturnino
E-mail: contact@saosat.com
Tel: +351 21 928 3192
Fax: +351 21 928 9685

Price Guide: (excluding VAT)
single €100-150
double/suite €120-180
sea view terrace €130-200

Quinta da Bela Vista

CAMINHO DO AVISTA NAVIOS 4, 9000 FUNCHAL, MADEIRA, PORTUGAL

It is a joy to stay in this traditional house, with its tall windows and green shutters, overlooking Funchal Bay and surrounded by 22,000m² of exotic gardens. The interiors are a blend of sophistication and rich, classical furnishings. Guests enjoy their apéritifs in the cheerful bar or on the sunny terraces before choosing between the elegant restaurant serving fine food and the best wines or the more informal dining room.

Surplombant la baie de Funchal et entourée de 22 000 m² de jardins exotiques, c'est un vrai plaisir de séjourner dans cette maison traditionnelle, avec ses grandes fenêtres et ses volets verts. L'intérieur est un mélange de sophistication et de richesse, avec des meubles classiques. Les visiteurs dégusteront leur apéritif dans le bar animé ou sur les terraces ensoleillées avant de se décider entre le restaurant élégant servant des plats fins et les meilleurs vins ou la salle à manger plus informelle.

Ein Aufenthalt in diesem traditionellen Haus mit seinen großen Fenstern und grünen Fensterläden, das auf die Bucht von Funchal blickt und von 22.000m² exotischen Gärten umgeben ist, bleibt unvergessen. Die Räume sind höchst elegant, üppig und klassisch eingerichtet. Die Gäste können in der gemütlichen Bar oder auf der sonnigen Terrasse einen Apéritif nehmen, bevor sie sich im informellen Speisesaal oder dem eleganten Restaurant von feinen Speisen und edlen Weinen verwöhnen lassen.

Our inspector loved: *The fine dining in the beautiful old house.*

Directions: Main road > Rua do Dr Pita. Madeira International Airport is a 30-minute drive.

Web: www.johansens.com/quintadabelavista
E-mail: info@belavistamadeira.com
Tel: +351 291 706400
Fax: +351 291 706401

Porto Moniz
Machico
Funchal

Price Guide:
single €118–209
double/twin €157–281
suite €299–339

89 35

Estalagem da Ponta do Sol

a member of design hotels™

QUINTA DA ROCHINHA, 9360 PONTA DO SOL, MADEIRA, PORTUGAL

Simply stunning, this special hotel is built on the edge of a cliff overlooking the ocean and pretty town of Ponta do Sol. Modern architecture and unique style combine with the original buildings to create a relaxing, luxurious atmosphere that does not detract from its breathtaking natural surroundings. The walls are adorned with black and white photographs and furnishings are cool and comfortable. An awe-inspiring pool seems to melt into the sea. Good local food is served in the restaurant, which has huge windows and spectacular views.

Tout simplement spectaculaire, cet hôtel très spécial est construit au bord de la falaise et surplombe l'océan et la ravissante ville de Ponta do Sol. Une architecture moderne et un style unique s'allient aux bâtiments d'origine afin de créer une atmosphère luxueuse et relaxante, sans porter atteinte à son environnement naturel à vous couper le souffle. Les murs sont couverts de photographies en noir et blanc et l'ameublement est design et confortable. La piscine, impressionnante, semble se fondre dans l'océan. Le restaurant offre des vues spectaculaires à travers ses baies vitrées.

Dieses eindrucksvolle Hotel liegt am Rande einer Klippe mit Blick auf das Meer und das hübsche Städtchen Ponta do Sol. Moderne Architektur und ein einzigartiger Stil verbinden sich mit den Originalgebäuden und schaffen eine entspannte, luxuriöse Atmosphäre, die jedoch keinesfalls von der atemberaubend schönen Umgebung ablenkt. Die Wände sind mit Schwarzweißfotografien geschmückt, und die Einrichtung ist kühl und komfortabel. Ein traumhafter Swimmingpool scheint mit dem Meer zu verschmelzen, und das Restaurant bietet herrliche Ausblicke.

Our inspector loved: *The simple yet elegant décor that highlights the natural surroundings and sea; a really peaceful retreat.*

Directions: Take the hotel's complimentary 35-minute shuttle bus ride from Madeira Airport.

Web: www.johansens.com/pontadosol
E-mail: info@pontadosol.com
Tel: +351 291 970 200
Fax: +351 291 970 209

Price Guide:
single €60-85
twin €70-110

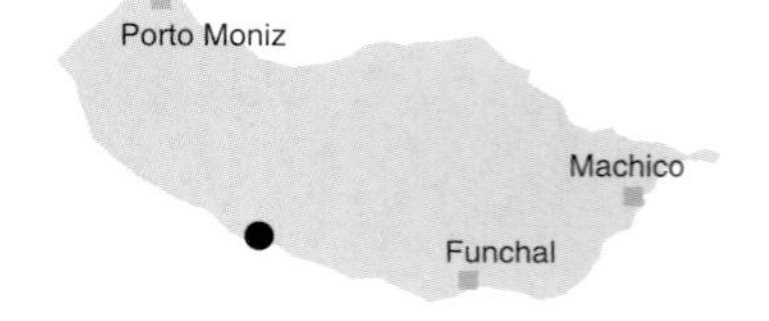

VINTAGE HOUSE

LUGAR DA PONTE, 5085-034 PINHÃO, PORTUGAL

On the very edge of the River Douro this elegant hotel is surrounded by the famous port vineyards of the world's oldest demarcated wine region. A former wine estate, dating back to the 18th century, its name is derived from the surrounding vineyards. Today, the owners run specialist wine tasting courses for enthusiasts, and the bar is situated in the former Port wine lodge. The hotel has been refurbished to reflect the building's heritage and now manages to combine the character of a period property with modern comforts and facilities.

Situé au bord du Douro et entouré par les vignobles fameux de Porto, la plus vieille région viticole du monde, cet élégant hotel se trouve sur une ancienne exploitation viticole du XVIIIe siècle, et tient son nom des vignobles environnants. Aujourd'hui, les propriétaires organisent des cours de dégustation pour les passionnés, et le bar se trouve dans les anciennes "cuves". L'hôtel a été meublé pour refléter l'héritage du bâtiment et arrive maintenant à combiner le caractère de l'ancienne propriété avec le confort et facilités modernes.

Direkt am Ufer des Douro liegt dieses elegante Hotel, umgeben von den berühmten Portweinbergen der ältesten Weinregion der Welt, die dem Hotel, einem ehemaligen Winzergut aus dem 18. Jahrhundert auch seinen Namen gaben. Heute werden hier spezielle Weinkurse für Weinliebhaber abgehalten, und die Bar befindet sich im früheren Portweinhaus. Das Hotel wurde sorgfältig restauriert und spiegelt nun das Erbe und den einstigen Charakter des Hauses wider, wobei modernste Einrichtungen und Komfort geboten werden.

Our inspector loved: *Being so close to the River Douro whilst relaxing at this absolutely lovely hotel.*

Directions: Porto > A4-IP4 > Vila Real > exit Mesão Frio/Régua > follow signs to Pinhão.

Web: www.johansens.com/vintagehouse
E-mail: vintagehouse@hotelvintagehouse.com
Tel: +351 254 730 230
Fax: +351 254 730 238

Price Guide:
single €107–155
double/twin €121–170
suite €206–310

Vidago Palace Hotel & Golf

PARQUE DE VIDAGO, 5425-307 VIDAGO, PORTUGAL

This is one of the most luxurious hotels in north-east Portugal. A true palace: majestic with tall windows and wrought-iron balconies overlooking vast parkland grounds of lawns, floral gardens and high pines. Wide stone steps lead visitors into an imposing reception hall with a magnificent staircase. Guest rooms have every comfort, lounges are sumptuous and excellent cuisine is served in the elegant restaurant, which has the welcoming atmosphere of a bygone era. Golf enthusiasts will enjoy the challenging 9-hole, par 66 mountain golf course designed by McKenzie Ross.

Ce palais est l'un des hôtels les plus luxueux du Nord Est du Portugal: majestueux avec de grandes fenêtres et des balcons en fer forgé surplombant de vastes pelouses, des jardins fleuris et des pins. De larges marches en pierres guident les visiteurs vers un imposant hall de réception d'où part un magnifique escalier. Les chambres possèdent tout le confort, les salons sont somptueux et une excellente cuisine est servie dans l'élégant restaurant, qui a gardé l'atmosphère accueillante d'autrefois. Des amateurs de golf apprécieront le parcours à 9 trous par 66 exigeant, dessiné par McKenzie Ross.

Dies ist eines der luxuriösesten Hotels im Nordosten Portugals. Ein wahrer Palast: majestätisch mit herrlich großen Fenstern und schmiedeeisernen Balkonen mit Blick auf die weitläufige Parklandschaft, blumengefüllten Gärten und hohen Pinien. Eine breite Steintreppe führt in die Eingangshalle mit ihrem wundervollen Treppenhaus. Die Zimmer bieten jeglichen Komfort und die Aufenthaltsräume sind opulent. Das elegante Restaurant mit dem einladenden Ambiente vergangener Zeiten serviert exzellente Speisen. Golfer schätzen den von Mc Kenzie Ross gestalteten 9-Loch Par 66 Golfplatz.

Our inspector loved: *The elegant and beautiful restaurant.*

Directions: Porto > Vila Real > Chaves.

Web: www.johansens.com/vidago
E-mail: vidagopalace@unicer.pt
Tel: +351 276 990 900
Fax: +351 276 907 359

Price Guide: (green fee €17.50)
single €73-130.50
double /twin €82.50-147
suite €121.50-217

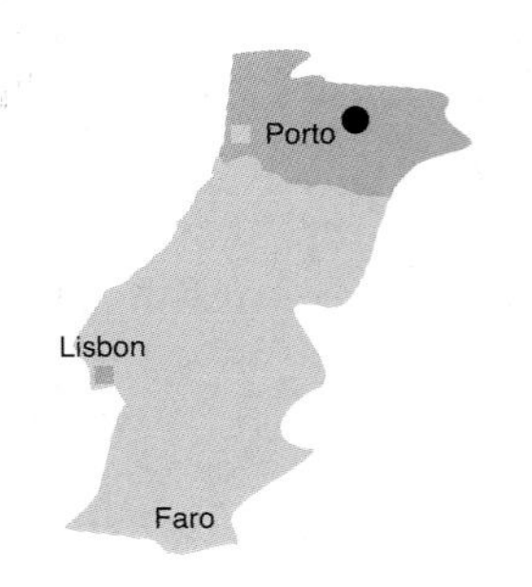

DELIGHTFULLY STILL
HILDON
AN ENGLISH
NATURAL MINERAL WATER
OF EXCEPTIONAL TASTE
www.hildon.com

Slovak Republic

Hotel location shown in red (hotel) or purple (spa hotel) with page number

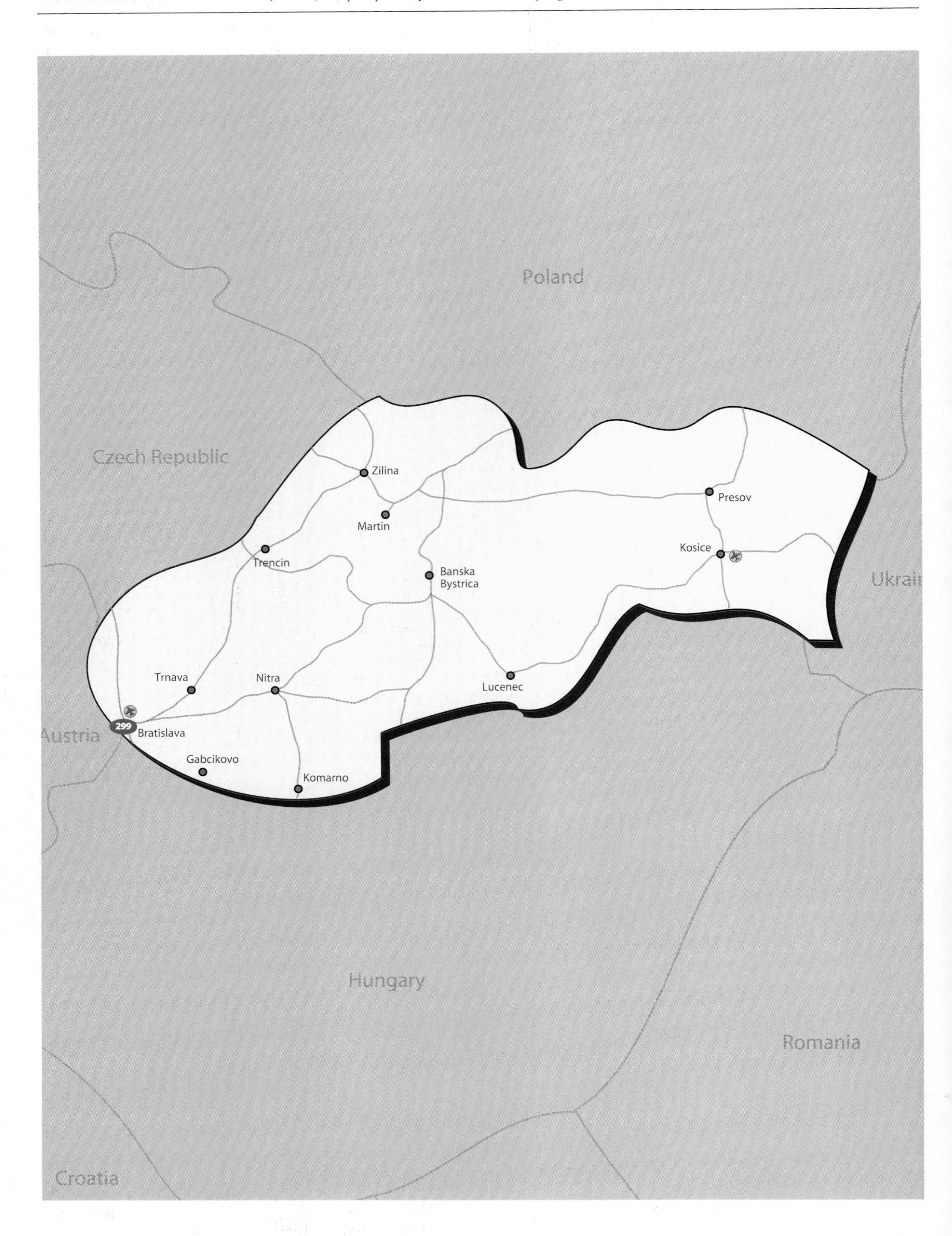

Hotel Marrol's

TOBRUCKÁ UL 4, 81102 BRATISLAVA, SLOVAK REPUBLIC

Hotel Marrol's décor invites guests to step back in time to the heyday of New York's "Cotton Club" years. Slovak furnishings are complemented by leather sofas to provide restful, elegant surroundings. A variety of guest rooms is available: executive rooms are perfect for families or business travellers and ladies chambers are ideal for the single woman. Italian cuisine is served in the spacious restaurant and al fresco dining can be taken on the terrace. Enjoy the Jasmine Spa with whirlpool, solarium and sauna.

Le décor de l'hôtel Marrol entraîne ses hôtes à l'époque ou le "Cotton Club" new-yorkais connu son apogée. Un ameublement slovaque complété de canapés en cuir offre un environnement tranquille et élégant. Plusieurs catégories de chambres sont disponibles : les chambres de luxe sont idéales pour les familles et les hommes d'affaires et il existe des chambres pour femmes seules. Une cuisine italienne est servie dans le spacieux restaurant ou en terrasse. Le Spa Jasmin avec bain à remous, solarium et sauna est à la disposition des clients.

Das Décor dieses Hotels läßt seine Gäste einen Schritt in die Vergangenheit tun, genauer gesagt in die Zeit des New Yorker „Cotton Clubs". Slowakische Einrichtung und Ledersofas schaffen eine entspannte, elegante Atmosphäre. Eine Vielzahl von Zimmern steht zur Verfügung: Executive-Zimmer sind ideal für Familien oder Geschäftsreisende, und es gibt spezielle Zimmer für alleinreisende Damen. Im großen Restaurant oder auf der Terrasse wird italienische Küche serviert, und im Jasmine Spa gibt es Whirlpool, Solarium und Sauna.

Our inspector loved: *The Jasmine Spa, and the flamed figs with mascarpone and three-coloured sauce.*

Directions: The nearest airports are Bratislava and Vienna. The hotel is opposite the River Danube in the old town.

Web: www.johansens.com/marrols
E-mail: johansens@hotelmarrols.sk
Tel: +421 25 77 84 600
Fax: +421 2 577 84 601

Zilina
Kosice
Bratislava

Price Guide:
single €163-234
double €185-234
suite €273-510

SPAIN

Hotel location shown in red (hotel) or purple (spa hotel) with page number

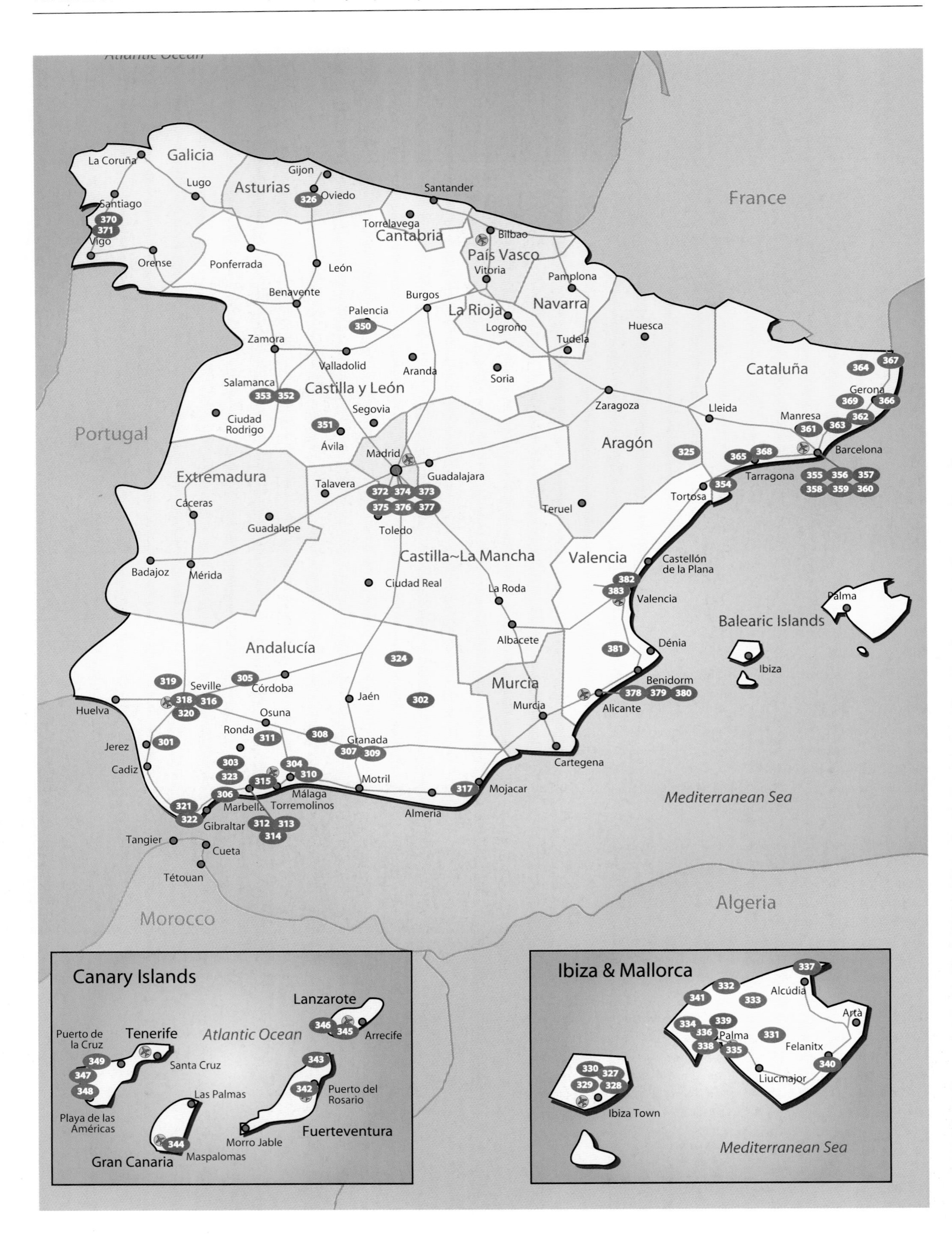

Hacienda El Santiscal

AVDA. EL SANTISCAL 129 (LAGO DE ARCOS), 11630 ARCOS DE LA FRONTERA, SPAIN

Surrounded by fields of sunflowers, this 15th-century manor house, exquisitely restored, offers glorious views of the lake and historic town of Arcos. A welcoming atmosphere envelopes the property as Señora Gallardo invites guests into her home to enjoy the ambience of a traditional Andalucían Hacienda. All rooms have been newly decorated. Traditional home-cooked dishes feature vegetables, olives and oranges grown in the Hacienda's own groves and gardens. A mobile phone is provided for the guests in each room.

Entouré de champs de tournesols, ce manoir du XVe siècle, restauré de façon exquise, offre des vues imprenables sur le lac et la ville historique d'Arcos. Une accueillante atmosphère caractérise la propriété, et Madame Gallardo invite les hôtes dans sa demeure afin de leur faire profiter de l'ambiance traditionnelle d'une Hacienda andalouse. Des plats traditionnels faits-maison sont composés des légumes, olives et oranges qui ont poussé dans le verger et le potager de la Hacienda. Un téléphone portable est mis à la disposition des clients dans chaque chambre.

Umgeben von Sonnenblumenfeldern bietet dieses perfekt restaurierte Herrenhaus aus dem 15. Jahrhundert herrliche Ausblicke auf den See und die historische Stadt Arcos. Eine herzliche Atmosphäre liegt über dem Anwesen und Señora Gallardo lädt ihre Gäste ein, das Ambiente einer typisch andalusischen Hazienda zu genießen. Für die traditionellen selbstgemachten Gerichte werden Gemüse, Oliven und Orangen aus den eigenen Hainen und Gärten verwendet. Die neu hergerichteten Zimmer sind mit Mobiltelefonen für die Gäste ausgestattet.

Our inspector loved: *Staying in a house that was inhabited during the time of America's discovery.*

Directions: Sevilla Cadiz motorway > exit Jerez > follow signs to Arcos de la Frontera > follow signs to Antequera > C372 towards El Bosque > follow signs to the hotel.

Barcelona
Madrid
Málaga

Web: www.johansens.com/haciendaelsantiscal
E-mail: reservas@santiscal.com
Tel: +34 956 70 83 13
Fax: +34 956 70 82 68

Price Guide: (room only, excluding VAT)
single €48-72
double/twin €65-99
suites €84-137

HOTEL PUERTA DE LA LUNA

C/ CANÓNIGO MELGARES RAYA S/N, 23440 BAEZA, JAÉN, SPAIN

Sophisticated elegance pervades this beautifully restored 16th-century palace, set in the heart of historic Baeza, next to its cathedral and steps from many sites of interest. Decorated with antiques and paintings with exposed beams, ceramic tiles and marble, this is a magnificent discovery for those seeking a refined and relaxing haven. An international and Mediterranean menu is served in the restaurant; before dining guests may enjoy an apéritif in the bar or on the exterior, landscaped patio. A massage service, sauna and Jacuzzi are available.

Une élégance sophistiquée domine ce palace du XVIe siècle superbement restauré, au coeur du Baeza historique, près de la cathédrale et des sites d'intérêt. Décoré avec des antiquités et tableaux, poutres apparentes, carrelages et marbres, c,est une découverte magnifique pour ceux qui recherchent un havre de paix raffiné. Un menu international et méditerranéen est servi au restaurant; avant le dîner, les invités peuvent déguster un apéritif au bar ou à l'extérieur sur le patio aménagé. Massages, sauna et jacuzzi sont disponibles.

Erlesene Eleganz durchzieht dieses herrlich restaurierte Palais aus dem 16. Jahrhundert, das mitten im historischen Baeza neben der Kathedrale und nur ein paar Meter von Monumenten und anderen Sehenswürdigkeiten entfernt liegt. Das mit Antiquitäten und Gemälden gefüllte Haus mit seinen Holzbalken, Keramikfliesen und Marmor ist ein wahrer Fund für Gäste, die eine elegante, entspannte Umgebung suchen. Im Restaurant werden internationale und Mittelmeerküche serviert, und die Bar oder der hübsche Innenhof laden zum Apéritif ein. Massagedienst, Sauna und Jacuzzi sind vorhanden.

Our inspector loved: *The tranquil setting, adjacent to the cathedral.*

Directions: Motorway from Málaga to Granada > continue inland on motorway to Jaén > A316 towards Úbeda.

Web: www.johansens.com/luna
E-mail: informacionyreservas@hotelpuertadelaluna.com
Tel: +34 953 747 019
Fax: +34 953 747 095

Price Guide: (room only, excluding VAT)
double €95-145
suites €166-210

Hotel Villa Padierna & Flamingos Golf Club

CTRA. DE CÁDIZ KM 166, 29679 MARBELLA, SPAIN

Reminiscent of an Italian villa, the hotel is surrounded by its own stunning golf course looking out across the Mediterranean and the mountains beyond. The impressive atrium complete with columns, statues, antique urns and a grand marble staircase, leads to a comfortable sitting room with doors opening onto a lovely sun-drenched terrace. Luxurious bedrooms are spacious with large bathrooms and windows and sumptuous furnishings. The manicured undulating lawns contain numerous trees, shrubs and flowers, providing colour and scent along with the breathtaking views.

Cet hôtel, qui rappelle une villa italienne, est entouré par son propre parcours de golf impressionnant, qui donne sur la Méditerranée et les montagnes lointaines. L'entrée avec des colonnes, statues, urnes anciennes et son grand escalier en marbre vous mène au salon confortable avec des portes donnant sur une terrasse ensoleillée. Les chambres luxueuses ont des meubles somptueux, grandes salles de bains et grandes fenêtres. Les jardins superbement entretenus avec toute une variété d'arbres, plantes et fleurs, fournissent des belles couleurs et du parfum ainsi que des vues imprenables.

Dieses an eine italienische Villa erinnernde Hotel liegt umgeben von seinem eigenen Golfplatz mit Blick auf das Mittelmeer und die Berge im Hintergrund. Vom Atrium mit seinen Säulen, Statuen, antiken Urnen und Marmortreppe gelangt man in einen bequemen Aufenthaltsraum, der auf eine sonnige Terrasse führt. Die luxuriösen, geräumigen Zimmer haben große Fenster und Bäder und sind stilvoll eingerichtet. Auf dem perfekt gepflegten, sanft hügeligen Rasen findet man zahlreiche Bäume, Sträucher und Blumen, die für Farbe und herrlichen Duft sorgen.

Our inspector loved: *The luxurious marble bathrooms with huge windows that open onto the golf lawns.*

Directions: Málaga - Cádiz motorway > exit Marbella > N340 towards Cádiz > exit km166 > signs to Flamingos Golf Club and Hotel.

Web: www.johansens.com/villapadierna
E-mail: info@hotelvillapadierna.com
Tel: +34 952 88 91 50
Fax: +34 952 88 91 60

Price Guide: (room only, excluding VAT)
single €157-285
double €193-430
suite €277-1,200

Hotel La Era

PARTIDO MARTINA, LOS CERRILLOS, P.85, 29566 CASARABONELA, MÁLAGA, SPAIN

This immaculate little hotel is a nature lover's paradise, sitting on a hilltop, surrounded by rare species of flora and fauna. The hotel is warm and inviting, with most bedrooms having their own terrace or balcony, and with lots of cosy spots in which to curl up with a book and enjoy the panoramic views. The dining room is excellent; both local and international delicacies are tailor-made for individual tastes and special diets.

Cet impeccable petit hôtel perché au sommet d'une colline et entouré de rares espèces de faune et de flore, est un paradis pour les amoureux de la nature. L'hôtel est chaleureux et accueillant, la plupart des chambres possédant ses propres terrasses ou balcons et avec de nombreux endroits où se pelotonner et admirer les vues panoramiques. La table est excellente : des mets d'inspirations locales et internationales sont concoctés afin de répondre à tous les goûts et toutes les alimentations.

Dieses makellose, auf einem Hügel umgeben von seltenen Pflanzen und Tieren gelegene kleine Hotel ist ein Paradies für Naturliebhaber. Das Hotel ist warm und einladend, die meisten Zimmer haben Terrasse oder Balkon, und es gibt dutzende von kleinen gemütlichen Winkeln, wo man sich mit einem Buch zurückziehen und die Aussicht bewundern kann. Der Speisesaal bietet exzellente Küche, und einheimische und internationale Gerichte werden je nach individuellem Geschmack oder nach speziellen Bedürfnissen zubereitet.

Our inspector loved: *The 360° views from the peaceful hilltop.*

Directions: Málaga - Cadiz road > exit Churriana and Cartana > Casarabonela > follow signs to hotel.

Web: www.johansens.com/laera
E-mail: info@hotellaera.es
Tel: +34 952 1125 25
Fax: +34 952 1120 09

Price Guide: (excluding VAT)
single €87
double €105-120
junior suite €135

Hotel Palacio de Los Granados

EMILIO CASTELAR 42, 41400 ÉCIJA (SEVILLA), SPAIN

This stylish little "palacio" has recently been lovingly and painstakingly restored by its owners, who fell in love with the building and the town it lies in. Seville is steeped in history, and the hotel retains a distinctly Moorish character. Lofty cloisters lead to elegant and stylish rooms, and a delightful garden with wooden galleries and pretty fountain. The welcome is as warm and attentive as the restoration project itself; a real little gem.

Cet élégant petit "palacio" a récemment été rénové avec le plus grand soin par son propriétaire tombé amoureux du bâtiment et de la ville. Séville est imprégnée d'histoire et l'hôtel garde distinctement un caractère mauresque. Les cloîtres élevés mènent aux chambres élégantes et à un charmant jardin avec des galeries en bois et une jolie fontaine. L'accueil est aussi chaleureux et attentif que la restauration elle-même. Un véritable petit bijou.

Dieses stilvolle kleine "Palacio" wurde kürzlich liebevoll von seinem Eigentümer restauriert, der sich in das Gebäude und die faszinierende, geschichtsträchtige Stadt, in der es sich befindet, verliebt hatte. Das Hotel besitzt immer noch seinen deutlich maurischen Charakter. Erhabene Kreuzgänge führen zu eleganten, edlen Zimmern und einem herrlichen Garten mit hölzernen Galerien und einem hübschen Springbrunnen. Der Gast wird hier mit der gleichen Aufmerksamkeit empfangen wie sie der Restaurierung des Hauses zukam. Ein wahres kleines Juwel.

Our inspector loved: *The peaceful and colourful back garden with its orange trees, pomegranates and geraniums.*

Directions: Sevilla - Córdoba motorway > exit Écija > hotel is signposted.

Web: www.johansens.com/granados
E-mail: info@palaciogranados.com
Tel: +34 955 905 344
Fax: +34 955 901 412

Price Guide: (excluding VAT)
double €120-150
suite €160-190

GRAN HOTEL ELBA ESTEPONA & THALASSO SPA

URB. ARENA BEACH, CTRA. ESTEPONA-CÁDIZ 151, 29680 ESTEPONA, SPAIN

Directions: From Gibraltar > Cádiz - Málaga road > Málaga > Km 151. From Málaga > Málaga - Cádiz road > Cádiz > Km 151.

Web: www.johansens.com/elbaestepona
E-mail: elbaestepona@hoteleselba.com
Tel: +34 952 809 200
Fax: +34 952 793 957

Price Guide: (excluding VAT)
double (single occupancy) €140-250
double €230-370
suite €265-1,050

Situated on a private beach, this magnificent hotel offers spacious guest rooms with breathtaking sea views. The traditional décor is interspersed with modern elements and the use of wooden furnishings, bathrooms, terraces and parquet floors creates a warm, cosy ambience. Dining is an unforgettable experience. The 3 restaurants, and 1 buffet restaurant for breakfast, offer a wide variety of gastronomic delights from traditional Spanish fare to exotic Asian cuisine. The largest thalasso spa in Andalucía, with over 60 treatments, is available and includes an ice room and log cabin sauna.

Situé sur une plage privée, cet hôtel offre de spacieux hébergements avec des vues sur la mer. Le décor traditionnel est parsemé d'éléments modernes et le présence de bois dans les salles de bains, sur le mobilier, les terrasses et les parquets crée une atmosphère chaleureuse. La table est superbe : 3 restaurants, plus 1 pour les buffets du petit-déjeuner, proposent un large choix de délices gastronomiques, de la cuisine traditionnelle espagnole aux saveurs exotiques asiatiques. Le plus grand Spa thalasso d'Andalucie a plus de 60 soins disponibles dont une cabine de glace et un sauna.

Dieses an einem Privatstrand gelegene Hotel bietet großzügige Zimmer und atemberaubende Blicke aufs Meer. Das traditionelle Décor wechselt sich mit modernen Details ab, und die Verwendung von Holz bei Mobiliar, Badezimmern, Terrassen und Parkettboden schafft eine gemütliche Atmosphäre. Die Küche ist hervorragend: In 3 Restaurants und einem für Frühstücksbüffets wird eine große kulinarische Auswahl serviert, von traditionell spanischen bis hin zu asiatischen Gerichten. Im größten Thalasso-Spa Andalusiens werden über 60 Thalasso-Behandlungen, ein Eisraum und eine Sauna angeboten.

Our inspector loved: *The fabulous spa.*

Hotel Casa Morisca

CUESTA DE LA VICTORIA 9, 18010 GRANADA, SPAIN

Situated in the historic "Albayzin" quarter with view of the Alhambra, this stunning, recently restored Moorish palace offers guests a true feel of this ancient city. The décor includes original features such as a beautiful Moorish brick façade, carved wooden ceilings dating from the 15th century, marble columns and old ceramic tiles. An interior courtyard with a skylight and fountains is surrounded by a 2-floor gallery, giving access to the 14 individually decorated bedrooms, some of which offer hydromassage baths.

Situé dans le quartier historique "Albayzin" avec vue de l'Alhambra, ce palais maure magnifique, récemment remis à neuf, offre une excellente impression de cette ville ancienne. Le décor comprend des caractéristiques originelles, telles que la façade en brique, des plafonds sculptés en bois datant du XVe siècle, des colonnes en marbre et des vieux carreaux en céramique. Une cour intérieure avec une lucarne et des fontaines est entourée par des galeries sur 2 niveaux, qui mènent aux 14 chambres décorées de façon individuelle, quelques-unes offrent des bains hydro-massage.

Dieses wundervolle Hotel im historischen Albayzin-Viertel mit Blick auf die Alhambra wurde kürzlich restauriert und bietet seinen Gästen ein authentisches Stück Granada. Ursprüngliche Merkmale wie die maurische Fassade, geschnitzte Holzdecken aus dem 15. Jahrhundert, Marmorsäulen und alte Keramikfliesen sind erhalten. Ein Innenhof mit Deckenlicht und Springbrunnen ist von einer 2-stöckigen Gallerie umgeben, von der man zu den 14 unterschiedlichen Zimmern gelangt, einige mit Hydromassagebad.

***Our inspector loved:** The breathtaking views of the Alhambra from room 15 and the magnificent carved wooden ceiling in room 8.*

Directions: Near the Alhambra in the town centre. The nearest airport is Málaga.

Web: www.johansens.com/morisca
E-mail: info@hotelcasamorisca.com
Tel: +34 958 221 100
Fax: +34 958 215 796

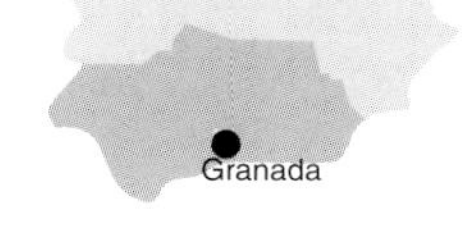

Price Guide: (room only, excluding VAT)
single €91.20-115.20
double €114-171
junior suite €196

SPAIN / ANDALUCÍA (GRANADA)

Hotel La Bobadilla

A member of The Leading Small Hotels of the World

FINCA LA BOBADILLA, APTO 144, 18300 LOJA, GRANADA, SPAIN

Directions: A92 Granada–Seville road > exit 175 Salinas.

Web: www.johansens.com/bobadilla
E-mail: info@la-bobadilla.com
Tel: +34 958 32 18 61
Fax: +34 958 32 18 10

Price Guide: (excluding VAT)
single €244–300
double/twin €264–320
suites €342–978

This hotel is a beautiful replica of an Andalucían village and a delight from the columned entrance hall to the enormous pool and the award-winning restaurant. The pretty bedrooms are spacious with sitting areas and decorated with typical local wood carved furniture; most have their own private terraces. The public areas have the atmosphere and décor of an Andalucían country manor. Guests can play tennis, go horse riding, (the hotel has its own stables with 6 horses) venture out in a beach buggy or bicycle or enjoy one of the hotel's falconry displays.

Cet hôtel est une réplique d'un village andalou où tout est un régal pour les sens, du hall à colonnes au restaurant primé en passant par l'immense piscine. Les jolies chambres spacieuses sont dotées d'un coin séjour et décorées de meubles en bois sculpté typiques de la région. La plupart d'entre elles disposent d'une terrasse privée. Les salles communes se distinguent par une atmosphère et un décor dignes d'un manoir andalou. Les visiteurs pourront jouer au tennis, faire de l'équitation – l'hôtel a 6 chevaux – et découvrir les environs en buggy ou à vélo, ou visiter une exposition de fauconnerie.

Diese Nachbildung eines andalusischen Dorfes ist zauberhaft, angefangen bei der Eingangshalle bis hin zum herrlich großen Swimmingpool und dem preisgekrönten Restaurant. Die hübschen Zimmer sind geräumig, haben Sitzecken und sind mit ortstypischen geschnitzten Holzmöbeln eingerichtet. Die meisten haben eine eigene Terrasse. Ambiente und Décor sind das eines andalusischen Landhauses. Zahlreiche Freizeit-möglichkeiten umfassen Tennis, Reiten – das Hotel besitzt 6 Pferde – und Ausflüge im Beach-Buggy oder mit dem Fahrrad, und Besuche der hoteleigenen Falknerei.

Our inspector loved: *The breathtaking reception hall, reminiscent of Andalucía's rich Moorish heritage.*

Hotel Palacio de Santa Inés

CUESTA DE SANTA INÉS 9, 18010 GRANADA, SPAIN

This restored 16th-century palace is located in a prime position from which to explore the magnificent sights of historic Granada. The impressive courtyard, with its fountain and magnificent paintings, leads guests into rooms decorated with a timeless elegance featuring original antique and contemporary furnishings. Some of the guest rooms look out to the Alhambra, and 3 conference rooms are available. Within walking distance of historical sites and convents, there are also bracing alpine walks in the surrounding Sierra Nevada to enjoy.

Ce palace restauré du XVIe siècle possède un emplacement unique pour explorer les magnifiques sites historiques de Grenade. De l'impressionnante cour intérieure avec sa fontaine et ses tableaux, les hôtes accèdent aux chambres à l'élégance intemporelle remplies d'antiquités et de meubles contemporains. Certaines des chambres ont vues sur l'Alhambra et 3 salles de conférences sont disponibles. Proches de sites historiques et de couvents à visiter, les hôtes peuvent également profiter des promenades vivifiantes dans la Sierra Nevada environnante.

Dieser restaurierte Palast aus dem 16. Jahrhundert ist ideal in unmittelbarer Nähe der vielen Sehenswürdigkeiten von Granada gelegen. Vom eindrucksvollen Innenhof mit seinem Springbrunnen und herrlichen Gemälden gelangt man in zeitlos elegant gestaltete Zimmer, die mit ursprünglichen antiken und zeitgenössischen Stücken eingerichtet sind. Einige Zimmer blicken auf die Alhambra, und 3 Räume stehen für Konferenzen zur Verfügung. Zahlreiche historische Stätten und Klöster liegen in unmittelbarer Nähe, außerdem bietet die Sierra Nevada hervorragende Wandermöglichkeiten.

Our inspector loved: *The treasure trove of monuments nearby.*

Directions: Located in the heart of Granada, 1 hour from Málaga Airport.

Web: www.johansens.com/sanaines
E-mail: sinespal@teleline.es
Tel: +34 958 22 23 62
Fax: +34 958 22 24 65

Barcelona
Madrid
Granada

Price Guide: (room only, excluding VAT)
single €80
double €105-155
suite €240

El Molino de Santillán

CTRA DE MACHARAVIAYA, KM 3, 29730 RINCÓN DE LA VICTORIA, MÁLAGA, SPAIN

Tucked away in its own large tract of hills, this Andalucían farmhouse is a rare gem. Each individually designed, rustic-styled bedrooms has a terrace and views over the manicured grounds. New bedrooms feature colour washed walls and CD players; the tower suite is exquisite. The sea is 5km away and can be glimpsed during a stroll down the delightful country paths. Granada, Seville, Córdoba and Málaga, with its airport, are within easy driving distance. Activities such as golf and horse riding can be arranged. 2 large conservatories can be used as meeting space.

Nichée au creux de ses propres collines, cette ferme andalouse est une vraie merveille. Chacune des chambres décorées de façon individuelle dispose d'une terrasse et jouit d'une vue sur le parc. Des nouvelles chambres ont des murs badigeonnés en couleur et des lecteurs CD, et la suite dans la tour est superbe. Une promenade de 5 km permet de rejoindre la mer, qui s'entrevoit tout au long de la descente par les chemins. Grenade, Séville, Cordoue et Málaga et l'aéroport ne sont pas loin et des activités comme le golf et l'équitation peuvent être organisées. 2 grands jardins d'hiver servent de salles de conférences.

Dieses andalusische Bauernhaus versteckt sich inmitten von Hügellandschaft und ist ein wahres Juwel. Jedes der ländlich individuell gestalteten Zimmer hat seine eigene Terrasse mit Blick auf den makellosen Rasen. Die neuen, bunt getünchten Zimmer bieten CD-Player, und die Turmsuite ist ein Traum. Das 5km entfernte Meer kann man auf einem Spaziergang erspähen, und Granada, Sevilla, Cordoba und Málaga und der Flughafen sind schnell zu erreichen. Aktivitäten wie Golf und Reiten können arrangiert werden. 2 große Wintergärten dienen auch als Konferenzräume.

Directions: Málaga – Almería road > exit No 258 Macharaviaya > hotel is signposted.

Web: www.johansens.com/molinodesantillan
E-mail: reservas@molinodesantillan.es
Tel: +34 952 40 09 49
Fax: +34 952 40 09 50

Price Guide: (breakfast €9, excluding VAT)
single €67.90–88.90
double €89.90–137.90
suites €141.90–257.90

Our inspector loved: *Its location: so close yet so far from the pace of the Costa.*

La Posada del Torcal

29230 VILLANUEVA DE LA CONCEPCIÓN, MÁLAGA, SPAIN

This idyllic Andalucían cortijo, 2001 recipient of Condé Nast Johansens Most Excellent Country Hotel award, is situated on a hilltop estate overlooking the El Torcal National Park. The 10 spacious and individually decorated rooms feature fine antiques and ceramics. Innovative Spanish and international cuisine is served in the winter dining room or the terrace restaurant. For leisure, there is tennis, horse riding, a heated swimming pool and spa facilities. Córdoba, Ronda, Granada and Seville are all nearby. Helicopter transfers from Málaga Airport can be arranged.

Ce charmant cortijo andalou, qui a reçu le prix Condé Nast Johansens de Plus Excellent Hôtel de Campagne en 2001, est situé au sommet d'une colline dominant le parc national El Torcal. Les 10 chambres spacieuses et décorées de manière individuelle sont parées de meubles anciens et de céramiques. Une cuisine espagnole et internationale est servie dans la salle à manger ou sur la fabuleuse terrasse. Les activités incluent tennis, équitation et il y a une piscine chauffée et un spa. Cordoue, Ronda, Grenade et Séville ne sont pas loin. Héliportage de l'aéroport de Málaga est possible.

Dieses idyllische andalusische Cortijo, Gewinner der Condé Nast Johansens Auzeichnung Bestes Landhotel 2001, liegt auf einer Anhöhe mit Blick auf den El Torcal Nationalpark. Die 10 geräumigen, individuell gestalteten Zimmer sind mit feinen Antiquitäten und Keramikarbeiten geschmückt. Innovative spanische und internationale Küche wird im Winterspeisesaal oder im sensationellen Terrassenrestaurant serviert. Das Freizeitangebot umfaßt Tennis, Reiten, beheizten Swimmingpool und Spa. Córdoba, Ronda, Granada und Sevilla sind schnell zu erreichen. Hubschraubertransfer vom Flughafen Málaga kann organisiert werden.

Our inspector loved: *The relaxing ambience, excellent service and great views.*

Directions: From Málaga, A45 > Antequera > exit 148 > Casabermeja > Villanueva de la Concepción towards La Jolla > the hotel is located before La Jolla and is signposted.

Web: www.johansens.com/posadadeltorcal
E-mail: hotel@eltorcal.com
Tel: +34 952 03 11 77
or +34 69 94 34 385
Fax: +34 952 03 10 06

Price Guide: (excluding VAT)
double/twin €125-180
suite €260

GRAN HOTEL GUADALPIN

BLVD PRÍNCIPE ALFONSO DE HOHELOHE, S/N 29600 MARBELLA, MÁLAGA, SPAIN

Directions: From Málaga: Málaga - Cadiz motorway. From Gibraltar: National Road 340 towards Málaga > Km 179.

Web: www.johansens.com/guadalpin
E-mail: info@granhotelguadalpin.com
Tel: +34 952 899 400
Fax: +34 952 899 401

Price Guide: (breakfast €20, excluding VAT)
double (single occupancy) €120-240
double €150-300
suite €200-400

Excellence, exclusivity, luxury. This sums up the 5-star Gran Hotel Guadalpin, a prestigious leisure and business retreat surrounded by a beautiful tropical garden on the main boulevard in Marbella, 200m from the beach and 500m from the city centre. It has ambience, superb décor, 127 spacious bedrooms and suites fitted with every comfort, including kitchenettes. Some have a Jacuzzi, all have a balcony or terrace, most have sea views. Award-winning cuisine is served in 3 restaurants, and there is an excellent fitness centre and spa.

Excellence, exclusivité, luxe au Gran Hotel Guadalpin. Cela résume les qualités de cet hôtel 5 étoiles, une retraite de loisirs et d'affaires prestigieuse entouré d'un beau jardin tropical sur le boulevard principal de Marbella, à 200 m des plages et 500 m du centre-ville. Il bénéficie d'une ambiance, d'un décor superbe, de 127 chambres et suites spacieuses avec tout le confort, y compris des petites cuisines. Certaines ont des jacuzzis, toutes un balcon ou terrasse et la plupart ont vue sur la mer. Une cuisine primée est servie dans les 3 restaurants, et il existe un excellent centre de remise en forme et bains.

Exklusivität und Luxus erster Klasse zeichnen dieses 5-Sterne-Hotel aus, ein prestigereiches, von einem herrlichen tropischen Garten umgebenes Urlaubs- und Businessresort am Hauptboulevard in Marbella, 200m vom Strand und 500m vom Stadtzentrum entfernt. Atmosphäre und edles Décor zeichnen die 127 geräumigen Zimmer und Suiten aus, die mit jeglichem Komfort inklusive Kochnischen ausgestattet sind. Einige haben Jacuzzi, alle bieten Balkon oder Terrasse, meist mit Meerblick. 3 Restaurants servieren preisgekrönte Küche, und es gibt ein hervorragendes Fitnesszentrum und Spa.

***Our inspector loved:** Relaxing in the Jacuzzi on the terrace of the bedroom whilst enjoying a drink and gazing at the Mediterranean.*

Hotel Los Monteros

CTRA CADIZ, KM 187, 29600 MARBELLA, SPAIN

Designed in the style of an Andalucían Pavilion, Los Monteros is spacious, light and airy. The hotel's communal areas open out onto gorgeous gardens bursting with colourful flowers, mature sub-tropical plants and tall shady trees. Cool colours contrast with bold prints in the ample-sized bedrooms, which all have balconies. Fresh seafood is a treat and the beach club is an idyllic place to have a drink under the stars on a perfect evening. There are many excellent golf courses nearby.

Créé dans le style de pavillons andalous, Los Monteros est un hôtel spacieux et clair. Les parties communes s'ouvrent sur de magnifiques jardins d'où jaillissent des fleurs de toutes les couleurs, des plantes sub-tropicales et de grands arbres. Les couleurs froides contrastent avec les imprimés vifs des vastes chambres, qui possèdent toutes un balcon. Les poissons frais sont un vrai délice et le beach-club est l'endroit idéal pour boire un verre sous les étoiles. Il y a beaucoup d'excellents parcours de golf à proximité.

Das im Stil eines andalusischen Pavillon gestaltete Los Monteros ist ein großräumiges, helles und luftiges Hotel. Von den Aufenthaltsräumen gelangt man in herrlichste Gärten, die mit bunten Blumen, subtropischen Pflanzen und hohen, schattenspendenden Bäumen gefüllt sind. Kühle Farben kontrastieren mit auffallenden Mustern in den großen Zimmern, die alle einen Balkon haben. Frischer Fisch und Meeresfrüchte sind ein Hochgenuss, und der Beachclub ist der ideale Ort für einen Drink unter freiem Himmel. Zahlreiche hervorragende Golfplätze liegen in nächster Nähe.

***Our inspector loved:** The fabulous beach club: La Bâbane.*

Directions: Málaga > Málaga - Cadiz road > Km 187 > the hotel is signposted.

Web: www.johansens.com/monteros
E-mail: hotel@monteros.com
Tel: +34 952 771 700
Fax: +34 952 825 846

Price Guide: (per person, room only, excluding VAT)
double superior €40-153
junior suite €52-226
(per room, room only, excluding VAT)
suite €368-1,400

Vasari Vacation Resort

URB. LA ALZAMBRA, EDIF. VASARI CENTER, 29660 MARBELLA, MÁLAGA, SPAIN

This stylish resort is perfect for a luxurious family holiday or short break. Large, well-tended gardens have lush foliage, palm trees and plenty of shade to escape the hot sun. The gorgeous Mediterranean-style serviced apartments each have open terraces and are tastefully decorated with cool relaxing shades and quality furnishings. The poolside bar offers a varied selection of drinks. A friendly and relaxed atmosphere can be found in the restaurant, which serves international and Italian cuisine as well as an excellent wine list from the hotel's well-stocked cellar.

Cet élégant resort est l'endroit idéal pour de luxueuses vacances en famille ou un court séjour. Les grands jardins bien entretenus, sont remplis de plantes luxuriantes, de palmiers et d'endroits ombragés. Les superbes appartements de style méditerranéen ont des terrasses ouvertes, sont avec service et décorés avec goût dans des tons relaxants et avec un mobilier de qualité. Le bar près de la piscine offre une grande sélection de boissons, et le restaurant a une ambiance amicable et détendue et sert des plats internationaux et italiens ainsi qu'un excellent choix de vins de la cave bien approvisionné de l'hôtel.

Dieses elegante Resort ist ideal für einen Familienurlaub oder Kurztrip. Die großen, gepflegten Gärten sind üppig mit schattenspendenden Palmen bepflanzt. Fantastische Appartements im mediterranen Stil bieten Hotelservice, haben eigene Terrassen und sind geschmackvoll in kühlen Farben gehalten und mit hochqualitativen Möbeln eingerichtet. An der Bar am Pool kann man einen Drink zu sich nehmen, und im freundlichen, legeren Restaurant wird internationale und italienische Küche und hervorragende Weine aus dem gutbestückten Weinkeller serviert.

Our inspector loved: *The space and privacy with every convenience of a hotel.*

Directions: Málaga motorway towards Cádiz > exit Marbella > go through town > Puerto Banus > Urb. Alzambra > Vasari Resort.

Web: www.johansens.com/vasari
E-mail: reservas@vasariresort.com
Tel: +34 952 907 806
Fax: +34 952 906 798

Price Guide: (excluding VAT, breakfast included)
apartment for 1 or 2 persons €135-260
apartment for 4 persons €180-400
apartment for 6 persons €280-525

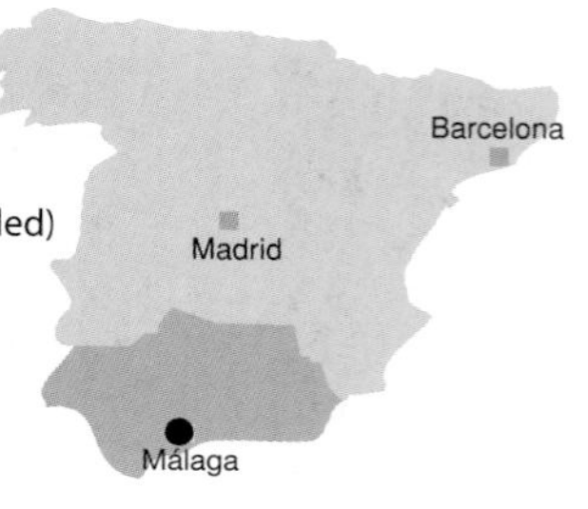

Hotel Byblos Andaluz

MIJAS GOLF, 29650 MIJAS~COSTA, MÁLAGA, SPAIN

This luxurious property offers glorious views over the surrounding mountains, gardens and golf courses. The comfortable, sybaritic bedrooms have excellent en-suite facilities. There are 2 delightful restaurants, El Byblos Andaluz, with its Sevillian courtyard, and the sophisticated Le Nailhac. The Louison Bobet Institute of Thalassotherapy together with La Prairie Beauty Centre cover a 2,500m spa area, the ideal place for relaxing, pampering and enjoying treatments.

Cette propriété luxueuse offre des vues imprenables sur les montagnes environnantes, les jardins et le terrain de golf. Les chambres confortables et sybarites ont de magnifiques salles de bains. L'hôtel a 2 délicieux restaurants, El Byblos Andaluz, avec sa cour sévillane et Le Nailhac plus sophistiqué. L'Institut Louison Bobet de Thalassothérapie et le centre de beauté « La Prairie » occupent une superficie de 2 500m, un endroit idéal pour des soins de relaxation et de beauté.

Dieses luxuriöse Anwesen trumpft mit traumhaften Blicken auf die umliegenden Berge, Parks und Golfplätze. Die gemütlichen Zimmer haben hervorragende En-suite-Annehmlichkeiten. Es gibt 2 exzellente Restaurants: El Byblos Andaluz mit seiner Sevillianer Innenhof, und das erlesene Le Nailhac. Das Louison Bobet Institut für Thalassotherapie und das La Prairie Beauty-Zentrum nehmen eine Fläche von 2.500m ein und bieten ein volles Entspannungs- und Verwöhnprogramm.

Our inspector loved: *The open spaces inside the hotel and the relaxing scenery.*

Directions: Málaga–Cádiz motorway > exit Fuengirola-Coin > follow signs.

Web: www.johansens.com/byblosandaluz
E-mail: comerical@byblos-andaluz.com
Tel: +34 952 47 30 50
Fax: +34 952 58 63 27

Barcelona
Madrid
Málaga

Price Guide: (excluding VAT)
mini suite (single occupancy) €215–280
mini suite €270
suite €475–1,280

Palacio Marqués de la Gomera

C/ San Pedro 20, 41640 Osuna, Seville, Spain

Set in a street full of wonderful old aristocratic houses, the façade of the Palace is one of the best examples of 18th-century Baroque architecture. Walking into its typical Andalucían central courtyard is like stepping back in time. Behind graceful colonnade arches lie public rooms filled with antiques and paintings and bedrooms all with their own special atmosphere and features, from wooden beams to stone walls, French windows and the classic Suite 7 as used in Zeffirelli's film "Callas Forever".

Situé dans une rue pleine de vieilles maisons aristocratiques, la façade du Palace est l'un des meilleurs exemples du Baroque XVIIIe siècle et entrer dans sa cour intérieure typiquement andalouse est un saut dans le passé. Derrière de belles arches à colonnades, se tiennent des pièces communes emplies d'antiquités et de particularités, des poutres en bois aux murs de pierre, portes-fenêtres et au Suite 7 classique comme celui du film de Zefferelli "Callas Forever".

Dieses Palacio, dessen Fassade eines der besten Beispiele für weltlichen Barock des 18. Jahrhunderts ist, liegt in einer Straße mit herrlichen alten Adelshäusern, und wenn man den typisch andalusischen Innenhof betritt, fühlt man sich sofort in die Vergangenheit zurückversetzt. Hinter dem eleganten Säulengang liegen mit Antiquitäten und Malereien geschmückte Aufenthaltsräume und Zimmer mit ihrer ganz eigenen Atmosphäre und Einrichtung aus Holzbalken, Steinwänden, großen Glastüren und dem klassischen Suite 7, wie man ihn aus Zeffirellis Film „Callas Forever" kennt.

Our inspector loved: *The unique charm of each bedroom that makes one feel like staying in a different one each night.*

Directions: From Seville > A92 to Osuna. From Málaga > Granada > Antequera > A92 to Osuna.

Web: www.johansens.com/palaciomarquesdelagomera
E-mail: info@hotelpalaciodelmarques.com
Tel: +34 95 4 81 22 23
Fax: +34 95 4 81 02 00

Price Guide: (room only, excluding VAT)
double (single occupancy) €68-95
standard double €88-125
upper-class double €108-150
suite €156-210

NH Almenara Golf Hotel & Spa

A-7 (NATIONAL ROAD), 11310 SOTOGRANDE, SPAIN

With stunning views over the countryside to the distant Mediterranean, this hotel is surrounded by 5 of Europe's finest golf courses. Bedrooms are tastefully furnished and fitted to the highest standard. Guests can choose from 2 restaurants: the Gaia, Mediterranean cuisine and the more casual Vein Tee Ocho. La Cabaña, Café del Mar and Tratoria are open during the summer. Keep fit in the impressive health club, with heated pool, laze around the spectacular outdoor pool or play golf on the hotel's 27-hole or new 18-hole golf course, La Reserva. 3 meeting rooms and 2 marquees are available.

Ce magnifique hôtel avec ses vues sur le paysage éloigné de la Méditerranée est entouré par 5 des plus prestigieux parcours de golf d,Europe. Les chambres sont meublées avec goût et pourvues des meilleurs équipements. Il y a 2 restaurants: le Gaia (cuisine méditerranéenne) et le Vein Tee Ocho plus décontracté. La Cabaña, Café del Mar et Tratoria sont ouverts en été. Les hôtes peuvent visiter le centre de remise en forme, lézarder autour de la superbe piscine, ou jouer au golf sur le parcours à 27 trous ou le nouveau parcours à 18 trous, La Reserva. Il y a 3 salles de réunions et 2 grandes tentes.

Dieses superbe Hotel mit Sicht auf das ferne Mittelmeer ist von 5 der besten Golfplätze Europas umgeben. Die Zimmer sind geschmackvoll und nach höchstem Standard eingerichtet. Für kulinarischen Genuss sorgen das Gaia (Mittelmeerküche) und das weniger formelle Café Vein Tee Ocho. La Cabaña, Café del Mar und Tratoria sind im Sommer geöffnet. Für sportliche Aktivitäten stehen ein Fitnesszentrum mit beheiztem Pool, ein Freibad und der hoteleigene 27-Loch- oder der neue 18-Loch-Golfplatz, La Reserva, zur Verfügung. 3 Konferenzräume und 2 Festzelte sind vorhanden.

Our inspector loved: *The outdoor aspect in this lovely natural setting.*

Directions: Málaga to Cádiz coast road E15 > exit 130.

Web: www.johansens.com/almenara
E-mail: nhalmenara@nh-hotels.com
Tel: + 34 956 58 20 00
Fax: +34 956 58 20 01

Barcelona
Madrid
Málaga

Price Guide: (breakfast €18, excluding VAT)
single €154–208
double/twin €159–228
suite €234–532

          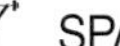   

Cortijo el Aguilon

CN 340, KM 68.3, FACINAS, 11391 TARIFA (CADIZ), SPAIN

Directions: Gibralter and Málaga motorway (CN340) towards Cádiz > pass Tarifa > km 68.3 > signposted.

Web: www.johansens.com/aguilon
E-mail: info@elaguilon.com
Tel: +34 637 424 251
Fax: +34 956 687 215

Price Guide:
double €200-300
suite €300

Just 5 minutes from the beach, bordering onto a Natural Park and surrounded by cork forests and rolling hills, this delightful property was originally built as a family home and offers only 6 charming bedrooms in a peaceful, secluded setting. Guests can lie by the pool in the shade of the orange grove, and a Turkish bath and further small pool are available for pampering. For active guests, there is windsurfing, and the hotel has its own tennis court and stable with 5 horses. Trips to Morocco can be arranged, and many interesting places are within easy reach.

A 5 minutes de la plage, à la limite d'un parc naturel et entouré par des forêts de liège et de nombreuses collines, cette charmante propriété fut à l'origine construite en maison de famille et n'offre que 6 chambres dans un cadre tranquille et retiré. Les clients peuvent se reposer près de la piscine à l'ombre de l'orangeraie. Un bain turc et un plus petit bassin sont à la disposition des clients. Pour les plus actifs, il y a de la planche à voile et l'hôtel à son propre terrain de tennis et écuries avec 5 chevaux. Des excursions au Maroc peuvent être organisées et de nombreux sites sont à proximité.

Nur 5 Minuten vom Strand entfernt, am Rande eines Naturparks und umgeben von Korkwäldern und sanften Hügeln befindet sich dieses zauberhafte, herrlich abgeschiedene, ursprünglich als Familienhaus erbaute Hotel mit nur 6 Zimmern. Man kann sich am Pool im Schatten von Orangenbäumen entspannen oder das Dampfbad und den kleinen Pool besuchen. Aktive Gäste können windsurfen, auf dem hoteleigenen Platz Tennis spielen und reiten – das Hotel hat 5 Pferde. Trips nach Marokko und zu den vielen interessanten Orten in der Umgebung werden arrangiert.

Our inspector loved: *Feeling like a welcome guest in a stylish Spanish country home.*

Cerro de Hijar Hotel

S/N - 29109 TOLOX, MÁLAGA, SPAIN

This delightful little hotel has the most stunning location, perched high on a mountain inside the Sierra de las Nieves Nature Reserve and looking down over the ancient thermal spa town of Tolox. Typically Andalucían in style, the hotel is charmingly decorated with a careful balance of rustic, Moorish features and modern-day luxuries, with many plants decorating the terraces and patio. A former chef, one of the owners prepares food for the dining room and is rapidly chasing his first Michelin star!

Ce charmant petit hôtel possède le plus bel emplacement : haut perché sur une montagne au cœur de la Réserve Naturelle de la Sierra de las Nieves et donnant sur l'ancienne ville thermale de Tolox. Typiquement andalou dans son style, l'hôtel est décoré de façon charmante avec un juste équilibre entre les éléments rustiques Mauresque et les équipements modernes. De nombreuses plantes décorent les terrasses et patios. Autrefois chef, le propriétaire prépare les repas et court après sa première étoile Michelin !

Dieses zauberhafte kleine Hotel ist fantastisch gelegen, hoch auf einem Berg im Sierra de la Nieves Naturreservat mit Blick auf die alte Kurstadt Tolox. Das typisch andalusische Hotel bietet eine hübsche und sorgfältig ausgewogene Mischung aus rustikalen maurischen Details und modernem Luxus, mit zahlreichen Pflanzen auf allen Terrassen. Einer der Besitzer ist ein Koch und kreiert die köstlichen Speisen, die ihm wohl bald seinen ersten Michelinstern einbringen werden.

Our inspector loved: *The sound of silence and the clouds below.*

Directions: Málaga - Coin road > Tolox > Balneario > follow signs "H" up the mountain.

Web: www.johansens.com/cerrodehija
E-mail: cerro@cerrodehijar.com
Tel: +34 952 11 21 11
Fax: +34 952 11 97

Price Guide: (room only, excluding VAT)
single €59-71
double €66-79
junior suite €79-92
suite €92-101

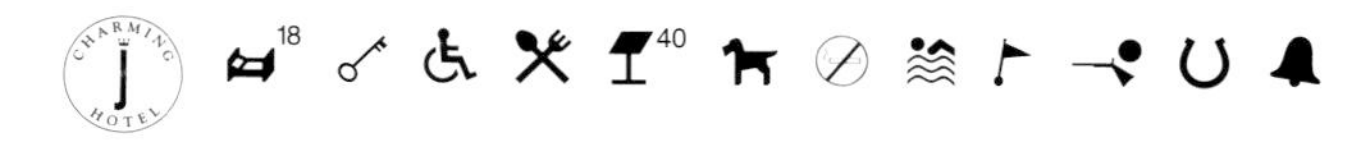

PALACIO DE LA RAMBLA

PLAZA DEL MARQUÉS 1, 23400 ÚBEDA, JAÉN, SPAIN

In the heart of the peaceful city of Úbeda stands this exclusive 16th-century palace, within walking distance of many local monuments and sights. Built in 1575, many original features remain and the air of relaxation is ensured by the friendly and attentive staff. Beyond the courtyard, with its archways and ivy-clad walls, special touches such as displays of fresh flowers pervade the palace, making this a unique place to stay. With only 8 bedrooms, a quiet, tranquil experience is guaranteed.

Au cœur de la paisible ville d'Ubeda, à quelques pas des nombreux sites et monuments locaux se dresse cet unique palace du 16ème siècle. Construit en 1575, de nombreuses caractéristiques subsistent et l'atmosphère reposante est renforcée par le personnel amical et attentif. Au delà de la cour, avec ses voûtes et ses murs couverts de lierre, des attentions particulières telles que la présence de fleurs fraîches se répandent dans le palace, en faisant ainsi un lieu de séjour unique. Avec seulement 8 chambres, calme et tranquillité sont garantis.

Dieses exklusive Palais aus dem 16. Jahrhundert liegt mitten im ruhigen Zentrum von Úbeda, nur ein paar Minuten von den zahlreichen Sehenswürdigkeiten der Stadt entfernt. Das 1575 erbaute Haus konnte viel von seinem ursprünglichen Charakter behalten, und das freundliche, aufmerksame Personal sorgt für Entspannung pur. Vom Innenhof mit seinen Torbögen und efeubewachsenen Wänden gelangt man ins Innere, wo kleine Extras wie frische Blumen das Haus in einen einzigartigen Ort verwandeln. Mit nur 8 Gästezimmern ist Erholung und Ruhe garantiert.

Our inspector loved: *This Renaissance palace, that exudes period charm with antique furnishings and a four poster bed.*

Directions: Málaga - Granada > motorway to Jaén > A316 toward Úbeda.

Web: www.johansens.com/rambla
E-mail: palaciorambla@terra.es
Tel: +34 953 75 01 96
Fax: +34 953 75 02 67

Price Guide:
single €72
double €100
suite €112

La Torre del Visco

44587 FUENTESPALDA, TERUEL, SPAIN

This beautiful, romantic 15th-century estate house has been superbly restored and is surrounded by lovely gardens and patios with fountains, at the end of a forest track in a remote river valley – the undiscovered "Spanish Provence". The Mediterranean cuisine, for which it is renowned, uses herbs and vegetables, olive oil and truffles from the 220-acre farm, and is complemented by wines from the well-stocked medieval wine cellar. British owners and Spanish staff create a friendly and peaceful atmosphere to be enjoyed all year round.

Ce beau domaine romantique et superbement restauré qui date du XVè siècle est entouré de beaux jardins et terrasses avec fontaines et situé au bout d'un chemin forestier dans une vallée écartée – la "Provence d'Espagne" non découverte. La cuisine méditerranéenne renommée emploie des herbes et légumes, huile d'olive et truffes de la ferme de 90 ha et elle est arrosée de vins de la cave médiévale bien fournie. Les propriétaires britanniques et le personnel espagnol offrent une ambiance accueillante et tranquille tout au long de l'année.

Dieses herrlich restaurierte, romantische Gutshaus aus dem 15. Jahrhundert ist umgeben von hübschen Gärten, Terrassen mit Springbrunnen und liegt am Ende eines Waldwegs in einem abgelegenen Flusstal – die unberührte "Spanische Provence". Die Mittelmeerküche, für die das Hotel berühmt ist, basiert auf Kräutern, Gemüse, Olivenöl und Trüffeln der eigenen 90ha Ländereien und wird von Weinen aus dem gutbestückten mittelalterlichen Keller abgerundet. Britische Besitzer und spanisches Personal schaffen das ganze Jahr über eine freundliche, friedliche Atmosphäre.

Our inspector loved: *The fresh flowers in the rooms and fresh food from the gardens and surrounding farms.*

Directions: The nearest airports are Valencia and Barcelona. From A7 > exit Reus > N420 - Calaceite > Valderrobres - Fuentespalda.

Zaragoza
Barcelona
Madrid
Málaga

Web: www.johansens.com/torredelvisco
E-mail: torredelvisco@torredelvisco.com
Tel: +34 978 76 90 15
Fax: +34 978 76 90 16

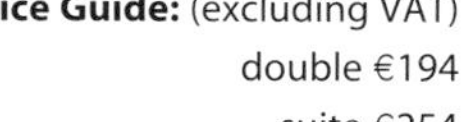

Price Guide: (excluding VAT)
double €194
suite €254

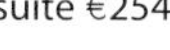

Palacio de Cutre

LA GOLETA S/N VILLAMAYOR, 33583 INFIESTO, ASTURIAS, SPAIN

Directions: Take the N634 Oviedo–Santander road > at Villamayor exit Borines > signposted.

Web: www.johansens.com/palaciodecutre
E-mail: hotel@palaciodecutre.com
Tel: +34 985 70 80 72
Fax: +34 985 70 80 19

Price Guide: (room only, excluding VAT)
single €78-85.60
double €108.07-145.52
suite €177.62-204.37

Built on a hill with incredible views of the surrounding mountains and farmland, this 16th-century farmhouse, with its own chapel, has been recently renovated and has a peaceful and friendly atmosphere. Great attention to detail, antique doll collections and small artefacts make every corner interesting. There is a delicious menu offering the region's seasonal specialities. Outdoor activities include canoeing, rafting, horse riding and hiking.

Construite sur une colline avec une vue imprenable sur les montagnes environnantes et les terres agricoles, cette ferme du XVIe siècle avec sa propre chapelle, a récemment été rénovée et bénéficie d'une atmosphère paisible et amicale. Une attention particulière au détail, des poupées antiques et de petits artefacts en rendent chaque recoin particulièrement intéressant. Un délicieux menu sert des spécialités régionales de saison. Pour activités de plein air, canoë, raft, randonne équestre et marche sont à disposition.

Auf einem Hügel mit herrlicher Sicht auf die umliegenden Berge und Felder liegt dieses kürzlich renovierte Bauernhaus aus dem 16. Jahrhundert mit seiner eigenen Kapelle. Die Atmosphäre ist ruhig und herzlich, und Liebe zum Detail, Sammlungen antiker Puppen und kleine Kunstgegenstände machen jeden Winkel interessant. Die verlockende Speisekarte bietet regionale Spezialitäten, die sich je nach Jahreszeit ändern. Aktivitäten sind z.B. Kanufahren, Rafting, Reiten und Wandern.

Our inspector loved: *The sumptuous fabrics in the newly decorated bedrooms.*

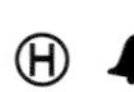

Atzaró Agroturismo

CTRA SAN JUAN, KM 15, 07840 SANTA EULALIA, IBIZA, BALEARIC ISLANDS

This century-old converted finca stands within exotic, tranquil gardens and a fragrant orange grove, surrounded by magnificent statues and fountains. The interior features Ibicencan, Arabic, Asian and African influences, with Arabic carpets and cushions, terracotta floors and rattan furniture. Each of the tastefully decorated bedrooms has a private terrace and bathroom decorated in colourful marble. International-Mediterranean cuisine is served in the refined and intimate restaurant; alternatively tapas may be enjoyed in the gardens.

Cette finca restaurée du siècle dernier, entourée de superbes statues et fontaines, se dresse au cœur de jardins exotiques et tranquilles et d'une orangeraie parfumée. La décoration à l'intérieur est d'influences arabe, africaine, asiatique et locale avec des tapis et des coussins arabes, des sols en terre cuite et des meubles en rotin. Chacune des chambres décorées avec goût possède sa propre terrasse et les salles de bains sont en marbre de couleur. Une cuisine d'inspiration internationale et méditerranéenne est servie dans le restaurant intime et raffiné et des tapas peuvent être dégustées dans le jardin.

Diese 100 Jahre alte umgebaute Finca liegt inmitten exotischer, ruhiger Gärten und eines duftigen Orangenhains und ist von herrlichen Statuen und Springbrunnen umgeben. Das Interieur spiegelt ein Kulturengemisch aus Ibiza, Arabien, Asien und Afrika wider und ist mit arabischen Teppichen, Terrakottaböden und Rattanmöbeln gefüllt. Jedes der geschmackvoll eingerichteten Zimmer hat eine eigene Terrasse und ein Marmorbad. International-mediterrane Küche wird im eleganten, gemütlichen Restaurant serviert, man kann aber auch im Garten Tapas genießen.

Our inspector loved: *The extensive Oriental gardens with pools, palms and art.*

Directions: Ibiza - San Joan de Labritja > hotel is then signposted.
Open all year.

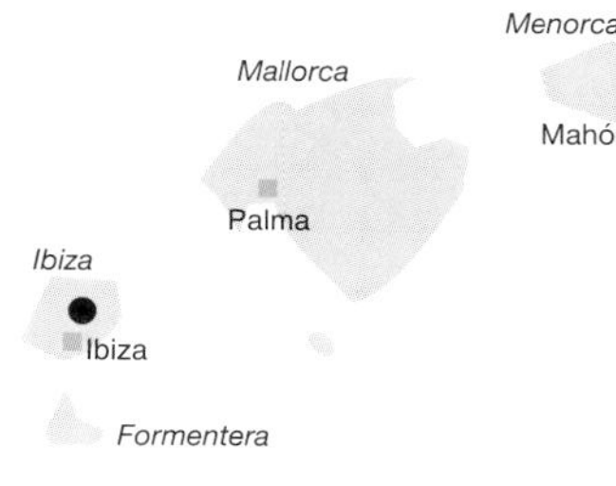

Web: www.johansens.com/atzaroagroturismo
E-mail: agroturismo@atzaro.com
Tel: +34 971 33 88 38
Fax: +34 971 33 16 50

Price Guide:
double €210-290
suite €250-330

SPAIN / BALEARIC ISLANDS (IBIZA)

Can Curreu

CTRA. SANT CARLES, KM 12, APDO. CORREOS 240, 07840 SANTA EULÀRIA, IBIZA, BALEARIC ISLANDS

Directions: Ibiza Airport > Santa Eulària > Sant Carles > hotel is on the left before the village.

Web: www.johansens.com/cancurreu
E-mail: hotel@cancurreu.com
Tel: +34 971 335 280
Fax: +34 971 335 280

Price Guide: (excluding VAT)
double €205-240
suite €275-370

Situated in the heart of the island, this charming residence is a truly exclusive retreat. Fresh fruit and flowers await guests in the beautifully appointed rooms, which are furnished with designer lamps and mirrors. All are individually housed and decorated providing total privacy; junior suites come complete with a kitchen area. Other facilities include Jacuzzi, television, hi-fi, telephone and fireplace. Can Curreu boasts many features for guests to enjoy such as a first-class restaurant, its own riding stables, a gymnasium and solarium, beautiful gardens and a boat for private excursions.

Situé au cœur de l'île, cette résidence de charme est un véritable havre de paix. Fruits et fleurs frais accueillent les clients dans les superbes chambres aux lampes et miroirs de designer. Toutes sont individuellement décorées et offrent une intimité totale. Les juniors suites possèdent toutes un coin cuisine. Les autres équipements comprennent jacuzzi, télévision, hi-fi, téléphone et cheminée. Can Curreu met également à la disposition de ses clients un restaurant de premier ordre, ses propres écuries, une salle de gym, un solarium, de superbes jardins et un bateau pour les excursions privées.

Dieses zauberhafte Hotel ist ein wahrhaft exklusives Versteck mitten auf der Insel. Frisches Obst und Blumen erwarten den Gast in den hübschen Zimmern, die mit Designerlampen und -spiegeln eingerichtet sind. Alle Zimmer sind individuell gestaltet und erlauben absolute Privatsphäre; die Junior-Suiten bieten eine Kochnische. Weitere Einrichtungen sind Jacuzzi, Fernseher, Hi-Fi und Kamin. Can Curreu bietet zahlreiche Attraktionen wie ein erstklassiges Restaurant, einen eigenen Reitstall, Fitnessraum und Solarium, herrliche Gärten und ein Boot für private Exkursionen.

Our inspector loved: *The feeling of privacy: no suite overlooks another.*

Can Lluc

CRTA. SANTA INÉS, KM 2, 07816 SAN RAFAEL, IBIZA, BALEARIC ISLANDS

Located in San Rafael, a valley in the heart of the island, Can Lluc perfectly captures the tranquillity and magic of rural Ibiza. Its main old farm building has retained sturdy stone walls and wooden beams, whilst skylights let in plenty of natural sunlight. Many of the bedrooms are housed in out-buildings, such as small houses with little terraces, and some feature fireplaces and hydromassage baths or showers. There is a restaurant service in summer, and nearby, guests can enjoy horse riding, rambling and cycling.

Situé à San Rafael, une vallée au cœur de l'île, Can Lluc représente parfaitement la tranquillité et la magie du véritable Ibiza. Ses anciens bâtiments fermiers ont gardé leurs robustes murs de pierre et poutres en bois tandis que les lucarnes au plafond laissent entrer un flot de lumière naturelle. La plupart des chambres sont situées dans des bâtiments extérieurs, sortes de petites maisons avec terrasses dont certaines offrent cheminées, bains ou douches à jets massant. L'été un service de restauration est disponible et à proximité les clients peuvent pratiquer de l'équitation, du vélo ou des randonnées.

Das in San Rafael, einem Tal mitten auf der Insel gelegene Can Lluc verkörpert perfekt die Ruhe und den Zauber des ländlichen Ibiza. Das alte Hauptgebäude hat immer noch seine robusten Steinwände und Holzbalken, und Dachfenster lassen die Sonne herein. Viele der Zimmer sind in Außengebäuden untergebracht, darunter kleine Häuschen mit Terrassen; einige bieten Kamine und Hydromassagebäder oder -duschen. Im Sommer gibt es ein Restaurant, und die Gäste können reiten, spazieren gehen oder Fahrrad fahren.

***Our inspector loved:** The warm, natural stone interiors punctuated by daylight from skylights and windows.*

Directions: Road to Santa Agnés > hotel is signposted.

Web: www.johansens.com/canlluc
E-mail: info@canlluc.com
Tel: +34 971 198 673
Fax: +34 971 198 547

Price Guide: (excluding VAT)
double €225-400

Cas Gasi

APDO. CORREOS 117, 07814 SANTA GERTRUDIS, IBIZA, BALEARIC ISLANDS

Directions: Ibiza Airport > Santa Eulalia > Santa Gertrudis > San Mateo > turning for San Antonio > hotel is on the right.

Web: www.johansens.com/casgasi
E-mail: info@casgasi.com
Tel: +34 971 197 700
Fax: +34 971 197 899

Price Guide: (excluding VAT)
double €204–276
suite €330–510

Set amidst pretty gardens, almond trees, orchards and olive groves, this former farmhouse has been completely renovated and extended to offer guests an exclusive stay in tranquil surroundings. The beautifully decorated bedrooms provide every modern comfort and are adorned with hand-painted tiles, terracotta floors and beamed ceilings. In the summer guests will enjoy the nightlife and beaches, and exploring the countryside on foot or by bicycle during the winter. The new spa features a Jacuzzi, sauna and fitness centre.

Au sein de charmants jardins, d'amandiers, de vergers et d'oliveraies, cet ancien corps de ferme a été complètement rénové et agrandi pour offrir à ses hôtes un séjour exclusif dans un environnement tranquille. Les chambres joliment décorées offrent tout le confort et sont ornées avec des carrelages peints à la main, des sols en terre cuite et des plafonds à poutres apparentes. En été, les hôtes peuvent profiter des plages et de la vie nocturne, alors qu'en hiver ils peuvent explorer la campagne à pied ou bicyclette. Le nouveau spa offre un jacuzzi, un sauna et un centre de remise en forme.

Inmitten von Gärten, Mandelbäumen, Obstgärten und Olivenhainen gelegen, bietet dieses einstige Bauernhaus, das komplett renoviert und erweitert wurde, einen exklusiven Aufenthalt in ruhiger Umgebung. Die hübschen Zimmer haben jeglichen modernen Komfort und sind mit handbemalten Fliesen, Terrakottaböden und Balkendecken geschmückt. Im Sommer kann man das Nachtleben und die Strände genießen, und im Winter läßt sich die Umgebung herrlich zu Fuß oder mit dem Fahrrad erkunden. Das neue Spa bietet Jacuzzi, Sauna und Fitnesszentrum.

Our inspector loved: *The warm, friendly service.*

Agroturismo Es Puig Moltó

CTRA. PINA-MONTUIRI, 07230 MONTUIRI, MALLORCA, BALEARIC ISLANDS

Just 30 minutes from the airport and set amidst 35ha of farmland, this charming hotel is one of the oldest documented country estates in the area and offers guests a warm welcome and friendly service. The views from the hotel and poolside are simply stunning. All 10 suites, many of which boast large terraces, are tastefully decorated in a contemporary rustic style in pale blue, peach and yellow, and furnished with beautiful antique pieces. A delicious menu, with fresh ingredients, is offered by request.

A 30 minutes seulement de l'aéroport et situé au milieu de 35ha de terres cultivées, cet hôtel charmant est un des plus vieilles terres dans la région appelée "Es Pla" et offre aux hôtes un accueil chaleureux et service amical. Les vues depuis l'hôtel et la piscine sont tout simplement magnifiques. Toutes les 10 suites, dont beaucoup ont une grande terrasse, sont décorées en style rustique en bleu, jaune et pêche pâle, et meublées avec des bels objets d'art. Un menu délicieux, préparé avec des ingrédients tous frais, est servi sur demande.

Nur eine halbe Stunde vom Flughafen entfernt und inmitten von 35ha Land liegt dieses zauberhafte Hotel, einer der ältesten dokumentierten Herrensitze der Region "Es Pla". Geboten wird hier ein herzlicher Empfang, freundlicher Service und eine atemberaubende Sicht auf die Umgebung. Alle 10 Suiten, viele davon mit großer Terrasse, sind geschmackvoll in zeitgenössischem ländlichen Stil in pastellblau, pfirsich und gelb gehalten und mit herrlichen antiken Möbeln eingerichtet. Auf Anfrage wird ein volles, mit frischesten Zutaten zubereitetes Menü serviert.

Our inspector loved: *The airy, spacious interior.*

Directions: Palma Mallorca Airport > road to Manacor > at Algaida take Pina Road.

Web: www.johansens.com/puigmolto
E-mail: puigmolto@airtel.net or info@puigmolto.com
Tel: +34 971 18 17 58
Fax: +34 971 18 17 58

Menorca
Mallorca
Mahón
Palma
Ibiza
Ibiza
Formentera

Price Guide:
single €117.70
double €128.40
junior suite €160.50
family room €214
superior junior suite €224.70

Ca's Xorc

CARRETERA DE DEIÀ, KM 56.1, 07100 SÓLLER, MALLORCA, BALEARIC ISLANDS

Majorcan tradition and contemporary style have been combined throughout this captivating hotel, surrounded by landscaped gardens. Stunning vistas of the Tramuntana mountains and the Mediterranean beyond are enjoyed from the terrace, where guests can sample delicacies from a constantly changing menu. Inside, the rooms with stone floors, exposed beams and white fabrics create an airy and romantic ambience. The hotel's enviable seclusion ensures a peaceful yet invigorating stay. A new Moroccan pavilion accommodates private functions such as wedding receptions (40 guests seated, 100 cocktail style).

Tradition majorquine et style contemporain se complètent à merveille dans cet hôtel d'exception, qui est entouré de jardins dessinés. De la terrasse, les visiteurs profitent d'une vue spectaculaire sur la Sierra de Tramuntana et la Méditerranée tout en dégustant des mets délicats chaque jour différents. À l'intérieur, les sols dallés, les poutres apparentes et les tissus blancs créent une ambiance claire et romantique. Grâce à son endroit retiré, l'hôtel offre des séjours paisibles et vivifiants. Un nouveau pavillon marocain est disponible aux célébrations comme des mariages (40 places assises ou 100 debout).

Mallorquinische Tradition und moderner Stil verbinden sich in diesem außergewöhnlichen, von Gärten umgebenen Hotel. Auf der Terrasse mit atemberaubender Sicht auf die Tramuntana-Berge und das Mittelmeer werden täglich neue Köstlichkeiten serviert. Die Innenräume beeindrucken mit ihren Steinböden, rohen Balken und weißen Stoffen und schaffen eine romantische und luftige Atmosphäre. Die abgeschiedene Lage garantiert einen ruhigen und erholsamen Aufenthalt. Ein neuer, marokkanischer Pavillon für Privatfeiern bietet Platz für 40 sitzende Gäste oder 100 bei einem Stehempfang.

Our inspector loved: *The amazing view of the mountains from the pool.*

Directions: Palma Airport > Sóller > past Sóller village > towards Deià > the hotel is on the left hand side.

Web: www.johansens.com/casxorc
E-mail: stay@casxorc.com
Tel: +34 971 63 82 80
Fax: +34 971 63 29 49

Price Guide:
interior room €160
vista room €180
superior room €220
de luxe room €290

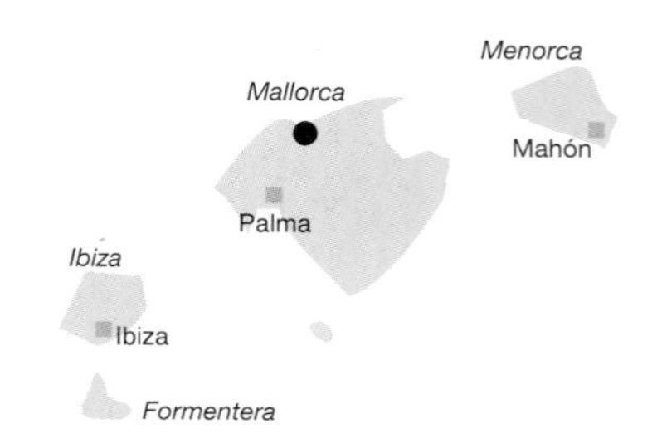

Can Furiós

CAMÍ VELL BINIBONA 11, BINIBONA, 07314 CAIMARI, MALLORCA, BALEARIC ISLANDS

Set amidst breathtaking mountain scenery, this enchanting 16th-century villa is the perfect place to unwind and relax. The villa has been carefully converted to provide all modern comforts whilst retaining its original character. The bedrooms are stunning, and the suites have terraces opening onto the landscaped gardens and pool area. Set in the old olive press room, which dates back to the 17th century, the restaurant serves exquisite modern Mediterranean and Majorcan dishes. Numerous activities to suit every taste can be arranged.

Au sein de beau paysage de montagne, cette villa enchanteur du XVIe siècle est l'endroit rêvé pour se relaxer et se dérouler. La villa a été soigneusement convertie pour offrir tout confort moderne, tout en gardant son caractère original. Les chambres sont fantastiques et les suites ont une terrasse donnant sur les jardins dessinés et la piscine. Situé dans l'ancienne salle de presse d'olives, datant du XVIIe siècle et construit en bois d'amande, le restaurant sert une cuisine moderne méditerranéenne et majorquine; les fruits de mer étant une spécialité. De nombreuses activités pour correspondre aux goûts de chacun peuvent être organisées.

Inmitten atemberaubender Berglandschaft liegt diese zauberhafte Villa aus dem 16. Jahrhundert - der ideale Erholungsort. Die Villa wurde sorgfältig in ein Hotel mit allen modernen Annehmlichkeiten umgewandelt, wobei der ursprüngliche Charakter erhalten blieb. Die Zimmer sind wundervoll, und die Suiten haben Terrassen mit Zugang zu den Gärten und zum Pool. Das im alten Olivenpresseraum aus dem 17. Jahrhundert gelegene Restaurant serviert moderne Mittelmeer- und mallorquinische Küche, die Spezialität sind Meeresfrüchte. Zahlreiche Aktivitäten können organisiert werden.

Our inspector loved: *The soft lighting and atmosphere in the bar.*

Directions: Palma Airport > Inca > Selva > the hotel is then signposted.

Web: www.johansens.com/can-furios
E-mail: info@can-furios.com
Tel: +34 971 51 57 51
Fax: +34 971 87 53 66

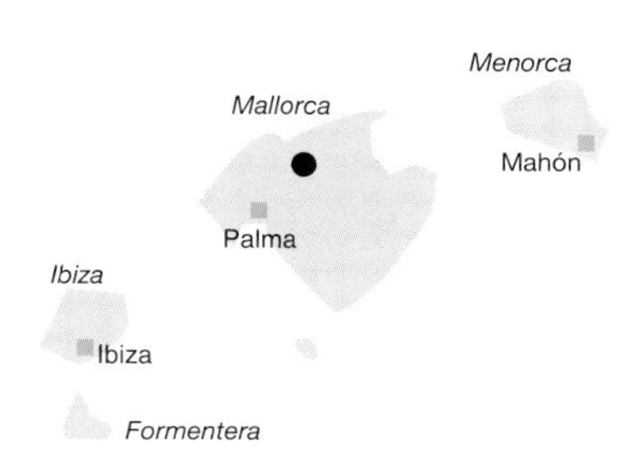

Price Guide: (excluding VAT)
double €150–220
suite €210–280

SPAIN / BALEARIC ISLANDS (MALLORCA)

Gran Hotel Son Net

07194 PUIGPUNYENT, MALLORCA, BALEARIC ISLANDS

This beautiful old finca dates back, in part, to 1672 and has been lovingly restored to the stunning hotel that it is today. 24 luxurious bedrooms and suites combine the traditional with the contemporary to create a truly stylish and individual hotel. The 30m swimming pool is surrounded by individual cabañas for private relaxation, and the restaurant L'Orangerie Mallorca has won many accolades.

Cette magnifique ancienne finca date en partie de 1672 et à été affectueusement restaurée et transformée en un superbe hôtel. 24 chambres et suites luxueuses associent le traditionnel et le contemporain et créent ainsi un hôtel élégant et unique. La piscine de 30 mètres est entourée de cabañas individuelles destinée à la relaxation en privée. Le restaurant L'Orangerie Mallorca à reçu de nombreuses consécrations

Diese zauberhafte alte Finca stammt zum Teil aus dem Jahr 1672 und wurde liebevoll restauriert und in das heutige fantastische Hotel umgewandelt. 24 luxuriöse Zimmer und Suiten verbinden Traditionelles und Zeitgenössisches in einem wahrhaft edlen und individuellen Hotel. Der 30-Meter-Swimmingpool ist von einzelnen Cabañas umgeben, die Privatsphäre bieten, und das Restaurant L'Orangerie Mallorca hat für seine Küche bereits zahlreiche Auszeichnungen gewonnen.

Our inspector loved: *The shady "Cabañas" to relax by the swimming pool.*

Directions: Palma Airport > Palma > Andratx > Puigpunyent.

Web: www.johansens.com/sonnet
E-mail: reservations@luxurylifestylehotels.com
Tel: +34 971 14 70 00
Fax: +34 971 14 70 01

Price Guide: (room only, excluding VAT)
single €180-320
double €180-490
suite €590-1,490

HOTEL DALT MURADA

C/ ALMUDAINA 6-A, 07001 PALMA DE MALLORCA, MALLORCA, BALEARIC ISLANDS

Situated in the gothic quarter of Palma and just a few metres away from the cathedral, this delightfully restored house dates back to the 16th century. A warm and friendly welcome awaits guests at this family-run hotel, which offers a simple Mediterranean chic combined with modern day luxuries. The rooms are carefully furnished with oil paintings, rugs, tapestries, traditional Majorcan glass lamps and antiques, and most incorporate giant Jacuzzi baths in the bathrooms.

Situé dans le quartier gothique de Palma, à quelques mètres de la cathédrale, cette charmante maison restaurée du XVIe siècle offre à ses hôtes un accueil amical et chaleureux. Cet hôtel familial offre une élégance méditerranéenne sans prétentions à laquelle se mélange le confort moderne. Les chambres sont meublées avec soin : peintures à l'huile, plaids, tapisseries, lampes traditionnelles majorquines, antiquités, et la plupart des salles de bains possède une énorme baignoire jacuzzi.

Im gotischen Viertel von Palma und nur ein paar Meter von der Kathedrale entfernt befindet sich dieses herrlich restaurierte Haus aus dem 16. Jahrhundert. Die Gäste erwartet ein sehr herzlicher Empfang in diesem familiengeführten Hotel, das einfachen mediterranen Chic und modernsten Komfort bietet. Die Zimmer sind sorgfältig mit Ölgemälden, Teppichen, Wandbehängen und traditionellen mallorquinischen Glaslampen und Antiquitäten eingerichtet, und die meisten Bäder sind mit einer riesigen Jacuzzibadewanne ausgestattet.

Our inspector loved: *The quiet little breakfast patio filled with orange and lemon trees.*

Directions: Palma Airport > centre of the old town.

Menorca
Mallorca
Mahón
Palma
Ibiza
Ibiza
Formentera

Web: www.johansens.com/daltmurada
E-mail: daltmurada@hotmail.com
Tel: +34 971 425 300
Fax: +34 971 719 708

Price Guide:
double from €140
suite €196
penthouse €280

8
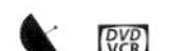
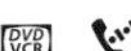

Hotel Maricel

CA'S CATALÀ. CARRETERA D'ANDRATX 11, 07181 CALVIÀ, MALLORCA, BALEARIC ISLANDS

Directions: Palma Airport > motorway to Andratx > exit Bendinat-Illetes > > return towards Illetes-Palma on coast road > the hotel is on the right.

Web: www.johansens.com/maricel
E-mail: maricel@hospes.es
Tel: +34 971 707 744
Fax: +34 971 707 745

Price Guide:
double €320-420
suite €470-620

Menorca
Mallorca
Mahón
Palma
Ibiza
Ibiza
Formentera

This stunning hotel is an eclectic fusion of old and new, with captivating views over the Mediterranean Sea. On arrival guests enter the impressive lobby where the high ceiling and glass windows enhance the magnificent scenery. The bedrooms are refined and contemporary with matte glass doors, dark wood floors, and bathrooms that possess traditional bathtubs. Visitors can dine al fresco or in the elegant restaurant. The award-winning gourmet breakfasts consist of a selection of small dishes, which satisfy even the heartiest of appetites.

Ce superbe hôtel est un mélange éclectique de l'ancien et du moderne avec de captivantes vues sur la mer Méditerranée. Dès leur arrivée, les clients pénètrent dans l'impressionnant lobby avec ses hauts plafonds et grandes fenêtres. Les chambres sont raffinées et contemporaines et ont des portes en verre mat, des sols en bois foncé et des baignoires traditionnelles dans les salles de bain. Les hôtes peuvent dîner à l'extérieur ou dans l'élégant restaurant. Le petit-déjeuner gourmet, mainte fois récompensé, est composé d'une sélection de petits plats et contente le plus féroce des appétits.

Dieses fantastische Hotel ist eine eigenwillige Mischung aus Alt und Neu, mit herrlicher Sicht aufs Mittelmeer. Die eindrucksvolle Rezeption mit ihrer hohen Decke und großen Glasfenstern unterstreicht die Schönheit der Umgebung. Die Zimmer sind edel und zeitgenössisch gestaltet und haben Milchglastüren, dunkle Holzböden und Bäder mit traditionellen Badewannen. Man diniert alfresco oder im eleganten Restaurant, und das preisgekrönte, aus einer Vielfalt kleiner Gerichte bestehende Frühstück wird selbst den größten Appetit stillen.

Our inspector loved: *The spacious, contemporary design.*

La Moraleja Hotel

URBANIZACIÓN LOS ENCINARES S/N, 07469 CALA SAN VICENTE, MALLORCA, BALEARIC ISLANDS

Set only 5 minutes' walk from beautiful sandy beaches, this 5-star hotel has retained the atmosphere of a private home. All of the large bedrooms have their own terrace, and the lounges boast antique furniture and original paintings. Guests can enjoy 2 swimming pools (one heated), or visit the showroom with its collection of 25 classic, convertible sports cars. Cristal serves an excellent à la carte menu, whilst a romantic new 8-table restaurant offers contemporary fusion cuisine, prepared by Masterchef Jaume of Es Convent. Internet access in the library. Open: 1st May - 30th October.

Situé 5 minutes de belles plages de sable, cet hôtel 5 étoiles a gardé son ambiance de maison privée. Les chambres sont grandes avec terrasse, et les salons sont meublés d'antiquités et de tableaux originaux. Les hôtes peuvent profiter de 2 piscines (une chauffée) ou visiter une exposition de 25 voitures de sport classiques décapotables. Cristal sert un dîner à la carte, alors qu'un nouveau restaurant romantique à 8 tables offre une cuisine contemporaine, préparée par maître cuisinier Jaume d'Es Convent. Accès à l'internet dans la bibliothèque. Ouvert 1 mai - 30 octobre.

Dieses 5-Sterne-Hotel mit der Atmosphäre eines Privathauses ist nur 5 Minuten von herrlichen Sandstränden entfernt. Die geräumigen Zimmer haben eigene Terrassen und die eleganten Aufenthaltsräume sind mit Antiquitäten und Originalgemälden gefüllt. Es gibt 2 Swimmingpools (einer beheizt), außerdem kann man einen Schauraum mit 25 klassischen Sportcabriolets bewundern. Im Cristal wird ein köstliches à la carte Menü serviert, während ein romantisches neues Restaurant zeitgenössische, von Meisterkoch Jaume vom Es Convent zubereitete Küche bietet. Internetzugang in der Bibliothek. Geöffnet 1. Mai - 30. Oktober.

Our inspector loved: *The atmosphere of discreet elegance.*

  17       

Directions: Palma Airport > motorway Inca-Pollensa > Cala San Vicente, turning off left. The hotel is on the main entry road.

Web: www.johansens.com/lamoraleja
E-mail: hotel@lamoraleja.net
Tel: +34 971 534 010
Fax: +34 971 533 418

Menorca
Mallorca
Mahón
Palma
Ibiza
Ibiza
Formentera

Price Guide:
superior twins €259-294
suites €330-369

Palacio Ca Sa Galesa

CARRER DE MIRAMAR 8, 07001 PALMA DE MALLORCA, BALEARIC ISLANDS

This 16th-century palacio is located in the heart of the Gothic quarter in the centre of Palma and is only a 2-minute walk from the cathedral. Original stained glass, floor tiles, chandeliers and tapestries adorn the beautiful public rooms, whilst the comfortable bedrooms are classically decorated, some with a very cosy feel. At 7pm, guests may enjoy an apéritif in the reading room, which has its own small library filled with books and magazines. The hotel boasts a small spa area complete with sauna and gymnasium; mountain bikes are available for excursions.

Ce palais du XVIe siècle est situé au cœur du quartier gothique de Palma et à deux pas de la cathédrale. Les vitraux originaux, des carreaux, des lustres et des tapisseries ornent les belles salles publiques, alors que les chambres sont décorées de façon classique, quelques-unes avec une ambiance très intime. A 19h, les hôtes peuvent prendre l'apéritif dans la salle de lecture avec sa propre bibliothèque rempli de libres et de magazines. L'hôtel s'enorgueillit d'un petit spa comprenant un sauna et une salle de remise en forme; des VTT sont disponibles pour des excursions.

Dieses Palacio aus dem 16. Jahrhundert liegt mitten im gotischen Viertel von Palma und ist nur 2 Minuten Fußmarsch von der Kathedrale entfernt. Ursprüngliche Details wie Buntglas, Fliesen, Lüster und Wandteppiche zieren die herrlichen Aufenthaltsräume, und die komfortablen Gästezimmer sind klassisch eingerichtet. Einige sind eher klein und gemütlich. Um 19 Uhr trifft man sich zum Apéritif im Lesesaal mit eigener Bibliothek. Das Hotel bietet einen kleinen Wellnessbereich mit Sauna und Fitnessraum. Mountainbikes für Exkursionen stehen ebenfalls zur Verfügung.

Our inspector loved: *The quiet, refined atmosphere - much appreciated after a hard day's sightseeing.*

Directions: The nearest airport is Palma. Take the motorway to Port and enter the old town behind the cathedral. At Plaça Santa Eulalia press the button at the police bollard to gain entry to the street.

Web: www.johansens.com/casagalesa
E-mail: reservas@palaciocasagalesa.com
Tel: +34 971 715 400
Fax: +34 971 721 579

Price Guide: (breakfast €20, excluding VAT)
double €230-292
suite €349-422

Read's

CA'N MORAGUES, 07320 SANTA MARÍA, MALLORCA, BALEARIC ISLANDS

Just 15 minutes from Palma and surrounded by 20,000m² of landscaped gardens, this 500-year-old countryside hotel is a genuine luxury retreat. There is an outdoor and indoor pool, gymnasium, sauna, solarium, Jacuzzi and tennis court. The restaurant, under the auspices of chef Marc Fosh, was recently awarded a Star by the prestigious Michelin guide and is currently No.1 in the Veuve Clicquot Top 10 of luxury restaurants. Open to non-residents; reservations recommended. Simpler meals can be enjoyed in the newly opened Bistro 33, housed in the olive press room with terrace.

Ce manoir de campagne de 500 ans, situé à 15 minutes de Palma, dans un parc de 20 000m², est un véritable hôtel de luxe. Il comprend une piscine extérieure et une couverte, gymnase, sauna, solarium, Jacuzzi et un court de tennis. Le restaurant, sous les auspices du chef Marc Fosh, a été attribué 1 étoile Michelin et actuellement il est 1er sur la liste de restaurants de luxe de Veuve Clicquot. Non-résidents sont conseillés de réserver une table en avance. Le Bistro 33, récemment ouvert, offre und cuisine plus simple, dans la salle des pressoirs d'olives, avec terrasse.

Dieser 500 Jahre alte Landsitz, nur 15 Minuten von Palma entfernt und umgeben von 20.000m² Garten, ist ein wahres Luxushotel. Es gibt Freibad, Hallenbad sowie Fitnessraum, Sauna, Solarium, Jacuzzi und Tennisplatz. Das Restaurant unter Führung von Chefkoch Marc Fosh bekam kürzlich einen Michelinstern und ist derzeit die Nr. 1 der Top 10 der Veuve Clicquot-Luxusrestaurants. Nicht-Gäste sollten unbedingt reservieren. Einfachere Küche gibt es im neueröffneten Bistro 33 mit seiner Terrasse, das im Olivenpresseraum untergebracht ist.

Our inspector loved: *Suite No 6, with a terrace overlooking the gardens.*

Directions: Palma Airport > Inca > Santa María. The hotel is then signposted.

Web: www.johansens.com/reads
E-mail: readshotel@readshotel.com
Tel: +34 971 14 02 62
Fax: +34 971 14 07 62

Price Guide:
double €190–360
suite €320–790

Sa Posada d'Aumallia

CAMINO SON PROHENS 1027, 07200 FELANITX, MALLORCA, BALEARIC ISLANDS

A fine example of Majorcan country architecture, this charming hotel is set amidst beautiful countryside in a secluded and peaceful position. Guests will receive the warmest of welcomes by the owners, the Martí Gomila family, who offer a truly wonderful stay in friendly surroundings. The public rooms are decorated with impeccable taste and boast antique furniture and paintings as well as fresh flowers, whilst the bedrooms are air-conditioned and have all modern amenities. The evenings are filled with fine dining accompanied by piano music played by Andrés Martí.

Un excellent exemple de l'architecture majorquin, ce charmant hôtel est situé en belle campagne dans un endroit retiré et paisible. Les propriétaires, la famille Martí Gomila, font les hôtes se sentir vraiment chez eux, offrant un séjour magnifique dans un cadre accueillant. Les salles communes sont ornées avec le meilleur goût et agrémentées d'antiquités et de tableaux originaux alors que les chambres sont climatisées et disposent de tout confort moderne. Les soirées sont remplies de bonne cuisine accompagnée du piano joué par Andrés Marti.

Dieses reizvolle Hotel ist ein hervorragende Beispiel für mallorquinische Architektur und liegt abgeschieden inmitten herrlicher Landschaft. Gäste erwartet ein herzlicher Empfang von der Familie Martí Gomila, die einen wundervollen Aufenthalt in freundlicher Umgebung bietet. Die geschmackvoll eingerichteten Aufenthaltsräume sind mit antiken Möbeln und Gemälden sowie frischen Blumen geschmückt, und die Gästezimmer sind klimatisiert und bieten jeglichen modernen Komfort. Abends genießt man hervorragende Speisen begleitet von Andrés Martí am Klavier.

Our inspector loved: *The fresh flowers and fresh breakfast eggs from the chickens.*

Directions: Palma Airport > road to Manacor > Felanitx > Porto Colom. Continue on this road, the hotel is signposted.

Web: www.johansens.com/posadadaumallia
E-mail: aumallia@aumallia.com
Tel: +34 971 58 26 57
Fax: +34 971 58 32 69

Price Guide: (excluding VAT)
double €120.20–144.31

SPAIN / BALEARIC ISLANDS (MALLORCA)

Valldemossa Hotel

CTRA. VIEJA DE VALLDEMOSSA S/N, 07170 VALLDEMOSSA, MALLORCA, BALEARIC ISLANDS

Set in flower-filled gardens on various levels, this romantic stone-built Majorcan house offers spectacular views over the village, the Bay of Palma and the Tramuntana mountain range. Built over 100 years ago, it has been converted into a luxurious hotel with superb facilities. No expense has been spared in the bedrooms, which vary in size and décor and display wonderful touches such as specially made hand-painted lamps. Superb cuisine is served in the Valldemossa restaurant, and there is a large outdoor pool, a small indoor pool and a sauna.

Dans un jardin rempli de fleurs sur plusieurs niveaux, cette maison majorquine romantique construite en pierre offre des vues spectaculaires sur le village, la baie de Palma et les montagnes de Tramuntana. Construite il y a plus de 100 ans, la maison a été convertie en hôtel luxueux avec des facilités superbes. Les chambres opulentes, qui ne manque aucun détail, varient en taille et décor et ont des agréments comme des lampes peintes à la main. Une cuisine superbe est servie dans le restaurant Valldemossa. L'hôtel dispose d'une piscine extérieure, petite piscine couverte et sauna.

In einem mit Blumen gefüllten Garten auf mehreren Ebenen liegt dieses romantische mallorquinische Steingebäude mit Blick auf das Dorf und die Tramuntanaberge. Das über 100 Jahre alte Haus wurde in ein luxuriöses Hotel umgewandelt und bietet hervorragende Einrichtungen. Bei der Ausstattung der unterschiedlich großen und individuell gestalteten Zimmer wurde nicht gespart, man findet zahlreiche Extras wie z.B. handbemalte Lampen. Im Valldemossa wird feinste Küche serviert, und ein großer Pool im Freien, ein kleines Hallenbad und eine Sauna sorgen für Entspannung.

Our inspector loved: *The breakfast terrace - a place to enjoy the peaceful country views.*

Directions: Palma Airport > Valldemossa. The hotel is signposted just before the entrance to the village.

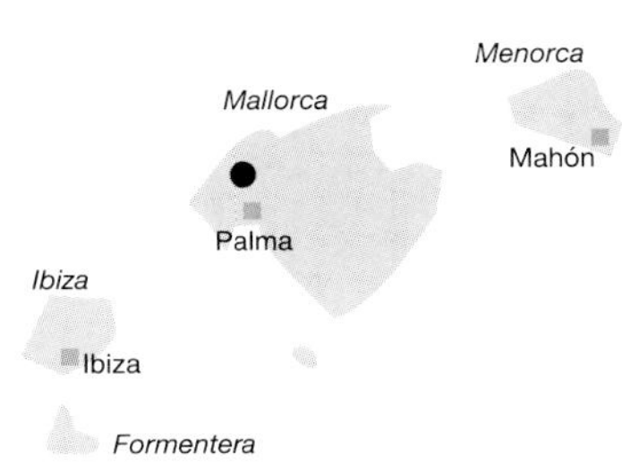

Web: www.johansens.com/valldemossa
E-mail: info@valldemossahotel.com
Tel: +34 971 61 26 26
Fax: +34 971 61 26 25

Price Guide: (excluding VAT)
single €200
double €300
suite €590

Elba Palace Golf Hotel

URB. FUERTEVENTURA GOLF CLUB, CTA DE JANDIA, KM11, 35610 ANTIGUA, FUERTEVENTURA, CANARY ISLANDS

Directions: 8km from Fuerteventura Airport > Caleta de Fuste > hotel is on the right.

Web: www.johansens.com/elbapalacegolfhotel
E-mail: epg@hoteleselba.com
Tel: +34 928 16 39 22
Fax: +34 928 16 39 23

Price Guide:
single €141-281
double €188–375
suite €288–475

Lanzarote
Tenerife
Arrecife
Santa Cruz
Las Palmas
Puerto del Rosario
Fuerteventura
Gran Canaria

This elegant new hotel is surrounded by a small garden with swimming pool, and beyond, an 18-hole golf course. Décor is sober and elegant combining parquet floors, hand-crafted wooden furniture, doors and ceilings, although the entrance hall does feature a stunning 4-metre chandelier. An basement wine cellar provides meeting space, as do the quiet library and cards room. Other activities include windsurfing, diving, sea fishing and sailing. A gymnasium and beauty centre (reservations required) are also available.

Cet nouvel hôtel élégant est entouré d'un petit jardin avec piscine, et plus loin se trouve un terrain de golf de 18 trous. Le décor est sobre et élégant grâce à une combinaison entre autres de parquets, de meubles, portes et plafonds en bois travaillés à la main. Dans l'entrée se tient un chandelier incroyable de près de quatré mètres. Le cellier à vin souterrain tout comme la bibliothèque tranquille et la salle de jeu, est un endroit agréable où se retrouver. Pour les sportifs, planche à voile, plongée, pêche en mer et voile ainsi qu'un gymnase et centre de beauté (réservation obligatoire) sont disponibles.

Dieses elegante neue Hotel ist von einem kleinen Garten mit Swimmingpool und einem 18-Loch Golfplatz umgeben. Das Décor ist nüchtern-elegant mit Parkettböden und handgefertigten Holzmöbeln und -decken, und die Eingangshalle ziert ein einzigartiger 4m hoher Kronleuchter. Der Weinkeller ist ein beliebter Treffpunkt, ebenso die ruhige Bibliothek und der Spieleraum. Aktivitäten sind Windsurfen, Tauchen, Angeln und Segeln, außerdem stehen ein Fitnessraum und eine Beautyfarm (Reservierung erforderlich) zur Verfügung.

Our inspector loved: *The truly palatial bathrooms in the suites, with outsized baths and massage showers.*

Gran Hotel Atlantis Bahía Real

AVENIDA GRANDES PLAYAS S/N, 35660 CORRALEJO, FUERTEVENTURA, CANARY ISLANDS

Owned by the reputable Atlantis Hotels and Resorts Group, Gran Hotel Atlantis Bahía Real opened on 1st November 2003. Adjacent to the sea and Las Dunas National Park, this Canarian hotel boasts magnificent views across Lobos Island and Lanzarote. 250 bedrooms have terraces or balconies and 7 bars and restaurants serve national, gourmet, Italian and Japanese cuisine whilst live entertainment is held in La Boheme. Bahia Vital Spa offers a wide range of health and beauty treatments (clients must be 16 years old), specialising in hydrotherapy.

Gran Hotel Atlantis Bahía Real, qui appartient au groupe bien réputé Atlantis Hotels and Resorts, a ouvert le 1er novembre 2003. A coté de la mer et du parc national de Las Dunas, cet hôtel canarien offre des vues imprenables sur l'île de Lobos et Lanzarote. Les 250 chambres ont des terrasses ou balcons et 7 bars et restaurants servent une cuisine nationale, gourmet, italienne et japonaise alors qu'il y a des spectacles sur scène à la Boheme. Bahia Vital Spa offre toute une gamme de traitements de beauté et de santé, spécialisant en l'hydrothérapie (âge minimum de 16 ans).

Dieses zur renommierten Gruppe der Atlantis Hotels and Resorts gehörende Hotel eröffnete am 1. November 2003. Direkt am Meer und neben dem Las Dunas Nationalpark gelegen, bietet es eine traumhafte Sicht auf die Insel Lobos und Lanzarote. Die 250 Zimmer haben Terrassen oder Balkone, und in 7 Bars und Restaurants wird spanische, Gourmet-, italienische und japanische Küche serviert. Im La Boheme finden Live-Unterhaltungsprogramme statt, und das auf Hydrotherapie spezialisierte Bahia Vital Spa bietet Gesundheits- und Schönheitsbehandlungen (Mindestalter 16 Jahre).

Our inspector loved: *The ocean view towards Lobos Island and Lanzarote.*

Directions: Fuerteventura Airport > Corralejo.

Web: www.johansens.com/atlantisbahiareal
E-mail: bahiareal@bahia-real.com
Tel: +34 928 53 64 44
Fax: +34 928 53 75 75

Price Guide:
single €159.50-204.50
double €213-272.50
suite €255.50-1,260

SPAIN / CANARY ISLANDS (GRAN CANARIA)

Gran Hotel Costa Meloneras

C/Mar Mediterráneo 1, 35100 Maspalomas, Gran Canaria, Canary Islands

Directions: Take the motorway south and exit at Pasito Blanco then follow signs to Maspalomas. The nearest airport is (Las Palmas de) Gran Canaria.

Web: www.johansens.com/costameloneras
E-mail: reservas@lopesanhr.com
Tel: +34 928 12 81 00
Fax: +34 928 12 81 47

Price Guide:
single €111–234
double €138–294
suite €210–1,764

Lanzarote
Arrecife
Tenerife
Santa Cruz
Las Palmas
Puerto del Rosario
Fuerteventura
Gran Canaria

Gran Hotel Costa Meloneras retains a sense of individuality and reflects the colonial and Canarian architecture of the island. Spacious public areas filled with exotic furniture and painted tile floors lead to beautifully landscaped gardens covering 76,000m², numerous swimming pools and the beach. Activities such as golf and water sports are close at hand, as well as a spa offering a superb variety of water, massage and innovative treatments. A wide selection of restaurants and bars all offer their own distinctive ambience.

Gran Hotel Costa Meloneras retient un sens d,individualité et ses décors reflètent l'architecture coloniale et canarienne de l'île. Les espaces publiques spacieux emplis de meubles exotiques et aux carrelages peints conduisent à de beaux jardins aménagés de 76 000 m² à de nombreuses piscines et à la plage. Des activités telles que golf et sports nautiques sont à potée, ainsi qu'un spa offrant une variété superbe comprenant des traitements innovatifs, d'eau et de massage. Il existe également une vaste sélection de restaurants et bars qui offrent tous leur propre ambiance.

Das Gran Hotel Costa Meloneras konnte sich ein Gefühl der Individualität bewahren und spiegelt die koloniale und kanarische Architektur der Insel wider. Die großen Aufenthaltsräume sind mit exotischem Mobiliar gefüllt und die gefliesten Böden führen zu herrlichen, 76.000m² großen Gärten, Swimmingpools und zum Strand. Golf und Wassersport können vor Ort betrieben werden, und es gibt ein Kurbad mit einer großen Auswahl an Wasser-, Massage- und innovativen Behandlungen. Zahlreiche Restaurants und Bars schaffen ein ganz besonderes Ambiente.

Our inspector loved: *The enormous spa complex - you could spend all day there.*

Hesperia Lanzarote Hotel

URB. CORTIJO VIEJO, PUERTO CALERO, 35570 YAIZA, LANZAROTE, CANARY ISLANDS

Hesperia Lanzarote Hotel is the ideal location from which to explore the island's capital. Whether a family holiday, romantic break or business trip, a wide range of accommodation and facilities are available. Many guest rooms have ocean views and terrace or balcony; 1 buffet and 2 à la carte restaurants and 5 bars offer something for every taste. Activities include 3 swimming pools, a children's pool, spa and wellness centre with fitness centre, steam room and beauty centre, 1 tennis and 1 squash court.

Hesperia Lanzarote est la base idéale pour explorer le capitale de l'île. Que ce soit une vacance en famille ou romantique ou un voyage d'affaires, toute une gamme de logement et de facilités est disponible. Plusieurs chambres ont une vue sur la mer et une terrasse ou un balcon. 1 restaurant aux buffets, 2 restaurants à la carte et 5 bars offrent quelque chose pour les goûts de chacun. Les facilités comprennent 3 piscines, une piscine pour des enfants, un centre de bien-être incluant un centre de remise en forme, hammam et centre de beauté, 1 court de tennis et 1 court de squash.

Dieses Hotel ist der ideale Ausgangsort, um die Inselhauptstadt zu erkunden. Ob Familienurlaub, romantischer Kurzurlaub oder Geschäftsreise – hier findet man eine große Auswahl an Unterkunft und Einrichtungen für jeden Zweck. Viele Zimmer haben Terrasse oder Balkon und Blick aufs Meer. 1 Buffetrestaurant, 2 à la carte Restaurants und 5 Bars bieten etwas für jeden Geschmack. Das Freizeitangebot umfasst 3 Swimmingpools, ein Kinderbecken, ein Wellness-Centre mit Fitness-Centre, Dampfbad und Beautysalon, sowie 1 Tennis- und 1 Squashplatz.

Our inspector loved: *The clean, modern architecture set against the open, coastal landscape of the island.*

Directions: Located 10km from the airport, directly on the seafront, adjacent to the exclusive Puerto Calero Yacht Harbour.

Lanzarote
Arrecife
Tenerife
Santa Cruz
Las Palmas
Puerto del Rosario
Fuerteventura
Gran Canaria

Web: www.johansens.com/hespialanzarote
E-mail: hotel@hesperia-lanzarote.com
Tel: +34 828 0808 00
Fax: +34 828 08 08 10

Price Guide: (room only, excluding VAT)
single €165-285
double €180-300
suite €275-760

PRINCESA YAIZA SUITE HOTEL*****

AVENIDA PAPAGAYO S/N, 35570 PLAYA BLANCA, YAIZA, LANZAROTE, CANARY ISLANDS

This sprawling, sparkling white modern resort featuring towers, domes and spacious balconies overlooks Playa Blanca beach. With restful gardens and a stylish interior enhanced by colonial-style furniture and wood-beamed ceilings, the Princesa Yaiza provides everything that a discerning guest could wish for. All suites and superior double rooms are tastefully furnished and decorated, and have luxury bathrooms and extensive facilities; many enjoy sea views. 4 restaurants serve Italian, Mexican, Japanese and international cuisine. Numerous leisure facilities are available.

Ce resort moderne, tentaculaire, d'un blanc étincelant avec ses tours, ses dômes et ses larges balcons surplombe la plage de Playa Blanca. Avec ses jardins reposants et une décoration de goût mise en valeur par des meubles de style coloniaux et des plafonds aux poutres apparentes, le Princesa Yaiza offre tout ce que désire un client avisé. Les suites et chambres pour deux supérieures sont toutes décorées avec goût, ont de somptueuses salles de bains et de nombreux équipements; beaucoup offrent la vue mer. 4 restaurants servent une cuisine italienne, mexicaine, japonaise et internationale. De nombreuses activités de loisirs sont disponibles.

Türme, Kuppeln und große Balkone zieren dieses ausgedehnte, strahlend weiße moderne Resort mit Blick auf die Playa Blanca. Mit seinen ruhigen Gärten und einem eleganten Interieur im Kolonialstil mit Holzbalkendecken bietet das Princesa Yaiza alles, was sich der anspruchsvolle Gast erträumt. Die Suiten und Doppelzimmer sind alle geschmackvoll kühl gestaltet und haben luxuriöse Bäder und umfassende Einrichtungen. Viele bieten Meerblick. In 4 Restaurants wird italienische, mexikanische, japanische und internationale Küche serviert. Zahlreiche Freizeitmöglichkeiten sind vorhanden.

***Our inspector loved:** The spacious rooms with their sunny terraces.*

Directions: Lanzarote Airport > Yaiza > Playa Blanca.

Web: www.johansens.com/yaiza
E-mail: info@princesayaiza.com
Tel: +34 928 519 222
Fax: +34 928 519 179

Price Guide:
single €140-240
double €200-300
suite €310-1,300

Lanzarote
Arrecife
Tenerife
Santa Cruz
Las Palmas
Puerto del Rosario
Fuerteventura
Gran Canaria

Gran Hotel Bahía del Duque Resort

C/ALCALDE WALTER PAETZMANN, S/N 38660 COSTA ADEJE, TENERIFE SOUTH, CANARY ISLANDS

This hotel is a private romantic village created on a gentle hill sloping down to the sea. 20 houses in turn-of-the-century Canarian architecture form this prestigious complex in a large estate with sculptured terraces and pools. The furniture has been specially designed, the floors are cool Spanish tiles and the bathrooms are luxurious. Descending towards the coast, guests will find a patio surrounded by 11 restaurants. The newly opened "El Mirador" section, decorated in soft, understated colours, offers its own restaurants and swimming pools.

Cet hôtel est un village romantique privé créé sur une pente douce descendant sur la mer. 20 maisons qui reflètent l'architecture canarienne du début du siècle forment un complexe prestigieux au milieu d'une grande propriété agrémentée de terrasses ornées et de piscines. Les meubles ont été spécialement conçus, les sols sont de céramiques espagnoles et les salles de bain sont luxueuses. En descendant vers la côte, les visiteurs trouveront un patio et 11 restaurants. La nouvelle section "El Mirador" est décorée en couleurs douces et dispose de ses propres restaurants et piscines.

Dieses romantische private Dorf liegt auf einem zum Meer abfallenden Hügel. Die renommierte Anlage besteht aus 20 Häusern im Stil kanarischer Architektur um die Jahrhundertwende, und liegt in einem ausgedehnten Grundstück mit gepflegten Terrassen und Pools. Das Mobiliar wurde eigens für das Hotel entworfen, die Böden sind mit spanischen Fliesen versehen und die Badezimmer sind reiner Luxus. In Richtung Meeresufer liegt ein von 11 Restaurants umrahmter Innenhof. Der neue, in sanften Farben gehaltene "El Mirador" Flügel hat eigene Restaurants und Swimmingpools.

Our inspector loved: *The enormous range of restaurants and bars within the complex; something for every taste.*

Directions: The nearest airport is Tenerife. Motorway to Playa Americas > San Eugenio exit.

Web: www.johansens.com/granhotelbahiadelduque
E-mail: comercial@bahia-duque.com
Tel: +34 922 74 69 00
Fax: +34 922 74 69 16

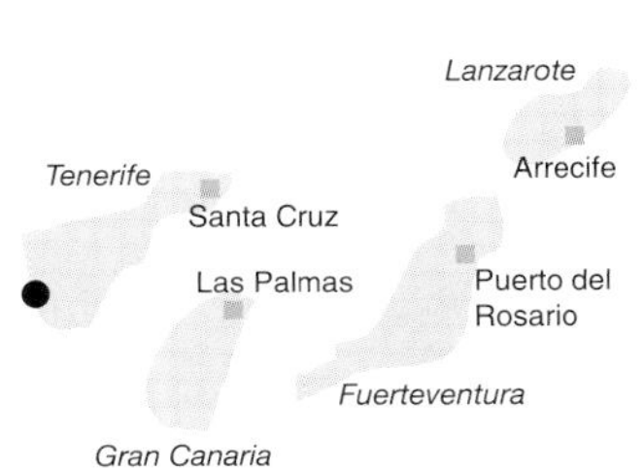

Price Guide:
single €229–415
double/twin €248–444
suite €452–2,103

Hotel Jardín Tropical

CALLE GRAN BRETAÑA, 38670 COSTA ADEJE, TENERIFE, CANARY ISLANDS

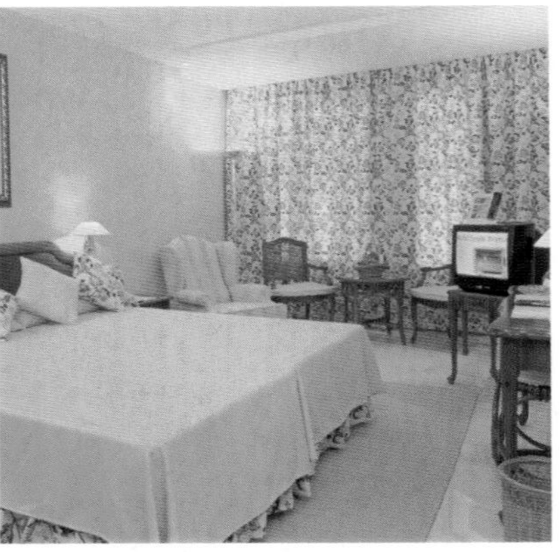

Built just 14 years ago, this magnificent Moorish palace with its brilliant white walls is enveloped by the exotic green foliage of its subtropical garden interspersed with blue pools and colourful flowers. The interior rooms display cool luxury, and the exclusive Las Adelfas Suites are phenomenal. Guests are spoilt for choice with the cuisine and may enjoy everything from poolside snacks to a gourmet feast in the El Patio restaurant. Beauty treatments are available in the Bio Centre.

Construit il y a tout juste 14 ans, ce magnifique palais mauresque a été embelli par des tours surmontées de dômes. L'hôtel se dresse au milieu d'un jardin exotique parsemé de bassins azur et de fleurs colorées. A l'intérieur, les chambres affichent un luxe sobre et les prestigieuses suites Las Adelfas sont remarquables. Les hôtes sont gâtés au niveau culinaire et pourront se régaler du simple snack au bord de la piscine jusqu'au festin gastronomique au restaurant El Patio. Il y a un "Bio Centre" pour des soins de beauté.

Dieser herrliche, vor 14 Jahren erbaute maurische Palast mit seinen strahlend weißen Wänden ist umgeben von exotischen subtropischen Gärten, leuchtendblauen Pools und bunten Blumen. Die Innenräume spiegeln kühlen Luxus wider, und die exklusiven Las Adelfas Suiten sind einfach prächtig. Was das Essen angeht, haben die Gäste die Qual der Wahl – vom Snack am Pool bis zum Gourmetdinner im El Patio ist alles geboten. Im "Bio Centre" werden Schönheitskuren angeboten.

Our inspector loved: *The Las Rocas beach bar overlooking the ocean.*

Directions: Airport > Tenerife South > motorway - Playa Americas > exit 29, San Eugenio.

Web: www.johansens.com/jardintropical
E-mail: hotel@jardin–tropical.com
Tel: +34 922 74 60 11/2/3
Fax: +34 922 74 60 14

Price Guide:
single €108.18-330.55
double/twin €150.25-811.36
suite €360.60-961.61

Hotel La Quinta Roja

GLORIETA DE SAN FRANCISCO, 38450 GARACHICO, TENERIFE, CANARY ISLANDS

This historical mansion is a fine example of Baroque architecture, and is set in the attractive town square of Garachico. The original building dates back to the 16th century and the wooden galleries, stone paving and marble fountain all create an atmosphere of a grand bygone era. Each bedroom is individually and tastefully decorated, and The Marquess Dining Room, rustic-style bar and restaurant serve fresh regional cuisine. The fitness club has a Jacuzzi, sauna and solarium.

Situé dans la place du marché de Garachico, ce manoir historique est un excellent exemple de l'architecture baroque. Le bâtiment original date du XVIe siècle et les galeries en bois, le pavé et la fontaine en marbre créent une ambiance d,une époque d'autrefois. Chacune des chambres est ornée avec goût et la salle à manger 'la Marquise', le bar rustique et le restaurant servent une cuisine fraîche et régionale. Il y a un jacuzzi, une sauna et un solarium dans le gymnase.

Dieses historische, am attraktiven Marktplatz der Stadt Garachio gelegene Haus ist ein hervorragendes Beispiel barocker Baukunst. Das ursprüngliche Gebäude stammt aus dem 16. Jahrhundert, und die hölzernen Galerien, der Steinboden und der Marmorbrunnen schaffen eine Atmosphäre vergangener Pracht. Jedes Zimmer ist individuell und geschmackvoll gestaltet, und im Speisesaal der „Marquise", der rustikalen Bar und dem Restaurant werden frische, regionale Köstlichkeiten serviert. Der Fitnessclub bietet Jacuzzi, Sauna und Solarium.

Our inspector loved: *The individual attention that every guest receives.*

Directions: From Highway Tenerife North to Puerto de la Crue > continue to Garachico > the hotel is in the village square.

Web: www.johansens.com/quintaroja
E-mail: hotelquintaroja@quintaroja.com
Tel: +34 922 13 33 77
Fax: +34 922 13 33 60

Price Guide:
double €84-158

POSADA DE LA CASA DEL ABAD DE AMPUDIA

PLAZA FRANCISCO MARTÍN GROMAZ 12, 34160 AMPUDIA (PALENCIA), SPAIN

Situated in the centre of a brilliantly restored village, where original wooden walkways and columns still stand, this breathtaking hotel is rich in history and enchantment. Originally an Abbot's house, all the rooms have been lovingly restored and are in full use, including the stables and wine press. Décor throughout blends original architecture, such as beamed ceilings and stone walls, with strong contemporary colours. In the kitchen, Joaquim Koerper of the Girasol creates fusion cuisine of the highest calibre.

Situé au cœur d'un village magnifiquement restauré avec ses allées et colonnes en bois d'origine, ce superbe hôtel est riche en histoire et en enchantement. Anciennement maison d'Abbé, toutes les pièces ont retrouvé leur éclat et sont utilisées, même les écuries et le pressoir. La décoration est un mélange d'architecture d'origine, tels que plafonds de poutres et murs en pierre, avec des couleurs vives contemporaines. Dans la cuisine, Joaquim Koerper, du restaurant Girasol, crée une cuisine du plus haut niveau.

Im Zentrum eines fantastisch restaurierten Dorfes mit ursprünglichen Holzwegen und Säulen befindet sich dieses atemberaubend schöne, geschichtsträchtige Hotel, einst das Haus eines Abtes. Alle Zimmer wurden liebevoll restauriert und werden als Gästezimmer angeboten, darunter die Stallungen und der Weinpresseraum. Das Décor ist eine gelungene Verbindung aus ursprünglicher Architektur, mit Holzbalkendecken und Steinwänden, und kräftigen, modernen Farben. In der Küche kreiert Joaquim Koerper vom Girasol Fusionsküche vom Feinsten.

Our inspector loved: *The restaurant in the old wine press; excellent food and service.*

Directions: Valladolid Airport > N620 - Palencia > exit Dueñas to Ampudia > hotel is in the centre of the village.

Web: www.johansens.com/abaddeampudia
E-mail: hotel@casadelabad.com
Tel: +34 979 768 008
Fax: +34 979 768 300

Price Guide: (room only, excluding VAT)
single €83-103
double €103-119
suite €144-170

EL MILANO REAL

C/TOLEO S/N, HOYOS DEL ESPINO, 05634 ÁVILA, SPAIN

This welcoming village hotel, surrounded by a beautiful landscaped garden, offers spectacular views of the Gredos mountains. Standard double bedrooms have recently been decorated and each superior guest room and suite has a hydromassage bath; the Nordic Suite has its very own sauna, and every suite boasts a wide screen TV. Guests can relax over an apéritif in the cosy lounge bar before enjoying excellent, creative cuisine in the attractive restaurant. This is an ideal "half-way stop" on route to the south.

Au cœur d'un beau jardin aménagé, cet hôtel de village accueillant offre une vue spectaculaire sur les montagnes de Gredos. Les chambres doubles ont été récemment décorées et chaque chambre supérieure et suite offrent une baignoire hydromassante. La suite Nordique a son propore sauna et chaque suite possède une téléviseur grand écran. Les hôtes peuvent se détendre à l'apéritif dans le confortable salon-bar avant de déguster une cuisine excellente et créative dans le charmant restaurant. C'est une étape idéale sur la route du sud.

Dieses einladende, von einem herrlichen Garten umgebene Dorfhotel bietet eine atemberaubende Sicht auf die Gredos-Berge. Die Standard-Doppelzimmer wurden kürzlich neu gestaltet, und die restlichen Zimmer und Suiten bieten Hydromassage-Bäder. Die Nordic Suite hat eine eigene Sauna, und alle Suiten haben Widescreen-Fernsehen. Die gemütliche Lounge lädt zum Apéritif ein, bevor man sich zu exquisiten, kreativen Speisen im Restaurant niederläßt. Ein ideale Haltestelle„ auf dem Weg in den Süden.

Our inspector loved: *The gourmet breakfast - a chance to sample everything.*

Directions: Madrid Airport > A6 > A51 towards Ávila > N502 towards Arenas de San Pedro in Venta Rasquilla > AV941 to Hoyos del Espino.

León
Barcelona
Madrid
Málaga

Web: www.johansens.com/elmilanoreal
E-mail: info@elmilanoreal.com
Tel: +34 920 349 108
Fax: +34 920 349 156

Price Guide:
single €102.72-132.68
double €127.33-161.57
suite €202.23

HOTEL RECTOR

RECTOR ESPERABÉ 10–APARTADO 399, 37008 SALAMANCA, SPAIN

This exclusive hotel stands by the walls of the citadel looking up to the cathedral, a magnificent golden vision at night when floodlit. The interior looks cool and elegant with archways between the spacious reception hall and the welcoming bar. Unique features in the main salon are 2 exquisite modern stained glass windows. There are 13 bedrooms, delightfully furnished with marble bathrooms. Breakfast is served in the hotel, and for dinner, there are numerous restaurants in the vicinity. Salamanca has been named City of Culture.

Cet hôtel exclusif se dresse à côté des remparts de la citadelle; elle même dominée par la cathédrale, qui devient une vision magique lorsqu'illuminée la nuit. L'intérieur est frais et élégant, avec de belles voûtes qui séparent le spacieux hall de réception et le bar accueillant. Le salon principal est orné de 2 ravissants vitraux modernes. L'hôtel compte treize chambres, délicieusement meublées avec salles de bain en marbre. Le petit déjeuner est servi à l'hôtel et de nombreux restaurants sont situés à proximité. En 2002, Salamanca a été appellé Ville Culturelle.

Dieses exklusive Hotel liegt an einer Zitadelle neben der Kathedrale, die nachts beleuchtet wird und ein herrlich goldenes Spektakel bietet. Das Interieur ist kühl und elegant, mit Bogengängen zwischen der großen Empfangshalle und der einladenden Bar. Hauptanziehungspunkte des Salons sind zweifellos 2 exquisite moderne Buntglasfenster. Die 13 Zimmer sind zauberhaft gestaltet und haben Marmorbäder. Frühstück wird im Hotel serviert, und am Abend locken zahlreiche Restaurants in der Umgebung. 2002 war Salamanca hat den Beinamen Stadt der Kultur.

Our inspector loved: *The impeccable neatness of this hotel.*

Directions: The nearest airports are Madrid and Valladolid. The hotel is south of the city centre.

Web: www.johansens.com/rector
E-mail: hotelrector@telefonica.net
Tel: +34 923 21 84 82
Fax: +34 923 21 40 08

Price Guide: (breakfast €10, excluding VAT)
single €89
double/twin €112-134
suite €146

Castillo de Buen Amor

CARRETERA NATIONAL 630 KM 317, 6 TOPAS 37799, SALAMANCA, SPAIN

This is a 13th-century castle with enough elegance, charm and atmosphere to satisfy the most discerning visitor. Majestic stone walls are topped with imposing battlements, a moat with swimming pool. The cool interior has all the attributes of a tranquil past era combined with the luxurious comforts of the 21st century. Public rooms are tall and spacious, their natural walls decorated with fine paintings and ancient artwork. Furnishings are in-keeping with the castle's age but the superb en-suite bedrooms are more contemporary.

Ce château du XIIIe siècle démontre de suffisamment d'élégance, de charme et d'atmosphère pour satisfaire les visiteurs les plus exigeants avec ses murs de pierre imposants surplombés de créneaux, ses douvres offrant une piscine. L'intérieur frais combine les attributs d'une époque passée au confort luxueux du XXIe siècle. Les salles communes sont hautes et spacieuses, leurs murs naturels décorés avec des tableaux de goût et d'anciennes œuvres d'art. Les tentures sont en accord avec l'âge du château mais les chambres superbes sont plus contemporaines.

Diese Burg aus dem 13. Jahrhundert bietet genug Eleganz, Charme und Atmosphäre für selbst den anspruchsvollsten Gast. Majestätische Steinwände sind von Zinnen gekrönt, und der Burggraben führt zum Swimmingpool. Im kühlen Interieur verbinden sich Details einer längst vergangenen Zeit mit dem Luxus des 21. Jahrhunderts, und die natürlichen Wände in den großen Aufenthaltsräumen sind mit edlen Gemälden und alten Kunstwerken geschmückt. Die Einrichtung ist dem Alter der Burg angemessen, doch die Zimmer sind zeitgenössisch und haben eigene Bäder.

Our inspector loved: *The beautiful bathrooms with strong colours and ceramic, hand painted wash basins.*

Directions: Madrid or Valladolid Airport > N630 - Salamanca - Zamora Road.

Web: www.johansens.com/buenamor
E-mail: castillo@buenamor.net
Tel: +34 923 355 002
Fax: +34 923 355 112

Price Guide: (excluding VAT)
double €182-245
suite €245-285

TANCAT DE CODORNIU

CTRA N340, KM 1059, 43530 ALCANAR, SPAIN

Directions: The nearest airports are Barcelona and Valencia. A7 > exit 42 towards Alcanar > N340. The hotel is closed 12th January - 12th February 2005.

Web: www.johansens.com/tancat
E-mail: info@tancatdecodorniu.com
Tel: +34 977 737 194
Fax: +34 977 737 231

Price Guide: (room only, excluding VAT)
double €100-140
suite €125-200

This striking 19th-century country house is delightfully set amongst orange groves and is only a short walk from unspoilt, stunning beaches. The simple, beautifully designed interiors are decorated with colourful modern artworks and relaxing armchairs, whilst the cool bedrooms are reflective and peaceful. There are 2 pools, one for children, and small pavilions to provide plenty of shade during the hottest hours. The new restaurant is set in the garden and offers freshly caught fish and lobster as a real treat.

Cette impressionnante maison de campagne du XIXe siècle est délicieusement située au milieu d'orangeraies et n'est qu'à quelques minutes de magnifiques plages désertes. Les intérieurs, simples et superbes, sont décorés d'illustrations modernes et colorées et de fauteuils accueillants tandis que les chambres sont claires et tranquilles. Il y a 2 piscines, dont une pour les enfants, et de nombreux petits pavillons offrent beaucoup d'ombre pendant les heures les plus chaudes. Le nouveau restaurant se trouve dans le jardin et propose poissons et homards frais.

Dieses eindrucksvolle Landhaus aus dem 19. Jahrhundert liegt idyllisch inmitten von Orangenhainen und ist nur einen kleinen Spaziergang von herrlichen unberührten Stränden entfernt. Das schöne, einfache Interieur ist mit modernen bunten Kunstwerken geschmückt, und die kühlen Zimmer bieten erholsame Ruhe. Es gibt 2 Pools, einer davon für Kinder, und kleine, schattenspendende Pavillons. Das neue Restaurant befindet sich im Garten, auf der Speisekarte stehen fangfrischer Fisch und als besondere Belohnung Hummer.

Our inspector loved: *Dining al fresco by the orange groves.*

CLARIS HOTEL

PAU CLARIS 150, 08009 BARCELONA, SPAIN

This former palace, close to the Paseo de Gracia still retains its graceful Renaissance façade whilst the interior is an example of avant-garde design with marble, glass and rare timbers. Art pieces and 5th-century Roman mosaics abound, and there is a collection of Egyptian art. The bedrooms are contemporary design with antique objets d'art. Creative Mediterranean cuisine and Spanish and French wines can be sampled in the gourmet restaurant and cocktail bar, East 47. There are also 2 other restaurants, La Terraza del Claris and the Claris. Wireless Internet connection available.

Cet ancien palais, près du Paseo de Gracia, conserve toujours sa gracieuse façade Renaissance alors que l'intérieur est un exemple d'avant-garde avec marbre, verre et des bois rares. Des œuvres d'art et des mosaïques romaines du Ve siècle abondent, et il y a une collection d'art égyptien. Les chambres ont un décor contemporain. Une cuisine méditerranéenne originale peut être dégustée au restaurant gourmet et bar-cocktail East 47, accompagnée des vins espagnols et français. Il existe également 2 autres restaurants, La Terraza del Clariset le Claris. Service Internet sans fil disponible.

Dieses einstige Palais nahe des Paseo de Gracia besitzt immer noch seine elegante Renaissancefassade, das Interieur dagegen ist ein Beispiel avantgardistischen Designs mit Marmor, Glas und seltenem Holz. Überall findet man Kunstgegenstände und römische Mosaiken aus dem 5. Jahrhundert, außerdem eine Sammlung ägyptischer Kunst. Die Zimmer sind zeitgenössisch mit antiken Objets d'art eingerichtet. Im Gourmetrestaurant und der Cocktailbar East 47 werden Mittelmeergerichte und spanische und französische Weine serviert, man kann aber auch das La Terraza del Claris oder das Claris besuchen. Drahtloser Internetzugang vorhanden.

Our inspector loved: *The rooftop terrace with wonderful views across the city.*

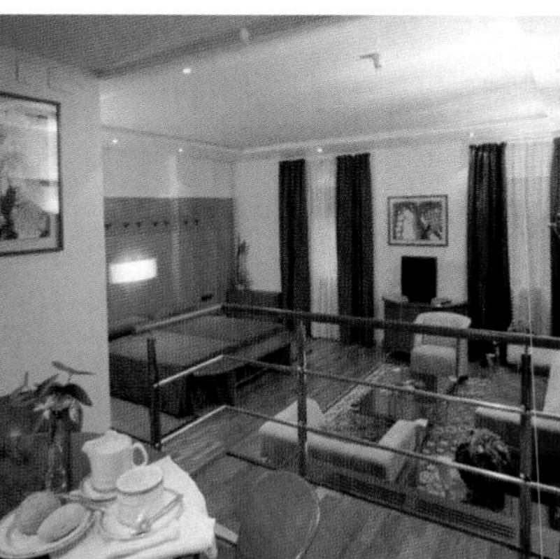

Directions: Pau Claris > Paseo de Gracia > Calle de Valencia. The hotel is in the centre of Barcelona.

Web: www.johansens.com/claris
E-mail: claris@derbyhotels.es
Tel: +34 934 87 62 62
Fax: +34 932 15 79 70

Barcelona
Madrid
Málaga

Price Guide: (breakfast €19, excluding VAT)
single €358
double/twin €398
suite €542-1,012

GALLERY HOTEL

ROSSELLÓ 249, 08008 BARCELONA, SPAIN

Directions: Between Rambla de Catalaña and Paseo de Gracia. Transfers are available from the airport to the hotel.

Web: www.johansens.com/gallery
E-mail: email@galleryhotel.com
Tel: +34 934 15 99 11
Fax: +34 934 15 91 84

Price Guide: (room only, excluding VAT)
single €232
double €264
suite €310

Visitors to the Gallery Hotel are enveloped by a warm ambience and are treated to a personal service whilst enjoying the fine standards of accommodation. Featuring a stylish blend of modern and classic décor, the bedrooms offer every amenity including fax. The Scotch Bar is ideal for a preprandial drink after which fine cuisine may be enjoyed in the atmospheric Café Del Gallery. A garden terrace, fitness centre and separate saunas offer revitalisation to visitors returning from a day exploring vibrant Barcelona. A business centre is available.

Les visiteurs du Gallery découvrent une atmosphère chaleureuse et un service personalisé, tout en profitant de cet établissement de grand standing. Les chambres, savant mélange d'éléments modernes et classiques, offrent tout le confort possible (incluant fax). Le Scotch Bar est idéal pour prendre l'apéritif à la suite de quoi une excellente cuisine vous est proposée au Café Del Gallery. Une terrasse au jardin, des saunas et un club de remise en forme attendent les visiteurs en quête de revitalisation après une journée de visite de Barcelone. Un centre d'affaires est disponible.

Die Gallery versprüht eine herzliche Atmosphäre, die von persönlichen Service noch verstärkt wird. Die Unterkunft ist erstklassig, und die Zimmer, sowohl modern als auch klassisch gestaltet, bieten jeden erdenklichen Komfort inklusive Fax. Die Scotch Bar ist ideal für einen Apéritif, und danach lässt man sich im charaktervollen Café Del Gallery von erlesenen Speisen verführen. Eine Gartenterrasse, ein Fitnesszentrum und separate Saunen sorgen nach einem langen Tag im lebhaften Barcelona für Entspannung. Ein Business-Zentrum ist vorhanden.

Our inspector loved: *Taking a drink on the green patio - a great city garden.*

SPAIN / CATALUÑA (BARCELONA)

GRAN HOTEL LA FLORIDA

CARRETERA VALLVIDRERA AL TIBIDABO 83-93, 08035 BARCELONA, SPAIN

With spectacular views overlooking the city and the Mediterranean Sea, this stunning new 5-star urban resort is filled with art and sculptures by internationally renowned artists. There are 74 amazing bedrooms and suites, including 8 designer suites with Jacuzzis, gardens and/or large terraces. Alfresco dining can be enjoyed at L'Orangerie, whilst the private Club Luna is the best venue in the city to enjoy live Jazz music. The Spa has a state-of-the-art gymnasium, sauna and a steam bath as well as a breathtaking 37-metre stainless steel indoor-outdoor swimming pool.

Offrant de superbes vues sur la ville de Barcelone et la Méditerranée, ce magnifique nouveau resort 5* est décoré de nombreuses œuvres d'art et sculptures d'artistes de renommée internationale. Il y a 74 chambres et suites dont 8 suites de designer avec jacuzzis, jardins et/ou terrasses. Les repas peuvent être pris en plein air au restaurant l'Orangerie et le club privé Club Luna est le meilleur endroit de la ville pour écouter du Jazz. Le spa a une salle de gym, un sauna et un hammam de pointe ainsi qu'une piscine intérieure-extérieure de 37 mètres en inox à couper le souffle.

Gran Hotel La Florida besticht mit spektakulären Panoramablicken über ganz Barcelona sowie das Mittelmeer. Das Luxushotel ist mit Kunst und Skulpturen international renomierter Künstler gefüllt. Es gibt 74 beeindruckende Zimmer, darunter 8 Designersuiten mit Jacuzzi, Garten und/oder Terrasse. Im L'Orangerie kann man al fresco dinieren, und der private Club Luna ist der beste Ort der Stadt für Live-Jazzmusik. Das Spa bietet einen hochmodernen Fitnessraum, Sauna, Dampfbad und einen atemberaubenden 37 Meter langen Außen- und Innenpool aus Stahl.

Our inspector loved: *The spectacular views of Barcelona.*

Directions: The nearest airport is Barcelona. Located 15 minutes from the city centre and 20 minutes from the airport.

Web: www.johansens.com/florida
E-mail: reservations@luxurylifestylehotels.com
Tel: +34 93 259 30 00
Fax: +34 93 259 30 01

Barcelona
Madrid
Málaga

Price Guide: (room only, excluding VAT)
single from €275
double from €275
suite €650-2,400

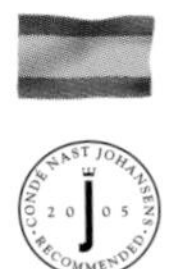

Hotel Casa Fuster

PASSEIG DE GRÀCIA 132, 08008 BARCELONA, SPAIN

Directions: The hotel is in the city centre. The nearest airport is Barcelona.

Web: www.johansens.com/fuster
E-mail: casafuster@holescenter.es
Tel: +34 93 255 30 00
Fax: +34 93 255 30 02

Price Guide: (room only, excluding VAT)
single €360
double €360-520
suite €750-1,750

Enjoying a central location, this recently opened, impressive 19th-century property affords stunning views over the city of Barcelona. The bedrooms and suites are decorated in a 1930s theme, painted in sumptuous shades of chocolate brown and rich red and embellished with potted plants and art déco furniture. The restaurant, serving contemporary Mediterranean cuisine, boasts similar modernist décor as well as a fantastic sweeping silver ceiling. After dining guests may relax in the bar area, sinking into huge, over stuffed sofas adorned with plush velvet cushions.

Bénéficiant d'un emplacement central, cet impressionnant bâtiment du XIXe siècle récemment ouvert offre de superbes vues sur la ville de Barcelone. Les chambres et suites sont décorées dans un style 1930, peintes dans de somptueux tons de marron chocolat et de rouge intense et embellies par des plantes et des meubles art déco. Le restaurant sert une cuisine méditerranéenne contemporaine dans un décor moderniste similaire et avec un somptueux plafond argent. Après dîner, les clients peuvent se relaxer au bar et se prélasser dans d'énormes canapés rembourrés couverts de coussins en peluche violets.

Dieses eindrucksvolle, zentral gelegene, kürzlich eröffnete Hotel aus dem 19. Jahrhundert bietet eine atemberaubende Sicht auf Barcelona. Die Zimmer und Suiten sind im 30er Jahre Stil gestaltet, in üppigen Tönen wie Schokoladenbraun und Tiefrot gestrichen und mit Topfpflanzen und Art Déco Mobiliar eingerichtet. Im Restaurant wird moderne Mittelmeerküche serviert, das Décor ist ähnlich modernistisch, mit einer fantastischen silberfarbenen Decke. Nach dem Essen ruft der Barbereich, wo man sich in riesige, üppig gepolsterte und mit Samtkissen verzierte Sofas fallen läßt.

Our inspector loved: *The bar, with ornamental columns and out-sized sofas.*

HOTEL COLÓN

AVENIDA DE LA CATEDRAL 7, 08002 BARCELONA, SPAIN

Situated in the old Gothic quarter, this hotel offers a combination of fine accommodation, excellent service and friendly staff resulting in a most inviting ambience. Vibrant décor with brightly coloured fabrics features throughout the hotel and the front rooms afford glorious views of the square and the 13th-century cathedral. The suites at the rear boast picturesque terraces. Drinks can be enjoyed in the classic, English-style bar. Seafood is a hotel speciality; with salmon, clams, squid and hake all used to create international and typical Catalan dishes.

Situé dans le vieux quartier gothique, cet hôtel offre un logement raffiné, un service excellent et un personnel amical qui donne une ambiance des plus sympathiques. L'hôtel est paré d'un décor vif avec des tissus de couleurs éclatantes. Les chambres de devant offrent des vues sur la place de la cathédrale du XIIIe siècle, alors que les suites à l'arrière ont des terrasses pittoresques. Les hôtes peuvent prendre un verre au bar classique d'un style anglais, et les fruits de mer sont la spécialité avec saumon, praires, poulpe et colin, tous cuisinés pour créer des plats internationaux et catalans.

Dieses einladende Hotel liegt im Gotischen Viertel und bietet gediegene Unterkunft, exzellenten Service und freundliches Personal. Kräftiges Décor mit bunten Stoffen ziert das gesamte Hotel. Die Zimmer an der Frontseite bieten einen Ausblick auf den Platz und die Kathedrale aus dem 13. Jahrhundert, während die Suiten an der Rückseite malerische Terrassen haben. Drinks kann man in der klassischen englischen Bar genießen, und auf der Speisekarte stehen internationale und katalanische Gerichte, vor allem Fisch und Meeresfrüchte wie Lachs, Muscheln, Tintenfisch und Seehecht.

Our inspector loved: *The English-style bar in the heart of a Spanish medieval square.*

 145

 150

Directions: Located in the Gothic quarter, in the centre of town. The nearest metro station is Jaume I. The nearest airport is Barcelona.

Barcelona
Madrid
Málaga

Web: www.johansens.com/colon
E-mail: info@hotelcolon.es
Tel: +34 933 01 14 04
Fax: +34 933 17 29 15

Price Guide: (room only, excluding VAT)
single €155–180
double/twin €220–310
suite €350

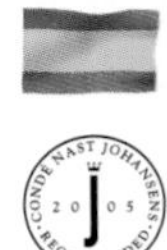

HOTEL OMM

ROSSELLÓ 265, 08008 BARCELONA, SPAIN

This stylishly modern hotel lies discreetly hidden among the many main streets of cosmopolitan Barcelona. The vast bedrooms are elegantly decorated with a minimal theme, and each has CD player and Internet access, with great emphasis being placed on soft, mood lighting. The restaurant Moo is run by the Roca brothers of Celler de Can Roca in Girona and each course comes with a recommended wine by the glass.

Cet hôtel moderne de style est discrètement caché parmi les rues principales de la cosmopolite Barcelone. Les vastes chambres sont élégamment décorées sur un thème minimaliste et ont toutes lecteur CD et accès internet. L'accent est mis sur une ambiance et un éclairage doux. Le restaurant Moo est géré par les frères Roca du Celler de Can Roca à Girona et chaque plat est accompagné d'un vin recommandé, servi au verre.

Dieses stilvolle moderne Hotel befindet sich versteckt inmitten der vielen Hauptstraßen von Barcelona. Die riesigen Zimmer sind elegant und minimalistisch gestaltet, jedes bietet CD-Player und Internetzugang. Große Betonung liegt auf sanfter, stimmungsvoller Beleuchtung. Das Restaurant Moo wird von den Roca-Brüdern vom Roca-Brüdern vom Celler de Can Roca in Girona geleitet, und jeder Gang wird von einem speziell empfohlenen Glas Wein ergänzt.

Our inspector loved: *The welcoming entrance; cosy yet full of light and life.*

Directions: Barcelona Airport > centre of the city.

Web: www.johansens.com/hotelomm
E-mail: reservas@hotelomm.es
Tel: +34 93 445 40 00
Fax: +34 93 445 40 04

Price Guide: (room only, excluding VAT)
single €290-350
double €290-420
suite €500

HOTEL URBISOL

CTRA MANRESA TO MOIÀ (N-141C), KM 20, 08279 CALDERS, BARCELONA, SPAIN

Visitors to this charming little country hotel, situated close to the lovely village of Calders, can expect a hospitable welcome together with high standards of accommodation and comfort. Furnishings and décor are stylishly contemporary and attractive. The 11 bedrooms and 2 suites offer every required amenity and picturesque views over the gardens and countryside. One suite features a four-poster bed, the other has a kitchen and open fireplace. There are cool terraces on which to relax and chat and a swimming pool.

Les clients de ce petit hôtel de charme de campagne, situé près du joli village de Calders, recevront un accueil chaleureux et d'excellents standards d'hébergement et de confort. Ameublements et décoration sont de style contemporain et élégants. Les 11 chambres et 2 suites offrent tous les équipements ainsi que des vues pittoresques sur les jardins et la campagne avoisinante. Une des suites est équipée d'un lit à baldaquin, une autre d'une cuisine et d'une cheminée. L'hôtel est pourvue de terrasses fraîches où se relaxer et également d'une piscine.

Wer dieses charmante kleine Landhotel in der Nähe des hübschen Dorfes Calders besucht, kann sich auf einen herzlichen Empfang, exzellente Unterkunft und höchsten Komfort freuen. Einrichtung und Décor sind elegant und zeitgenössisch, und die 11 Zimmer und 2 Suiten sind mit jeglichem Detail ausgestattet und haben eine malerische Sicht auf die Gärten und Umgebung. Eine der Suiten bietet ein Himmelbett, die andere eine Küche und einen offenen Kamin. Entspannen kann man sich wunderbar auf den kühlen Terrassen und am Swimmingpool.

Our inspector loved: *The spacious suites with their beautiful views across the hills.*

Directions: The nearest airport is Barcelona. C-58 to Sabadell, Terrassa, Manresa > C-16 to Manresa > exit St Fruitòs de Bages, Navarcles > Moià. The hotel is just beyond the village of Calders, just before Moià.

Web: www.johansens.com/urbisol
E-mail: info@hotelurbisol.com
Tel: +34 93 830 9153
Fax: +34 93 830 92 62

Price Guide:
double €115-130
superior €145-160
suite €175-190

Hotel Santa Marta

PLAYA DE SANTA CRISTINA, 17310 LLORET DE MAR, SPAIN

Directions: The nearest airports are Gerona and Barcelona. N11 to Blanes > 2km along coast road > north to Lloret de Mar.

Web: www.johansens.com/santamarta
E-mail: info@hstamarta.com
Tel: +34 972 364 904
Fax: +34 972 369 280

Price Guide: (excluding breakfast and tax)
single €90-162
double €106-264
suite €180-370

Surrounded by pine-covered hills and with extensive gardens sloping down to a spectacular sandy beach and the Mediterranean's warm, translucent waters, this attractive hotel offers tranquillity and comfort together with an extensive range of sport and leisure facilities. Furnishings and décor are classic, public rooms spacious, en-suite guest rooms light and with shaded balconies from which to enjoy sea, garden or hillside views. First-class cuisine is served in a traditional-style restaurant with charming features such as wall displays of copper pans.

Entouré de collines de pins et avec de vastes jardins descendant directement sur une superbe plage de sable blanc et sur les eaux tièdes et transparentes de la Méditerranée, ce bel hôtel offre tranquillité et confort mais également un large choix d'activités de sports et de loisirs. Ameublements et décoration sont de style classique, les salons sont spacieux et les chambres offrent un balcon ombragé d'où l'on peut admirer la mer, le jardin ou les collines. Une cuisine de premier ordre est servie dans un cadre traditionnel avec de charmants détails tes qu'un mur de casseroles en cuivre.

Umgeben von mit Pinien bedeckten Hügeln und ausgedehnten Gärten, die sich bis zu einem herrlichen Sandstrand und dem warmen, klaren Wasser des Mittelmeers erstrecken, bietet dieses attraktive Hotel Ruhe, Komfort und eine riesige Auswahl an Sport- und Freizeitaktivitäten. Einrichtung und Décor sind klassisch, die Aufenthaltsräume großzügig, und jedes der hellen Zimmer hat ein eigenes Bad und einen beschatteten Balkon mit Blick auf Meer, Garten oder Hügellandschaft. Erstklassige Küche wird im traditionell gestalteten Restaurant serviert, in dem man bezaubernde Details wie z.B. Kupferpfannen an der Wand findet.

Our inspector loved: *The secluded sandy beach in front of the hotel.*

     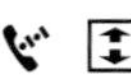  

Rigat Park & Spa Hotel

AV. AMERICA 1, PLAYA DE FENALS, 17310 LLORET DE MAR, COSTA BRAVA, GERONA, SPAIN

Surrounded by lush gardens and pine trees exuding their distinctive aroma, the Rigat Park is an ideal base for exploring the beaches of Costa Brava and the nearby Catalan towns. The 21 beautiful Mediterranean-style suites have tiled floors and marble bathrooms and 3 have motorised posturing beds. Guests may play billiards, swim in the pool or take advantage of the newly opened spa that offers sauna, Jacuzzi, mineralised water and indoor heated pool.

Entouré de jardins luxuriants et de pins exsudant leur senteur particulière, le Rigat Park Hôtel est une base idéale pour explorer les plages de la Costa Brava et les viles catalanes proches. Les 21 belles suites méditerranéennes ont un sol carrelés et des salles de bain en marbre et 3 ont des lits à position réglable motorisés. Les hôtes peuvent jouer au billard, profiter de la piscine ou des nouveaux Bains avec sauna, jacuzzi, eau minérale et piscine intérieure chauffée.

Dieses von üppigen Gärten und duftenden Pinienbäumen umgebene Hotel mit seiner Landhausatmosphäre ist der ideale Ausgangspunkt für Ausflüge an die Costa Brava und die umliegenden katalonischen Städte. Die 21 zauberhaften Suiten im mediterranen Stil bieten Fliesenböden und Marmorbäder und 3 haben automatisch verstellbare Betten. Man kann Billiard spielen, schwimmen oder das neueröffnete Spa mit Sauna, Jacuzzi, mineralisiertem Wasser und beheiztem Hallenbad besuchen

Our inspector loved: *The spacious bars and lounge areas, inside and out.*

Directions: A7 > exit 9 > Lloret de Mar > Fenals Beach. Barcelona and Gerona Airports are nearby.

Web: www.johansens.com/rigatpark
E-mail: info@rigat.com
Tel: +34 972 36 52 00
Fax: +34 972 37 04 11

Price Guide:
single €170-220
double €190-300
suite €300-1,300

99 SPA

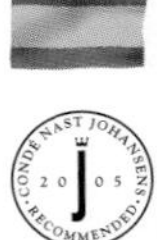

MAS FALGARONA

AVINYONET DE PUIGVENTOS, 17742 GERONA, SPAIN

In this well restored 16th-century farmhouse, décor is contemporary with a mixture of white drapes, terracotta floors, intriguing lighting and original wooden beams. All bathrooms are individually furnished with Mallorcan hand-painted tiles. Care is taken by the owners to offer an attentive and personal service, and dinner menus change daily. The hotel is situated in the open countryside with bicycles provided and golf nearby. Other places of interest include Avinyonet, Figueres and Cadaques.

Dans cette ferme du XVIe siècle joliment restaurée, le décor est contemporain avec un mélange de tentures blanches, des sols terracotta, des lumières fascinantes et poutres d'origine. Toutes les salles de bain sont décorées individuellement avec des carrelages majorquins peints à la main. Les propriétaires prennent soin d'offrir un service personnalisé et attentif, et les menus du dîner changent quotidiennement. L'hôtel est situé en pleine campagne, les bicyclettes sont fournies et le golf est proche. Dans les environs, Avinyonet, Figueres and Cadaques sont à visiter.

Das Décor dieses herrlich restaurierten Bauernhauses aus dem 16. Jahrhundert ist zeitgenössisch mit einer Mischung aus weißen Stoffen, Terrakottaböden, interessanter Beleuchtung und Original-Holzbalkendecken. Alle Bäder sind individuell mit handbemalten mallorquinischen Fliesen gestaltet. Der Service ist aufmerksam und persönlich und die Speisekarte ändert sich täglich. Die ländliche Umgebung lädt zu Fahrradtouren ein, man kann Golf spielen oder Avinyonet, Figueres und Cadaques besuchen.

Our inspector loved: *The thoughtful design of the rooms; everything is exactly where you need it.*

Directions: A7 motorway > exit 4 > Figueres-Olot > N260. The nearest airports are Barcelona, Gerona and Perpignon.

Web: www.johansens.com/masfalgarona
E-mail: email@masfalgarona.com
Tel: +34 972 54 66 28
Fax: +34 972 54 70 71

Price Guide:
single €135–255
double €168–195
junior suite €225–290
suite €265–320

HOTEL MAS PASSAMANER

CAMÍ DE LA SERRA 52, 43470 LA SELVA DEL CAMP (TARRAGONA), SPAIN

Set in a hazelnut orchard, this 1920s building has been magnificently restored in a modernist style featuring fabulous sculptures and ceramics. Splashes of vibrant colours contrast with neutral marble and stone flooring enhanced by ambient lighting. The superior double bedrooms and suites are exquisitely chic, and the delicious seasonal menu is supervised by a 2 Michelin-star awarded chef. Extensive hydrotherapy, electrotherapy and massage treatments are available; alternatively guests may enjoy archery and the on-site football pitch.

Situé dans un verger de noisetiers, ce bâtiment des années 20 a été superbement restauré dans un style moderniste, offrant de magnifiques sculptures et céramiques. Les touches de couleurs vives sont en contraste avec le ton neutre du marbre et le sol en pierre, mis en valeur par l'éclairage ambiant. Les chambres doubles supérieures et les suites sont très chics, et le délicieux menu de saison est sous la supervision d'un chef à 2 étoiles Michelin. Hydrothérapie, électrothérapie et soins manuels sont disponibles. Les hôtes peuvent également s'essayer au tir à l'arc ou se défouler sur le terrain de foot.

Dieses inmitten eines mit Haselnussbäumen gefüllten Gartens gelegene Haus aus den 20er Jahren wurde perfekt restauriert und bietet nun modernistischen Stil mit herrlichen Skulpturen und Keramiken. Kraftvolle Farben kontrastieren mit neutralen Marmor- und Steinböden, deren Wirkung durch atmosphärische Beleuchtung noch verstärkt wird. Die eleganten Zimmer und Suiten sind exquisit, und ein 2-Michelinsterne-Chefkoch sorgt für kulinarischen Genuss. Umfassende Hydro- und Elektrotherapiebehandlungen und Massagen werden angeboten, ebenso Bogenschießen und Fußball.

Our inspector loved: *The Royal Suites - contemporary duplexes with their own private pools.*

Directions: Barcelona/Revs Airports > A7 > exit 34 to Montblanc > Selva del Camp.

Web: www.johansens.com/passamaner
E-mail: hotel@maspassamaner.com
Tel: +34 977 766 333
Fax: +34 977 766 336

Price Guide: (room only, excluding VAT)
single €135-175
double €170-215
suite €240-510

HOTEL DEL TEATRE

PLAÇA MAJOR S/N, 17214 REGENCÓS, COSTA BRAVA, GIRONA, SPAIN

Formerly two 18th-century farmhouses, this attractive hotel stands in the main square of a village oozing serenity and historical ambience. The cool interior, featuring bleached beams and pastel tinted walls, combines traditional and 21st-century furniture and fittings. Each bedroom is designed to an impeccable standard, offering privacy and attentive service. Pre-dinner apèritifs are enjoyed in the garden bar, overlooking the secluded swimming pool, before taking meals in the elegant dining room.

Autrefois deux métairies du XVIIIe siècle, ce superbe hôtel se dresse sur la place du village d'où il émane sérénité et une atmosphère historique. L'intérieur, avec ses poutres décolorées et ses murs couleurs pastels, associe des meubles et installations traditionnelles avec celles du XXIe siècle. Chaque chambre est absolument impeccable et offre intimité ainsi qu'un service attentif. Le bar du jardin, qui surplombe la piscine, est le lieu idéal pour prendre l'apéritif avant de dîner dans l'élégante salle à manger.

Dieses attraktive Hotel, einst zwei Bauernhäuser aus dem 18. Jahrhundert, befindet sich direkt am Hauptplatz eines hübschen Dorfes mit historischem Ambiente. Das kühle Interieur mit seinen gebleichten Holzbalken und pastellfarbenen Wänden verbindet traditionelle Möbel und Einrichtungen mit denen des 21. Jahrhunderts. Privatsphäre und aufmerksamer Service sind garantiert, und jedes Zimmer ist absolut makellos. In der Gartenbar mit Blick auf den etwas abgeschieden gelegenen Swimmingpool kann man einen Apéritif genießen, bevor der elegante Speisesaal zum Abendessen einlädt.

Our inspector loved: *The modern facilities incorporated in a traditional setting.*

Directions: Girona/Barcelona Airport > A7 > exit 6 > La Bisbal c31 from Palafrugell to Regencós.

Web: www.johansens.com/teatre
E-mail: info@hoteldelteatre.com
Tel: +34 972 30 62 70
Fax: +34 972 30 62 73

Price Guide: (room only, excluding VAT)
double €110-155
suite €150-170

ROMANTIC VILLA - HOTEL VISTABELLA

CALA CANYELLES PETITES, PO BOX 3, 17480 ROSES (GERONA), SPAIN

Overlooking a spectacular sandy beach, this tranquil, unique hotel offers 30 bedrooms, including 8 suites. The Royal Suite features 2 bedrooms. All rooms are individually furnished and most have a sea view. The hotel can organise activities such as scuba diving, water skiing, sky diving and various mountain sports and guests may board the hotel's boat for private excursions. Every Friday and Saturday the gastronomic feasts are not to be missed and with 4 restaurants the hotel serves a sumptuous range of cuisine. The Dali Museum is nearby.

Avec ses vues magnifiques de la plage, cet hôtel tranquille propose 30 chambres, dont 8 sont des suites. La suite royale a 2 chambres. Chaque pièce est meublée de manière individuelle et la plupart ont une vue sur la mer. L'hôtel organise des sports comme la plongée sous-marine, le ski nautique, le parachutisme en chute libre et de divers sports de montagne. Son bateau est à la disposition des clients pour des excursions privées. Le vendredi et samedi il faut déguster la délicieuse cuisine, avec ses 4 restaurants les hôtes ont l'embarras du choix. Le musée Dali n'est pas très loin.

Dieses ruhige, luxuriöse Hotel mit Blick auf einen spektakulären Sandstrand bietet 8 Suiten mit separatem Wohnzimmer, die Royal Suite besitzt 2 Schlafzimmer. Alle Zimmer sind individuell gestaltet, die meisten haben Meerblick. Aktivitäten wie Tauchen, Wasserski, Skydiving und verschiedene Bergsportarten können organisiert werden, und das hoteleigene Boot steht den Gästen für Privatausflüge zur Verfügung. Die Gourmetabende jeden Freitag und Samstag sollte man sich nicht entgehen lassen, und die 4 Restaurants sorgen für kulinarische Vielfalt. In der Nähe befindet sich das Dali Museum.

Our inspector loved: _The Dali Suite - the spirit of the artist is truly captured._

Directions: The nearest airport is Girona or Perpignan. Alternatively Barcelona International Airport is still nearby. Vistabella is 2km past Roses, along the coast road.

Web: www.johansens.com/vistabella
E-mail: info@vistabellahotel.com
Tel: +34 972 25 62 00
Fax: +34 972 25 32 13

Price Guide:
double €160–280
suite €280–410

San Sebastian Playa Hotel

CALLE PORT ALEGRE 53, 08870 SITGES (BARCELONA), SPAIN

Located in the cosmopolitan town of Sitges, this hotel offers a sense of peace and tranquillity and extremely friendly Spanish hospitality. The spacious bedrooms have balconies, whilst the bathrooms boast thermostatic showers. El Posit, set directly on the sea, specialises in seafood dishes and uses the finest of local produce. With no less than 17 beaches, an abundance of restaurants and museums, activities for all tastes are catered for. Extensive, state-of-the-art audio-visual equipment is available with a professional conference team on hand to help organise a variety of events.

Situé dans la ville cosmopolite de Sitges, cet hôtel offre un sentiment de paix et de tranquillité et l'extrêmement amicale hospitalité espagnole. Chaque chambre est spacieuse et a un balcon, et les salles de bain bénéficient de douches thermostatiques. El Posit, qui donne directement sur la mer, sert poissons et fruits de mer et utilise les meilleurs produits locaux. Avec 17 plages, un grand nombre de restaurants et musées, il y a des activités pour tous les goûts. Des équipements audio-visuels ultramodernes combinent avec un personnel très professionnel qui aide à l'organisation d'une variété d'événements.

Dieses in der kosmopoliten Stadt Sitges gelegene Hotel bietet ein Gefühl von Ruhe und Frieden und freundlichste spanische Gastfreundschaft. Die großen Zimmer haben Balkone, und die Bäder sind mit thermostatischen Duschen ausgestattet. Im El Posit direct am Meer genießt man fangfrischen Fisch und beste einheimische Zutaten. 17 Strände und eine Fülle von Restaurants und Museen bieten Unterhaltung für jeden Geschmack. Hochmoderne audiovisuelle Ausstattung ist vorhanden, und das erfahrene Konferenzteam hilft bei der Organisation jeglicher Veranstaltungen.

Directions: Barcelona Airport > motorway to Sitges > hotel is signposted.

Web: www.johansens.com/sebastian
E-mail: hotelsansebastian@hotelsansebastian.com
Tel: +34 93 894 86 76
Fax: +34 93 894 04 30

Price Guide: (room only)
single €105-201
double €115-230
suite €195-330

Our inspector loved: *The pretty poolside garden area.*

Hotel Torre Martí

C/ RAMON LLULL 11, 08504 ST JULIÀ DE VILATORTA, SPAIN

This family-run hotel, reminiscent of a French Riviera mansion, sits at the foot of Guilleries, the Catalan pre-Pyrenees. The public rooms reflect 19th-century style with magnificent furnishings and artefacts and soothing pastel colours create a relaxing atmosphere in the bedrooms, which feature 1950s-style bathrooms. Chef patron, Pere Morral, serves creative cuisine from locally produced ingredients in the art nouveau dining room. Relax in the lounge or explore the surrounding area with its many churches and monasteries.

Cet hôtel familial, dont l'architecture rappelle celle des hôtels particuliers de la Côte d'Azur, est situé au pied des pre-pyrénées catalans. L'intérieur est décoré dans un style du XIXe siècle avec de magnifiques meubles et bibelots. Les chambres de couleurs pastels sont très accueillantes et les salles de bains ont un style années 50. Le chef propriétaire, Pere Morral, propose une cuisine créative à partir d'ingrédients locaux, servie dans une salle à manger art nouveau. Les hôtes peuvent se relaxer dans le salon ou visiter les environs riches d'églises et de monastères.

Dieses an ein Haus an der Französischen Riviera erinnernde, familiengeführte Hotel liegt am Fuße der Guilleries, der katalanischen Pyrenäen. Die Aufenthaltsräume spiegeln mit herrlicher Einrichtung und Kunstgegenständen den Stil des 19. Jahrhunderts wider, und Pastellfarben schaffen eine entspannende Atmosphäre in den Zimmern, deren Bäder im 50er Jahre Stil gehalten sind. Chefkoch Pere Morral serviert kreative, aus einheimischen Zutaten zubereitete Speisen in einem Jugendstil-Speisesaal. Entspannt wird in der Lounge, und die Umgebung mit ihren Kirchen und Klöstern lädt zur Erkundung ein.

Our inspector loved: *The furniture and lamps; every piece is fascinating.*

Directions: Girona/Barcelona Airport > Vic > St Julià de Vilatorta is indicated off Vic > Girona road (C25).

Web: www.johansens.com/marti
E-mail: hoteltorremarti@yahoo.es
Tel: +34 938 88 83 72
Fax: +34 938 88 83 74

Price Guide: (excluding VAT)
single €88-110
double €88-135
suite €215

Gran Hotel Hesperia La Toja

ISLA DE LA TOJA S/N, 36991 PONTEVEDRA, SPAIN

Directions: Santiago de Compostela Airport > A9 to Pontevedra > O Grove > La Toja.

Web: www.johansens.com/latoja
E-mail: hotel@granhotelhesperia-latoja.com
Tel: +34 986 73 00 25
Fax: +34 986 73 00 26

Price Guide: (room only, excluding VAT)
single €123-216
double €155-216
suite €218-309

Traditional and elegant, this hotel enjoys a wonderful location on the coast of a small island, overlooking the Mediterranean Sea and surrounded by pine woodland. On arrival guests are enveloped by the warm hospitality and attentive service of the staff. The comfortable bedrooms are well appointed and the à la carte restaurant offers a wide selection of mouthwatering dishes. The large fitness area includes a sauna, indoor pool and gym that incorporates a separate health spa providing a wide variety of treatments.

Traditionnel et élégant, cet hôtel, entouré de pins et surplombant la Méditerannéee, est idéalement situé sur la côte d'une petite île. Dès leur arrivée, les hôtes sont séduits par l'accueil chaleureux et l'attention du personnel. Les chambres confortables sont bien agencées et le restaurant à la carte propose une large sélection de plats alléchants. Le vaste centre de remise en forme est composé d'un sauna, d'une piscine intérieure, d'une salle de gym et d'un spa offrant un grand choix de soins.

Dieses traditionelle, elegante Hotel liegt herrlich an der Küste einer kleinen Insel mit Blick aufs Mittelmeer und umgeben von Pinienwäldern. Die Herzlichkeit und der aufmerksame Service des Personals sorgen schon bei der Ankunft für Wohlbehagen. Die komfortablen Zimmer sind gut ausgestattet und die umfassende Speisekarte im Restaurant verspricht kulinarischen Genuss. Der große Fitnessbereich bietet Sauna, Hallenbad und Fitnessraum mit separatem Spa und einer Vielzahl von Behandlungen.

Our inspector loved: *The elegant atmosphere and impeccable service.*

Hesperia Isla de la Toja

ISLA DE LA TOJA, S/N 36991 PONTEVEDRA, SPAIN

This spectacular hotel and spa was built in 2001 and boasts the ultimate in contemporary design. The charming estuary setting can be enjoyed from the indoor swimming pool with its floor length windows, and the spa offers some of the very latest thermal, beauty, slimming and anti-stress treatments. The atmosphere is young and informal and ideally suited for a relaxing break or business function.

Ce spectaculaire hôtel et spa fut construit en 2001 et offre le summum du design contemporain. Depuis la piscine intérieure, au travers de grandes baies vitrées on peut admirer le décor du charmant estuaire. Les derniers-nés des soins thermaux, de beauté, d'anti-stress et d'amaigrissement sont disponibles au spa. L'atmosphère est jeune et informelle et s'adapte parfaitement aux séjours de loisirs et d'affaires.

Dieses spektakuläre Hotel und Spa wurde 2001 erbaut und bietet ultimatives zeitgenössisches Design. Die zauberhafte Lage bewundert man am besten vom Hallenbad mit seinen wandhohen Fenstern aus, und im Spa kann man sich von den neuesten Thermal-, Beauty-, Abnehm- und Anti-Stress-Behandlungen verwöhnen lassen. Die Atmosphäre ist jung und informell und ideal für ein Entspannungswochenende oder ein Geschäftstreffen.

Our inspector loved: *The huge indoor swimming pool with views over the sea.*

Directions: Santiago de Compostela or Oporto Airports. E01 > O Grove > La Toja.

Web: www.johansens.com/isladelatoja
E-mail: hotel@hesperia-isladelatoja.com
Tel: +34 986 73 00 50
Fax: +34 986 73 01 01

Price Guide: (room only, excluding VAT)
single €107-124
double €134-155
suite €159-190

Antiguo Convento

C/ DE LAS MONJAS, S/N BOADILLA DEL MONTE, 28660 MADRID, SPAIN

Dating from the 17th century, this old convent has been beautifully refurbished with modern fittings, antiques and harmonious period details. The former nun cells have been imaginatively decorated as bedrooms and guests can enjoy a stroll through the exquisite ornamental gardens. Impressive skylights and a large covered patio create light and space. The new restaurant offers superb cuisine and extensive business facilities are provided. Madrid is nearby with excellent shopping and tourist attractions.

Ce vieux couvent du XVIIe siècle a été admirablement rénové avec des installations modernes, antiquités et d'harmonieux détails d'époque. La décoration des anciennes cellules des nonnes en chambres est originale et les hôtes peuvent se promener dans les charmants jardins ornementaux. Des lucarnes impressionnantes associées à un grand patio couvert créent lumière et espace. Une cuisine superbe est servie dans le nouveau restaurant, et l'hôtel dispose d'un centre d'affaires. Madrid est proche pour du shopping de qualité et des visites touristiques.

Dieses einstige Kloster aus dem 17. Jahrhundert wurde harmonisch mit modernen und antiken Elementen renoviert. Die ehemaligen Zellen wurden phantasievoll in Schlafzimmer umgewandelt, und die exquisit gestalteten Gärten sind herrlich für Spaziergänge. Eindrucksvolle Deckenfenster und eine große überdachte Terrasse schaffen Licht und Raum. Im neuen Restaurant wird hervorragende Küche serviert. Umfassende Konferenzeinrichtungen sind vorhanden, und Madrid und die Umgebung laden zu Besichtigungen und Einkaufstrips ein.

Directions: M40 out of Madrid towards A Coruña > M511 to Boadilla del Monte.

Web: www.johansens.com/elconvento
E-mail: informacion@elconvento.net
Tel: + 34 91 632 22 20
Fax: +34 91 633 15 12

Price Guide:
single €138.23
double €156.26
suite €300.50

Our inspector loved: *The storks nestling above the beautiful belfry.*

Gran Meliá Fénix

HERMOSILLA 2, 28001 MADRID, SPAIN

Standing majestically on the Avenida Castellana in the exclusive heart of Madrid, this superb hotel is the epitome of elegance and luxury with standards of comfort and service that exceed its 5-star rating. Behind a grand exterior are sumptuously decorated and furnished public and guest rooms that will satisfy the most discerning visitor. Each en-suite bedroom and suite has every modern facility, and the Presidential Suite, with 3 Jacuzzis, 2 terraces, gym and butler service, is probably the most luxurious in the city.

Se tenant majestueusement sur l'Avenida Castellana dans le centre chic de Madrid, cet hôtel superbe est l'exemple même de l'élégance et du luxe avec des standards de confort et de service excédant son classement 5 étoiles. Derrière un extérieur magnifique, on trouve des salles somptueusement décorées et meublées et des chambres qui satisferont les plus exigeants. Chaque chambre a sa salle de bain et bénéficie, comme les suites, de tout le confort moderne. La Suite Présidentielle, avec ses 3 jacuzzis, 2 terrasses, salle de gym et son service Maître d'Hôtel est probablement la plus luxueuse de la ville.

Dieses majestätisch an der Avenida Castellana im exklusiven Herzen Madrids gelegene Hotel ist der Inbegriff von Eleganz und Luxus, dessen Niveau an Komfort und Service seine 5 Sterne bei weitem übertrifft. Hinter einer edlen Fassade verbergen sich üppig ausgestattete Aufenthaltsräume und Zimmer, die selbst den anspruchsvollsten Gast beeindrucken. Jedes der Zimmer und Suiten mit Bad bietet jeglichen modernen Komfort, und die Präsidentensuite mit 3 Jacuzzis, 2 Terrassen, Fitnessraum und Butler-Service ist wohl die luxuriöseste Suite der ganzen Stadt.

Our inspector loved: *The Presidential Suite, lacking no luxurious detail.*

Directions: Located on the Castellana, centre Madrid.

Web: www.johansens.com/meliafenix
E-mail: comercial.gran.melia.fenix@solmelia.com
Tel: +34 91 431 67 00
Fax: +34 91 576 06 61

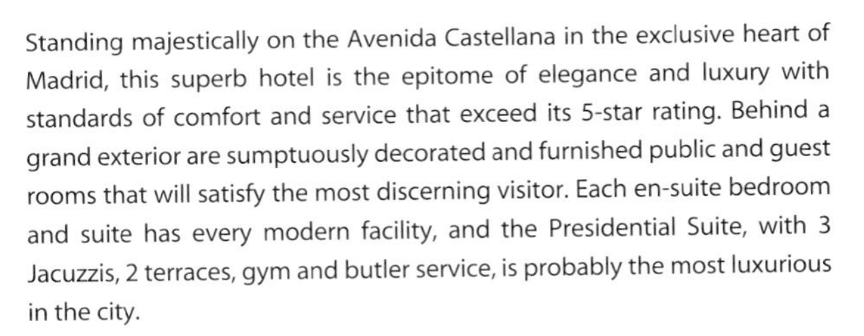

Price Guide: (per person, breakfast €25, excluding VAT)
de luxe €325-€365
single €375
double €436
suite €725-2,500

Hotel Orfila

C/ORFILA, NO 6, 28010 MADRID, SPAIN

Located in a quiet residential area and surrounded by stately residences within minutes of the city centre, this 19th-century palace has been converted into a hotel and refurbished to a high standard. Each bedroom is individually decorated with antique pieces and equipped with hydro-massage baths. Guests can savour haute cuisine in the small restaurant, which opens onto a terrace and pretty garden, whilst the cocktails served in the intimate bar are reputed to be amongst the best in Madrid. Guests can enjoy the facilities of a nearby fitness centre with indoor pool.

Situé dans un quartier résidentiel calme et entouré par des résidences majestueuses à quelques minutes du centre ville, ce palais datant du XIXe siècle a été converti en hôtel et remis à neuf. Chaque chambre est ornée de façon individuelle avec des antiquités et équipée avec bain hydro-massage. Les hôtes peuvent savourer la haute cuisine dans le petit restaurant qui donne sur une terrasse et joli jardin, alors que les cocktails servis dans le bar intime sont réputés être parmi les meilleurs à Madrid. Les hôtes peuvent profiter d'un centre de remise en forme avec piscine couverte tout près.

Dieses in ein wundervolles Hotel umgewandelte Palais aus dem 19. Jahrhundert liegt in einer ruhigen Wohngegend, umgeben von herrschaftlichen Häusern nur ein paar Minuten vom Stadtzentrum entfernt. Alle Zimmer sind unterschiedlich gestaltet, mit Antiquitäten gefüllt und bieten Hydromassagebäder. Im kleinen Restaurant mit Terrasse und Garten wird Haute Cuisine serviert, und die Cocktails, die man in der gemütlichen Bar bekommt, gehören bekanntlich zu den besten in Madrid. Ein nahegelegenes Fitnesszentrum mit Hallenbad steht zur Verfügung.

Our inspector loved: *The landscaped terrace garden with central wall-mounted fountain; charming for candle-lit al fresco dining.*

Directions: The hotel is located within minutes of the city centre.

Web: www.johansens.com/orfila
E-mail: inforeservas@hotelorfila.com
Tel: +34 91 702 77 70
Fax: +34 91 702 77 72

Price Guide: (room only, excluding VAT)
double €297-365
suite €409-1,184

Hotel Quinta de los Cedros

C/ALLENDESALAZAR 4, 28043 MADRID, SPAIN

Surrounded by cedar trees and affording fine views across the city, this charming hotel was built in the elegant style of a Tuscan villa and provides an impeccably high standard of service and the utmost in comfort. Each of its 22 bedrooms and 10 terraced bungalows in the grounds is themed differently and features all modern amenities. The intimate and romantic Los Cedros restaurant serves traditional and modern cuisine with Mediterranean flavours. Guests may enjoy their meals on the terrace overlooking the beautiful gardens. A meeting room is available.

Entouré par des arbres de cèdre avec des vues spectaculaires de la ville, cet hôtel charmant fut construit dans le style élégant d'une villa toscane et offre un excellent niveau de service et confort. Chacune des 22 chambres et 10 pavillons en terrasses est décorée avec un thème différent et équipée avec toutes les facilités modernes. Le restaurant intime et romantique Los Cedros sert des plats traditionnels et modernes avec des saveurs de la Méditerranée. Les hôtes peuvent dîner sur la terrasse donnant sur les beaux jardins. Une salle de réunion est disponible.

Umgeben von Zedern und mit einer herrlichen Sicht auf die Stadt, bietet dieses charmante, im Stil einer eleganten toskanischen Villa erbaute Hotel ein extrem hohes Maß an Service und höchsten Komfort. Alle 22 Zimmer und 10 Bungalows auf dem Gelände sind unterschiedlich gestaltet und mit modernsten Einrichtungen ausgestattet. Im gemütlichen und romantischen Restaurant Los Cedros werden traditionelle und moderne Gerichte mit mediterraner Note serviert, die man auch auf der Terrasse inmitten des herrlichen Gartens genießen kann. Ein Konferenzraum steht zur Verfügung.

***Our inspector loved:** The ambience and décor reminiscent of the Tuscan villas of Italy.*

Directions: The hotel is north of Madrid's centre, adjacent to C/Arturo Soria. Close to Chamartin train station and 10km from Madrid Airport.

Web: www.johansens.com/loscedros
E-mail: reservas@quintadeloscedros.com
Tel: +34 91 515 2200
Fax: +34 91 415 2050

Price Guide: (breakfast €9, excluding VAT)
single €167
double €210-244
suite €311

Hotel Villa Real

PLAZA DE LAS CORTES 10, 28014 MADRID, SPAIN

Directions: Located in the centre of the city.

Web: www.johansens.com/vilareal
E-mail: info@derbyhotels.es
Tel: +34 914 20 37 67
Fax: +34 914 20 25 47

Price Guide: (breakfast €18, excluding VAT)
single €322
double/twin €360
suite €470-1,012

Surrounded by cultural attractions, this prestigious hotel offers impeccable service and a palatial interior, filled with wonderful antiques and mirrors, handsome rugs on marble floors, Roman mosaics and Greek ceramics. The newly refurbished Royal and Imperial Suites offer hydro-massage baths; one of the suites has a small sauna. Guests can sample exquisite dishes in the gourmet restaurant Europa or enjoy creative cuisine in the East 47. The hotel boasts a fantastic new fitness centre with separate saunas and relaxation areas for men and women. Wireless Internet connection available.

Entouré des attractions culturelles, ce prestigieux hôtel bénéficie d'un service impeccable et d'un intérieur grandiose, orné des antiquités et des miroirs, de beaux tapis sur des sols de marbre, des mosaïques romaines et céramiques grecques. Les suites Royale et Impériale disposent d'un bain hydro-massage; une a un sauna. Il y a 2 restaurants: le restaurant gastronomique Europa et l'East 47, où une cuisine créative est servie. L'hôtel s'enorgueillit d'un nouveau centre de remise en forme avec sauna et aire de détente séparés pour les hommes et les femmes. Service internet sans fil disponible.

In diesem von kulturellen Attraktionen umgebenen Hotel findet man tadellosen Service und ein palastartiges Interieur gefüllt mit Antiquitäten, Spiegeln, hübschen Teppichen auf Marmorböden, römischen Mosaiken und griechischen Keramiken. Die kürzlich renovierten Royal und Imperial Suiten bieten Hydromassagebäder, eine besitzt sogar eine integrierte Sauna. Im Europa wird Gourmet-, im East 47 kreative Küche serviert. Das Hotel besitzt ein neues Fitnesszentrum mit separaten Saunen und Relaxzonen für Männer und Frauen. Drahtloser Internetzugang vorhanden.

Our inspector loved: *The Roman mosaics and art treasures exhibited around the hotel; one of the finest private collections in Europe.*

Mirasierra Suites Hotel

C/ Alfredo Marquerie 43, 28034 Madrid, Spain

Recently opened, Mirasierra Suites Hotel is ideally located at a very short distance from Madrid's main business areas. A shuttle service takes guests to Paseo de la Castellana in 5 minutes, to Juan Carlos I Exhibition Centre (IFEMA) in 8, and to Madrid-Barajas International Airport in 10. All 182 rooms are suites with a minimum size of 60m²; there is a 1,300m² fitness centre-spa, an outdoor and an indoor swimming pool, 13 function rooms with a total area of 2,000m², a distinguished gastronomic offer and, on the executive 10th floor, the sophisticated Juban Club.

Cet hôtel récemment ouvert est idéalement situé à seulement quelques minutes des centres névralgiques les plus importants de Madrid. Grâce à son service de navette, ses clients sont à moins de 5 minutes du Paseo de la Castellana, 8 minutes du Parc des Expositions Juan Carlos I (IFEMA) et 10 minutes de l'Aéroport International de Madrid-Barajas. L'hôtel combine à la fois 182 suites, chacune, au minimum, de 60 m², un fitness center/spa de 1300 m², 2 piscines – une extérieure et une intérieure – 13 salons d'un total de 2000 m², une offre gastronomique remarquable et un étage «exécutif» au 10ème étage, le Juban Club.

Dieses ideal gelegene, kürzlich neu eröffnete Hotel ist nur wenige Minuten von Madrids Hauptattraktionen entfernt. Ein Shuttle-Service bringt die Gäste in 5 Minuten zum Paseo de la Castellana, in 8 zum Juan Carlos I. Exhibition Centre (IFEMA) und in 10 zum internationalen Flughafen Madrid-Barajas. Jede der 182 Suiten ist mindestens 60m² groß, geboten werden ein 1300m² großes Fitnesszentrum/Spa, ein Hallen- und ein Freibad, 13 Veranstaltungsräume mit einer Fläche von 2000m², gastronomischer Hochgenuss und der exclusive Juban Club in der Chefetage im 10 stockwerk.

***Our inspector loved:** The domed reception lobby, a genuine architectural feat.*

Directions: Situated in the north of Madrid and 8 minutes from exhibition venues. 15 minutes from the city centre.

Web: www.johansens.com/mirasierra
E-mail: msh@jubanhoteles.com
Tel: +34 91 727 79 00
Fax: +3491 727 79 18

Barcelona
Madrid
Málaga

Price Guide: (room only, excluding VAT)
suite €295-951

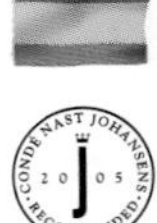

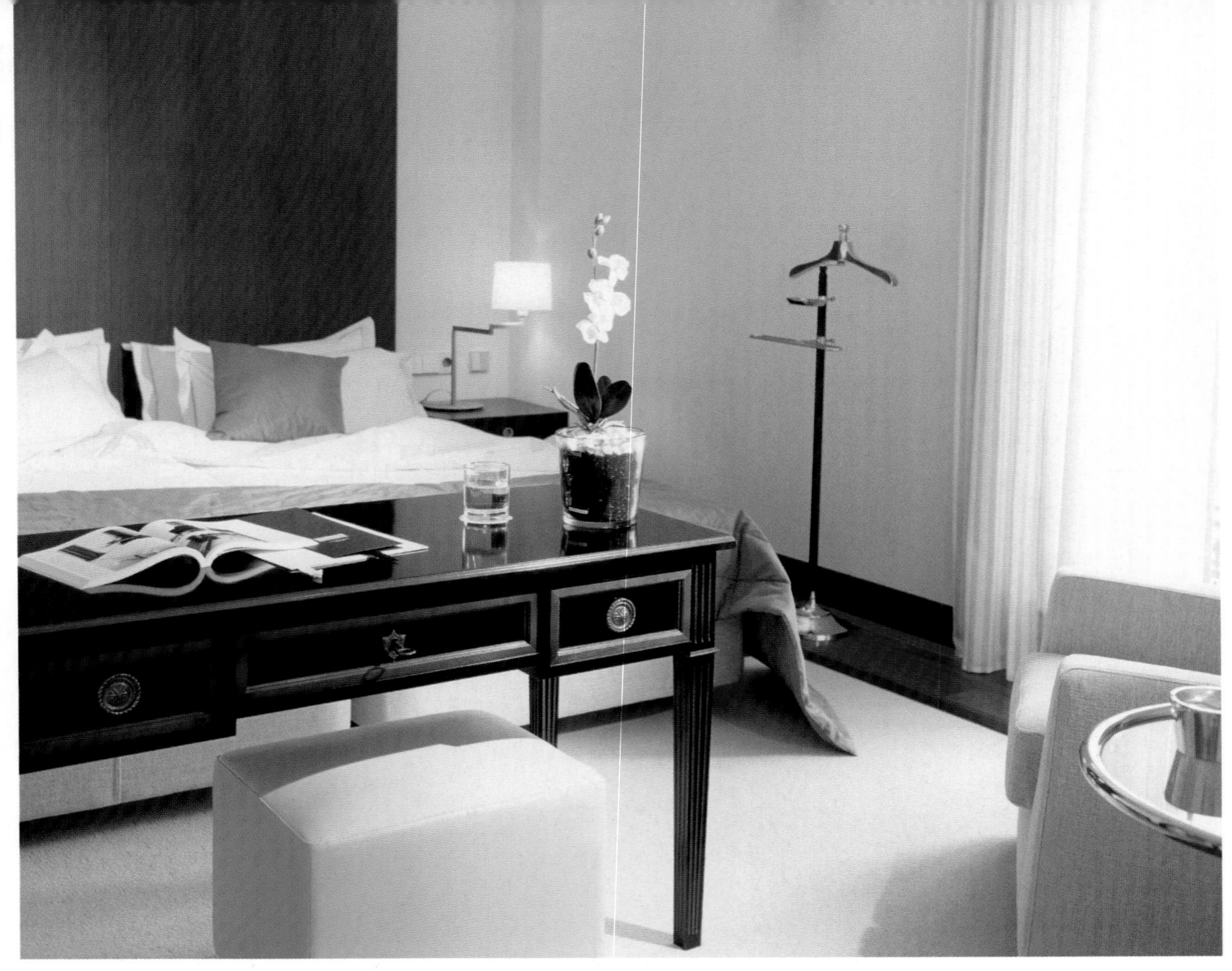

AMÉRIGO

C/ RAFAEL ALTAMIRA 7, 03002 ALICANTE, SPAIN

Directions: Alicante Airport > city centre > city council/hall street.

Web: www.johansens.com/amerigo
E-mail: amerigo@hospes.es
Tel: +34 965 14 65 70
Fax: +34 965 14 65 71

Price Guide:
single €120-220
double €150-250
suite €600

Situated in the old quarter of Alicante this restored 16th-century convent is a short stroll from the marina and seafront promenade. The interior features marble, stone, wood, leather, glass and chrome cleverly blended to create a luxurious yet functional 21st-century ambience. The spacious bedrooms and bathrooms boast contemporary décor and possess all modern technological features. For relaxation, guests can take advantage of the attractive roof terrace with fitness centre, sauna, indoor/outdoor pool and bar.

Situé dans le vieux quartier d'Alicante, ce convent restauré du XVIe siècle n'est qu'à quelques pas du port de plaisance et du bord de mer. L'intérieur est composé de marbre, de pierres, de bois, de cuir, de verre et de chrome habilement mélangés pour créer une atmosphère luxueuse et fonctionnelle du XXIe siècle. Les chambres et salles de bain spacieuses sont décorées de manière contemporaine et possèdent toute la technologie moderne. Pour la relaxation, les clients peuvent profiter de l'attirante terrasse sur le toit où se trouvent un centre de remise en forme, sauna, piscine intérieure et bar.

Dieses in der Altstadt von Alicante gelegene restaurierte Kloster aus dem 16. Jahrhundert ist nur einen Katzensprung von der Hafenpromenade entfernt. Die Verbindung aus Marmor, Stein, Holz, Leder, Glas und Chrom schafft ein luxuriöses und doch funktionelles Ambiente des 21. Jahrhunderts. Die geräumigen Zimmer und Bäder bieten zeitgenössisches Décor und jegliche modernen technologischen Details. Zur Entspannung steht eine attraktive Dachterrasse mit Fitnesszentrum, Sauna, Hallenbad und Bar zur Verfügung.

Our inspector loved: *The hotel's epicurean breakfast consisting of tasty morsels.*

Hesperia Alicante Golf, Spa, Hotel

AVENIDA DE LAS NACIONES, S/N PLAYA DE SAN JUAN, 03540 ALICANTE, SPAIN

This stunning modern hotel is nestled amongst the fairways and greens of a magnificent 18-hole golf course designed by Severiano Ballesteros and is only 5 minutes' walk from many fine sandy beaches. Mediterranean-style décor uses marble, wood, wrought iron and cool pastel shades to create a wonderful atmosphere of light and spaciousness whilst bedrooms are the ultimate in chic comfort with views over the golf course, beautifully tended gardens and pool. The hotel has extensive spa facilities.

Ce superbe hôtel moderne est niché au sein des fairways et greens de ce magnifique golf 18 trous créé par Severiano Ballesteros et est à seulement 5 minutes de marche de nombreuses plages de sable fins. Le décor de style méditerranéen utilise marbre, bois, fers forgés et des tons de couleur pastel pour créer une atmosphère merveilleuse de lumière et d'espace. Les chambres sont ce qui se fait de mieux en confort chic avec vues sur le parcours de golf, les jardins superbement entretenus et la piscine. Cet hôtel dispose également de services de soins.

Dieses eindrucksvolle moderne Hotel liegt inmitten der Fairways und Greens eines herrlichen, von Severiano Ballesteros gestalteten 18-Loch-Golfplatzes und ist nur 5 Minuten zu Fuß von mehreren Sandstränden entfernt. Das Mittelmeerdécor mit Marmor, Holz, Schmiedeeisen und kühlen Pastelltönen schafft eine luftige, geräumige Atmosphäre. Die Zimmer sind höchst elegant und blicken auf den Golfplatz, die wundervollen Gärten und den Pool. Umfassende Kureinrichtungen sind vorhanden.

Our inspector loved: *The light and spacious ambience.*

Directions: Situated 5 minutes from Alicante city centre along the Avenida de las Naciones.

Web: www.johansens.com/hesperiaalicante
E-mail: hotel@hesperia-alicante.com
Tel: +34 965 23 50 00
Fax: +34 965 26 82 42

Price Guide: (room only)
single €135-176
double €196-220
suite €700

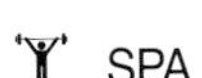

HOTEL SIDI SAN JUAN & SPA

PLAYA DE SAN JUAN, 03540 ALICANTE, SPAIN

This excellent hotel is situated on a long, sandy beach near Cabo de Las Huertas and is only 10 minutes away from Alicante, renowned for its cultural activities and sights. With 8,000m² of beautiful gardens filled with over 250 palm trees, this is just the place for a long relaxing stroll. All rooms and suites have magnificent views of the sea. The restaurant, Grill Sant Joan, offers a wide range of international specialities, healthy Mediterranean cuisine and exquisite wines. The hotel has 1 indoor and 1 outdoor swimming pool, 5 tennis and 2 paddle courts as well as a spa.

Cet excellent hôtel est situé sur une longue plage de sable près de Cabo de Las Huertas, à 10 minutes d'Alicante, célèbre pour ses attractions culturelles. Avec ses 8000m² de jardins merveilleux remplis de plus de 250 palmiers, c'est un endroit parfait pour des longues promenades relaxantes. Toutes les chambres et suites ont des vues sur la mer. Le restaurant, Grill Sant Joan, offre des specialités internationales, une cuisine méditerranéenne saine et des vins exquis. L'hôtel dispose d'une piscine couverte, une en plein air, 5 courts de tennis et 2 de paddle ainsi qu'un spa.

Dieses exzellente Hotel liegt in bevorzugter Lage direkt an einem etwa 5km langen Sandstrand in unmittelbarer Nähe vom Cabo de Las Huertas. Alicante mit seinen kulturellen Sehenswürdigkeiten ist in 10 Minuten zu erreichen. Ein 8000m² großer Garten mit über 250 Palmen lädt zum Verweilen ein. Alle Zimmer und Suiten verfügen über Blick aufs Meer. Wahrhafte Genüsse bietet das Restaurant Grill Sant Joan: internationale Spezialitäten, ausgewogene Mittelmeerküche und erlesene Weine. Ein Hallenbad, Swimmingpool, 5 Tennis- und 2 Paddleplätze sowie ein Spa stehen für Wellness pur.

Our inspector loved: *The sea views from the sauna, indoor pool and hydro-massage pool. What a way to relax!*

Directions: From Alicante follow the signs to Playa San Juan. 12km from the city centre the hotel is on the beachfront.

Web: www.johansens.com/sanjuan
E-mail: reservas@sanjuan.hotelessidi.es
Tel: +34 96 516 13 00
Fax: +34 96 516 33 46

Price Guide: (room only, excluding VAT)
single €148-172
double €184-214
suite €645-735

SPAIN / VALENCIA (ONTINYENT)

Santa Elena

KM9, CARETERRA CV655 ONTINYENT/FONTANARS, PARTIDA DE LA UMBRIA, ONTINYENT, VALENCIA, SPAIN

Santa Elena is a charming rural hotel in the heart of Valencia countryside. Terracotta, wood and rustic Spanish period features are combined with pastel walls, open fireplaces and English antiques to create an eclectic mix of traditional styles. Luxurious bedrooms have all the personal touches of home and are decorated with wrought-iron beds, rich fabrics and lion's claw baths. Al fresco dining offers tasty Mediterranean dishes on a sun-warmed terrace.

Santa Elena est un hôtel de charme rural au cœur de la campagne de Valence. Terre cuite, bois et éléments rustiques d'époque associés à des murs de couleurs pastels, des cheminées et des antiquités anglaises produisent un mélange éclectique de styles traditionnels. Les chambres luxueuses décorées avec des lits en fer forgé, de superbes tissus et des baignoires à pied possèdent toutes les touches particulières que l'on trouve dans une demeure privée. De délicieux plats méditerranéens sont dégustés à la belle étoile sur une terrasse chauffée par le soleil.

Santa Elena ist ein zauberhaftes ländliches Hotel mitten im Herzen der Landschaft von Valencia. Terrakotta, Holz und rustikale spanische Einrichtung schaffen zusammen mit pastellfarbenen Wänden, offenen Kaminen und englischen Antiquitäten eine eigenwillige Mischung traditioneller Stile. Die luxuriösen Zimmer haben eine heimelige, persönliche Note und sind mit schmiedeeisernen Betten, üppigen Stoffen und freistehenden Badewannen ausgestattet. Auf einer sonnenbeschienenen Terrasse kann man mediterrane Köstlichkeiten genießen.

Our inspector loved: *The tasteful combination of curtain fabrics, fresh bed linen and bedroom décor.*

Directions: From Alicante > Madrid motorway > Fontanares. From Fontanares > Bocairent > 5km on right. A 1-hour drive from Valencia and Alicante Airports.

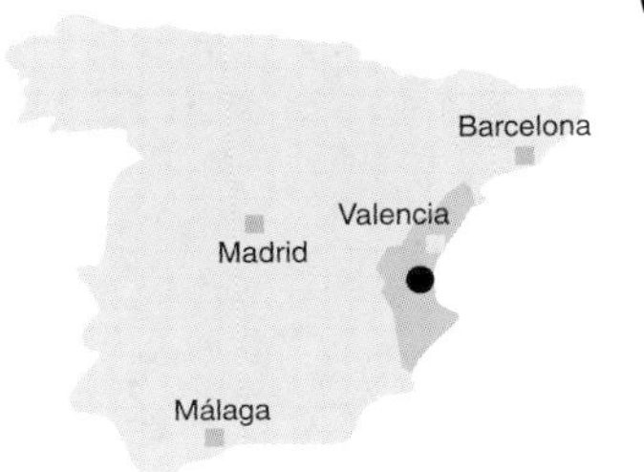

Web: www.johansens.com/santaelena
E-mail: info@santaelenahotel.com
Tel: +34 96 291 16 56
Fax: +34 96 238 36 29

Price Guide: (room only)
double €120
luxury double €160

Hotel Sidi Saler & Spa

PLAYA EL SALER, 46012 VALENCIA, SPAIN

Directions: From Valencia take the coastal road and follow signs to El Saler. The hotel is 12km further on.

Web: www.johansens.com/saler
E-mail: reservas@saler.hotelessidi.es
Tel: +34 961 61 04 11
Fax: +34 961 61 08 38

Price Guide: (excluding VAT)
single €172-206
double €220-245
suite €680-758

This 5-star hotel is situated on the long sandy beach of El Saler, within the Albufera Nature Park, which features a beautiful lake and habitat for all kinds of birds. All rooms and suites enjoy magnificent views of the Mediterranean. The Les Dunes à la carte restaurant offers a wide range of regional and international dishes accompanied by live jazz, blues and country music. Whether it is a ride on a mountain bike or a swim in either the outdoor or the indoor swimming pool, a game of tennis or a session in the beauty salon, there is always some form of exercise or relaxation on offer.

Cet hôtel 5 étoiles est situé sur la longue plage de sable de El Saler, au parc naturel d'Albufera avec sa grande variété d'oiseaux et son lac magnifique. Toutes les chambres et suites ont des vues merveilleuses de la Méditerranée. Le restaurant Les Dunes offre un menu à la carte de plats régionaux et internationaux accompagnés de musique sur scène de jazz, blues et country. Les hôtes peuvent faire du VTT, nager dans la piscine couverte ou en plein air, jouer au tennis ou se dorloter au salon de beauté – il y a toujours des possibilités d'activité ou de détente.

Die Lage dieses 5-Sterne Hotels ist unübertreffbar: direkt an einem langen Sandstrand und im Bereich des Albufera-Naturparks, ein Vogelparadies mit einem herrlichen See. Von allen Zimmern und Suiten aus hat man einen wunderschönen Blick auf das Mittelmeer. Das à-la-carte Restaurant Les Dunes bietet neben höchsten regionalen und internationalen Genüssen auch Live-Jazz, Blues und Country-Musik. Ob mit dem Mountainbike oder im Hallenbad bzw. Swimmingpool, auf den Tennisplätzen oder im Beauty-und Wellnesscenter, überall ist eine aktive Erholung möglich.

Our inspector loved: *The setting within a natural park, with the gardens leading out onto the dunes and beach.*

Palau de la Mar

NAVARRO REVERTER 14, 46004 VALENCIA, SPAIN

Located in the heart of Valencia, close to Puente de las Flores, this renovated aristocratic property is a creative blend of luxury and style. The hotel consists of 2 adjacent buildings visible only from the exterior due to the different façades; once inside the ambience is homogenous. Each floor enjoys an individual design yet maintains a graceful harmony, with some of the accommodation situated around an open landscaped patio. The staircase is an exceptional feature with its magnificent stained-glass skylight depicting the waves of the sea.

Situé au cœur de la ville de Valencia, cette noble demeure rénovée est un créatif mélange de luxe et de style. L'hôtel est composé de 2 bâtiments attenants aux façades différentes mais dont l'ambiance intérieure est homogène. Chaque étage a son propre design mais une harmonie gracieuse et maintenue et certaines chambres se trouvent autour d'un patio paysager ouvert. L'escalier est un élément exceptionnel avec un magnifique vitrail au plafond représentant les vagues de la mer.

Dieses im Herzen von Valencia gelegene aristokratische Anwesen stellt eine kreative Mischung aus Luxus und Stil dar. Das Hotel besteht aus 2 Gebäuden, die sich nur durch ihre unterschiedlichen Fassaden unterscheiden – das Innere ist in beiden gleich. Jede Etage ist individuell, anmutig und harmonisch gestaltet, einige Zimmer sind um eine offene, edel bepflanzte Terrasse herum angeordnet. Das außergewöhnliche Treppenhaus bietet ein fantastisches Dachfenster aus Buntglas, auf dem die Wellen des Meeres abgebildet sind.

Our inspector loved: *The eclectic 21st-century interior design and stimulating sensual ambience.*

Directions: Valencia Airport > city centre > Plaza Porta de la Mar.

Web: www.johansens.com/palaudelamar
E-mail: palaudelamar@hospes.es
Tel: +34 96 316 2884
Fax: +34 96 316 2885

Barcelona
Valencia
Madrid
Málaga

Price Guide: (room only, excluding VAT)
single €140-230
double €160-250
suite €500

SWEDEN

Hotel location shown in red (hotel) or purple (spa hotel) with page number

Hestravikens Wärdshus

VIK, 33027, HESTRA, SMÅLAND, SWEDEN

Behind the traditional yellow country house façade lie 7 immaculately maintained suites, tastefully decorated with contemporary designer furnishings. Some include Jacuzzi baths and fireplaces, whilst all have terraces or balconies. A small relaxation room offers guests the perfect end to the day having taken advantage of Småland's wealth of outdoor pursuits, from walking in the National Park to canoeing in the Nissan river running alongside the Hotel. Excellent cuisine and a generous Scandinavian breakfast is served in the adjacent restaurant and conservatory.

Derrière la traditionnelle façade jaune de cette maison de campagne se tiennent 7 suites immaculées, décorées avec goût dans un mobilier contemporain de designer. Certaines contiennent un jacuzzi et une cheminée, et toutes disposent d'une terrasse ou d'un balcon. Une petite pièce de relaxation offre une fin de journée parfaite aux hôtes qui ont profité de la myriade d'activités en plein air offerte à Småland, des randonnées dans le Park National au canoë sur la rivière Nissan qui coule le long de l'hôtel. Une cuisine excellente et un petit-déjeuner scandinave copieux sont servis dans le restaurant adjacent et la serre.

Hinter der traditionellen gelben Landhausfassade verstecken sich 7 makellose Suiten, die geschmackvoll in zeitgenössischem Design eingerichtet sind. Einige haben Whirlpoolbäder und Kamine, alle bieten Terrassen oder Balkone. In einem kleinen Entspannungsraum kann man den Tag ausklingen lassen, nachdem man Smålands riesiges Freizeitangebot von Wanderungen im Nationalpark bis hin zu Kanufahrten auf dem am Hotel vorbeifließenden Nissan genutzt hat. Hervorragende Küche und ein großzügiges Frühstück werden im Restaurant und Wintergarten serviert.

Our inspector loved: *The comfort of Suite 47 with its spacious bathroom.*

Directions: Jönköping > 26 > Hestra.

Web: www.johansens.com/hestravikenswardshus
E-mail: info@hestraviken.se
Tel: +46 370 33 68 00
Fax: +46 370 33 62 90

Price Guide:
double SEK1,380–1,580
suite SEK1,780–2,680

SWITZERLAND

Hotel location shown in red (hotel) or purple (spa hotel) with page number

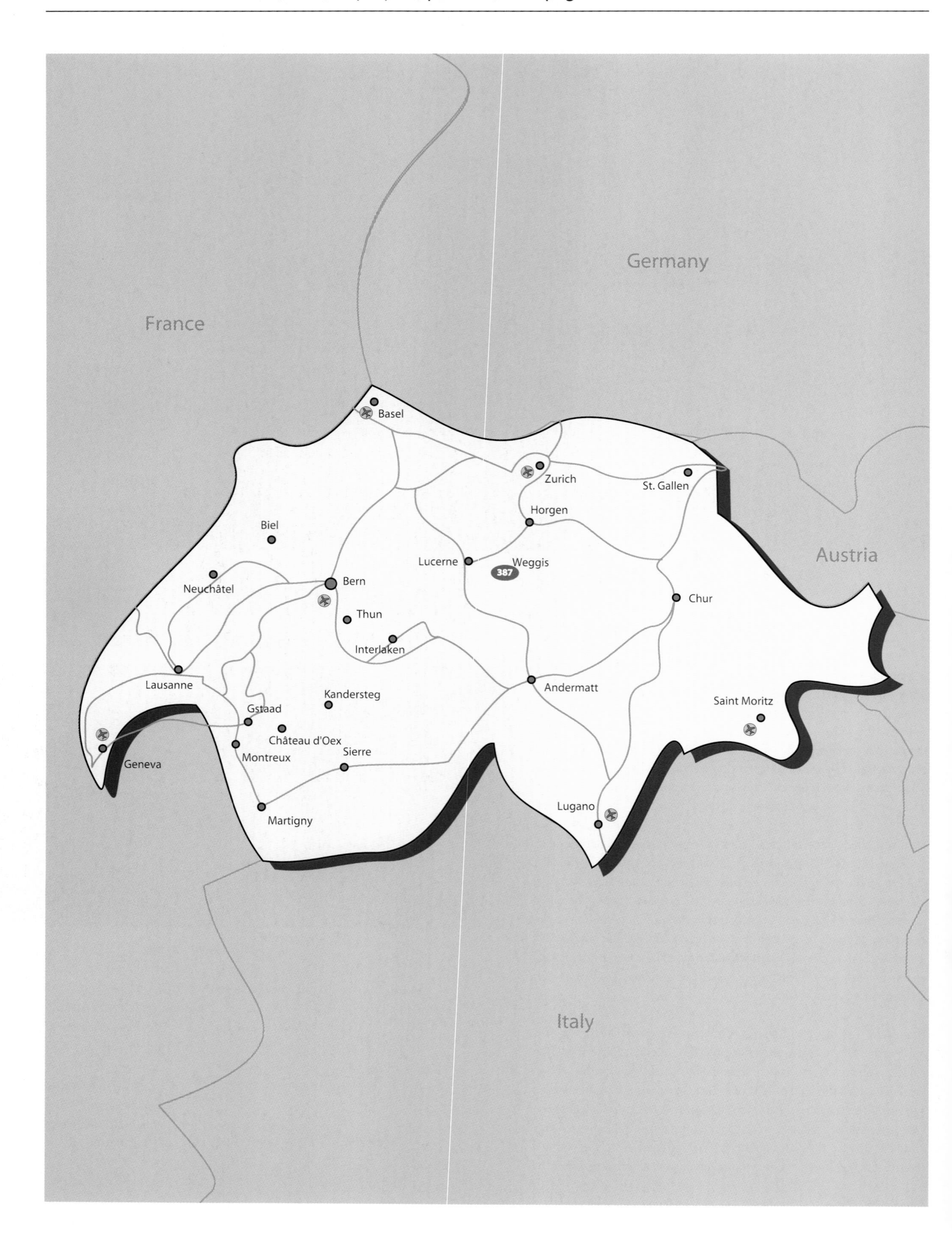

PARK HOTEL WEGGIS

HERTENSTEINSTRASSE 34, CH - 6353 WEGGIS, SWITZERLAND

Set in magnificent parkland with a private beach and breathtaking views over Lake Lucerne and the Alps, this unique hotel blends traditional charm and elegance with modern flair. Emphasis is on relaxation, and the 6 private SPA-Cottages offer a full range of beauty and massage treatments. The award-winning Annex restaurant serves French cuisine, whilst the bedrooms and suites are stylishly decorated with Designers Guild fabrics, Philippe Starck lighting and Molteni furniture.

Situé dans un magnifique parc avec une plage privée et des vues imprenables sur le lac Lucerne et les Alpes, cet hôtel unique marie à merveille le charme et l'élégance traditionnels avec un style moderne. L'accent est sur la détente, et les 6 villas-SPA offrent un choix complet de soins et traitements de beauté et massage. Une Cuisine française est servie au restaurant primé Annex. Les chambres et suites élégantes sont ornées avec goût avec des tissus de Designers Guild, lampes de Philippe Starck et meubles de Molteni.

Inmitten eines herrlichen Parks mit eigenem Strand und herrlicher Sicht auf den Vierwaldstätter See und die Alpen bietet dieses einzigartige Hotel traditionelle Eleganz mit modernem Flair. Die Betonung liegt auf Entspannung, und in den 6 SPA-Cottages erhält man umfassende Beauty- und Massagebehandlungen. Im preisgekrönten Annex Restaurant werden einfallsreiche Speisen der französischen Küche serviert, und die Zimmer und Suiten sind stilvoll mit Stoffen von Designers Guild, Philippe Starck-Lampen und Molteni-Möbeln eingerichtet.

Our inspector loved: *The Bonsai trees in the Japanese meditation garden and the Rachmaninoff Suite.*

Directions: 60 minutes by car from Zurich Airport. The hotel is in the resort town of Weggis, on the shores of Lake Lucerne.

Web: www.johansens.com/weggis
E-mail: info@phw.ch
Tel: +41 41 392 05 05
Fax: +41 41 392 05 28

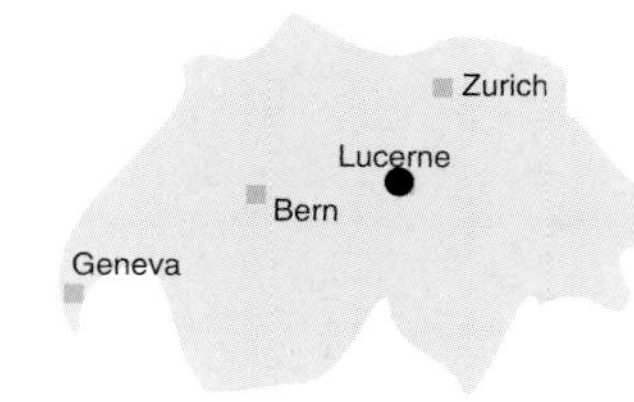

Price Guide: (per person)
single €163-203
double €110-177
suite €170-370

TURKEY

Hotel location shown in red (hotel) or purple (spa hotel) with page number

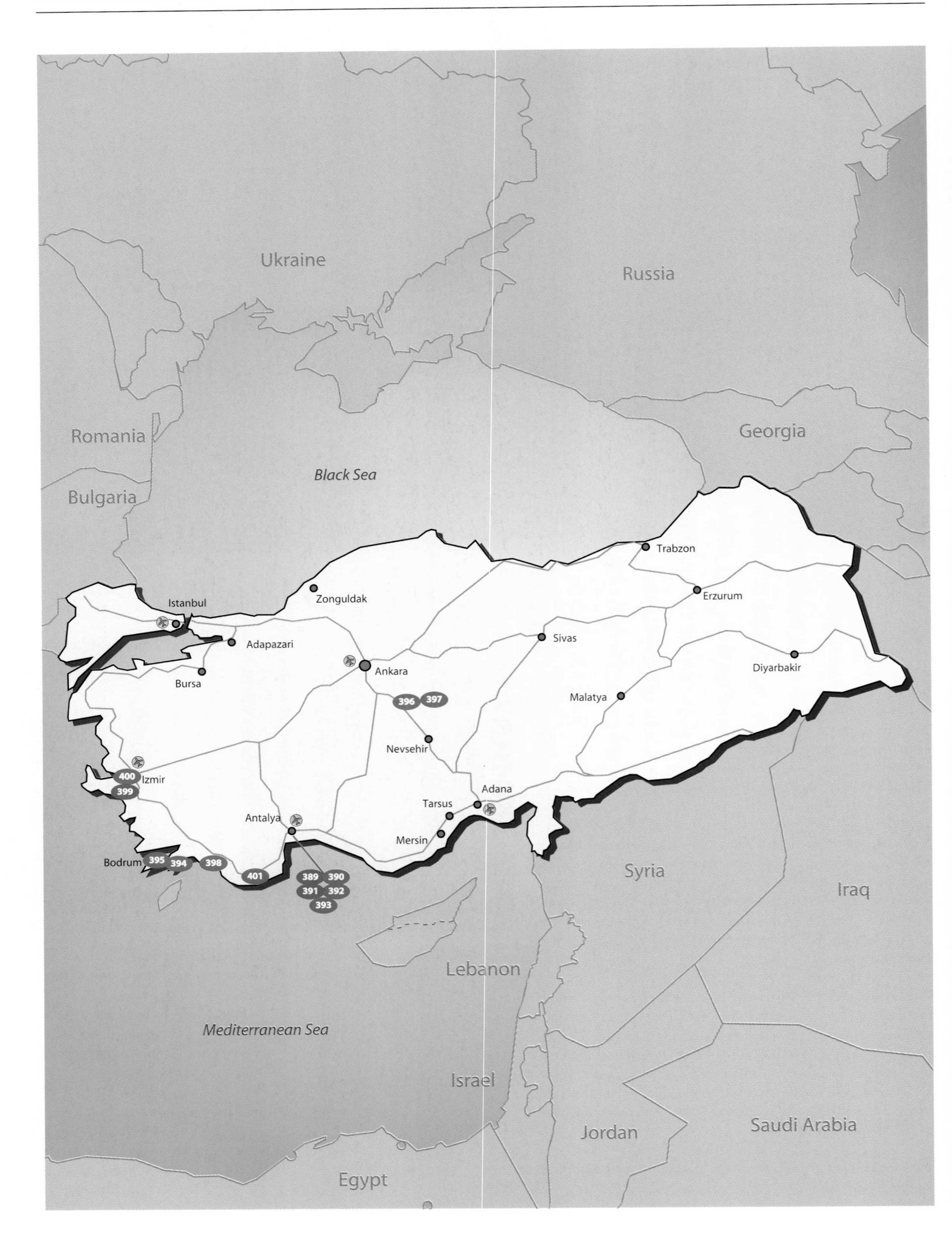

Gloria Select Villas

ACISCU MEVKII, BELEK, ANTALYA, TURKEY

Situated at the eastern end of the famous Turkish Riviera, Gloria Select Villas lies within Belek's best golf resort. Each villa boasts views across the swimming pool and gardens and has a private entrance, veranda and sun deck. Furnishings include fully-equipped kitchens and luxuriously decorated bedrooms and bathrooms with accommodation for up to 4 people. Guests can enjoy all of the activities of the resort along with its golf amenities, beach, restaurants and Thalasso spa.

Situé à l'est de la célèbre riviera turque, Gloria Select Villas se tient au sein de la meilleure station de golf de Belek. Chaque villa offre une vue sur la piscine et les jardins et une entrée privée, véranda et solarium. Les logements conçus pour 4 personnes incluent une cuisine toute équipée et des chambres et salles de bain luxueusement décorées. Les hôtes peuvent profiter de toutes les activités de la station y compris les services de golf, plage, restaurants et services Thalasso.

Die Gloria Select Villas befinden sich am Ostende der berühmten türkischen Riviera, inmitten des besten Golfresorts von Belek. Jede Villa bietet Platz für bis zu 4 Personen, blickt auf den Swimmingpool und die Gärten und hat einen eigenen Eingang, eine Veranda und eine Sonnenterrasse, sowie eine voll ausgestattete Küche und luxuriöse Schlafzimmer und Bäder. Die Gäste können sämtliche Einrichtungen des Resorts benutzen, darunter die Golfanlage, den Strand, die Restaurants und das Thalasso-Spa.

Our inspector loved: *The peaceful gardens.*

Directions: Antalya Airport is 22km away. Airport > left towards Antalya - Belek > right at Belek > pass village.

Web: www.johansens.com/gloriavillas
E-mail: sales@gloriagolf.com
Tel: +90 242 715 2410
Fax: +90 242 715 2419

Istanbul
Ankara
Antalya

Price Guide: (all inclusive elegance package, please contact resort for details)
select villa €690-1,090
presidential villa €3,000-4,000

Olympos Lodge

PO BOX 38, ÇIRALI - KEMER, ANTALYA, TURKEY

Peacefully secluded, each of these magnificent bungalows is idyllically located directly on a beautiful Mediterranean beach, with a pine forest backdrop. Most of the bungalows boast sea views whilst others overlook the garden. Bedrooms are light and airy with minimalist bathrooms, and views of the Olympos mountain and sea are enjoyed whilst sampling the sumptuous cuisine. Visit the beaches of Olympos and Çirali, simply relax in a hammock surrounded by citrus trees, hike along the Taurus coastal mountains or hire a motorboat.

Tranquillement isolés, chacun de ces magnifiques bungalows est idéalement situé sur une superbe plage de Méditerranée avec une forêt de pins en toile de fond. La plupart des bungalows ont vue mer, les autres ont vue jardin. Les chambres sont claires et spacieuses et ont des salles de bain minimalistes. Les montagnes Olympos et la mer peuvent être admirés en dégustant la délicieuse cuisine. Les hôtes peuvent visiter les plages d'Olympos et de Çirali, se relaxer dans un hamac entouré de citronniers, marcher dans les montagnes le long de la côte ou louer un bateau à moteur.

Jeder dieser herrlich abgeschiedenen Bungalows ist idyllisch am Strand gelegen, und ein Pinienwald bildet den Hintergrund. Die meisten bieten Blick aufs Meer, einige blicken auf den Garten. Die Zimmer sind hell und luftig und haben minimalistische Bäder, und eine Sicht auf den Berg Olympos und das Meer genießt man am besten bei üppiger Küche im Restaurant. Auf dem Programm stehen Besuche der Strände von Olympos und Çirali, Entspannung in der Hängematte umgeben von Zitronenbäumen, Wanderungen im an der Küste gelegenen Taurus-Gebirge und Motorbootfahrten.

Our inspector loved: *The heavenly gardens - breathtaking.*

Directions: Antalya to Kemer > pass Tekirova > turn left at Çirali > 7kms > turn right. Airport transfers available upon request.

Web: www.johansens.com/olympos
E-mail: info@olymposlodge.com.tr
Tel: +90 242 825 7171
Fax: +90 242 825 7173

Price Guide:
single €140
double €175
suite €200

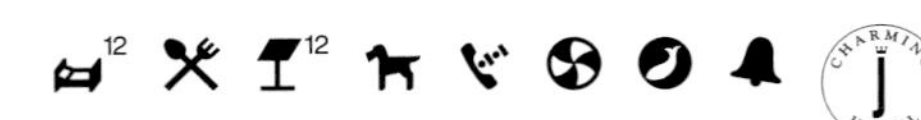

Renaissance Antalya Beach Resort & Spa

PO BOX 654, 07004 BELDIBI - KEMER, ANTALYA, TURKEY

Surrounded by spectacular scenery and set in extensive gardens, various types of accommodation, from spacious rooms with first-class amenities to self-catering units in the garden, are on offer. Enjoy a drink in the Piano Bar or by the pool before sampling delicious Turkish and international cuisine in one of the 5 restaurants. An extensive range of sports and leisure facilities include the 950m² spa complex, Harmonia Rebirth Wellness and Spa Centre, where "Kneipp" treatments are offered. Alternatively, there is the new Cigar Bar, outdoor pool and private quay at the beach.

Entouré de paysages extraordinaires et situé dans des grands jardins, ce centre de séjour offre divers types de logements dans des grandes pièces avec des équipements de qualité, y compris des unités de cuisine dans le jardin. Le service est excellent et les hôtes peuvent prendre un verre au Piano Bar ou au bord de la piscine avant de déguster la délicieuse cuisine turque et internationale de l'un des 5 restaurants. Le choix de loisirs est tres étendu, avec le spa de 950m², le Harmonia Rebirth Wellness and Spa Centre, qui offre des traitements "Kneipp". Il y a aussi un nouveau Cigar Bar, une piscine extérieure et un quai privé à la plage.

Umgeben von atemberaubender Landschaft und ausgedehnten Gärten bietet dieses Resort großzügige, erstklassig eingerichtete Zimmer und Garten-Appartements. Der Service ist hervorragend, und nach einem Drink in der Pianobar oder am Pool kann man in 5 Restaurants türkische oder internationale Köstlichkeiten genießen. Das Sport- und Freizeitangebot ist riesig, darunter der 950m² große Spa-Komplex, das Harmonia Rebirth Wellness and Spa Centre, das Kneipp-Kuren bietet. Außerdem gibt es die neue Cigar Bar, ein Freibad und eine private Anlegestelle am Strand.

Our inspector loved: *The new restaurant serving unbeatable Turkish cuisine.*

Directions: Antalya towards Kemer > after 30km turn left at Bedibi 2 exit.

Web: www.johansens.com/antalyaresort
E-mail: info@renaissanceantalya.com
Tel: +90 242 824 84 31
Fax: +90 242 824 84 30

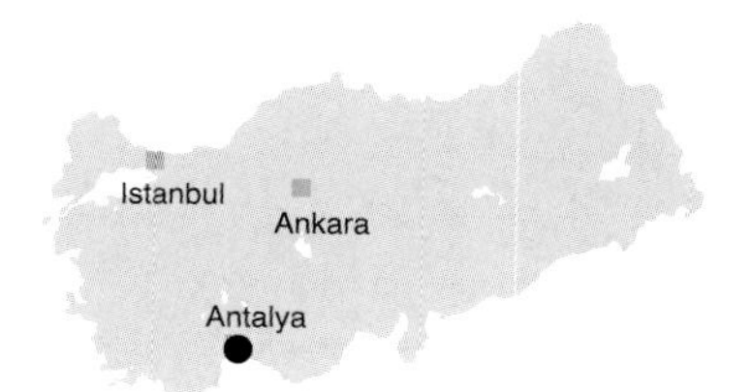

Price Guide:
single US$90–200
double US$130–250
suite US$145–1,000

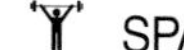

TURKEY (ANTALYA)

TEKELI KONAKLARI

DIZDAR HASAN SOKAK, KALEIÇI, ANTALYA, TURKEY

Situated in the heart of the award-winning city of Antalya, just minutes away from the Marina, these 6 restored mansions, dating back to the Ottoman Empire, comprise 8 beautifully appointed spacious rooms overlooking 2 courtyards. All rooms recreate 18th-century Ottoman wealth and the à la carte restaurant and patisserie are both excellent. A friendly and professional personal touch of the management gives a cosy, homely atmosphere to the hotel making guests feel special.

Situées au cœur de la ville primée d'Antalya, à quelques minutes seulement de la marina, ces 6 demeures datant de l'empire ottoman, offrent 8 belles chambres spacieuses surplombant 2 cours. Toutes les chambres recréent l'abondance ottomane et le restaurant à la carte et la pâtisserie sont tous deux excellents. Les hôtes se sentent spéciaux grâce à l'atmosphère chaleureuse procurée par une direction très amicale et professionnelle.

Mitten im Herzen der preisgekrönten Stadt Antalya und nur ein paar Schritte von der Uferpromenade entfernt befinden sich diese 6 restaurierten Häuser, die aus der Zeit des Ottomanischen Reiches stammen. Die 8 zauberhaft eingerichteten, großen Zimmer bieten Blick auf 2 Innenhöfe, und alle spiegeln die Opulenz des 18. Jahrhunderts wider. Das á la carte Restaurant und die Patisserie sind hervorragend, und der freundliche, persönliche Service sorgt für eine heimelige Atmosphäre.

Our inspector loved: *The charming and relaxing courtyard.*

Directions: Old city > Clock Tower > turn right at end of road > hotel is situated 20m along.

Web: www.johansens.com/tekelikonaklari
E-mail: mirya@superonline.com
Tel: +90 242 244 54 65
Fax: +90 242 242 67 14

Price Guide:
single US$90-120
double US$110-140

Tuvana Residence

TUZCULAR MAHALLESI, KARANLIK SOKAK 7, 07100 KALEIÇI - ANTALYA, TURKEY

Set in Kaleiçi, Antalya's old quarter, this is the newest of the 3 distinct Tuvana hotels. All rooms are beautifully decorated and offer all modern amenities, and wooden floors and ceilings create a warm and cosy atmosphere. Delightful Turkish cuisine can be sampled in one of the 3 restaurants, and guests have full use of the swimming pool and gardens of the Tuvana Hotel across the road. The historic parts of Antalya such as the old harbour as well as numerous shops, restaurants and beaches are within easy reach.

Situé à Kaleiçi, le vieux quartier d'Antalya, celui-ci est le plus récent des 3 différents hôtels Tuvana. Toutes les chambres sont superbement décorées et offrent toutes les facilités modernes. Planchers et plafonds en bois créent une atmosphère chaleureuse et douillette. Une délicieuse cuisine turque peut être dégustée dans l'un des 3 restaurants et les hôtes peuvent utiliser la piscine et les jardins de l'hôtel Tuvana de l'autre côte de la route. Les quartiers historiques d'Antalya tel que le vieux port, ainsi que de nombreux magasins, restaurants et plages sont d'accès facile.

Dieses in Antalyas Altstadt Kaleiçi gelegene Hotel ist das neueste der 3 Tuvana Hotels. Alle Zimmer sind hübsch eingerichtet und bieten jeden modernen Komfort, Holzböden und -decken schaffen ein warmes Ambiente. In 3 Restaurants wird köstliche türkische Küche serviert, und die Gäste haben Zugang zum Swimmingpool und Garten im gegenüberliegenden Tuvana Hotel. Die historischen Teile Antalyas wie der alte Hafen, sowie zahlreiche Geschäfte, Restaurants und Strände liegen in nächster Nähe.

Our inspector loved: *Its "old quarter" location.*

Directions: The nearest airport is Antalya. From the clock tower turn left > left again after 200 metres.

Web: www.johansens.com/tuvanaresidence
E-mail: tuvanaotel@superonline.com
Tel: +90 242 247 60 15
Fax: +90 242 241 19 81

Price Guide:
single US$80–125
double US$100–150

ADA HOTEL

BAGARASI MAHALLESI, TEPECIK CADDESI, NO 128, PO BOX 350, GÖLTÜRKBÜKÜ, 48400 BODRUM, TURKEY

Directions: From Milas-Bodrum Airport head towards Bodrum, then right at the junction of Güvercinlik/Yalikavak after 11km. Turn right at Türkbükü and follow signs to hotel.

Web: www.johansens.com/adahotel
E-mail: info@adahotel.com
Tel: +90 252 377 5915
Fax: +90 252 377 5379

Price Guide:
double US$250-320
suite US$290-595

Situated on a slope overlooking Göl-Türbükü bay, this charming and luxurious hotel offers its guests a magical experience. The 14 bedrooms and suites are well-appointed and include a Penthouse Suite and a Presidential Suite, both sharing a private pool and sun terrace. Guests can enjoy a candle-lit dinner and exquisite wines at the exclusive Mahzen restaurant or choose the hotel's beach club, which is a 10-minute walk or a shuttle ride away. The hotel's 2-level health centre boasts a swimming pool, Jumbo Jacuzzi and a magnificent Turkish bath.

Situé sur une colline surplombant la baie de Göl-Türbükü, ce charmant hôtel luxueux offre une expérience magique à ses hôtes. Les 14 chambres et suites sont bien équipées, et la Penthouse Suite et Presidential Suite partagent une piscine et une terrasse privée. On peut savourer un dîner aux chandelles et des vins fins au restaurant exclusif Mahzen, alors que la plage privée est seulement 10 minutes à pied ou quelques minutes avec la navette. L'hôtel dispose d'un centre de remise en forme en deux étages avec piscine, Jumbo Jacuzzi et un bain turc merveilleux.

Auf einem Hügel mit Blick auf die Bucht von Göl-Türbükü gelegen, bietet dieses zauberhafte Luxushotel seinen Gästen einen märchenhaften Aufenthalt. Es gibt 14 Zimmer und Suiten, darunter die Penthouse und die Presidential Suite, die einen Pool und eine Sonnenterrasse teilen. Man kann im exklusiven Mahzen Restaurant bei Kerzenschein feinste Küche und Weine genießen oder den Beach Club besuchen, der in 10 Minuten zu Fuß oder mit dem Shuttle zu erreichen ist. Der zweistöckige Health Club bietet Swimmingpool, Jumbo-Jacuzzi und ein herrliches Türkisches Bad.

Our inspector loved: *The elegance and dreamy atmosphere.*

Divan Bodrum Palmira

KELESHARIM CADDESI 6, 48483 GÖLTÜRKBÜKÜ, 48483 BODRUM, TURKEY

Stone walls and wooden balconies give real charm to this wonderful beachfront hotel, which has a lovely colourful garden and a bright lobby with eye-catching paintings. The comfortable rooms are spacious and beautifully decorated; some have sea views. Tasty Mediterranean cuisine is served either al fresco by the swimming pool or in the cosy restaurant. Guests can take advantage of the excellent fitness facilities, water sports, tennis, snooker and basketball or explore the many historical sights nearby.

Des murs de pierre et balcons en bois ajoutent au charme de ce merveilleux hôtel de bord de plage, qui a un ravissant jardin coloré et un hall clair avec des tableaux accrocheurs. Les chambres douillettes sont spacieuses et joliement décorées; certaines ont vue sur la mer. Une cuisine méditerranéenne délicieuse est servie au frais au bord de la piscine ou dans le confortable restaurant. Les hôtes peuvent profiter des excellents équipements de remise en forme, des sports nautiques, tennis, billard et basket ou explorer les sites historiques proches.

Steinwände und hölzerne Balkone sorgen für zusätzlichen Charme in diesem zauberhaften Strandhotel mit seinem farbenfrohen Garten und mit interessanten Bildern geschmückten Empfangsraum. Die attraktiven Zimmer sind komfortabel und geräumig und einige haben Sicht auf das Meer. Köstliche Mittelmeerküche wird am Pool oder im gemütlichen Restaurant serviert. Hervorragende Fitnesseinrichtungen stehen zur Verfügung, Wassersport, Tennis, Billiard und Basketball sind möglich und zahlreiche historische Stätten liegen in der Nähe.

Our inspector loved: *The relaxing atmosphere and sipping a cocktail at the beach bar.*

Directions: Bodrum-Milas Airport > follow signs for Türkbükü > follow signs for Divan Palmira towards beach.

Web: www.johansens.com/divanpalmira
E-mail: divan@divanpalmira.com.tr
Tel: +90 252 377 5601
Fax: +90 252 377 5952

Price Guide: (excluding VAT)
rooms €230-450

SACRED HOUSE

KARAHANDERE MAHALLESI, BARBAROS HAYRETTIN, SOKAK, NO 25, 50400 ÜRGÜP, TURKEY

Directions: Kayseri Airport > Nevsehir > turn left for Ürgüp > take the road opposite historical Hamam.

Web: www.johansens.com/sacredhouse
E-mail: info@sacred-house.com
Tel: +90 384 341 7102
Fax: +90 384 341 6986

Price Guide:
double US$80-250

Stylish, elegant and private, Sacred House, a former medieval mansion, is a boutique hotel that has lost none of its historic charm. History, art and modern comforts combine with attentive service to provide guests with a relaxing and luxurious visit in a refined setting with beautiful décor and antique furnishings throughout. 4 of the bedrooms open onto a vine-hung courtyard, 5 have fireplaces and all are furnished to a high standard. Excellent meals created from ancient recipes are served in the unique, cave-style restaurant.

Chic, élégant et prive, Sacred House, ancienne demeure médiévale, est un hôtel boutique qui n'a perdu aucun de son charme historique. Histoire, art et confort moderne sont associés à un service attentif, procurant aux hôtes une visite luxueuse et de détente dans une location raffinée aux superbes décors et un mobilier ancien. 4 des chambres donnent sur une cour où pend la vigne vierge, 5 ont des cheminées et toutes sont meublées dans les meilleurs goûts. D'excellents repas basés sur des recettes anciennes sont servis dans l'exceptionnel restaurant cave.

Das elegante, stilvolle und private Sacred House, einst ein mittelalterliches Herrenhaus, ist heute ein Boutique-Hotel, das nichts von seinem historischen Charme eingebüßt hat. Geschichte, Kunst und moderner Komfort verbinden sich mit aufmerksamem Service und schaffen ein entspanntes und luxuriöses Haus mit edlem Ambiente, herrlichem Décor und antiken Einrichtungen. 4 der Zimmer führen auf einen mit Weinlaub geschmückten Innenhof, 5 haben offene Kamine und alle sind hervorragend ausgestattet. Im einzigartigen Kellerrestaurant werden exquisite, nach alten Rezepten zubereitete Speisen serviert.

Our inspector loved: *The elegant and comfortable rooms.*

ÜRGÜP EVI

ESBELLI MAHALLESI 54, 50400 ÜRGÜP-NEVSEHIR, TURKEY

Winner of the Condé Nast Johansens Most Excellent European Value for Money Award 2004, Ürgüp Evi is situated in the old district of charming Ürgüp; lovingly restored to create an intimate cave hotel. Bedrooms have wooden floors, cave-carved cupboards, handmade furniture and modern bathrooms, most have sun-drenched terraces to enjoy the view over the town. Gorgeous meals are served in the terrace restaurant and guests will enjoy the friendly informal atmosphere of the hotel.

Ürgüp Evi, gagnant du prix Condé Nast Johansens Most Excellent European Value for Money Award 2004, est un intime et joliment restauré hôtel-cave situé dans le vieux district du charmant Ürgüp. Les chambres ont des planchers, des penderies creusées dans les caves, des meubles faits main et des salles de bain modernes; la plupart disposent également de terrasses inondées de soleil d'où apprécier la vue sur la ville. De superbes repas sont servis sur e restaurant en terrasse et les hôtes peuvent profiter de l'atmosphère amicale et informelle de l'hôtel.

Ürgüp Evi, mit dem Condé Nast Johansens Most Excellent European Value for Money Award 2004 ausgezeichnet, liegt in der Altstadt des zauberhaften Ürgüp und wurde liebevoll in ein gemütliches Höhlenhotel umgewandelt. Die Zimmer sind mit Holzböden, in den Felsen gehauenen Schränken, handgefertigtem Mobiliar und modernen Bädern ausgestattet, und die meisten bieten sonnige Terrassen, von denen man auf die Stadt blickt. Die Gäste können im Terrassenrestaurant köstliche Mahlzeiten genießen und sich in der freundlichen und ungezwungenen Atmosphäre wunderbar entspannen.

Our inspector loved: *The new garden terrace - the perfect place to unwind.*

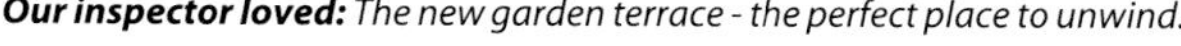

Directions: Neveshir > Ürgüp Main Road > left to Esbelli Quartes.

Web: www.johansens.com/urgupevi

E-mail: faruk@urgupevi.com

Tel: +90 384 341 3173

Fax: +90 384 341 6269

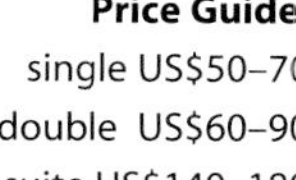

Istanbul

Ankara

Antalya

Price Guide:

single US$50–70

double US$60–90

suite US$140–180

Swissôtel Göcek Marina & Spa Resort

CUMHURIYET MAHALLESI, PO BOX 15, GÖCEK-FETHIYE/MUGLA, 48310 GÖCEK, TURKEY

Directions: Dalaman Airport > pass Göcek > turn right at petrol station > turn left and follow signs.

Web: www.johansens.com/gocekmarina
E-mail: emailus.gocek@swissotel.com
Tel: +90 252 645 2760
Fax: +90 252 645 2767

Price Guide:
standard US$120-170
superior US$140-190
de luxe US$160-210

Close to Port Göcek, this chic hotel is ideal for sailing and motorboat enthusiasts. Next to a pine forest and amidst pretty gardens, each bedroom has a balcony or terrace with sea or mountain views. Breakfast and lunch can be enjoyed in the Olive Tree Restaurant and Sundowner Restaurant serves light lunches and an à la carte menu during the evening and buffets on Friday and weekend nights. The Verandah Restaurant, set on the marina, is a short walk away. Exclusive use of a 280m-long beach, sailing trips, yacht charters, jeep safaris and wild water rafting.

Près du port de Göcek, cet hôtel sophistiqué est idéal pour les enthousiastes de la voile et du bateau à moteur. Près d'une forêt de pins et au sein de jardins, chaque chambre bénéficie de balcon ou terrasse avec vue sur la mer ou la montagne. Les petits déjeuners et déjeuners sont servis au restaurant Olive Tree, alors que le Sundowner sert des déjeuners légers, un dîner à la carte et des buffets le vendredi soir et le week-end. Le Véranda, sur les bords de la marina, est tout proche à pied. Il y a une plage privée de 280m, et des tours en voilier, en charters yacht, safaris en jeep et rafting peuvent être organisés.

Dieses nahe am Hafen von Göcek gelegene Hotel ist ein Paradies für Segler und Motorbootfreunde, umgeben von hübschen Gärten und Pinienwald. Jedes Zimmer hat Balkon oder Terrasse mit Blick aufs Meer oder die Berge. Im Olive Tree Restaurant gibt es Frühstück und Mittagessen, abends speist man im Sundowner Restaurant, und freitags und am Wochenende wird ein Büffet serviert. Das Veranda Restaurant am Meer ist nur ein paar Gehminuten entfernt. Ein 280m langer Strand steht exklusiv zur Verfügung, Segeltörns, Jachtcharter, Jeep-Safaris und Wildwasser-Rafting werden arrangiert.

Our inspector loved: *The tranquil setting of the complex.*

Sisus

DALYANKÖY YAT LIMANI MEVKII, ÇESME - ÍZMÍR, TURKEY

This new and exciting hotel lies in the quiet Bay of Çesme next to a small marina. The hotel has been designed with a Feng Shui philosophy and includes state-of-the-art technology to create a haven of modern luxury. The beautiful atrium has a wonderful airy atmosphere and all of the bedrooms and suites have carefully chosen décor and cool marble bathrooms. The restaurant offers some excellent examples of both Aegean and Mediterranean cuisine, and the kind staff offer the most attentive service.

Ce nouveaux et sensationnel hôtel se trouve dans la tranquille baie de Çesme, à côté du petit port de plaisance. L'hôtel a été conçu selon le principe du Feng Shui et comprend un système de technologie de pointe créant ainsi un havre moderne de luxe. Le magnifique atrium est clair et spacieux et toutes les chambres et suites ont une décoration soigneusement choisie et d'agréables salles de bain en marbre. Le restaurant sert d'excellents échantillons de la cuisine égéenne et méditerranéenne et le personnel offre un service des plus attentifs.

Dieses neue, spannende Hotel befindet sich in der ruhigen Bucht von Çesme neben einem kleinen Hafen. Das Hotel wurde gemäß der Feng-Shui-Philosophie gestaltet und ist eine reine Oase aus modernem Luxus mit hochmoderner Technologie. Das herrliche Atrium besitzt eine wundervoll luftige Atmosphäre und alle Zimmer und Suiten sind mit sorgfältigem Décor und kühlen Marmorbädern ausgestattet. Im Restaurant werden hervorragende ägäische und mediterrane Köstlichkeiten serviert, und das freundliche Personal sorgt für unübertroffenen Service.

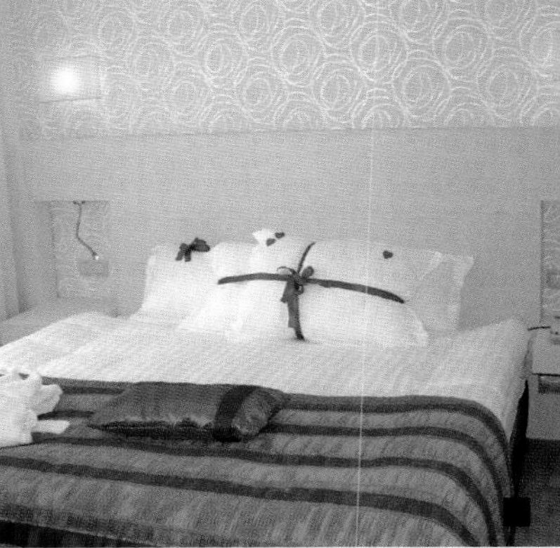

Directions: Çesme Highway > Dalyanköy at Çesme junction.

Web: www.johansens.com/sisus
E-mail: info@sisushotel.com
Tel: +90 232 724 0330
Fax: +90 232 724 9656

Price Guide:
single €120-170
double €160-220
suite €225-900

Our inspector loved: *The fantastic view of Dalyanköy at night.*

Tas Otel

KEMALPASA CADDESI NO 132, ALAÇATI/ÇESME - ÍZMÍR, TURKEY

This sparkling white stone built hotel, with attractive pale blue window shutters, is the ideal retreat for those who enjoy cosmopolitan village life, sandy beaches and windsurfing. Built as a family home 150 years ago, Tas Otel has been beautifully restored and converted into a charming boutique hotel with 8 individually decorated, delightfully furnished guest rooms, a large ground floor lounge with open fire, and a lovely breakfast room opening onto a flower-filled, vine-shaded garden with swimming pool.

Cet hôtel en pierre blanche éclatante avec ses jolis volets bleus pâles est la retraite idéale pour ceux qui aiment la vie de village cosmopolite et l'animation d'un petit port actif. Maison de famille construite il y a 150 ans, Tas Otel a été superbement restauré et converti en un charmant petit hôtel avec 8 chambres décorées individuellement et meublées avec goût, un salon spacieux au rez-de-chaussée avec une grande cheminée, et une salle adorable pour le petit déjeuner qui ouvre sur un jardin avec piscine, couvert de fleurs et ombragé grâce à la vigne vierge.

Dieses strahlend weiße, aus Stein erbaute Hotel mit seinen hübschen hellblauen Fensterläden ist der ideale Ort für Gäste, die ein kosmopolites Dorfleben und den Trubel eines kleinen Hafens schätzen. Das vor 150 Jahren als Privathaus erbaute Tas Otel wurde ausgiebig restauriert und in ein Boutiquehotel umgewandelt, und bietet nun 8 individuell gestaltete, zauberhaft eingerichtete Zimmer, einen großen Aufenthaltsraum mit offenem Kamin und einen hübschen Frühstückssaal, von dem man in einen mit Blumen gefüllten, von Weinlaub beschatteten Garten mit Swimmingpool gelangt.

Our inspector loved: *The charming entrance.*

Directions: Ízmír - Çesme Highway > Alaçati > follow signs in the village.

Web: www.johansens.com/tasotel
E-mail: zeynep@tasotel.com
Tel: +90 232 716 7772
Fax: +90 232 716 8517

Price Guide:
single €75
double €100

Hotel Villa Mahal

PO BOX 4 KALKAN, 07960 ANTALYA, TURKEY

This intimate hotel stands on a hillside, overlooking the spectacular bay of Kalkan, and is surrounded by olive trees. Stone steps plunge to the villa's own beach platforms, and the pool suite has a private swimming pool and terrace. The bright and airy bedrooms, all with seaview, accommodate a maximum of 26 guests, and the ambience is more like that of a private house than a hotel. Breakfast is a delicious buffet enjoyed on the rooftop terrace, and the Beach Restaurant serves succulent Turkish specialities for lunch and dinner.

Cet hôtel intime, entouré d'oliviers et perché sur une colline, surplombe la baie spectaculaire de Kalkan. Un escalier donne accès à la plage privée (plate-formes), et la suite piscine possède une terrasse et une piscine privée. Les chambres spacieuses et lumineuses, pouvant accueillir jusqu'à 26 hôtes, ont toutes vue sur la mer et l'ambiance ressemble plus à celle d'une maison particulière qu'à celle d'un hôtel. Le petit-déjeuner est un superbe buffet servi sur la terrasse du toit et le restaurant de la plage propose des spécialités turques pour le déjeuner et le dîner.

Dieses kleine, von Olivenbäumen umgebene Hotel liegt auf einem Hügel mit Blick über die spektakuläre Bucht von Kalkan. Eine Treppe führt von der Villa hinunter zum Privatsteg. Die Pool Suite bietet einen privaten Pool und Terrasse, und die hellen und luftigen Zimmer haben Meerblick und beherbergen maximal 26 Gäste. Das Ambiente ähnelt eher einem privaten Haus als einem Hotel. Zum Frühstück gibt es ein köstliches Buffet auf der Dachterrasse, und mittags und abends können die Gäste im Strandrestaurant türkische Spezialitäten genießen.

Our inspector loved: *The tranquil setting and fantastic view from this charming hotel.*

Directions: Dalaman Airport > Kas > Kalkan sign > left > beach.

Web: www.johansens.com/villamahal
E-mail: info@villamahal.com
Tel: +90 242 844 32 68
Fax: +90 242 844 21 22

Price Guide:
single €117
double/twin €130–220
suite €225–245

Mini Listings Great Britain & Ireland

Condé Nast Johansens are delighted to recommend over 620 properties across Great Britain and Ireland.
These properties can be found in *Recommended Hotels & Spas - GB & Ireland 2005* and *Recommended Country Houses, Small Hotels & Inns - GB & Ireland 2005.* Call +44 1323 649350 or see the order forms on page 437 to order Guides.

Recommended Hotels & Spas Great Britain & Ireland 2005

England

The Bath Priory Hotel And Restaurant	Bath & NE Somerset	+44 (0)1225 331922
The Bath Spa Hotel	Bath & NE Somerset	+44 (0)1225 444424
Combe Grove Manor Hotel & Country Club	Bath & NE Somerset	+44 (0)1225 834644
The Francis Hotel	Bath & NE Somerset	+44 (0)1225 424105
Homewood Park	Bath & NE Somerset	+44 (0)1225 723731
Hunstrete House	Bath & NE Somerset	+44 (0)1761 490490
The Royal Crescent Hotel	Bath & NE Somerset	+44 (0)1225 823333
The Windsor Hotel	Bath & NE Somerset	+44 (0)1225 422100
Moore Place Hotel	Bedfordshire	+44 (0)1908 282000
Cliveden	Berkshire	+44 (0)1628 668561
Donnington Valley Hotel & Golf Club	Berkshire	+44 (0)1635 551199
Fredrick's – Hotel Restaurant Spa	Berkshire	+44 (0)1628 581000
The French Horn	Berkshire	+44 (0)1189 692204
Monkey Island Hotel	Berkshire	+44 (0)1628 623400
Newbury Manor Hotel	Berkshire	+44 (0)1635 528838
The Regency Park Hotel	Berkshire	+44 (0)1635 871555
Sir Christopher Wren's House Hotel & Spa	Berkshire	+44 (0)1753 861354
Stirrups	Berkshire	+44 (0)1344 882284
The Swan At Streatley	Berkshire	+44 (0)1491 878800
The Vineyard At Stockcross	Berkshire	+44 (0)1635 528770
Hotel Du Vin & Bistro	Birmingham	+44 (0)121 200 0600

New Hall	**Birmingham**	**+44 (0)121 378 2442**
Hotel Du Vin & Bistro	Bristol	+44 (0)117 925 5577
Danesfield House Hotel And Spa	Buckinghamshire	+44 (0)1628 891010
Hartwell House Hotel, Restaurant & Spa	Buckinghamshire	+44 (0)1296 747444
Stoke Park Club	Buckinghamshire	+44 (0)1753 717171
Taplow House Hotel	Buckinghamshire	+44 (0)1628 670056
The Cambridge Belfry	Cambridgeshire	+44 (0)1954 714600
The Haycock	Cambridgeshire	+44 (0)1780 782223
Hotel Felix	Cambridgeshire	+44 (0)1223 277977
The Alderley Edge Hotel	Cheshire	+44 (0)1625 583033
The Chester Crabwall Manor	Cheshire	+44 (0)1244 851666
The Chester Grosvenor and Grosvenor Spa	Cheshire	+44 (0)1244 324024
Crewe Hall	Cheshire	+44 (0)1270 253333
Green Bough Hotel	Cheshire	+44 (0)1244 326241
Hillbark Hotel	Cheshire	+44 (0)151 625 2400
Mere Court Hotel	Cheshire	+44 (0)1565 831000
Nunsmere Hall	Cheshire	+44 (0)1606 889100
Rowton Hall Hotel	Cheshire	+44 (0)1244 335262
The Stanneylands Hotel	Cheshire	+44 (0)1625 525225
Alverton Manor	Cornwall	+44 (0)1872 276633
Budock Vean - The Hotel On The River	Cornwall	+44 (0)1326 252100
Fowey Hall Hotel & Restaurant	Cornwall	+44 (0)1726 833866
The Garrack Hotel & Restaurant	Cornwall	+44 (0)1736 796199
The Greenbank Hotel	Cornwall	+44 (0)1326 312440
Hell Bay	Cornwall	+44 (0)1720 422947
The Lugger Hotel	Cornwall	+44 (0)1872 501322
Meudon Hotel	Cornwall	+44 (0)1326 250541
The Nare Hotel	Cornwall	+44 (0)1872 501111
The Rosevine Hotel	Cornwall	+44 (0)1872 580206
Talland Bay Hotel	Cornwall	+44 (0)1503 272667
Treglos Hotel	Cornwall	+44 (0)1841 520727
Trenython Manor Hotel & Spa	Cornwall	+44 (0)1726 814797
The Well House	Cornwall	+44 (0)1579 342001
Armathwaite Hall Hotel	Cumbria	+44 (0)17687 76551
Gilpin Lodge	Cumbria	+44 (0)15394 88818
Holbeck Ghyll Country House Hotel	Cumbria	+44 (0)15394 32375
The Inn on the Lake	Cumbria	+44 (0)17684 82444
Lakeside Hotel On Lake Windermere	Cumbria	+44 (0)1539 530001
Linthwaite House Hotel	Cumbria	+44 (0)15394 88600
The Lodore Falls Hotel	Cumbria	+44 (0)17687 77285
Lovelady Shield Country House Hotel	Cumbria	+44 (0)1434 381203
Netherwood Hotel	Cumbria	+44 (0)15395 32552
Rampsbeck Country House Hotel	Cumbria	+44 (0)17684 86442
Rothay Manor	Cumbria	+44 (0)15394 33605
Sharrow Bay Country House Hotel	Cumbria	+44 (0)17684 86301
Storrs Hall	Cumbria	+44 (0)15394 47111
Tufton Arms Hotel	Cumbria	+44 (0)17683 51593
Callow Hall	Derbyshire	+44 (0)1335 300900
Cavendish Hotel	Derbyshire	+44 (0)1246 582311
East Lodge Country House Hotel	Derbyshire	+44 (0)1629 734474
Fischer's	Derbyshire	+44 (0)1246 583259
Hassop Hall	Derbyshire	+44 (0)1629 640488
The Izaak Walton Hotel	Derbyshire	+44 (0)1335 350555
The Lee Wood Hotel & Restaurant	Derbyshire	+44 (0)1298 23002
Riber Hall	Derbyshire	+44 (0)1629 582795
Ringwood Hall Hotel	Derbyshire	+44 (0)1246 280077
Riverside House	Derbyshire	+44 (0)1629 814275
The Arundell Arms	Devon	+44 (0)1566 784666
Bovey Castle	Devon	+44 (0)1647 445016
Buckland-Tout-Saints	Devon	+44 (0)1548 853055
Combe House Hotel & Restaurant	Devon	+44 (0)1404 540400
Fairwater Head Country House Hotel	Devon	+44 (0)1297 678349
Hotel Riviera	Devon	+44 (0)1395 515201
Ilsington Country House Hotel	Devon	+44 (0)1364 661452
Langdon Court Hotel & Restaurant	Devon	+44 (0)1752 862358
Lewtrenchard Manor	Devon	+44 (0)1566 783222
Mill End	Devon	+44 (0)1647 432282
Northcote Manor Country House Hotel	Devon	+44 (0)1769 560501
Orestone Manor Hotel & Restaurant	Devon	+44 (0)1803 328098
The Osborne Hotel & Langtry's Restaurant	Devon	+44 (0)1803 213311
The Palace Hotel	Devon	+44 (0)1803 200200
Percy's Country Hotel & Restaurant	Devon	+44 (0)1409 211236
Soar Mill Cove Hotel	Devon	+44 (0)1548 561566
The Tides Reach Hotel	Devon	+44 (0)1548 843466
Watersmeet Hotel	Devon	+44 (0)1271 870333
Woolacombe Bay Hotel	Devon	+44 (0)1271 870388
The Avonmouth Hotel and Restaurant	Dorset	+44 (0)1202 483434
Langtry Manor	Dorset	+44 (0)1202 553887
Moonfleet Manor	Dorset	+44 (0)1305 786948
Plumber Manor	Dorset	+44 (0)1258 472507
The Priory Hotel	Dorset	+44 (0)1929 551666
Headlam Hall	Durham	+44 (0)1325 730238
Five Lakes Resort	Essex	+44 (0)1621 868888
Greenwoods Estate	Essex	+44 (0)1277 829990
Maison Talbooth	Essex	+44 (0)1206 322367
Barnsley House	Gloucestershire	+44 (0)1285 740000
The Bear Of Rodborough	Gloucestershire	+44 (0)1453 878522

Mini Listings Great Britain & Ireland

Condé Nast Johansens are delighted to recommend over 620 properties across Great Britain and Ireland.
These properties can be found in *Recommended Hotels & Spas - GB & Ireland 2005* and *Recommended Country Houses, Small Hotels & Inns - GB & Ireland 2005.*
Call +44 1323 649350 or see the order forms on page 437 to order Guides.

Burleigh Court	Gloucestershire	+44 (0)1453 883804
Calcot Manor	Gloucestershire	+44 (0)1666 890391
Charingworth Manor	Gloucestershire	+44 (0)1386 593555
Corse Lawn House Hotel	Gloucestershire	+44 (0)1452 780479
Cotswold House Hotel	Gloucestershire	+44 (0)1386 840330
The Dial House	Gloucestershire	+44 (0)1451 822244
Fosse Manor	Gloucestershire	+44 (0)1451 830354
The Grapevine Hotel	Gloucestershire	+44 (0)1451 830344
The Greenway	Gloucestershire	+44 (0)1242 862352
Hatton Court	Gloucestershire	+44 (0)1452 617412
Hotel On The Park	Gloucestershire	+44 (0)1242 518898
Lords Of The Manor Hotel	Gloucestershire	+44 (0)1451 820243
Lower Slaughter Manor	Gloucestershire	+44 (0)1451 820456
The Manor House Hotel	Gloucestershire	+44 (0)1608 650501
The Noel Arms Hotel	Gloucestershire	+44 (0)1386 840317
The Painswick Hotel	Gloucestershire	+44 (0)1452 812160
The Swan Hotel At Bibury	Gloucestershire	+44 (0)1285 740695
The Unicorn Hotel	Gloucestershire	+44 (0)1451 830257
Washbourne Court Hotel	Gloucestershire	+44 (0)1451 822143
Thornbury Castle	South Gloucestershire	+44 (0)1454 281182
Careys Manor Hotel & Senspa	Hampshire	+44 (0)1590 623551
Chewton Glen	Hampshire	+44 (0)1425 275341
Chilworth Manor	Hampshire	+44 (0)23 8076 7333
Esseborne Manor	Hampshire	+44 (0)1264 736444
Hotel Du Vin & Bistro	Hampshire	+44 (0)1962 841414
Le Poussin at Whitley Ridge	Hampshire	+44 (0)1590 622354
The Montagu Arms Hotel	Hampshire	+44 (0)1590 612324
New Park Manor	Hampshire	+44 (0)1590 623467
Passford House Hotel	Hampshire	+44 (0)1590 682398
Tylney Hall	Hampshire	+44 (0)1256 764881
Down Hall Country House Hotel	Hertfordshire	+44 (0)1279 731441
The Grove Hotel	Hertfordshire	+44 (0)1923 807807
The Pendley Manor Hotel	Hertfordshire	+44 (0)1442 891891
Sopwell House	Hertfordshire	+44 (0)1727 864477
St Michael's Manor	Hertfordshire	+44 (0)1727 864444
The Priory Bay Hotel	Isle of Wight	+44 (0)1983 613146
Chilston Park	Kent	+44 (0)1622 859803
Eastwell Manor	Kent	+44 (0)1233 213000
Hotel Du Vin & Bistro	Kent	+44 (0)1892 526455
Rowhill Grange Hotel And Spa	Kent	+44 (0)1322 615136
The Spa Hotel	Kent	+44 (0)1892 520331
The Gibbon Bridge Hotel	Lancashire	+44 (0)1995 61456
Northcote Manor	Lancashire	+44 (0)1254 240555
The Pines Hotel	Lancashire	+44 (0)1772 338551
Quorn Country Hotel	Leicestershire	+44 (0)1509 415050
Stapleford Park Hotel, Spa, Golf & Sporting Estate	Leicestershire	+44 (0)1572 787 522
The Angel and Royal Hotel	Lincolnshire	+44 (0)1476 565816
The George Of Stamford	Lincolnshire	+44 (0)1780 750750
The Lincoln Hotel	Lincolnshire	+44 (0)1522 520348
41	London	+44 (0)20 7300 0041
47 Park Street	London	+44 (0)20 7491 7282
51 Buckingham Gate	London	+44 (0)20 7769 7766
The Athenaeum Hotel & Apartments	London	+44 (0)20 7499 3464
Beaufort House	London	+44 (0)20 7584 2600
Cannizaro House	London	+44 (0)208 879 1464
The Carlton Tower	London	+44 (0)20 7235 1234
The Cranley	London	+44 (0)20 7373 0123
Dolphin Square Hotel	London	+44 (0)20 7834 3800
The Dorchester	London	+44 (0)20 7629 8888
Dorset Square Hotel	London	+44 (0)20 7723 7874
Draycott House Apartments	London	+44 (0)20 7584 4659
The Goring	London	+44 (0) 20 7396 9000
Kensington House Hotel	London	+44 (0)20 7937 2345
The Leonard	London	+44 (0)20 7935 2010
The Lowndes Hotel	London	+44 (0)20 7823 1234
The Mayflower Hotel	London	+44 (0)20 7370 0991
The Milestone Hotel & Apartments	London	+44 (0)20 7917 1000
Number Sixteen	London	+44 (0)20 7589 5232
Pembridge Court Hotel	London	+44 (0)20 7229 9977
The Richmond Gate Hotel And Restaurant	London	+44 (0)20 8940 0061
The Ritz	London	+44 (0)20 7493 8181
The Royal Park	London	+44 (0)20 7479 6600
Sofitel St James	London	+44 (0)20 7747 2200
Twenty Nevern Square	London	+44 (0)20 7565 9555

▼

Warren House	**London**	**+44 (0)20 8547 1777**
West Lodge Park Country House Hotel	London	+44 (0)20 8216 3900
Didsbury House	Greater Manchester	+44 (0)161 448 2200
Etrop Grange	Greater Manchester	+44 (0)161 499 0500
Congham Hall	Norfolk	+44 (0)1485 600250
Park Farm Country Hotel & Leisure	Norfolk	+44 (0)1603 810264
Fawsley Hall	Northamptonshire	+44 (0)1327 892000
Whittlebury Hall	Northamptonshire	+44 (0)1327 857857
Marshall Meadows Country House Hotel	Northumberland	+44 (0)1289 331133
Matfen Hall	Northumberland	+44 (0)1661 886500
Tillmouth Park	Northumberland	+44 (0)1890 882255
Hart's Hotel	Nottinghamshire	+44 (0)115 988 1900
Lace Market Hotel	Nottinghamshire	+44 (0)115 852 3232
Langar Hall	Nottinghamshire	+44 (0)1949 860559
The Bay Tree Hotel	Oxfordshire	+44 (0)1993 822791
Bignell Park Hotel & Restaurant	Oxfordshire	+44 (0)1869 326550
The Cotswold Lodge Hotel	Oxfordshire	+44 (0)1865 512121
Fallowfields	Oxfordshire	+44 (0)1865 820416
The Feathers Hotel	Oxfordshire	+44 (0)1993 812291
Hawkwell House	Oxfordshire	+44 (0)1865 749988
Phyllis Court Club	Oxfordshire	+44 (0)1491 570500
The Spread Eagle Hotel	Oxfordshire	+44 (0)1844 213661
The Springs Hotel & Golf Club	Oxfordshire	+44 (0)1491 836687
Weston Manor	Oxfordshire	+44 (0)1869 350621
Hambleton Hall	Rutland	+44 (0)1572 756991
The Lake Isle	Rutland	+44 (0)1572 822951
Dinham Hall	Shropshire	+44 (0)1584 876464
Madeley Court	Shropshire	+44 (0)1952 680068
Bindon Country House Hotel	Somerset	+44 (0)1823 400070
Daneswood House Hotel	Somerset	+44 (0)1934 843145
Holbrook House Hotel & Spa	Somerset	+44 (0)1963 824466
Mount Somerset Country House Hotel	Somerset	+44 (0)1823 442500
Ston Easton Park	Somerset	+44 (0)1761 241631
Hoar Cross Hall Spa Resort	Staffordshire	+44 (0)1283 575671
Angel Hotel	Suffolk	+44 (0)1284 714000
Black Lion Hotel & Restaurant	Suffolk	+44 (0)1787 312356
Brudenell Hotel	Suffolk	+44 (0)1728 452071
Hintlesham Hall	Suffolk	+44 (0)1473 652334

Mini Listings Great Britain & Ireland

Condé Nast Johansens are delighted to recommend over 620 properties across Great Britain and Ireland.
These properties can be found in *Recommended Hotels & Spas - GB & Ireland 2005* and *Recommended Country Houses, Small Hotels & Inns - GB & Ireland 2005*.
Call +44 1323 649350 or see the order forms on page 437 to order Guides.

The Hotel Victoria	Suffolk	+44 (0)1502 574433
Ravenwood Hall Country Hotel & Restaurant	Suffolk	+44 (0)1359 270345
Salthouse Harbour Hotel	Suffolk	+44 (0)1473 226789
Seckford Hall	Suffolk	+44 (0)1394 385678
The Swan Hotel	Suffolk	+44 (0)1502 722186
The Swan Hotel	Suffolk	+44 (0)1787 247477
Swynford Paddocks Hotel And Restaurant	Suffolk	+44 (0)1638 570234
Foxhills	Surrey	+44 (0)1932 704500
Great Fosters	Surrey	+44 (0)1784 433822
Langshott Manor	Surrey	+44 (0)1293 786680
Lythe Hill Hotel & Spa	Surrey	+44 (0)1428 651251
Oatlands Park Hotel	Surrey	+44 (0)1932 847242
Pennyhill Park Hotel	Surrey	+44 (0)1276 471774
Ashdown Park Hotel And Country Club	East Sussex	+44 (0)1342 824988
Dale Hill	East Sussex	+44 (0)1580 200112
The Grand Hotel	East Sussex	+44 (0)1323 412345
Horsted Place Country House Hotel	East Sussex	+44 (0)1825 750581
Hotel Du Vin & Bistro	East Sussex	+44 (0)1273 718588
Newick Park	East Sussex	+44 (0)1825 723633
The PowderMills	East Sussex	+44 (0)1424 775511
White Lodge Country House Hotel	East Sussex	+44 (0)1323 870265
Alexander House Hotel	West Sussex	+44 (0)1342 714914
Amberley Castle	West Sussex	+44 (0)1798 831992
The Angel Hotel	West Sussex	+44 (0)1730 812421
Bailiffscourt Hotel & Health Spa	West Sussex	+44 (0)1903 723511
Ghyll Manor	West Sussex	+44 (0)845 345 3426
The Millstream Hotel	West Sussex	+44 (0)1243 573234
Ockenden Manor	West Sussex	+44 (0)1444 416111
South Lodge Hotel	West Sussex	+44 (0)1403 891711
The Spread Eagle Hotel & Health Spa	West Sussex	+44 (0)1730 816911
The Vermont Hotel	Tyne & Wear	+44 (0)191 233 1010
Alveston Manor	Warwickshire	+44 (0)1789 205478
Ardencote Manor Hotel, Country Club & Spa	Warwickshire	+44 (0)1926 843111
Billesley Manor	Warwickshire	+44 (0)1789 279955
Ettington Park	Warwickshire	+44 (0)1789 450123
The Glebe At Barford	Warwickshire	+44 (0)1926 624218
Mallory Court	Warwickshire	+44 (0)1926 330214
Nailcote Hall	Warwickshire	+44 (0)2476 466174
Nuthurst Grange	Warwickshire	+44 (0)1564 783972
Wroxall Abbey Estate	Warwickshire	+44 (0)1926 484470
Bishopstrow House	Wiltshire	+44 (0)1985 212312
Howard's House	Wiltshire	+44 (0)1722 716392
The Manor House Hotel & Golf Club	Wiltshire	+44 (0)1249 782206
The Old Bell	Wiltshire	+44 (0)1666 822344
The Pear Tree At Purton	Wiltshire	+44 (0)1793 772100
The Broadway Hotel	Worcestershire	+44 (0)1386 852401
Brockencote Hall	Worcestershire	+44 (0)1562 777876
The Cottage In The Wood	Worcestershire	+44 (0)1684 575859
Dormy House	Worcestershire	+44 (0)1386 852711
The Elms	Worcestershire	+44 (0)1299 896666
The Evesham Hotel	Worcestershire	+44 (0)1386 765566
The Lygon Arms	Worcestershire	+44 (0)1386 852255
Wood Norton Hall	Worcestershire	+44 (0)1386 425780
Willerby Manor Hotel	East Riding of Yorkshire	+44 (0)1482 652616
Aldwark Manor	North Yorkshire	+44 (0)1347 838146
The Boar's Head Hotel	North Yorkshire	+44 (0)1423 771888
The Devonshire Arms Country House Hotel	North Yorkshire	+44 (0)1756 718111
The Feversham Arms Hotel	North Yorkshire	+44 (0)1439 770766
The Grange Hotel	North Yorkshire	+44 (0)1904 644744
Grants Hotel	North Yorkshire	+44 (0)1423 560666
Hackness Grange	North Yorkshire	+44 (0)1723 882345
Hazlewood Castle Hotel	North Yorkshire	+44 (0)1937 535353
Hob Green Hotel And Restaurant	North Yorkshire	+44 (0)1423 770031
Hotel Du Vin & Bistro	North Yorkshire	+44 (0)1423 856800
Judges Country House Hotel	North Yorkshire	+44 (0)1642 789000
Middlethorpe Hall Hotel, Restaurant & Spa	North Yorkshire	+44 (0)1904 641241
Monk Fryston Hall Hotel	North Yorkshire	+44 (0)1977 682369
The Pheasant	North Yorkshire	+44 (0)1439 771241
The Royal Hotel	North Yorkshire	+44 (0)1723 364333
Rudding Park Hotel & Golf	North Yorkshire	+44 (0)1423 871350
Simonstone Hall	North Yorkshire	+44 (0)1969 667255
Swinton Park	North Yorkshire	+44 (0)1765 680900
The Worsley Arms Hotel	North Yorkshire	+44 (0)1653 628234
Wrea Head Country Hotel	North Yorkshire	+44 (0)1723 378211
Charnwood Hotel	South Yorkshire	+44 (0)114 258 9411
Hellaby Hall Hotel	South Yorkshire	+44 (0)1709 702701
Whitley Hall Hotel	South Yorkshire	+44 (0)114 245 4444
42 The Calls	West Yorkshire	+44 (0)113 244 0099
Chevin Country Park Hotel	West Yorkshire	+44 (0)1943 467818
Haley's Hotel & Restaurant	West Yorkshire	+44 (0)113 278 4446
Holdsworth House Hotel & Restaurant	West Yorkshire	+44 (0)1422 240024
Wood Hall	West Yorkshire	+44 (0)1937 587271
Woodlands	West Yorkshire	+44 (0)113 238 1488

Channel Islands

The Atlantic Hotel	Jersey	+44 (0)1534 744101
Château La Chaire	Jersey	+44 (0)1534 863354

N. Ireland

Bushmills Inn Hotel	Antrim	+44 (0)28 2073 3000

Ireland

Dromoland Castle	Clare	+353 61 368144
Harvey's Point	Donegal	+353 74 972 2208
Rathmullan House	Donegal	+353 74 915 8188
Renvyle House Hotel	Galway	+353 95 43511
Cahernane House Hotel	Kerry	+353 64 31895
Park Hotel Kenmare & Sámas	Kerry	+353 64 41200

▼

Parknasilla Hotel	**Kerry**	**+353 64 45122**
Killashee House Hotel	Kildare	+353 45 879277
Mount Juliet Conrad	Kilkenny	+353 56 777 3000
Glin Castle	Limerick	+353 68 34173
Ashford Castle	Mayo	+353 94 95 46003
Knockranny House Hotel & Spa	Mayo	+353 98 28600
Nuremore Hotel And Country Club	Monaghan	+353 42 9661438
Dunbrody Country House & Cookery School	Wexford	+353 51 389 600
Kelly's Resort Hotel	Wexford	+353 53 32114
Marlfield House	Wexford	+353 55 21124

Mini Listings Great Britain & Ireland

Condé Nast Johansens are delighted to recommend over 620 properties across Great Britain and Ireland.
These properties can be found in *Recommended Hotels & Spas - GB & Ireland 2005* and *Recommended Country Houses, Small Hotels & Inns - GB & Ireland 2005*.
Call +44 1323 649350 or see the order forms on page 437 to order Guides.

Scotland

Darroch Learg	Aberdeenshire	+44 (0)13397 55443
Ardanaiseig	Argyll & Bute	+44 (0)1866 833333
Cameron House	Argyll & Bute	+44 (0)1389 755565
Loch Melfort Hotel & Restaurant	Argyll & Bute	+44 (0)1852 200233

▼

Stonefield Castle	**Argyll & Bute**	**+44 (0)1880 820836**
Balcary Bay Hotel	Dumfries & Galloway	+44 (0)1556 640217
Cally Palace Hotel	Dumfries & Galloway	+44 (0)1557 814341
Kirroughtree House	Dumfries & Galloway	+44 (0)1671 402141
Knockinaam Lodge	Dumfries & Galloway	+44 (0)1776 810471
The Bonham	Edinburgh	+44 (0)131 623 9301
Bruntsfield Hotel	Edinburgh	+44 (0)131 229 1393
Channings	Edinburgh	+44 (0)131 623 9302
The Chester Residence	Edinburgh	+44 (0)131 226 2075
Christopher North House	Edinburgh	+44 (0)131 225 2720
The Edinburgh Residence	Edinburgh	+44 (0)131 623 9304
The Howard	Edinburgh	+44 (0)131 623 9303
The Old Manor Country House Hotel	Fife	+44 (0)1333 320368
One Devonshire Gardens	Glasgow	+44 (0)141 3392001
Bunchrew House Hotel	Highland	+44 (0)1463 234917
Cuillin Hills Hotel	Highland	+44 (0)1478 612003
Culloden House	Highland	+44 (0)1463 790461
Glen Mhor Hotel	Highland	+44 (0)1463 234308
The Glenmoriston Town House Hotel & La Riviera Restaurant	Highland	+44 (0)1463 223777
The Golf View Hotel & Leisure Club	Highland	+44 (0)1667 458800
Inverlochy Castle	Highland	+44 (0)1397 702177
Kincraig House Hotel	Highland	+44 (0)1349 852587
Loch Torridon Country House Hotel	Highland	+44 (0)1445 791242
Muckrach Lodge Hotel & Restaurant	Highland	+44 (0)1479 851257
The Royal Golf Hotel	Highland	+44 (0)1667 458800
Royal Marine Hotel	Highland	+44 (0)1408 621252
Skeabost Country House	Highland	+44 (0)1470 532202
Dalhousie Castle And Spa	Midlothian	+44 (0)1875 820153
Knockomie Hotel	Moray	+44 (0)1309 673146
Ballathie House Hotel	Perth & Kinross	+44 (0)1250 883268
Cromlix House	Perth & Kinross	+44 (0)1786 822125
Gleneagles	Perth & Kinross	+44 (0)1764 662231
Kinnaird	Perth & Kinross	+44 (0)1796 482440
The Royal Hotel	Perth & Kinross	+44 (0)1764 679200
Castle Venlaw	Scottish Borders	+44 (0)1721 720384
Cringletie House	Scottish Borders	+44 (0)1721 725750
Dryburgh Abbey Hotel	Scottish Borders	+44 (0)1835 822261
Ednam House Hotel	Scottish Borders	+44 (0)1573 224168
The Roxburghe Hotel & Golf Course	Scottish Borders	+44 (0)1573 450331
Enterkine Country House	South Ayrshire	+44 (0)1292 520580
Buchanan Arms Hotel & Leisure Club	Stirling	+44 (0)1360 660588

Wales

Llechwen Hall	Cardiff	+44 (0)1443 742050
Bodysgallen Hall & Spa	Conwy	+44 (0)1492 584466
St Tudno Hotel & Restaurant	Conwy	+44 (0)1492 874411
Wild Pheasant Hotel	Denbighshire	+44 (0)1978 860629
Hotel Maes-Y-Neuadd	Gwynedd	+44 (0)1766 780200
Palé Hall	Gwynedd	+44 (0)1678 530285
Penmaenuchaf Hall	Gwynedd	+44 (0)1341 422129
The Trearddur Bay Hotel	Isle of Anglesey	+44 (0)1407 860301
Allt-Yr-Ynys Hotel	Monmouthshire	+44 (0)1873 890307
Llansantffraed Court Hotel	Monmouthshire	+44 (0)1873 840678
Lamphey Court Hotel	Pembrokeshire	+44 (0)1646 672273
Penally Abbey	Pembrokeshire	+44 (0)1834 843033
Warpool Court Hotel	Pembrokeshire	+44 (0)1437 720300
Gliffaes Country House Hotel	Powys	+44 (0)1874 730371
The Lake Country House	Powys	+44 (0)1591 620202
Lake Vyrnwy Hotel	Powys	+44 (0)1691 870 692
Llangoed Hall	Powys	+44 (0)1874 754525
Morgans	Swansea	+44 (0)1792 484856

Recommended Country Houses, Small Hotels & Inns Great Britain & Ireland 2004

England

The County Hotel	Bath & NE Somerset	+44 (0)1225 425003
Dorian House	Bath & NE Somerset	+44 (0)1225 426336
Oldfields	Bath & NE Somerset	+44 (0)1225 317984
The Ring O' Roses	Bath & NE Somerset	+44 (0)1761 232478
Tasburgh House Hotel	Bath & NE Somerset	+44 (0)1225 425096
Mill House Hotel & Restaurant	Bedfordshire	+44 (0)1234 781678
Cantley House	Berkshire	+44 (0)118 978 9912
The Cottage Inn	Berkshire	+44 (0)1344 882242
Crown & Garter	Berkshire	+44 (0)1488 668325
The Inn on the Green	Berkshire	+44 (0)1628 482638
The Leatherne Bottel Riverside Restaurant	Berkshire	+44 (0)1491 872667
The Royal Oak Restaurant & Hotel	Berkshire	+44 (0)1635 201325
The Dinton Hermit	Buckinghamshire	+44 (0)1296 747473
The Greyhound	Buckinghamshire	+44 (0)1753 883404
The Ivy House	Buckinghamshire	+44 (0)1494 872184
The Nags Head	Buckinghamshire	+44 (0)1494 862945
The Meadowcroft Hotel	Cambridgeshire	+44 (0)1223 346120
Broxton Hall	Cheshire	+44 (0)1829 782321
Frogg Manor Hotel & Restaurant	Cheshire	+44 (0)1829 782629
Willington Hall Hotel	Cheshire	+44 (0)1829 752321
Cormorant On The River, Hotel & Riverside Restaurant	Cornwall	+44 (0)1726 833426
Highland Court Lodge	Cornwall	+44 (0)1726 813320
The Old Quay House Hotel	Cornwall	+44 (0)1726 833302
Tredethy House	Cornwall	+44 (0)1208 841262
Trehaven Manor	Cornwall	+44 (0)1503 262028
Trehellas House Hotel & Restaurant	Cornwall	+44 (0)1208 72700
Trelawne Hotel – The Hutches Restaurant	Cornwall	+44 (0)1326 250226
Trevalsa Court Country House Hotel	Cornwall	+44 (0)1726 842468
Wisteria Lodge & Country Spa	Cornwall	+44 (0)1726 810800
Broadoaks Country House	Cumbria	+44 (0)1539 445566
Crosby Lodge Country House Hotel	Cumbria	+44 (0)1228 573618
Dale Head Hall Lakeside Hotel	Cumbria	+44 (0)17687 72478
Fayrer Garden House Hotel	Cumbria	+44 (0)15394 88195
Gilpin Lodge	Cumbria	+44 (0)15394 88818
Grizedale Lodge	Cumbria	+44 (0)15394 36532

Mini Listings Great Britain & Ireland

Condé Nast Johansens are delighted to recommend over 620 properties across Great Britain and Ireland.
These properties can be found in *Recommended Hotels & Spas - GB & Ireland 2005* and *Recommended Country Houses, Small Hotels & Inns - GB & Ireland 2005.*
Call +44 1323 649350 or see the order forms on page 437 to order Guides.

The Leathes Head	Cumbria	+44 (0)17687 77247
Linthwaite House Hotel	Cumbria	+44 (0)15394 88600
The Pheasant	Cumbria	+44 (0)17687 76234
The Queen's Head Hotel	Cumbria	+44 (0)15394 36271
Sawrey House Country Hotel & Restaurant	Cumbria	+44 (0)15394 36387
Temple Sowerby House Hotel	Cumbria	+44 (0)17683 61578
Underwood	Cumbria	+44 (0)1229 771116

▼

Boar's Head Hotel	**Derbyshire**	**+44 (0)1283 820344**
The Chequers Inn	Derbyshire	+44 (0)1433 630231
Dannah Farm Country House	Derbyshire	+44 (0)1773 550273
Kegworth House	Derbyshire	+44 (0)1509 672575
Littleover Lodge Hotel	Derbyshire	+44 (0)1332 510161
The Peacock At Rowsley	Derbyshire	+44 (0)1629 733518
The Plough Inn	Derbyshire	+44 (0)1433 650319
The Wind In The Willows	Derbyshire	+44 (0)1457 868001
Bickleigh Castle	Devon	+44 (0)1884 855363
Browns Hotel, Wine Bar & Brasserie	Devon	+44 (0)1822 618686
Combe House Hotel & Restaurant	Devon	+44 (0)1404 540400
The Edgemoor	Devon	+44 (0)1626 832466
The Galley Restaurant & Rooms	Devon	+44 (0)1392 876078
Gidleigh Park	Devon	+44 (0)1647 432367
Hewitt's - Villa Spaldi	Devon	+44 (0)1598 752293
Home Farm Hotel	Devon	+44 (0)1404 831278
Ilsington Country House Hotel	Devon	+44 (0)1364 661452
Kingston House	Devon	+44 (0)1803 762 235
The New Inn	Devon	+44 (0)1363 84242
Percy's Country Hotel & Restaurant	Devon	+44 (0)1409 211236
Yeoldon House Hotel	Devon	+44 (0)1237 474400
The Grange At Oborne	Dorset	+44 (0)1935 813463
Kemps Country Hotel & Restaurant	Dorset	+44 (0)1929 462563
The Lord Bute	Dorset	+44 (0)1425 278884
Summer Lodge	Dorset	+44 (0)1935 482000
Yalbury Cottage Hotel	Dorset	+44 (0)1305 262382
The Cricketers' Arms	Essex	+44 (0)1799 543210
The Crown House	Essex	+44 (0)1799 530515
The Mistley Thorn	Essex	+44 (0)1206 392821
The Pump House Apartment	Essex	+44 (0)1277 656579
Bibury Court	Gloucestershire	+44 (0)1285 740337
Charlton Kings Hotel	Gloucestershire	+44 (0)1242 231061
Lower Brook House	Gloucestershire	+44 (0)1386 700286
The Malt House	Gloucestershire	+44 (0)1386 840295
New Inn At Coln	Gloucestershire	+44 (0)1285 750651
The Snooty Fox	Gloucestershire	+44 (0)1666 502436
Three Choirs Vineyards Estate	Gloucestershire	+44 (0)1531 890223
The Wild Duck Inn	Gloucestershire	+44 (0)1285 770310
Langrish House	Hampshire	+44 (0)1730 266941
The Mill At Gordleton	Hampshire	+44 (0)1590 682219
The Nurse's Cottage	Hampshire	+44 (0)1590 683402
Thatched Cottage Hotel & Restaurant	Hampshire	+44 (0)1590 623090
Whitley Ridge Country House Hotel	Hampshire	+44 (0)1590 622354
Ford Abbey	Herefordshire	+44 (0)1568 760700
Glewstone Court	Herefordshire	+44 (0)1989 770367
The Pilgrim Hotel	Herefordshire	+44 (0)1981 540742
Rhydspence Inn	Herefordshire	+44 (0)1497 831262
The Verzon	Herefordshire	+44 (0)1531 670381
Wilton Court Hotel	Herefordshire	+44 (0)1989 562569
Redcoats Farmhouse Hotel And Restaurant	Hertfordshire	+44 (0)1438 729500
The White House and Lion & Lamb Bar & Restaurant	Hertfordshire	+44 (0)1279 870257
Rylstone Manor	Isle of Wight	+44 (0)1983 862806
The Wellington Hotel	Isle of Wight	+44 (0)1983 856600
The George Hotel	Kent	+44 (0)1580 713348
Hempstead House	Kent	+44 (0)1795 428020
Ringlestone Inn and Farmhouse Hotel	Kent	+44 (0)1622 859900
Romney Bay House Hotel	Kent	+44 (0)1797 364747
Wallett's Court Hotel & Spa	Kent	+44 (0)1304 852424
The Inn At Whitewell	Lancashire	+44 (0)1200 448222
Tree Tops Country House Restaurant & Hotel	Lancashire	+44 (0)1704 572430
Abbots Oak Country House	Leicestershire	+44 (0)1530 832 328
Horse & Trumpet	Leicestershire	+44 (0)1858 565000
The Red House	Leicestershire	+44 (0)1664 822429
Rothley Court Hotel	Leicestershire	+44 (0)116 237 4141
Sysonby Knoll Hotel	Leicestershire	+44 (0)1664 563563
The Crown Hotel	Lincolnshire	+44 (0)1780 763136
The Lea Gate Inn	Lincolnshire	+44 (0)1526 342370
Washingborough Hall	Lincolnshire	+44 (0)1522 790340
Racquet Club	Merseyside	+44 (0)151 236 6676
Beechwood Hotel	Norfolk	+44 (0)1692 403231
Broom Hall Country Hotel	Norfolk	+44 (0)1953 882125
Brovey Lair	Norfolk	+44 (0)1953 882706
Catton Old Hall	Norfolk	+44 (0)1603 419379
Elderton Lodge Hotel & Langtry Restaurant	Norfolk	+44 (0)1263 833547
Felbrigg Lodge	Norfolk	+44 (0)1263 837588
The Great Escape Holiday Company	Norfolk	+44 (0)1485 518717
Idyllic Cottages At Vere Lodge	Norfolk	+44 (0)1328 838261
The Manor House	Norfolk	+44 (0)1328 820597
The Moat House	Norfolk	+44 (0)1508 570149
The Norfolk Mead Hotel	Norfolk	+44 (0)1603 737531
The Old Rectory	Norfolk	+44 (0)1603 700772
The Stower Grange	Norfolk	+44 (0)1603 860210
The White Horse	Norfolk	+44 (0)1485 210262
The Falcon Hotel	Northamptonshire	+44 (0)1604 696200
The Windmill At Badby	Northamptonshire	+44 (0)1327 702363
The Otterburn Tower	Northumberland	+44 (0)1830 520620
Waren House Hotel	Northumberland	+44 (0)1668 214581
Cockliffe Country House Hotel	Nottinghamshire	+44 (0)1159 680179
The Saracens Head Hotel	Nottinghamshire	+44 (0)1636 812701
Duke Of Marlborough Country Inn	Oxfordshire	+44 (0)1993 811460
The George Hotel	Oxfordshire	+44 (0)1865 340404
The Kings Head Inn & Restaurant	Oxfordshire	+44 (0)1608 658365
The Lamb Inn	Oxfordshire	+44 (0)1993 823155
The Plough At Clanfield	Oxfordshire	+44 (0)1367 810222
The White Hart Hotel	Oxfordshire	+44 (0)1491 641245
Barnsdale Lodge	Rutland	+44 (0)1572 724678
The Hundred House Hotel, Norton	Shropshire	+44 (0)1952 730353
The Old Vicarage Hotel	Shropshire	+44 (0)1746 716497
Overton Grange Hotel	Shropshire	+44 (0)1584 873500
Pen-Y-Dyffryn Hall Hotel	Shropshire	+44 (0)1691 653700
Soulton Hall	Shropshire	+44 (0)1939 232786
Ashwick Country House Hotel	Somerset	+44 (0)1398 323868
Beryl	Somerset	+44 (0)1749 678738
Compton House	Somerset	+44 (0)1934 733944

Mini Listings Great Britain & Ireland

Condé Nast Johansens are delighted to recommend over 620 properties across Great Britain and Ireland. These properties can be found in *Recommended Hotels & Spas - GB & Ireland 2005* and *Recommended Country Houses, Small Hotels & Inns - GB & Ireland 2005.*

Call +44 1323 649350 or see the order forms on page 437 to order Guides.

Farthings Hotel & Restaurant	Somerset	+44 (0)1823 480664
Glencot House	Somerset	+44 (0)1749 677160
Karslake House Hotel & Restaurant	Somerset	+44 (0)1643 851242
The Old Rectory	Somerset	+44 (0)1460 54364
Porlock Vale House	Somerset	+44 (0)1643 862338
Three Acres Country House	Somerset	+44 (0)1398 323730
Somerford Hall	Staffordshire	+44 (0)1902 850108
The Brome Grange Hotel	Suffolk	+44 (0)1379 870456
Clarice House	Suffolk	+44 (0)1284 705550
Worlington Hall Country House Hotel	Suffolk	+44 (0)1638 712237
Chase Lodge	Surrey	+44 (0)20 8943 1862
Stanhill Court Hotel	Surrey	+44 (0)1293 862166
The Hope Anchor Hotel	East Sussex	+44 (0)1797 222216
Crouchers Country Hotel & Restaurant	West Sussex	+44 (0)1243 784995
The Mill House Hotel	West Sussex	+44 (0)1903 892426
The Old Tollgate Restaurant And Hotel	West Sussex	+44 (0)1903 879494
The Royal Oak Inn	West Sussex	+44 (0)1243 527434
The George Inn	Wiltshire	+44 (0)1985 840396
Hinton Grange	Wiltshire	+44 (0)117 937 2916
Lucknam Park, Bath	Wiltshire	+44 (0)1225 742777
The Old Manor Hotel	Wiltshire	+44 (0)1225 777393
Stanton Manor	Wiltshire	+44 (0)1666 837552
Whatley Manor	Wiltshire	+44 (0)1666 822888
Widbrook Grange	Wiltshire	+44 (0)1225 864750
The Boot Inn	Worcestershire	+44 (0)1386 462658
Buckland Manor	Worcestershire	+44 (0)1386 852626
Colwall Park	Worcestershire	+44 (0)1684 540000
The Old Rectory	Worcestershire	+44 (0)1527 523000
The Old Windmill	Worcestershire	+44 (0)1386 792801
Riverside Restaurant And Hotel	Worcestershire	+44 (0)1386 446200
The White Lion Hotel	Worcestershire	+44 (0)1684 592551
The Austwick Traddock	North Yorkshire	+44 (0)15242 51224
The Boar's Head Hotel	North Yorkshire	+44 (0)1423 771888
Dunsley Hall	North Yorkshire	+44 (0)1947 893437
Hob Green Hotel And Restaurant	North Yorkshire	+44 (0)1423 770031
The Kings Head Hotel	North Yorkshire	+44 (0)1748 850220
Middleham Grange	North Yorkshire	+44 (0)1969 622630
The Red Lion	North Yorkshire	+44 (0)1756 720204
Rookhurst Country House Hotel	North Yorkshire	+44 (0)1969 667454
Stow House Hotel	North Yorkshire	+44 (0)1969 663635
Hey Green Country House Hotel	West Yorkshire	+44 (0)1484 844235

Channel Islands

The White House	Herm Island	+44 (0)1481 722159
Eulah Country House	Jersey	+44 (0)1534 626626
Aval du Creux Hotel	Sark	+44 (0)1481 832036
La Sablonnerie	Sark	+44 (0)1481 832061

Ireland

Gregans Castle	Clare	+353 65 7077005
Ballylickey Manor House	Cork	+353 27 50071
Merrion Hall Hotel	Dublin	+353 1 668 1426
Ross Lake House Hotel	Galway	+353 91 550109
Zetland Country House Hotel	Galway	+353 95 31111
Caragh Lodge	Kerry	+353 66 9769115
Emlagh House	Kerry	+353 66 915 2345
Gorman's Clifftop House & Restaurant	Kerry	+353 66 9155162
Coopershill House	Sligo	+353 71 9165108

Scotland

Balgonie Country House	Aberdeenshire	+44 (0)13397 55482
Castleton House Hotel	Angus	+44 (0)1307 840340
Ballachulish House	Argyll & Bute	+44 (0)1855 811266
The Frog At Port Dunstaffnage	Argyll & Bute	+44 (0)1631 567005
Highland Cottage	Argyll & bute	+44 (0)1688 302030
Ptarmigan House	Argyll & Bute	+44 (0)1688 302863
Castle Campbell Hotel	Clackmannanshire	+44 (0)1259 742519
Fernhill Hotel	Dumfries & Galloway	+44 (0)1776 810220
Gillbank Guest House	Dumfries & Galloway	+44 (0)1848 330597
Trigony House Hotel	Dumfries & Galloway	+44 (0)1848 331211

▼

Corriegour Lodge Hotel	**Highland**	**+44 (0)1397 712685**
The Cross at Kingussie	Highland	+44 (0)1540 661166
Hotel Eilean Iarmain	Highland	+44 (0)1471 833332
The Steadings Hotel	Highland	+44 (0)1808 521314
Toravaig House Hotel	Highland	+44 (0)1471 833231
Cairn Lodge Hotel	Perth & Kinross	+44 (0)1764 662634
The Four Seasons Hotel	Perth & Kinross	+44 (0)1764 685333
Knockendarroch House	Perth & Kinross	+44 (0)1796 473473
The Lake Hotel	Perth & Kinross	+44 (0)1877 385258
Monachyle Mhor	Perth & Kinross	+44 (0)1877 384622
Traquair House	Scottish Borders	+44 (0)1896 830323
Culzean Castle – The Eisenhower Apartment	South Ayrshire	+44 (0)1655 884455

Wales

The Great House	Bridgend	+44 (0)1656 657644
The Inn At The Elm Tree	Cardiff	+44 (0)1633 680225
Ty Mawr Country Hotel	Carmarthenshire	+44 (0)1267 202332
Conrah Country House Hotel	Ceredigion	+44 (0)1970 617941
Ynyshir Hall	Ceredigion	+44 (0)1654 781209
The Old Rectory Country House	Conwy	+44 (0)1492 580611
Tan-Y-Foel	Conwy	+44 (0)1690 710507
Bae Abermaw	Gwynedd	+44 (0)1341 280550
Llwyndu Farmhouse	Gwynedd	+44 (0)1341 280144
Plas Dolmelynllyn	Gwynedd	+44 (0)1341 440273
Porth Tocyn Country House Hotel	Gwynedd	+44 (0)1758 713303
Ye Olde Bull's Head	Isle of Anglesey	+44 (0)1248 810329
The Bell At Skenfrith	Monmouthshire	+44 (0)1600 750235
Parva Farmhouse And Restaurant	Monmouthshire	+44 (0)1291 689411
The Gower Hotel & Orangery Restaurant	Pembrokeshire	+44 (0)1834 813452
Wolfscastle Country Hotel & Restaurant	Pembrokeshire	+44 (0)1437 741225
Felin Fach Griffin	Powys	+44 (0)1874 620111
Fairyhill	Swansea	+44 (0)1792 390139
Egerton Grey	Vale Of Glamorgan	+44 (0)1446 711666

HISTORIC HOUSES, CASTLES & GARDENS

Incorporating Museums & Galleries

We are pleased to feature over 150 places to visit during your stay at a Condé Nast Johansens recommended hotel.

England

Bedfordshire

Woburn Abbey - Woburn, Bedfordshire MK17 9WA. Tel: 01525 290666

Berkshire

Anderton house - The Landmark Trust, Shottesbrooke, Maidenhead, Berkshire SL6 3SW. Tel: 01628 825920

Dolbelydr - The Landmark Trust, Shottesbrooke, Maidenhead, Berkshire SL6 3SW. Tel: 01628 825920

Old Campden House - The Landmark Trust, Shottesbrooke, Maidenhead, Berkshire SL6 3SW. Tel: 01628 825920

Savill Garden - Windsor Great Park, Berkshire. Tel: 01753 847518

Taplow Court - Berry Hill, Taplow, Nr Maidenhead, Berkshire SL6 0ER. Tel: 01628 591209

Buckinghamshire

Hughenden Manor - High Wycombe, Buckinghamshire HP14 4LA. Tel: 01494 755573

Stowe Landscape Gardens - Stowe, Buckingham, Buckinghamshire MK18 5EH. Tel: 01280 818809

Waddesdon Manor - Waddesdon, Nr Aylesbury, Buckinghamshire HP18 0JH. Tel: 01296 653211

Cambridgeshire

Ely Cathedral - The Chapter House, The College, Ely, Cambridgeshire CB7 4DL. Tel: 01353 667735

The Manor of Green Knowe - Hemingford Grey, Cambridgeshire PE28 9BN. Tel: 01480 463134

Cheshire

Dorfold Hall - Nantwich, Cheshire CW5 8LD. Tel: 01270 625245

Gawsworth Hall - Gawsworth, Macclesfield, Cheshire SK11 9RN. Tel: 01260 223456

Norton Priory Museum & Gardens - Tudor Road, Manor Park, Cheshire WA7 1SX. Tel: 01928 569895

Tabley House Stately Home - Tabley House, Knutsford, Cheshire WA16 0HB. Tel: 01565 750151

Co Durham

Raby Castle - Staindrop, Darlington, Co Durham DL2 3AH. Tel: 01833 660207 / 660202

Cornwall

Mount Edgcumbe House & Park - Cremyll, Nr. Plymouth, Cornwall PL10 1HZ. Tel: 01752 822236

Royal Cornwall Museum - River Street, Truro, Cornwall TR1 2SJ. Tel: 01872 272205

Cumbria

Dove Cottage & The Wordsworth Museum - Grasmere, Cumbria LA22 9SH. Tel: 015394 35544

Isel Hall - Cockermouth, Cumbria CA13 0QG.

Levens Hall & Gardens - Kendal, Cumbria LA8 0PD. Tel: 01539 560321

Mirehouse & Keswick - Mirehouse, Keswick, Cumbria CA12 4QE. Tel: 01768 772287

Windermere Steamboat Centre - Rayrigg Road, Windermere, Cumbria LA23 1BN. Tel: 01539 445565

Derbyshire

Haddon Hall - Bakewell, Derbyshire DE45 1LA. Tel: 01629 812855

Melbourne Hall & Gardens - Melbourne, Derbyshire DE73 1EN. Tel: 01332 862502

Devon

▼
Bickleigh Castle - Bickleigh, Tiverton, Devon EX16 8RP. Tel: 01884 855363

Downes Estate at Crediton - Crediton, Devon EX17 3PL. Tel: 01392 439046

Ugbrooke Park - Ugbrooke, Chudleigh, Devon TQ13 0AD. Tel: 01626 852179

Dorset

Chiffchaffs - Chaffeymoor, Bourton, Gillingham, Dorset SP8 5BY. Tel: 01747 840841

Cranborne Manor Garden - Cranborne, Wimborne, Dorset BH21 5PP. Tel: 01725 517248

Deans Court Garden - Deans Court, Wimborne, Dorset BH21 1EE. Tel: 01202 886116

Lulworth Castle - The Lulworth Estate, East Lulworth, Wareham, Dorset BH20 5QS. Tel: 01929 400352

Mapperton - Mapperton, Beaminster, Dorset DT8 3NR. Tel: 01308 862645

Russell-Cotes Art Gallery & Museum - East Cliff, Bournemouth, Dorset BH1 3AA. Tel: 01202 451800

Essex

Ingatestone Hall - Hall Lane, Ingatestone, Essex CM4 9NR. Tel: 01277 353010

The Gardens of Easton - Warwick House, Easton Lodge, Essex CM6 2BB. Tel: 01371 876979

Gloucestershire

Cheltenham Art Gallery & Museum - Clarence Street, Cheltenham, Gloucestershire GL50 3JT. Tel: 01242 237431

Hardwicke Court - Gloucester, Gloucestershire GL2 4RS. Tel: 01452 720212

Hampshire

Beaulieu - John Montagu Building, Beaulieu, Hampshire SO42 7ZN. Tel: 01590 612345

Beaulieu Vineyard and Gardens - Beaulieu Estate, John Montagu Building, Beaulieu, Hampshire SO42 7ZN. Tel: 01590 612345

Broadlands - Romsey, Hampshire SO51 9ZD. Tel: 01794 505010

Gilbert White's House and The Oates Museum - Selborne, Hampshire GU34 3JH. Tel: 01420 511275

Greywell Hill House - Greywell, Hook, Hampshire RG29 1DG.

Pylewell House - South Baddesley, Lymington, Hampshire SO41 5SJ. Tel: 01329 833130

Herefordshire

Eastnor Castle - Eastnor, Ledbury, Herefordshire HR8 1RL. Tel: 01531 633160

Kentchurch Court - Kentchurch, Nr Pontrilas, Hereford, HR2 0DB. Tel: 01981 240228

Hertfordshire

Ashridge - Ringshall, Berkhamsted, Hertfordshire HP4 1NS. Tel: 01442 843491

Hatfield House, Park & Gardens - Hatfield, Hertfordshire AL9 5NQ. Tel: 01707 287010

Isle of Wight

Deacons Nursery - Moor View, Godshill, Isle of Wight PO38 3HW. Tel: 01983 840750

Kent

Cobham Hall - Cobham, Kent DA12 3BL. Tel: 01474 823371

Graham Clarke Up the Garden Studio - Green Lane, Boughton Monchelsea, Maidstone, Kent ME17 4LF. Tel: 01622 743938

Groombridge Place Gardens & Enchanted Forest - Groombridge, Tunbridge Wells, Kent TN3 9QG. Tel: 01892 861444

Hever Castle & Gardens - Edenbridge, Kent TN8 7NG. Tel: 01732 865224

Leeds Castle - Maidstone, Kent ME17 1PL. Tel: 01622 765400

Marle Place Gardens - Marle Place Road, Brenchley, Kent TN12 7HS. Tel: 01892 722304

Mount Ephraim Gardens - Hernhill, Nr Faversham, Kent ME13 9TX. Tel: 01227 751496

Penshurst Place & Gardens - Penshurst, Nr Tonbridge, Kent TN11 8DG. Tel: 01892 870307

Scotney Castle, Garden & Estate - Lamberhurst, Tunbridge Wells, Kent TN3 8JN. Tel: 01892 891081

The New College of Cobham - Cobhambury Road, Graves End, Kent DA12 3BG. Tel: 01474 814280

Lancashire

Townhead House - Slaidburn, Via Clitheroe, Lancashire BBY 3AG.

London

Pitzhanger Manor House - Walpole Park, Mattock Lane, Ealing, London W5 5EQ. Tel: 020 8567 1227

Sir John Soane's Museum - 13 Lincoln's Inn Fields, London WC2A 3BP. Tel: 020 7405 2107

Spencer House - 27 St. James's Place, London SW1A 1NR. Tel: 0207-514 1964

Merseyside

Knowsley Hall - Prescot, Merseyside L32 4AF. Tel: 0151 489 4437 / 0468 698640

Middlesex

Syon Park - London Road, Brentford, Middlesex TW8 8JF. Tel: 020 8560 0882

Norfolk

Walsingham Abbey Grounds - c/o The Estate Office, Little Walsingham, Norfolk NR22 6BP. Tel: 01328 820259 / 820510

Wolterton and Mannington Estate - Mannington Hall, Norwich, Norfolk NR11 7BB. Tel: 01263 584175

Northamptonshire

Althorp - Northampton, Northamptonshire NN7 4HQ. Tel: 01604 770107

Boughton House - Kettering, Northamptonshire NN14 1BJ. Tel: 01536 515731

Coton Manor Garden - Coton, Nr Guilsborough, Northamptonshire NN6 8RQ. Tel: 01604 740219

Cottesbrooke Hall and Gardens - Cottesbrooke, Northampton, Northamptonshire NN6 8PF. Tel: 01604 505808

Haddonstone Show Garden - The Forge House, Church Lane, East Haddon, Northamptonshire NN6 8DB. Tel: 01604 770711

Northumberland

Alnwick Castle - Alnwick, Northumberland NE66 1NQ. Tel: 01665 510777/ 511100

Chipchase Castle - Chipchase, Wark on Tyne, Hexham, Northumberland NE48 3NT. Tel: 01434 230203

Paxton House & Country Park - Berwick-upon-Tweed, Northumberland TD15 1SZ. Tel: 01289 386291

Seaton Delaval Hall - Seaton Sluice, Whitley Bay, Northumberland NE26 4QR. Tel: 0191 237 1493 / 0786

Oxfordshire

Kingston Bagpuize House - Kingston Bagpuize, Abingdon, Oxfordshire OX13 5AX. Tel: 01865 820259

Mapledurham House - Mapledurham, Nr Reading, Oxfordshire RG4 7TR. Tel: 01189 723350

River & Rowing Museum - Mill Meadows, Henley-on-Thames, Oxfordshire RG9 1BF. Tel: 01491 415600

Wallingford Castle Gardens - Castle Street, Wallingford, Oxfordshire. Tel: 01491 835373

Shropshire

Hawkstone Park & Follies - Weston-under-Redcastle, Shrewsbury, Shropshire SY4 5UY. Tel: 01939 200 611

Hodnet Hall Gardens - Hodnet, Market Drayton, Shropshire TF9 3NN. Tel: 01630 685786

The Dorothy Clive Garden - Willoughbridge, Market Drayton, Shropshire TF9 4EU. Tel: 01630 647237

Weston Park - Weston-under-Lizard, Nr Shifnal, Shropshire TF11 8LE. Tel: 01952 852100

Somerset

▼
Cothay Manor & Gardens - Cothay Manor, Greenham, Nr Wellington, Somerset TA21 OJR. Tel: 01823 672283

Great House Farm - Wells Road, Theale, Wedmore, Somerset BS28 4SJ. Tel: 01934 713133

Museum of Costume & Assembly Rooms - Bennett Street, Bath, Somerset BA1 2QH. Tel: 01225 477789 / 477785

Robin Hood's Hut - Halswell, Goathurst, Somerset. Tel: 01628 825920

Roman Baths & Pump Room - Abbey Church Yard, Bath, Somerset BA1 1LZ. Tel: 01225 477785

Staffordshire

Ancient High House - Greengate Street, Stafford, Staffordshire ST16 2JA. Tel: 01785 223181

Izaak Walton's Cottage - Shallowford, Nr Stafford, Staffordshire ST15 OPA. Tel: 01785 760 278

Stafford Castle - Newport Road, Stafford, Staffordshire ST16 1DJ. Tel: 01785 257 698

Whitmore Hall - Whitmore, Newcastle-under-Lyme, Staffordshire ST5 5HW. Tel: 01782 680478

Suffolk

Ancient House - Clare, Suffolk CO10 8NY. Tel: 01628 825920

Freston Tower - Nr Ipswich, Suffolk. Tel: 01628 825920

Newbourne Hall - Newbourne, Nr Woodbridge, Suffolk IP12 4NP. Tel: 01473 736764

Shrubland Park Gardens - Shrubland Estate, Coddenham, Ipswich, Suffolk IP6 9QQ. Tel: 01473 830221

Surrey

Claremont House - Claremont Drive, Esher, Surrey KT10 9LY. Tel: 01372 467841

Goddards - Abinger Common, Dorking, Surrey RH5 6TH. Tel: 01628 825920

Painshill Landscape Garden - Portsmouth Road, Cobham, Surrey KT11 1JE. Tel: 01932 868113

East Sussex

Merriments Gardens - Hurst Green, E Sussex TN19 7RA. Tel: 01580 860666

Firle Place - The Estate Office, Lewes, East Sussex BN8 6NS. Tel: 01273 858043

Garden and Grounds of Herstmonceux Castle - Herstmonceux Castle, Hailsham, East Sussex BN27 1RN. Tel: 01323 833816

Wilmington Priory - Wilmington, Nr Eastbourne, East Sussex BN26 5SW. Tel: 01628 825920

West Sussex

Borde Hill Garden - Balcombe Road, West Sussex RH16 1XP. Tel: 01444 450326

Denmans Garden - Clock House, Denmans, Fontwell, West Sussex BN18 0SU. Tel: 01243 542808

Goodwood House - Goodwood, Chichester, West Sussex PO18 0PX. Tel: 01243 755000

High Beeches Gardens - High Beeches, Handcross, West Sussex RH17 6HQ. Tel: 01444 400589

Weald and Downland Open Air Museum - Singleton, Chichester, West Sussex PO21 4JU. Tel: 01243 811363

West Dean Gardens - West Dean, Chichester, West Sussex PO18 0QZ. Tel: 01243 818210

Warwickshire

Arbury Hall - Nuneaton, Warwickshire CV10 7PT. Tel: 024 7638 2804

Shakespeare Houses - The Shakespeare Centre, Henley Street, Stratford-upon-Avon, Warwickshire CV37 6QW. Tel: 01789 204016

Barber Institute of Fine Arts - The University of Birmingham, Edgbaston, Birmingham, West Midlands B15 2TS. Tel: 0121 414 7333

Castle Bromwich Hall Gardens - Chester Road, Castle Bromwich, Birmingham, West Midlands B36 9BT. Tel: 0121 749 4100

Coventry Cathedral - 7 Priory Row, Coventry, West Midlands CV1 5ES. Tel: 0203 227597

The Birmingham Botanical Gardens and Glasshouses - Westbourne Road, Edgbaston, Birmingham, West Midlands B15 3TR. Tel: 0121 454 1860

HISTORIC HOUSES, CASTLES & GARDENS

HISTORIC HOUSES CASTLES & GARDENS incorporating Museums&Galleries

Incorporating Museums & Galleries

www.historichouses.co.uk

North Yorkshire

Allerton Park - Knaresborough, North Yorkshire HG5 OSE. Tel: 01423 330927

Duncombe Park - Helmsley, York, North Yorkshire YO62 5EB. Tel: 01439 770213

Kiplin Hall - Nr Scorton, Richmond, North Yorkshire. Tel: 01748 818178

Newby Hall & Gardens - Ripon, North Yorkshire HG4 5AE. Tel: 01423 322583

Ripley Castle - Ripley Castle Estate, Harrogate, North Yorkshire HG3 3AY. Tel: 01423 770152

Skipton Castle - Skipton, North Yorkshire BD23 1AQ. Tel: 01756 792442

The Forbidden Corner - The Tupgill Park Estate, Coverham, Middleham, North Yorkshire DL8 4TJ. Tel: 01969 640638

Thorp Perrow Arboretum & The Falcons of Thorp Perrow - Bedale, North Yorkshire DL8 2PR. Tel: 01677 425323

West Yorkshire

Bramham Park - Estate Office, Bramham Park, Wetherby, West Yorkshire LS23 6ND. Tel: 01937 846000

Harewood House - The Harewood House Trust, Moorhouse, Harewood, Leeds, West Yorkshire LS17 9LQ. Tel: 0113 218 1010

Ledston Hall - Hall Lane, Ledstone, West Yorkshire WF10 3BB. Tel: 01423 523 423

Lotherton Estate & Garden - Aberford, Leeds, West Yorkshire LS25 3EB. Tel: 0113 281 3259

Temple Newsam House & Estate - Leeds, West Yorkshire LS15 0AE. Tel: 0113 264 7321

Wiltshire

Charlton Park House - Charlton, Malmesbury, Wiltshire SN16 9DG. Tel: 01666 824389

Hamptworth Lodge - Landford, Salisbury, Wiltshire SP5 2EA. Tel: 01794 390215

▼

Longleat - Warminster, Wiltshire BA12 7NW. Tel: 01985 844400

Salisbury Cathedral - Visitor Services, 33 The Close, Salisbury, Wiltshire SP1 2EJ. Tel: 01722 555120

Worcester

Harvington Hall - Harvington, Kidderminister, Worcestershire DY10 4LR. Tel: 01562 777846

Spetchley Park Gardens - Spetchley Park, Worcester Worcestershire WR5 1RS. Tel: 01453 810303

Little Malvern Court - Nr Malvern, Worcestershire WR14 4JN. Tel: 01684 892988

N. Ireland

Co Down

Seaforde Gardens - Seaforde, Downpatrick, Co Down BT30 8PG. Tel: 028 4481 1225

Ireland

Co Cork

Bantry House & Gardens - Bantry, Co Cork. Tel: + 353 2 750 047

Co Offaly

Birr Castle Demesne & Ireland's Historic Science Centre - Birr, Co Offaly. Tel: + 353 509 20336

Scotland

Aberdeenshire

Craigston Castle - Turriff, Aberdeenshire AB53 5PX. Tel: 01888 551228

Ayrshire

Auchinleck House - Ochiltree, Ayrshire. Tel: 01628 825920

Blairquhan Castle and Gardens - Straiton, Maybole, Ayrshire KA19 7LZ. Tel: 01655 770239

Maybole Castle - Maybole, Ayrshire KA19 7BX. Tel: 01655 883765

Isle of Skye

Armadale Castle, Gardens & Museum of the Isles - Armadale, Sleat, Isle of Skye IV45 8RS. Tel: 01471 844305

Kincardineshire

Arbuthnott House and Garden - Arbuthnott, Laurencekirk, Kincardineshire AB30 1PA. Tel: 0561 361226

Orkney Islands

Balfour Castle - Shapinsay, Orkney Islands KW17 2DL. Tel: 01856 711282

Peebles

▼

Traquair House - Innerleithen, Peebles EH44 6PW. Tel: 01896 830323

Scottish Borders

Bowhill House & Country Park - Bowhill, Selkirk, Scottish Borders TD7 5ET. Tel: 01750 22204

West Lothian

Newliston - Kirkliston, West Lothian EH29 9EB. Tel: 0131 333 3231

Wales

Flintshire

Golden Grove - Llanasa, Nr. Holywell, Flintshire CH8 9NA. Tel: 01745 854452

Gwynedd

Plas Brondanw Gardens - Menna Angharad, Plas Brondanw, Llanfrothen, Gwynedd LL48 6SW. Tel: 01766 770484

Pembrokeshire

St Davids Cathedral - The Deanery, The Close, St. David's, Pembrokeshire SA62 6RH. Tel: 01437 720199

Powys

The Judge's Lodging - Broad Street, Presteigne, Powys LD8 2AD. Tel: 01544 260650

Continental Europe

France

Château Royal D'Amboise - Chateau Royal, B.P. 271, 37403 Amboise, France. Tel: +33 2 47 57 00 98

The Netherlands

Palace Het Loo National Museum - Koninklijk Park 1, 7315 JA Apeldoorn, The Netherlands. Tel: +31 55 577 2400

Mini Listings North America

Condé Nast Johansens are delighted to recommend over 240 properties across North America, Mexico, Bermuda, The Caribbean, The Pacific. Call +44 1323 649 349 or see the order forms on page 437 to order guides.

ARIZONA - SEDONA

Canyon Villa Bed & Breakfast Inn

125 Canyon Circle Drive, Sedona, Arizona 86351
Tel: 1 928 284 1226
Fax: 1 928 284 2114

ARIZONA - SEDONA

L'Auberge De Sedona

301 L'Auberge Lane, Sedona, Arizona 86336
Tel: 1 928 282 1661
Fax: 1 928 282 1064

ARIZONA - SEDONA

The Lodge at Sedona - A Luxury Bed & Breakfast Inn

125 Kallof Place, Sedona, Arizona 86336
Tel: 1 928 204 1942
Fax: 1 928 204 2128

ARIZONA - TUCSON

Arizona Inn

2200 East Elm Street, Tucson, Arizona 85719
Tel: 1 520 325 1541
Fax: 1 520 881 5830

ARIZONA - TUCSON

Tanque Verde Ranch

14301 East Speedway, Tucson, Arizona 85748
Tel: 1 520 296 6275
Fax: 1 520 721 9426

ARIZONA - TUCSON

White Stallion Ranch

9251 West Twin Peaks Road, Tucson, Arizona 85743
Tel: 1 520 297 0252
Fax: 1 520 744 2786

ARKANSAS - EUREKA SPRINGS

The 1886 Crescent Hotel & Spa

75 Prospect Avenue, Eureka Springs, Arkansas 72632
Tel: 1 479 253 9766
Fax: 1 479 253 5296

ARKANSAS - LITTLE ROCK

The Empress of Little Rock

2120 South Louisiana, Little Rock, Arkansas 72206
Tel: 1 501 374 7966
Fax: 1 501 375 4537

ARKANSAS - LITTLE ROCK

The Peabody Little Rock

3 Statehouse Plaza, 72201 Arkansas
Tel: 1 501 375 5000
Fax: 1 501 375 4721

CALIFORNIA - BEL AIR

The Hotel Bel Air

701 Stone Canyon Road, Bel Air, California 90077
Tel: 1 310 472 1211
Fax: 1 310 909 1601

CALIFORNIA - BORREGO SPRINGS

La Casa del Zorro Desert Resort

3845 Yaqui Pass Road, Borrego Springs, California 92004
Tel: 1 760 767 5323
Fax: 1 760 767 5963

CALIFORNIA - CARMEL

Quail Lodge

8000 Valley Greens Drive, Carmel, California 93923
Tel: 1 831 624 2888
Fax: 1 831 624 3726

CALIFORNIA - CARMEL VALLEY

Bernardus Lodge

415 Carmel Valley Road, Carmel Valley California 93924
Tel: 1 831 658 3400
Fax: 1 831 659 3529

CALIFORNIA - CARMEL-BY-THE-SEA

Tradewinds Inn

Mission Street at Third, Carmel-by-the-Sea, California 93921
Tel: 1 831 624 2776
Fax: 1 831 624 0634

CALIFORNIA - EUREKA

Carter House

301 L Street, Eureka, California 95501
Tel: 1 707 444 8062
Fax: 1 707 444 8067

CALIFORNIA - FERNDALE

Gingerbread Mansion Inn

400 Berding Street, Ferndale, California 95536
Tel: 1 707 786 4000
Fax: 1 707 786 4381

CALIFORNIA - FORESTVILLE

Farmhouse Inn and Restaurant

7871 River Road, Forestville, California 95436
Tel: 1 707 887 3300
Fax: 1 707 887 3311

CALIFORNIA - GLEN ELLEN

The Gaige House

13540 Arnold Drive, Glen Ellen, California 95442
Tel: 1 707 935 0237
Fax: 1 707 935 6411

CALIFORNIA - HEALDSBURG

The Grape Leaf Inn

539 Johnson Street, Healdsburg, California 95448
Tel: 1 707 433 8140
Fax: 1 707 433 3140

CALIFORNIA - KENWOOD

The Kenwood Inn and Spa

10400 Sonoma Highway, Kenwood, California 95452
Tel: 1 707 833 1293
Fax: 1 707 833 1247

Mini Listings North America

Condé Nast Johansens are delighted to recommend over 240 properties across North America, Mexico, Bermuda, The Caribbean, The Pacific. Call +44 1323 649 349 or see the order forms on page 437 to order guides.

CALIFORNIA - LA JOLLA

The Bed & Breakfast Inn At La Jolla
7753 Draper Avenue, La Jolla, California 92037
Tel: 1 858 456 2066
Fax: 1 858 456 1510

CALIFORNIA - LOS GATOS

Hotel Los Gatos & Spa
210 Main Street, Los Gatos, California 95030
Tel: 1 408 335 1700
Fax: 1 408 335 1750

CALIFORNIA - MENDOCINO

The Joshua Grindle Inn
44800 Little Lake Road, Mendocino, California 95460
Tel: 1 707 937 4143
Fax: 1 801 751 4998

CALIFORNIA - MENDOCINO

The Stanford Inn By The Sea
Coast Highway One & Comptche-Ukiah Road, Mendocino, California 95460
Tel: 1 707 937 5615
Fax: 1 707 937 0305

CALIFORNIA - MILL VALLEY

Mill Valley Inn
165 Throckmorton Avenue, Mill Valley, California 94941
Tel: 1 415 389 6608
Fax: 1 415 389 5051

CALIFORNIA - MONTEREY

Old Monterey Inn
500 Martin Street, California 93940
Tel: 1 831 375 8284
Fax: 1 831 375 6730

CALIFORNIA - NAPA

The Carneros Inn
4048 Sonoma Highway, California 94559
Tel: 1 707 299 4900
Fax: 1 707 299 4950

CALIFORNIA - NAPA

Milliken Creek
1815 Silverado Trail, Napa, California 94558
Tel: 1 707 255 1197
Fax: 1 707 255 3112

CALIFORNIA - NAPA VALLEY

1801 First Inn
1801 First Street, Napa, California 94559
Tel: 1 707 224 3739
Fax: 1 707 224 3932

CALIFORNIA - OLEMA

Olema Druids Hall
9870 Shoreline Highway One, Olema, California 94950
Tel: 1 415 663 8727
Fax: 1 415 663 1830

CALIFORNIA - PALM SPRINGS

Caliente tropics Resort
411 East Palm Canyon Drive, Palm Springs, California 92264
Tel: 1 760 327 1391
Fax: 1 760 318 1883

CALIFORNIA - PLAYA DEL REY

Inn At Playa Del Rey
435 Culver Boulevard Playa del Rey, Comer, California 90293
Tel: 1 310 574 1920
Fax: 1 310 574 9920

CALIFORNIA - RANCHO SANTA FE

The Inn at Rancho Santa Fe
5951 Linea del Cielo, Rancho Santa Fe, California 92067
Tel: 1 858 756 1131
Fax: 1 858 759 1604

CALIFORNIA - SAN FRANCISCO

Nob Hill Lambourne
725 Pine Street, San Francisco, California 94108
Tel: 1 415 433 2287
Fax: 1 415 433 0975

CALIFORNIA - SAN FRANCISCO

Union Street Inn
2229 Union Street, San Francisco, California 94123
Tel: 1 415 346 0424
Fax: 1 415 922 8046

CALIFORNIA - SAN FRANCISCO BAY AREA

Gerstle Park Inn
34 Grove Street, San Rafael, California 94901
Tel: 1 415 721 7611
Fax: 1 415 721 7600

CALIFORNIA - SAN JOSE

Hotel Valencia Santana Row
355 Santana Row, San Jose, California 95128
Tel: 1 408 551 0010
Fax: 1 408 551 05550

CALIFORNIA - SANTA BARBARA

Inn of the Spanish Garden
915 Garden Street, Santa Barbara, California 93101
Tel: 1 805 564 4700
Fax: 1 805 564 4701

CALIFORNIA - SANTA YNEZ

The Santa Ynez Inn
3627 Sagunto Street, Santa Ynez, California 93460-0628
Tel: 1 805 688 5588
Fax: 1 805 686 4294

CALIFORNIA - TIBURON

Waters Edge Hotel
25 Main Street, Tiburon, California 94920
Tel: 1 415 789 5999
Fax: 1 415 789 5888

Mini Listings North America

Condé Nast Johansens are delighted to recommend over 240 properties across North America, Mexico, Bermuda, The Caribbean, The Pacific.
Call +44 1323 649 349 or see the order forms on page 437 to order guides.

CALIFORNIA - BIG SUR

Ventana Inn and Spa
Highway 1, Big Sur, California 93920
Tel: 1 831 667 2331
Fax: 1 831 667 2419

COLORADO - BEAVER CREEK

The Inn at Beaver Creek
10 Elk Track Lane, Beaver Creek Resort, Colorado, 81620
Tel: 1 970 845 5990
Fax: 1 970 845 5911

COLORADO - DENVER

The Brown Palace Hotel
321 17th Street, Denver, Colorado 80202
Tel: 1 303 297 3111
Fax: 1 303 297 2954

COLORADO - DENVER

Castle Marne
1572 Race Street, Denver, Colorado 80206
Tel: 1 303 331 0621
Fax: 1 303 331 0623

COLORADO - EAGLE

Inn & Suites at Riverwalk
27 Main Street, Edwards, Colorado 81632
Tel: 1 970 926 0606
Fax: 1 970 926 0616

COLORADO - ESTES PARK

Taharaa Mountain Lodge
3110 So. St. Vrain, Estes Park, Colorado 80517
Tel: 1 970 577 0098
Fax: 1 970 577 0819

COLORADO - MANITOU SPRINGS

The Cliff House at Pikes Peak
306 Cañon Avenue, Manitou Springs, Colorado 80829
Tel: 1 719 685 3000
Fax: 1 719 685 3913

COLORADO - STEAMBOAT SPRINGS

Vista Verde Guest Ranch
PO Box 770465, Steamboat Springs, Colorado 80477
Tel: 1 970 879 3858
Fax: 1 970 879 1413

DELAWARE - WILMINGTON

The Inn at Montchanin
Route 100 & Kirk Road, Montchanin, Delaware 19710
Tel: 1 302 888 2133
Fax: 1 302 888 0389

DELAWARE - REHOBOTH BEACH

Boardwalk Plaza Hotel
Olive Avenue & The Boardwalk, Rehoboth Beach, Delaware 19971
Tel: 1 302 227 7169
Fax: 1 302 227 0561

DISTRICT OF COLUMBIA - WASHINGTON D.C.

The Hay Adams
Sixteenth & H Streets N.W., Washington D.C. 20006
Tel: 1 202 638 6600
Fax: 1 202 638 2716

DISTRICT OF COLUMBIA - WASHINGTON D.C.

The Madison
15th and M Streets, N.W., Washington D.C. 20005
Tel: 1 202 862 1600
Fax: 1 202 587 2696

FLORIDA - KEY WEST

Simonton Court Historic Inn & Cottages
320 Simonton Street, Key West, Florida 33040
Tel: 1 305 294 6386
Fax: 1 305 293 8446

FLORIDA - LITTLE TORCH KEY

Little Palm Island Resort & Spa
28500 Overseas Highway, Little Torch Key, Florida 33042
Tel: 1 305 872 2524
Fax: 1 305 872 4843

FLORIDA - MIAMI BEACH

Fisher Island Hotel & Resort
One Fisher Island Drive, Fisher Island, Florida 33109
Tel: 1 305 535 6080
Fax: 1 305 535 6003

FLORIDA - MIAMI BEACH

The Tides
1220 Ocean Drive, Miami Beach, Florida 33139
Tel: 1 305 604 5070
Fax: 1 305 604 5180

FLORIDA - NAPLES

LaPlaya Beach & Golf Resort
9891 Gulf Shore Drive, Naples, Florida 34108
Tel: 1 239 597 3123
Fax: 1 239 597 8283

FLORIDA - ORLANDO

Celebration Hotel
700 Bloom Street, Celebration, Florida 34747
Tel: 1 407 566 6000
Fax: 1 407 566 6001

FLORIDA - ORLANDO

Portofino Bay Hotel
5601 Universal Boulevard, Orlando, Florida 32819
Tel: 1 407 503 1000
Fax: 1 407 503 1010

FLORIDA - ORLANDO

Villas of Grand Cypress
One North Jacaranda, Orlando, Florida 32836
Tel: 1 407 239 4700
Fax: 1 407 239 7219

Mini Listings North America

Condé Nast Johansens are delighted to recommend over 240 properties across North America, Mexico, Bermuda, The Caribbean, The Pacific.
Call +44 1323 649 349 or see the order forms on page 437 to order guides.

FLORIDA - PALM COAST
The Lodge at Ocean Hammock
105 16th Road, Palm Coast, Florida 32137
Tel: 1 386 447 4600
Fax: 1 386 447 4601

FLORIDA - SEAGROVE BEACH
WaterColor Inn & Resort
34 Goldenrod Circle, Seagrove Beach, Florida 32459
Tel: 1 850 534 5030
Fax: 1 850 534 5001

FLORIDA - ST. AUGUSTINE
Casablanca Inn
24 Avenida Menendez, St. Augustine, Florida 32084
Tel: 1 904 829 0928
Fax: 1 904 826 1892

FLORIDA - ST. PETE BEACH
Don CeSar Beach Resort
3400 Gulf Boulevard, St. Pete Beach, Florida 33706
Tel: 1 727 360 1881
Fax: 1 727 367 3609

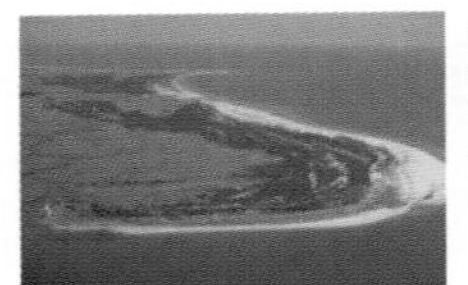

GEORGIA - LITTLE ST. SIMONS ISLAND
The Lodge on Little St. Simons Island
PO Box 21078, Little St. Simons Island, Georgia 31522-0578
Tel: 1 912 638 7472
Fax: 1 912 634 1811

GEORGIA - PERRY
Henderson Village
125 South Langston Circle, Perry, Georgia 31069
Tel: 1 478 988 8696
Fax: 1 478 988 9009

GEORGIA - SAVANNAH
The Eliza Thompson House
5 West Jones Street, Savannah, Georgia 31401
Tel: 1 912 236 3620
Fax: 1 912 238 1920

HAWAII - HILO
Shipman House
131 Ka'iulani Street, Hilo, Hawaii 96720
Tel: 1 808 934 8002
Fax: 1 808 934 8002

HAWAII - HONOMU
The Palms Cliff House
28-3514 Mamalahoa Highway 19, PO Box 189, Honomu, Hawaii 96728-0189
Tel: 1 808 963 6076
Fax: 1 808 963 6316

HAWAII - LAHAINA
Lahaina Inn
127 Lahainaluna Road, Lahaina, Maui, Hawaii 96761
Tel: 1 808 661 0577
Fax: 1 808 667 9480

HAWAII - LAHAINA
The Plantation Inn
174 Lahainaluna Road, Lahaina, Maui, Hawaii 96761
Tel: 1 808 667 9225
Fax: 1 808 667 9293

IDAHO - MCCALL
The Whitetail Club
501 West Lake Street, McCall, Idaho 83638
Tel: 1 208 634 2244
Fax: 1 208 634 7504

LOUISIANA - NAPOLEONVILLE
Madewood Plantation House
4250 Highway 308, Napoleonville, Louisiana 70390
Tel: 1 985 369 7151
Fax: 1 985 369 9848

LOUISIANA - NEW ORLEANS
Hotel Maison De Ville
727 Rue Toulouse, New Orleans, Louisiana 70130
Tel: 1 504 561 5858
Fax: 1 504 528 9939

LOUISIANA - NEW ORLEANS
The LaFayette Hotel
600 St. Charles Avenue, New Orleans, Louisiana 70130
Tel: 1 504 524 4441
Fax: 1 504 962 5537

LOUISIANA - ST. FRANCISVILLE
The Lodge at the Bluffs
Highland 965 at Freeland Road, 70748 Louisiana
Tel: 1 225 634 3410
Fax: 1 225 634 3528

MARYLAND - FROSTBURG
Savage River Lodge
1600 Mt. Aetna Road, Frostburg, Maryland 21536
Tel: 1 301 689 3200
Fax: 1 301 689 2746

MARYLAND - TANEYTOWN
Antrim 1844
30 Trevanion Road, Taneytown, Maryland 21787
Tel: 1 410 756 6812
Fax: 1 410 756 2744

MISSISSIPPI - JACKSON
Fairview Inn
734 Fairview Street, Jackson, Mississippi 39202
Tel: 1 601 948 3429
Fax: 1 601 948 1203

MISSISSIPPI - NATCHEZ
Dunleith
84 Homochitto Street, Natchez, Mississippi 39120
Tel: 1 601 446 8500
Fax: 1 601 446 8554

Mini Listings North America

Condé Nast Johansens are delighted to recommend over 240 properties across North America, Mexico, Bermuda, The Caribbean, The Pacific.
Call +44 1323 649 349 or see the order forms on page 437 to order guides.

MISSISSIPPI - NATCHEZ

Monmouth Plantation

36 Melrose Avenue At John A. Quitman Parkway, Natchez, Mississippi 39120
Tel: 1 601 442 5852
Fax: 1 601 446 7762

MISSISSIPPI - VICKSBURG

Anchuca Historic Mansion & Inn

1010 First East Street, Vicksburg, Mississippi 39183
Tel: 1 601 661 0111
Fax: 1 601 661 0111

MISSOURI - ST. LOUIS

The Chase Park Plaza

212-232 North Kingshighway Boulevard, St. Louis, Missouri 63108
Tel: 1 314 633 3000
Fax: 1 314 633 1144

MISSOURI - KANSAS CITY

The Raphael Hotel

325 Ward Parkway, Kansas City, Missouri 64112
Tel: 1 816 756 3800
Fax: 1 816 802 2131

MONTANA - BIG SKY

The Big EZ Lodge

7000 Beaver Creek Road, Big Sky, Montana 59716
Tel: 1 406 995 7000
Fax: 1 406 995 7007

NEW ENGLAND / CONNECTICUT - ESSEX

Copper Beech Inn

46 Main Street, Ivoryton, Connecticut 06442
Tel: 1 860 767 0330
Fax: 1 860 767 7840

NEW ENGLAND / CONNECTICUT - GREENWICH

Delamar Greenwich Harbor Hotel

500 Steamboat Road, Greenwich, Connecticut 06830
Tel: 1 203 661 9800
Fax: 1 203 661 2513

NEW ENGLAND / CONNECTICUT - WESTPORT

The Inn at National Hall

2 Post Road West, Westport, Connecticut 06880
Tel: 1 203 221 1351
Fax: 1 203 221 0276

NEW ENGLAND / MAINE - GREENVILLE

The Lodge At Moosehead Lake

Upon Lily Bay Road, Box 1167, Greenville, Maine 04441
Tel: 1 207 695 4400
Fax: 1 207 695 2281

NEW ENGLAND / MAINE - KENNEBUNKPORT

The Captain Lord Mansion

6 Pleasant Street, Kennebunkport, Maine 04046-0800
Tel: 1 207 967 3141

NEW ENGLAND / MAINE - NEWCASTLE

The Newcastle Inn

60 River Road, Newcastle, Maine 04553
Tel: 1 207 563 5685
Fax: 1 207 563 6877

NEW ENGLAND / MASSACHUSETTS - BOSTON

The Charles Street Inn

94 Charles Street, Boston, Massachusetts 02114–4643
Tel: 1 617 314 8900
Fax: 1 617 371 0009

NEW ENGLAND / MASSACHUSETTS - BOSTON

The Lenox

61 Exeter Street at Boylston, Boston, Massachusetts 02116
Tel: 1 617 536 5300
Fax: 1 617 267 1237

NEW ENGLAND / MASSACHUSETTS - CAPE COD

Wequassett Inn Resort and Golf Club

On Pleasant Bay, Chatham, Cape Cod, Massachusetts 02633
Tel: 1 508 432 5400
Fax: 1 508 430 3131

NEW ENGLAND / MASSACHUSETTS - LENOX

Cranwell Resort, Spa & Golf Club

55 Lee Road, Route 20, Lenox, Massachusetts 01240
Tel: 1 413 637 1364
Fax: 1 413 637 4364

NEW ENGLAND / MASSACHUSETTS - MARTHA'S VINEYARD

Hob Knob Inn

128 Main Street, Edgartown, Massachusetts 02539
Tel: 1 508 627 9510
Fax: 1 508 627 4560

NEW ENGLAND / MASSACHUSETTS - MARTHA'S VINEYARD

The Victorian Inn

24 South Water Street, Edgartown, Massachusetts 02539
Tel: 1 508 627 4784

NEW ENGLAND / MASSACHUSETTS - MARTHA'S VINEYARD

The Winnetu Inn & Resort at South Beach

31 Dunes Road, Edgartown, Massachusetts 02539
Tel: 1 978 443 1733
Fax: 1 978 443 0479

NEW ENGLAND / MASSACHUSETTS - ROCKPORT

Seacrest Manor

99 Marmion Way, Rockport, Massachusetts 01966
Tel: 1 978 546 2211

NEW ENGLAND / NEW HAMPSHIRE - ASHLAND

The Glynn House Inn

59 Highland Street, Ashland, New Hampshire 03217
Tel: 1 603 968 3775
Fax: 1 603 968 9415

Mini Listings North America

Condé Nast Johansens are delighted to recommend over 240 properties across North America, Mexico, Bermuda, The Caribbean, The Pacific.
Call +44 1323 649 349 or see the order forms on page 437 to order guides.

NEW ENGLAND / NEW HAMPSHIRE - JACKSON

The Wentworth
Jackson Village, New Hampshire 03846
Tel: 1 603 383 9700
Fax: 1 603 383 4265

NEW ENGLAND / RHODE ISLAND - BLOCK ISLAND

The Atlantic Inn
Po Box 1788, Block Island, Rhode Island 02807
Tel: 1 401 466 5883
Fax: 1 401 466 5678

NEW ENGLAND / RHODE ISLAND - NEWPORT

The Agincourt Inn
120 Miantonomi Avenue, Newport, Rhode Island 02842
Tel: 1 401 847 0902
Fax: 1 401 848 6529

RHODE ISLAND - NEWPORT

The Chanler at Cliff Walk
117 Memorail Boulevard, Newport, Rhode Island 02840
Tel: 1 401 847 1300
Fax: 1 401 847 3620

NEW ENGLAND / VERMONT - KILLINGTON

Fox Creek Inn
49 Dam Road, Chittenden, Vermont 05737
Tel: 1 802 483 6213
Fax: 1 802 483 2623

NEW ENGLAND / VERMONT - KILLINGTON

Mountain Top Inn & Resort
195 Mountain Top Road, Chittenden, Vermont 05737
Tel: 1 802 483 2311
Fax: 1 802 483 6373

NEW ENGLAND / VERMONT - KILLINGTON

Red Clover Inn
Woodward Road, Mendon, Vermont 05701
Tel: 1 802 775 2290
Fax: 1 802 773 0594

NEW ENGLAND / VERMONT - MANCHESTER CENTER

Inn at Ormsby Hill
Route 7A, 1842 Main Street, Manchester Center, Vermont 05255
Tel: 1 802 362 1163
Fax: 1 802 362 5176

NEW ENGLAND / VERMONT - STOWE

The Green Mountain Inn
18 Main Street, Stowe, Vermont 05672
Tel: 1 802 253 7301
Fax: 1 802 253 5096

NEW ENGLAND / VERMONT - STOWE

The Mountain Road Resort At Stowe
PO Box 8, 1007 Mountain Road, Stowe, Vermont 05672
Tel: 1 802 253 4566
Fax: 1 802 253 7397

NEW ENGLAND / VERMONT - WOODSTOCK

Woodstock Inn & Resort
Fourteen The Green, Woodstock, Vermont 05091-1298
Tel: 1 802 457 1100
Fax: 1 802 457 6699

NEW MEXICO - SANTA FE

The Bishop's Lodge Resort & Spa
PO Box 2367, Santa Fe, New Mexico 87504
Tel: 1 505 983 6377
Fax: 1 505 989 8739

NEW MEXICO - SANTA FE

Hotel St. Francis
210 Don Gaspar Avenue, Santa Fe, New Mexico 87501
Tel: 1 505 983 5700
Fax: 1 505 989 7690

NEW MEXICO - SANTA FE

Inn of the Anasazi
113 Washington Avenue, Santa Fe, New Mexico 87501
Tel: 1 505 988 3030
Fax: 1 505 988 3277

NEW MEXICO - SANTA FE

The Inn of The Five Graces
150 E Devargas Street, Santa Fe, New Mexico 87501
Tel: 1 505 992 0957
Fax: 1 505 955 0549

NEW MEXICO - SANTA FE

Inn of the Turquoise Bear
342 E. Buena Vista Street, Santa Fe, New Mexico 87505-2623
Tel: 1 505 983 0798
Fax: 1 505 988 4225

NEW YORK - AURORA

The Aurora Inn
391 Main Street, Aurora, new York 13026
Tel: 1 315 364 8888
Fax: 1 315 364 8887

NEW YORK - CAZENOVIA

The Brewster Inn
6 Ledyard Avenue, Cazenovia, New York 13035
Tel: 1 315 655 9232
Fax: 1 315 655 2130

NEW YORK - DOVER PLAINS

Old Drovers Inn
196 East Duncan Hill Road, Dover Plains, New York 12522
Tel: 1 845 832 9311
Fax: 1 845 832 6356

NEW YORK - EAST AURORA

Roycroft Inn
40 South Grove Street, East Aurora, New York 14052
Tel: 1 716 652 5552
Fax: 1 716 655 5345

Mini Listings North America

Condé Nast Johansens are delighted to recommend over 240 properties across North America, Mexico, Bermuda, The Caribbean, The Pacific.
Call +44 1323 649 349 or see the order forms on page 437 to order guides.

NEW YORK - GENEVA

Geneva On The Lake

1001 Lochland Road (Route 14), Geneva, New York 14456
Tel: 1 315 789 7190
Fax: 1 315 789 0322

NEW YORK - LAKE GEORGE

The Sagamore

110 Sagamore Road, Bolton Landing, New York 12814
Tel: 1 518 644 9400
Fax: 1 518 644 2851

NEW YORK - LAKE PLACID

Lake Placid Lodge

Whiteface Inn Road, New York 12946
Tel: 1 518 523 2700
Fax: 1 518 523 1124

NEW YORK - LONG ISLAND

Inn at Great Neck

30 Cutter Mill Road, Great Neck, New York 11021
Tel: 1 516 773 2000
Fax: 1 516 773 2020

NEW YORK - LONG ISLAND

The Mill House Inn

31 North Main Street, East Hampton New York 11937
Tel: 1 631 324 9766
Fax: 1 631 324 9793

NEW YORK - MOUNT TREMPER

The Emerson Inn & Spa

146 Mount Pleasant Road, Mount Tremper, New York 12457
Tel: 1 845 688 7900
Fax: 1 845 688 2789

NEW YORK - NEW YORK CITY

The Benjamin

125 East 50th Street, New York, New York 10022
Tel: 1 212 320 8002
Fax: 1 212 465 3697

NEW YORK - NEW YORK CITY

Hotel Plaza Athenee

37 East 64th Street, New York 10021
Tel: 1 212 734 9100
Fax: 1 212 772 0958

NEW YORK - NEW YORK CITY

The Inn at Irving Place

56 Irving Place, New York, New York 10003
Tel: 1 212 533 4600
Fax: 1 212 533 4611

NEW YORK - SARANAC LAKE

The Point

Saranac Lake, New York 12983
Tel: 1 518 891 5674
Fax: 1 518 891 1152

NORTH CAROLINA - BEAUFORT

The Cedars Inn

305 Front Street, Beaufort, North Carolina 28516
Tel: 1 252 728 7036
Fax: 1 252 728 1685

NORTH CAROLINA - BLOWING ROCK

Gideon Ridge Inn

202 Gideon Ridge Road, Blowing Rock, North Carolina 28605
Tel: 1 828 295 3644
Fax: 1 828 295 4586

NORTH CAROLINA - CASHIERS

Millstone Inn

119 Lodge Lane, Highway 64 West, Cashiers, North Carolina 28717
Tel: 1 828 743 2737
Fax: 1 828 743 0208

NORTH CAROLINA - CHARLOTTE

Ballantyne Resort

10000 Ballantyne Commons Parkway, Charlotte, North Carolina 28277
Tel: 1 704 248 4000
Fax: 1 704 248 4099

NORTH CAROLINA - CHARLOTTE

The Park

2200 Rexford Road, Charlotte, North Carolina 28211
Tel: 1 704 364 8220
Fax: 1 704 365 4712

NORTH CAROLINA - HENDERSONVILLE

Claddagh Inn

755 North Main Street, Hendersonville, North Carolina 28792
Tel: 1 828 697 7778
Fax: 1 828 697 8664

NORTH CAROLINA - HIGHLANDS

Old Edwards Inn and Spa

445 Main Street, Highlands, North Carolina 28741
Tel: 1 828 526 8008
Fax: 1 828 526 8301

NORTH CAROLINA - NEW BERN

Aerie Inn

509 Pollock Street, New Bern, North Carolina 28562
Tel: 1 252 636 5553
Fax: 1 252 514 2157

NORTH CAROLINA - RALEIGH - DURHAM

The Siena Hotel

1505 E Franklin Street, Chapel Hill, North Carolina 27514
Tel: 1 919 929 4000
Fax: 1 919 968 8527

NORTH CAROLINA - ROBBINSVILLE

Snowbird Mountain Lodge

275 Santeetlah Road, Robbinsville, North Carolina 28771
Tel: 1 828 479 3433
Fax: 1 828 479 3473

Mini Listings North America

Condé Nast Johansens are delighted to recommend over 240 properties across North America, Mexico, Bermuda, The Caribbean, The Pacific. Call +44 1323 649 349 or see the order forms on page 437 to order guides.

NORTH CAROLINA - TRYON

Pine Crest Inn

85 Pine Crest Lane, Tryon, North Carolina 28782
Tel: 1 828 859 9135
Fax: 1 828 859 9136

NORTH CAROLINA - WILMINGTON

Graystone Inn

100 South Third Street, Wilmington, North Carolina 28401
Tel: 1 910 763 2000
Fax: 1 910 763 5555

OHIO - CINCINNATI

The Cincinnatian Hotel

601 Vine Street, Cincinnati, Ohio 45202-2433
Tel: 1 513 381 3000
Fax: 1 513 651 0256

OKLAHOMA - BARTLESVILLE

Inn at Price Tower

510 Dewey Avenue, Bartlesville, Oklahoma 74003
Tel: 1 918 336 1000
Fax: 1 918 336 7117

OREGON - ASHLAND

The Winchester Inn & Restaurant

35 South Second Street, Ashland, Oregon 97520
Tel: 1 541 488 1113
Fax: 1 541 488 4604

OREGON - EUGENE

The Campbell House

252 Pearl Street, Eugene, Oregon 97401
Tel: 1 541 343 1119
Fax: 1 541 343 2258

OREGON - GOLD BEACH

Tu Tu' Tun Lodge

96550 North Bank Rogue, Gold Beach, Oregon 97444
Tel: 1 541 247 6664
Fax: 1 541 247 0672

OREGON - PORTLAND

The Benson Hotel

309 Southwest Broadway, Portland, Oregon 97205
Tel: 1 503 228 2000
Fax: 1 503 471 3920

OREGON - PORTLAND

Portland's White House

1914 North East 22nd Avenue, Portland, Oregon 97212
Tel: 1 503 287 7131
Fax: 1 503 249 1641

PENNSYLVANIA - HANOVER

Sheppard Mansion

117 Frederick Street, Hanover, Pennsylvania 17331
Tel: 1 717 633 8075
Fax: 1 717 633 8074

PENNSYLVANIA - LEOLA

Leola Village Inn & Suites

38 Deborah Drive, Route 23, Leola, Pennsylvania 17540
Tel: 1 717 656 7002
Fax: 1 717 656 7648

PENNSYLVANIA - NEW BERLIN

The Inn at New Berlin

321 Market Street, New Berlin, Pennsylvania 17855-0390
Tel: 1 570 966 0321
Fax: 1 570 966 9557

PENNSYLVANIA - PHILADELPHIA

Rittenhouse Square European Boutique Hotel

1715 Rittenhouse Square, Philadelphia, Pennsylvania 19103
Tel: 1 215 546 6500
Fax: 1 215 546 8787

PENNSYLVANIA - SKYTOP

Skytop Lodge

One Skytop, Skytop, Pennyslvania 18357
Tel: 1 800 345 7759
Fax: 1 570 595 8917

SOUTH CAROLINA - CHARLESTON

The Boardwalk Inn at Wild Dunes Resort

5757 Palm Boulevard, Isle of Palms, South Carolina 29451
Tel: 1 843 886 6000
Fax: 1 843 886 2916

SOUTH CAROLINA - CHARLESTON

Vendue Inn

19 Vendue Range, Charleston, South Carolina 29401
Tel: 1 843 577 7970
Fax: 1 843 577 2913

SOUTH CAROLINA - KIAWAH ISLAND

The Sanctuary at Kiawah Island

1 Sanctuary Beach Drive, Kiawah Island, South Carolina 29455
Tel: 1 843 768 6000
Fax: 1 843 768 5150

SOUTH CAROLINA - PAWLEYS ISLAND

Litchfield Plantation

Kings River Road, Box 290, Pawleys Island, South Carolina 29585
Tel: 1 843 237 9121
Fax: 1 843 237 1041

SOUTH CAROLINA - TRAVELERS REST

La Bastide

10 Road Of Vines, Travelers Rest, South Carolina 29690
Tel: 1 864 836 8463
Fax: 1 864 836 4820

TEXAS - AUSTIN

The Mansion at Judges' Hill

1900 Rio Grande, Austin, Texas 78705
Tel: 1 512 495 1800
Fax: 1 512 691 4461

Mini Listings North America

Condé Nast Johansens are delighted to recommend over 240 properties across North America, Mexico, Bermuda, The Caribbean, The Pacific.
Call +44 1323 649 349 or see the order forms on page 437 to order guides.

TEXAS - GLEN ROSE
Rough Creek Lodge
PO Box 2400, Glen Rose, Texas 76043
Tel: 1 254 965 3700
Fax: 1 254 918 2570

TEXAS - SAN ANTONIO
Hotel Valencia Riverwalk
150 East Houston Street, San Antonio, Texas 78205
Tel: 1 210 227 9700
Fax: 1 210 227 9701

TEXAS - SAN ANTONIO SAN ANTONIO
Beauregard House
215 Beauregard Street, San Antonio, Texas 78204
Tel: 1 210 222 1198
Fax: 1 210 222 9338

VIRGINIA - CHARLOTTESVILLE
200 South Street Inn
200 South Street, Charlottesville, Virginia 22902
Tel: 1 434 979 0200
Fax: 1 434 979 4403

VIRGINIA - CHARLOTTESVILLE
The Clifton Inn
1296 Clifton Inn Drive, Charlottesville, Virginia 22911
Tel: 1 434 971 1800
Fax: 1 434 971 7098

WASHINGTON - BELLINGHAM
The Chrysalis Inn & Spa
804 10th Street, Bellingham, Washington 98225
Tel: 1 360 756 1005
Fax: 1 360 647 0342

WASHINGTON - FRIDAY HARBOR
Friday Harbor House
130 West Street, Washington 98250
Tel: 1 360 378 8455
Fax: 1 360 378 8453

WASHINGTON - SEATTLE
Sorrento Hotel
900 Madison Street, Seattle, Washington 98104-1297
Tel: 1 206 622 6400
Fax: 1 206 343 6155

WASHINGTON - SEATTLE
Woodmark Hotel on Lake Washington
1200 Carillon Point, Kirkland, Washington 98033
Tel: 1 425 822 3700
Fax: 1 425 822 3699

WASHINGTON - SPOKANE
The Davenport Hotel
10 South Post Street, Spokane, Washington 99201
Tel: 1 509 455 8888
Fax: 1 509 624 4455

WASHINGTON - UNION
Alderbrook Resort & Spa
10 East Alderbrook Drive, Union, Washington 98592
Tel: 1 360 898 2200
Fax: 1 360 898 4610

WASHINGTON - WOODINVILLE
The Herbfarm
14590 North East 145th Street, Woodinville, Washington 98072
Tel: 1 425 485 5300
Fax: 1 425 424 2925

WASHINGTON - WOODINVILLE
Willows Lodge
14580 N.E. 145th Street, Woodinville, Washington 98072
Tel: 1 425 424 3900
Fax: 1 425 424 2585

WYOMING - CHEYENNE
Nagle Warren Mansion
222 East 17Th Street, Cheyenne, Wyoming 82001
Tel: 1 307 637 3333
Fax: 1 307 638 6879

WYOMING - JACKSON
The Rusty Parrot Lodge
175 North Jackson Street, Jackson, Wyoming 83001
Tel: 1 307 733 2000
Fax: 1 307 733 5566

WYOMING - JACKSON HOLE
Spring Creek Ranch
1800 Spirit Dance Road, Wyoming 83001
Tel: 1 307 733 8833
Fax: 1 307 733 1524

WYOMING - MORAN
Jenny Lake Lodge
Inner Park Loop Road, Grand Teton National Park, Wyoming 83013
Tel: 1 307 543 3300
Fax: 1 307 543 3358

MEXICO - ACAPULCO
Quinta Real Acapulco
Paseo de la Quinta 6, Desarrollo Turistico Real Diamante, Acapulco, Guerrero 39907
Tel: 52 744 469 1500
Fax: 52 744 469 1516

MEXICO - AGUASCALIENTES
Quinta Real Aguascalientes
Av. Aguascalientes Sur 601, Jardines de la Asuncion, Aguascalientes, Aguascalientes 20070
Tel: 52 449 978 5818
Fax: 52 449 978 5616

MEXICO - BAJA CALIFORNIA
Casa Natalia
Blvd Mijares 4, San Jose Del Cabo, Baja California Sur 23400
Tel: 52 624 14 251 00
Fax: 52 624 14251 10

Mini Listings North America

Condé Nast Johansens are delighted to recommend over 240 properties across North America, Mexico, Bermuda, The Caribbean, The Pacific.
Call +44 1323 649 349 or see the order forms on page 437 to order guides.

MEXICO - CANCUN

Villas Tacul Boutique Hotel
Boulevard Kukulkan, KM 5.5, Cancun, Quintana Roo 77500
Tel: 52 998 883 00 00
Fax: 52 998 849 70 70

MEXICO - GUADALAJARA

Quinta Real Guadalajara
Av. Mexico 2727 Fraccionamiento Monraz, Guadalajara, Jalisco 44680
Tel: 52 33 3669 0600
Fax: 52 33 3669 0601

MEXICO - GUANAJUATO

Quinta Las Acacias
Paseo de la Presa 168, Guanajuato, Guanajuato 36000
Tel: 52 473 731 1517
Fax: 52 473 731 1862

MEXICO - GUANAJUATO

Quinta Real Casa de Sierra Nevada
Hospicio 35, San Miguel de Allende, Guanajuato 37700
Tel: 52 415 152 7040
Fax: 52 415 152 1436

MEXICO - HUATULCO

Quinta Real Huatulco
Paseo Benito Juarez Lote 2, Bahia de Tangolunda, Huatulco, Oaxaca 70989
Tel: 52 958 58 10428
Fax: 52 958 58 10429

MEXICO - ISLA MUJERES

Secreto
Sección Rocas, Lote 11, Punta Norte, Isla Mujeres, Quintana Roo 77400
Tel: 52 998 877 1039
Fax: 52 998 877 1048

MEXICO - MÉRIDA

Hacienda Xcanatun & Casa de Piedra
Carretera Mérida-Progreso, Km 12, Mérida, Yucatán 97300
Tel: 52 999 941 0273
Fax: 52 999 941 0319

MEXICO - MONTERREY

Quinta Real Monterrey
Diego Rivera 500, Fracc. Valle Oriente, Monterrey, Nuevo León 66260
Tel: 52 81 83 68 1000
Fax: 52 81 83 68 1070

MEXICO - MORELIA

Hotel Los Juaninos
Morelos Sur 39, Centro, Morelia, Michoacán 58000
Tel: 52 443 312 00 36
Fax: 52 443 312 00 36

MEXICO - MORELIA

Villa Montaña Hotel & Spa
201 Patzimba Vista Bella, Morelia, Michoacán 58090
Tel: 52 443 314 02 31
Fax: 52 443 315 14 23

MEXICO - NUEVO VALLARTA

Grand Velas All Suites & Spa Resort
Av. Cocoteros 98 Sur, Nuevo Vallarta, Nayarit 63735
Tel: 52 322 226 8000
Fax: 52 322 297 2005

MEXICO - OAXACA

Casa Cid de Leon
Av. Morelos 602, Centro, Oaxaca, Oaxaca 68000
Tel: 52 951 514 1893
Fax: 52 951 514 7013

MEXICO - OAXACA

Casa Oaxaca
Calle García Vigil 407, Centro, Oaxaca, Oaxaca 68000
Tel: 52 951 514 4173
Fax: 52 951516 4412

MEXICO - OAXACA

Hacienda Los Laureles - Spa
Hildago 21, San Felipe del Agua, Oaxaca 68020
Tel: 52 951 501 5300
Fax: 52 951 501 5301

MEXICO - PUERTO VALLARTA

Las Alamandas Resort
Carretera Barra de Navidad - Puerto Vallarta km 83.5, Col. Quemaro, Jalisco 48980
Tel: 52 322 285 5500
Fax: 52 322 285 5027

MEXICO - PUERTO VALLARTA

Quinta Real Puerto Vallarta
Pelicanos 311, Fracc. Marina Vallarta, Puerto Vallarta, Jalisco 48354
Tel: 52 322 226 6688
Fax: 52 322 226 6699

MEXICO - SALTILLO

Quinta Real Saltillo
Colosio 1385, Saltillo, Coahuila, 25205
Tel: 52 844 485 0471
Fax: 52 844 485 0470

MEXICO - SONORA

Hacienda de los Santos Resort & Spa
Calle Molina 8, Alamos, Sonora 85760
Tel: 52 647 428 0222
Fax: 52 647 428 0367

MEXICO - ZACATECAS

Quinta Real Zacatecas
Av. Ignacio Rayon 434, Centro, Zacatecas, Zacatecas 98000
Tel: 52 492 92 29104
Fax: 52 492 922 8440

MEXICO - ZIHUATANEJO

Hotel Villa Del Sol
Playa La Ropa S/N, Zihuatanejo, Guerrero 40880
Tel: 52 755 555 5500
Fax: 52 755 554 2758

Mini Listings North America

Condé Nast Johansens are delighted to recommend over 240 properties across North America, Mexico, Bermuda, The Caribbean, The Pacific.

Call +44 1323 649 349 or see the order forms on page 437 to order guides.

BAHAMAS - HARBOUR ISLAND

Pink Sands

Chapel Street, Harbour Island, Bahamas
Tel: 1 242 333 2030
Fax: 1 242 333 2060

BERMUDA - DEVONSHIRE

Ariel Sands

34 South Shore Road, Devonshire, Bermuda
Tel: 1 441 236 1010
Fax: 1 441 236 0087

BERMUDA - HAMILTON

Rosedon Hotel

P.O. Box Hm 290, Hamilton Hmax, Bermuda
Tel: 1 441 295 1640
Fax: 1 441 295 5904

BERMUDA - PAGET

Fourways Inn

PO Box Pg 294, Paget Pg Bx, Bermuda
Tel: 1 441 236 6517
Fax: 1 441 236 5528

BERMUDA - SOMERSET

Cambridge Beaches

Kings Point, Somerset, MA02 Bermuda
Tel: 1 441 234 0331
Fax: 1 441 234 3352

BERMUDA - SOUTHAMPTON

The Reefs

56 South Shore Road, Southampton, SN02 Bermuda
Tel: 1 441 238 0222
Fax: 1 441 238 8372

BERMUDA - WARWICK

Surf Side Beach Club

90 South Shore Road, Warwick, Bermuda
Tel: 1 441 236 7100
Fax: 1 441 236 9765

CARIBBEAN - ANGUILLA

Cap Juluca

Maundays Bay, Anguilla, Leeward Islands, British West Indies
Tel: 1 264 497 6666
Fax: 1 264 497 6617

CARIBBEAN - ANTIGUA

Blue Waters

PO BOX 256, ST. JOHN'S, ANTIGUA, WEST INDIES
Tel: 1 870 360 1245
Fax: 1 870 360 1246

CARIBBEAN - ANTIGUA

Curtain Bluff

P.O. Box 288, Antigua, West Indies
Tel: 1 268 462 8400
Fax: 1 268 462 8409

CARIBBEAN - ANTIGUA

Galley Bay

Five Islands, PO Box 305, St. John's, Antigua, West Indies
Tel: 1 268 462 0302
Fax: 1 268 462 4551

CARIBBEAN - ANTIGUA

The Inn at English Harbour

Po Box 187, St. John's, Antigua, West Indies
Tel: 1 268 460 1014
Fax: 1 268 460 1603

CARIBBEAN - BARBADOS

Coral Reef Club

St. James, Barbados, West Indies
Tel: 1 246 422 2372
Fax: 1 246 422 1776

CARIBBEAN - BARBADOS

The House at Tamarind Cove

Paynes Bay, St. James, Barbados, West Indies
Tel: 1 246 432 5525
Fax: 1 246 432 5255

CARIBBEAN - BARBADOS

Little Arches

Enterprise Beach Road, Christ Church, Barbados, West Indies
Tel: 1 246 420 4689
Fax: 1 246 418 0207

CARIBBEAN - BARBADOS

Lone Star Hotel

Mount Standfast, St. James, Barbados, West Indies
Tel: 1 246 419 0599
Fax: 1 246 419 0597

CARIBBEAN - BARBADOS

The Sandpiper

Holetown, St. James, Barbados, West Indies
Tel: 1 246 422 2251
Fax: 1 246 422 0900

CARIBBEAN - BRITISH VIRGIN ISLANDS (TORTOLA)

Long Bay Beach Resort & Villas

Long Bay, Tortola, British Virgin Islands
Tel: 1 954 481 8787
Fax: 1 954 481 1661

CARIBBEAN - CURAÇAO

Avila Beach Hotel

Penstraat 130, Willemstad, Curaçao, Netherlands Antilles, West Indies
Tel: 599 9 461 4377
Fax: 599 9 461 1493

CARIBBEAN - GRENADA

Spice Island Beach Resort

Grand Anse Beach, Box 6, St. George's, Grenada, West Indies
Tel: 1 473 444 4423/4258
Fax: 1 473 444 4807

Mini Listings North America

Condé Nast Johansens are delighted to recommend over 240 properties across North America, Mexico, Bermuda, The Caribbean, The Pacific.
Call +44 1323 649 349 or see the order forms on page 437 to order guides.

CARIBBEAN - JAMAICA

Half Moon
Montego Bay, Jamaica, West Indies
Tel: 1 876 953 2211
Fax: 1 876 953 2731

CARIBBEAN - JAMAICA

Round Hill Hotel and Villas
P.O. Box 64, Montego Bay, Jamaica, West Indies
Tel: 1 876 956 7050
Fax: 1 876 956 7505

CARIBBEAN - JAMAICA

The Tryall Club
PO Box 1206, Montego Bay, Jamaica, West Indies
Tel: 1 800 238 5290
Fax: 1 876 956 5673

CARIBBEAN - JAMAICA

Sans Souci Resort & Spa
PO Box 103, Ocho Rios, St. Ann, Jamaica, West Indies
Tel: 1 876 994 1206
Fax: 1 876 994 1544

CARIBBEAN - NEVIS

The Hermitage
Figtree Parish, PO Box 497, Charlestown, Nevis, West Indies
Tel: 1 869 469 3477
Fax: 1 869 469 2481

CARIBBEAN - NEVIS

Montpelier Plantation Inn
Montpelier Estate, PO Box 474, Nevis, West Indies
Tel: 1 869 469 3462
Fax: 1 869 469 2932

CARIBBEAN - NEVIS

Nisbet Plantation Beach Club
St. James Parish, Nevis, West Indies
Tel: 1 869 469 9325
Fax: 1 869 469 9864

CARIBBEAN - ST. KITTS

Ottley's Plantation Inn
P.o. Box 345, Basseterre, St. Kitts, West Indies
Tel: 1 869 465 7234
Fax: 1 869 465 4760

CARIBBEAN - SAINT-BARTHÉLEMY

Carl Gustaf Hotel
BP 700, Rue des Normands, Gustavia, 97099 Saint-Barthélemy, French West Indies
Tel: 1 590 590 297 900
Fax: 1 590 590 278 237

CARIBBEAN - ST. LUCIA

Anse Chastanet
SoufriÈre, St. Lucia, West Indies
Tel: 1 758 459 7000
Fax: 1 758 459 7700

CARIBBEAN - ST. LUCIA

The Body Holiday at LeSport
Cariblue Beach, Castries, St. Lucia, West Indies
Tel: 1 758 457 7800
Fax: 1 758 450 0368

CARIBBEAN - ST. LUCIA

Windjammer Landing Villa Beach Resort & Spa
Labrelotte Bay, Castries, St. Lucia, West Indies
Tel: 1 954 481 8787
Fax: 1 954 481 1661

CARIBBEAN - THE GRENADINES (MUSTIQUE)

Firefly
Mustique Island, St. Vincent & The Grenadines
Tel: 1 784 488 8414
Fax: 1 784 488 8514

CARIBBEAN - THE GRENADINES (PALM ISLAND)

Palm Island
St. Vincent & The Grenadines, West Indies
Tel: 1 954 481 8787
Fax: 1 954 481 1661

CARIBBEAN - TURKS & CAICOS

Point Grace
P.O. Box 700, Providenciales, Turks & Caicos Islands, British west indies
Tel: 1 649 946 5096
Fax: 1 649 946 5097

CARIBBEAN - TURKS & CAICOS

Turks & Caicos Club
PO Box 687, Providenciales, Turks & Caicos, British West Indies
Tel: 1 649 946 5800
Fax: 1 649 946 5858

PACIFIC - FIJI ISLANDS (LABASA)

Nukubati Island
P.O. Box 1928, Labasa, Fiji Islands
Tel: 61 2 93888 196
Fax: 61 2 93888 204

PACIFIC - FIJI ISLANDS (LAUTOKA)

Blue Lagoon Cruises
183 Vitogo Parade, Lautoka, Fiji Islands
Tel: 1 679 6661 622
Fax: 1 679 6664 098

PACIFIC - FIJI ISLANDS (QAMEA ISLAND)

Qamea Resort & Spa
P.A. Matei, Tajeuni, Fiji Islands
Tel: 679 888 0220
Fax: 679 888 0092

PACIFIC - FIJI ISLANDS (SAVU SAVU)

Jean-Michel Cousteau Fiji Islands Resort
Lesiaceva Point, Savu Savu, Fiji Islands
Tel: 415 788 5794
Fax: 415 788 0150

Gastronomic restaurant

▼

ORDER FORM

CONDÉ NAST JOHANSENS

Up to €30 off when you order more than one guide...

Order 4 guides get €30 off, 3 guides get €15 off, 2 guides €8 off

Hotels & Spas
Great Britain & Ireland
€29.95

QUANTITY €

Country Houses
Great Britain & Ireland
€26.95

QUANTITY €

Hotels & Spas
Europe & Mediterranean
€26.95

QUANTITY €

Hotels, Inns & Resorts
N. America, Caribbean
€21.95

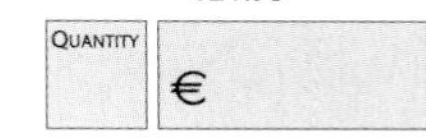
QUANTITY €

Business Venues
(published Feb 2005)
€38.00

QUANTITY €

Save over €74 when you order the **The International Collection...**

The International Collection
€100.00

QUANTITY €

a boxed presentation set of the four leisure guides,

PLUS the Business Venues Guide,

PLUS our exclusive silver plated luggage tag.

A great offer for only €100 ***(RRP €174.80)***

(Silver plated luggage tag RRP €23, presentaion box RRP €8)

DISCOUNT - Discount does not apply to the International Collection 2 Guides = €8 off ☐ 3 Guides = €15 off ☐ 4 Guides = €30 off ☐

PACKING & DELIVERY - All orders outside the UK add €9 per guide or €38 for The International Collection. €

GRAND TOTAL - Don't forget to deduct your discount €

☐ Please charge my Visa/Mastercard/Amex/Switch ☐ I enclose a cheque payable to Condé Nast Johansens

Card No.: Exp. Date: Issue No. (Switch only): Start Date:

Name: Signature:

Address:

Postcode: Tel: E-mail:

Please tick if you would like to receive information or offers from The Condé Nast Publications Ltd by telephone ☐ or SMS ☐ or E-mail ☐
Please tick if you would like to receive information or offers from other selected companies by telephone ☐ or SMS ☐ or E-mail ☐
Please tick this box if you prefer not to receive direct mail from The Condé Nast Publications Ltd ☐ and other reputable companies ☐

Mail to Condé Nast Johansens, Unit 1, 16 Maple Road, Eastbourne, Great Britain, BN23 6ZW
or fax your order on +44 1323 649 350 or register online at www.cnjguides.co.uk quoting reference below

OR CALL OUR HOTLINE NOW ON +44 1323 649 349, quote ref: G008

GUEST SURVEY REPORT

Evaluate your stay in a Condé Nast Johansens Recommendation

Dear Guest,

Following your stay in a Condé Nast Johansens recommendation, please spare a moment to complete this Guest Survey Report. This is an important source of information for Johansens, to maintain the highest standards for our recommendations and to support the work of our team of inspectors.

It is also the prime source of nominations for Condé Nast Johansens Awards for Excellence, which are made annually to those properties worldwide that represent the finest standards and best value for money in luxury, independent travel.

Thank you for your time and I hope that when choosing future accommodation Condé Nast Johansens will be your guide.

Yours faithfully,

Andrew Warren
Managing Director

p.s. Guest Survey Reports may also be completed online at www.johansens.com

1. Your details

Your name: ....

Your address: ....

....

....

Postcode: ....

Telephone: ....

E-mail: ....

2. Hotel details

Name of hotel: ....

....

Location: ....

Date of visit: ....

3. Your rating of the hotel

Please tick one box in each category below (as applicable)

	Excellent	Good	Disappointing	Poor
Bedrooms	❍	❍	❍	❍
Public Rooms	❍	❍	❍	❍
Food/Restaurant	❍	❍	❍	❍
Service	❍	❍	❍	❍
Welcome/Friendliness	❍	❍	❍	❍
Value For Money	❍	❍	❍	❍

4. Any other comments

If you wish to make additional comments, please write separately to the Publisher, Condé Nast Johansens Ltd, 6-8 Old Bond Street, London W1S 4PH

....

....

....

....

....

Please return to **Condé Nast Johansens, Unit 1, 16 Maple Road, Eastbourne, Great Britain, BN23 6NY**
or alternatively send by fax on +44 1323 649350

Please tick if you would like to receive information or offers from The Condé Nast Publications Ltd by telephone ☐ or SMS ☐ or E-mail ☐
Please tick if you would like to receive information or offers from other selected companies by telephone ☐ or SMS ☐ or E-mail ☐
Please tick this box if you prefer not to receive direct mail from The Condé Nast Publications Ltd ☐ and other reputable companies ☐

Bon de Commande

€30 de remise si vous commandez au moins 2 Guides

Commandez 4 Guides et recevez une remise de €30,
3 Guides et une remise de €15, 2 Guides et une remise de €8

Hotels & Spas
Great Britain & Ireland
€29.95

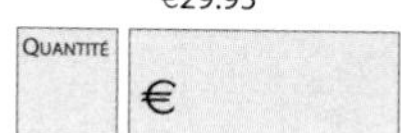

Country Houses
Great Britain & Ireland
€26.95

Hotels & Spas
Europe & Mediterranean
€26.95

Hotels, Inns & Resorts
N. America, Caribbean
€21.95

Business Venues
(published février 2005)
€38.00

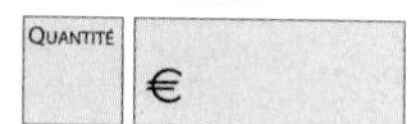

Economisez €74 en commandant la **Collection Internationale**

The International Collection
€100.00

QUANTITÉ | €

une présentation en boîte des 4 Guides de loisirs,

PLUS le guide des lieux de conférence,

PLUS notre exclusif marque bagage en argent.

Une superbe offre pour seulement €100
(€174.80 prix public conseillé)
(Prix public conseillé du marque bagage €23, de la boîte €8)

REMISE - aucune remise s'applique pour la Collection Internationale — 2 Guides = €8 de remise ☐ 3 Guides = €15 de remise ☐ 4 Guides = €30 de remise ☐

FRAIS D'ENVOI - Merci d'ajouter €9 par guide pour toute commande en dehors du Royaume Uni et €38 pour la Collection Internationale. €

GRAND TOTAL - N'oubliez pas de déduire vos remises €

☐ Merci de débiter ma carte Visa/Mastercard/Amex ☐ Je joint un chèque à l'ordre de Condé Nast Johansens

CB No.: Expire le:

Titulaire: Signature:

Adresse:

Code postal/ville: Tel: E-mail:

Merci de cocher si vous souhaitez recevoir des informations de The Condé Nast Publications Ltd par téléphone ☐ ou SMS ☐ ou E-mail ☐
Merci de cocher si vous souhaitez recevoir des informations ou des offres de sociétés sélectionnées par téléphone ☐ ou SMS ☐ ou E-mail ☐
Merci de cocher si vous ne souhaitez pas recevoir des informations ou des offres de The Condé Nast Publications Ltd ☐ ou d'autres sociétés sélectionnées ☐

Envoyez à Condé Nast Johansens Condé Nast Johansens, Unit 1, 16 Maple Road, Eastbourne, Great Britain, BN23 6NY
ou faxez votre bon de commande au +44 1323 649 350 ou www.cnjGuides.co.uk, en mentionnant la référence: G008

OU APPELEZ NOTRE NUMÉRO VERT AU +44 1323 649 349, en mentionnant la référence: G008

ENQUÊTE DE SATISFACTION

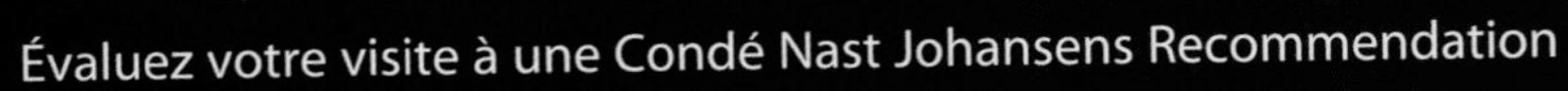

Évaluez votre visite à une Condé Nast Johansens Recommendation

Cher client,

Nous espérons que vous avez apprécié votre séjour dans cet établissement recommandé par Johansens. Merci de nous accorder un peu de votre temps pour compléter le questionnaire d'évaluation ci-joint. Ce document est essentiel pour Johansens, non seulement afin de maintenir les standards de qualité de nos Recommandations, mais également afin d'aider le travail de nos inspecteurs.

C'est aussi la meilleure source pour les nominations aux Prix d'Excellence que remet chaque année Johansens aux établissements qui représentent les meilleurs standards et valeurs de l'hébergement indépendant de luxe à travers le monde.

Merci pour votre aide et j'espère que la prochaine fois que vous choisirez un établissement de qualité en Grande-Bretagne, en Irelande, en Europe, en Amérique du Nord, aux Bermudes, aux Caraïbes ou au Pacifique, vous laisserez Johansens être votre guide.

Cordialement,

Andrew Warren
Managing Director

P.S. Vous pouvez également compléter ce questionnaire en tapant sur www.johansens.com

1. Vos détails

Votre nom: ....

Votre adresse: ....

....

Code Postal: ....

Pays: ....

Téléphone: ....

E-mail: ....

2. Détails de l'hôtel

Nom de l'hôtel: ....

....

Ville/Lieu: ....

Date de séjour: ....

3. Votre évaluation de l'hotel

Une seule croix par catégorie:

	Excellent	Bon	Décevant	Médiocre
Chambres	❍	❍	❍	❍
Lieux publiques	❍	❍	❍	❍
Cuisine/Restaurant	❍	❍	❍	❍
Service	❍	❍	❍	❍
Accueil	❍	❍	❍	❍
Rapport qualité prix	❍	❍	❍	❍

4. Commentaires

Pour de plus amples commentaires, merci de nous écrire séparément à
Condé Nast Johansens Ltd, 6-8 Old Bond Street, London W1S 4PH, Grande-Bretagne

....

....

....

....

....

Merci de compléter et d'envoyer ce coupon à: **Condé Nast Johansens, Unit 1, 16 Maple Road, Eastbourne, Great Britain, BN23 6NY**
ou par fax au +44 1323 649350

Merci de cocher si vous souhaitez recevoir des informations de The Condé Nast Publications Ltd par téléphone téléphone ☐ ou SMS ☐ ou E-mail ☐
Merci de cocher si vous souhaitez recevoir des informations ou des offres de sociétés selectionnées par téléphone ☐ ou SMS ☐ ou E-mail ☐
Please tick this box if you prefer not to receive direct mail from de The Condé Nast Publications Ltd ☐ ou autres sociétés selectionnées ☐

Bestellformular

Sparen Sie bis zu €30 wenn Sie mehr als einen Guide bestellen

4 Guides €30 Rabatt, 3 Guides €15 Rabatt, 2 Guides €8 Rabatt

Hotels & Spas
Großbritannien & Irland
€29.95

Country Houses
Großbritannien & Irland
€26.95

Hotels & Spas
Europa & Mittelmeerraum
€26.95

Hotels, Inns & Resorts
Nordamerika & Karibik
€21.95

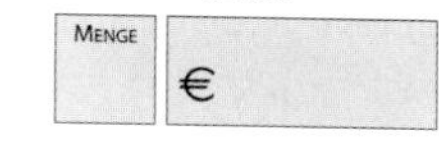

Business Venues
(erscheint Febr. 2005)
€38.00

Sparen Sie über €74 wenn Sie die **The International Collection** bestellen...

Die International Collection
€100.00

Die vier Urlaubs-Guides im Geschenkformat

+ der Business Venues Guide,

+ der exklusive versilberte Gepäckanhänger.

Ein fantastisches Angebot für nur €100

(Normalpreis €174.80)

(Normalpreis versilberter Gepäckanhänger: €23, Geschenkbox €8)

RABATT - gilt nicht für die International Collection 2 Guides = €8 Rabatt ☐ 3 Guides = €15 Rabatt ☐ 4 Guides = €30 Rabatt ☐

VERPACKUNGS- UND VERSANDKOSTEN - Bestellungen außerhalb UK zzgl. €9 pro Guide/€38 für die International Collection. €

GESAMTSUMME - Vergessen Sie nicht, Ihren Rabatt abzuziehen €

☐ Ich bezahle per Visa/Mastercard/Amex ☐ Ein Scheck, zahlbar an Condé Nast Johansens, liegt bei

Kartennummer: gültig bis:

Name: Unterschrift:

Straße: PLZ/Ort:

Land: Telefon: E-mail:

Bitte kreuzen Sie das entsprechende Kästchen an, wenn Sie Information oder Angebote von The Condé Nast Publications Ltd per Telefon ☐ oder SMS ☐ oder E-mail ☐ erhalten möchten.
Bitte kreuzen Sie das entsprechende Kästchen an, wenn Sie Information oder Angebote anderer, sorgfältig ausgewählter Firmen per Telefon ☐ oder SMS ☐ oder E-mail ☐ erhalten möchten.
Bitte kreuzen Sie das entsprechende Kästchen an, wenn Sie nicht von The Condé Nast Publications Ltd ☐ und anderen sorgfältig ausgewählten Firmen ☐ kontaktiert werden möchten.

Bitte senden Sie dieses Formular an Condé Nast Johansens, Unit 1, 16 Maple Road, Eastbourne, Großbritannien BN23 6NY
oder schicken Sie Ihre Bestellung per Fax an +44 1323 649 350 oder registrieren Sie sich online unter www.cnjguides.co.uk (Referenznummer: G008)

ODER RUFEN SIE UNSERE HOTLINE UNTER +44 1323 649 349 an (Referenznummer: G008)

Gastbericht

Lieber Gast,

Ich hoffe, Sie haben Ihren Aufenthalt in diesem von Johansens empfohlenen Hotel genossen. Bitte nehmen Sie sich einen Moment Zeit, diesen Gastbericht auszufüllen. Er stellt eine äußerst wichtige Informationsquelle dar und ist entscheidend dafür, dass wir das hohe Niveau der von uns empfohlenen Hotels aufrechterhalten und unser Team von Inspektoren bei ihrer Arbeit unterstützen können.

Außerdem bildet dieser Bericht die Basis für die "Johansens Awards for Excellence" (Auszeichnungen für besondere Qualität), die jährlich weltweit an die Hotels vergeben werden, die höchste Exklusivität und das beste Preis-Leistungs-Verhältnis für unabhängige Luxusreisen repräsentieren.

Vielen Dank für Ihre Zeit. Ich hoffe, dass Sie sich, wenn Sie zukünftig nach erstklassiger Unterkunft in Großbritannien, Irland, Europa, Nordamerika, Bermuda, der Karibik und dem Pazifikraum suchen, von Johansens beraten lassen.

Mit freundlichen Grüßen,

Andrew Warren
Managing Director

P.S. Sie können den Gastbericht auch online ausfüllen: www.johansens.com

1. Angaben zu Ihrer Person

Ihr Name: ....

Ihre Adresse: ....

....

Postleitzahl/Ort: ....

Land: ....

Telefon: ....

E-mail: ....

2. Angaben zum Hotel

Name des Hotels: ....

....

Ort: ....

Datum des Aufenthalts: ....

3. Ihre Hotelbenotung

Kreuzen Sie bitte ein Kästchen in jeder Kategorie an:

	Hervorragend	Gut	Enttäuschend	Schlecht
Gästezimmer	❍	❍	❍	❍
Aufenthaltsräume	❍	❍	❍	❍
Küche/Restaurant	❍	❍	❍	❍
Bedienung/Service	❍	❍	❍	❍
Empfang/Freundlichkeit	❍	❍	❍	❍
Preis-Leistg.-Verhältnis	❍	❍	❍	❍

4. Anmerkungen

Wenn Sie noch weitere Anmerkungen machen möchten, senden Sie diese bitte separat an Condé Nast Johansens Ltd, 6-8 Old Bond Street, London W1S 4PH, Großbritannien

....

....

....

....

....

Bitte senden Sie das ausgefüllte Formular an **Condé Nast Johansens, Unit 1, 16 Maple Road, Eastbourne, Great Britain, BN23 6NY**
oder per Fax an +44 1323 649350

Bitte kreuzen Sie das entsprechende Kästchen an, wenn Sie Information oder Angebote von The Condé Nast Publications Ltd per Telefon ☐ oder SMS ☐ oder E-mail ☐ erhalten möchten.
Bitte kreuzen Sie das entsprechende Kästchen an, wenn Sie Information oder Angebote anderer, sorgfältig ausgewählter Firmen per Telefon ☐ oder SMS ☐ oder E-mail ☐ erhalten möchten.
Bitte kreuzen Sie das entsprechende Kästchen an, wenn Sie nicht von The Condé Nast Publications Ltd _ und anderen sorgfältig ausgewählten Firmen ☐ kontaktiert werden möchten.

ORDER FORM

CONDÉ NAST
JOHANSENS

Up to €30 off when you order more than one guide...

Order 4 guides get €30 off, 3 guides get €15 off, 2 guides €8 off

Hotels & Spas
Great Britain & Ireland
€29.95

Country Houses
Great Britain & Ireland
€26.95

Hotels & Spas
Europe & Mediterranean
€26.95

Hotels, Inns & Resorts
N. America, Caribbean
€21.95

Business Venues
(published Feb 2005)
€38.00

Save over €74 when you order the **The International Collection...**

The International Collection
€100.00

a boxed presentation set of the four leisure guides,
PLUS the Business Venues Guide,
PLUS our exclusive silver plated luggage tag.

A great offer for only €100 *(RRP €174.80)*

(Silver plated luggage tag RRP €23, presentaion box RRP €8)

DISCOUNT - Discount does not apply to the International Collection 2 Guides = €8 off ☐ 3 Guides = €15 off ☐ 4 Guides = €30 off ☐

PACKING & DELIVERY - All orders outside the UK add €9 per guide or €38 for The International Collection. €

GRAND TOTAL - Don't forget to deduct your discount €

☐ Please charge my Visa/Mastercard/Amex/Switch ☐ I enclose a cheque payable to Condé Nast Johansens

Card No.: Exp. Date: Issue No. (Switch only): Start Date:

Name: Signature:

Address:

Postcode: Tel: E-mail:

Please tick if you would like to receive information or offers from The Condé Nast Publications Ltd by telephone ☐ or SMS ☐ or E-mail ☐
Please tick if you would like to receive information or offers from other selected companies by telephone ☐ or SMS ☐ or E-mail ☐
Please tick this box if you prefer not to receive direct mail from The Condé Nast Publications Ltd ☐ and other reputable companies ☐

Mail to Condé Nast Johansens, Unit 1, 16 Maple Road, Eastbourne, Great Britain, BN23 6ZW
or fax your order on +44 1323 649 350 or register online at www.cnjguides.co.uk quoting reference below

OR CALL OUR HOTLINE NOW ON +44 1323 649 349, quote ref: G008

GUEST SURVEY REPORT

Evaluate your stay in a Condé Nast Johansens Recommendation

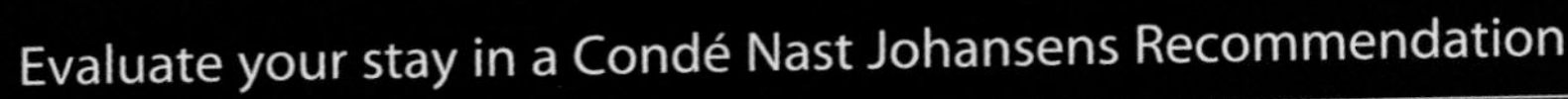

Dear Guest,

Following your stay in a Condé Nast Johansens recommendation, please spare a moment to complete this Guest Survey Report. This is an important source of information for Johansens, to maintain the highest standards for our recommendations and to support the work of our team of inspectors.

It is also the prime source of nominations for Condé Nast Johansens Awards for Excellence, which are made annually to those properties worldwide that represent the finest standards and best value for money in luxury, independent travel.

Thank you for your time and I hope that when choosing future accommodation Condé Nast Johansens will be your guide.

Yours faithfully,

Andrew Warren
Managing Director

p.s. Guest Survey Reports may also be completed online at www.johansens.com

1. Your details

Your name: ....

Your address: ....

....

....

Postcode: ....

Telephone: ....

E-mail: ....

2. Hotel details

Name of hotel: ....

....

Location: ....

Date of visit: ....

3. Your rating of the hotel

Please tick one box in each category below (as applicable)

	Excellent	Good	Disappointing	Poor
Bedrooms	❍	❍	❍	❍
Public Rooms	❍	❍	❍	❍
Food/Restaurant	❍	❍	❍	❍
Service	❍	❍	❍	❍
Welcome/Friendliness	❍	❍	❍	❍
Value For Money	❍	❍	❍	❍

4. Any other comments

If you wish to make additional comments, please write separately to the Publisher, Condé Nast Johansens Ltd, 6-8 Old Bond Street, London W1S 4PH

....

....

....

....

....

Please return to **Condé Nast Johansens, Unit 1, 16 Maple Road, Eastbourne, Great Britain, BN23 6NY**
or alternatively send by fax on +44 1323 649350

Please tick if you would like to receive information or offers from The Condé Nast Publications Ltd by telephone ☐ or SMS ☐ or E-mail ☐
Please tick if you would like to receive information or offers from other selected companies by telephone ☐ or SMS ☐ or E-mail ☐
Please tick this box if you prefer not to receive direct mail from The Condé Nast Publications Ltd ☐ and other reputable companies ☐